**SPRINGER PUBLISHING**

MW00837172

GET THE MOST FROM YOUR BOOK

SPRINGER PUBLISHING
CONNECT™

VOUCHER CODE:

MU90WCF9

Online Access

Your print purchase of *Nursing Home Administration, Eighth Edition,* includes **online access via Springer Publishing Connect**™ to increase accessibility, portability, and searchability.

Insert the code at https://connect.springerpub.com/content/book/978-0-8261-4847-6 today!

Having trouble? Contact our customer service department at cs@springerpub.com

Instructor Resource Access for Adopters

Let us do some of the heavy lifting to create an engaging classroom experience with a variety of instructor resources included in most textbooks SUCH AS:

INSTRUCTOR'S MANUAL

POWERPOINTS

TEST BANK

Visit **https://connect.springerpub.com/** and look for the **"Show Supplementary"** button on your **book homepage** to see what is available to instructors! First time using Springer Publishing Connect?

Email **textbook@springerpub.com** to create an account and start unlocking valuable resources.

Nursing Home Administration

Michael Mileski, DC, MPH, MHA, MSHEd, LNFA, FACHCA, is currently continuing his work in long-term care and acute care environments as a field consultant. He also shares his extensive and diverse experience with upcoming administrators through his associate professorship at Texas State University, where he is program director of the Long-Term Care Administration Program in the School of Health Administration. Dr. Mileski received his doctor of chiropractic degree at Texas Chiropractic College and his master of public health, master of health administration, and master of higher education from Purdue University Global. He has been a licensed nursing facility administrator for more than 20 years and is a Fellow of the American College of Health Care Administrators. Dr. Mileski's active research focus, with many peer-reviewed publications, is long-term care efficacy and effectiveness in addition to his work on patient experience improvement and efficiency. When possible, he enjoys traveling and exploring exotic historic and artisanal beverages and cultures.

Rebecca McClay, DNP, MS, ACNPC-AG, CCRN-CMC-CSC, TCRN, NPD-BC, is currently working in intensive care as part of a hospitalist team. Her strong clinical background and high level of clinical and administrative acumen have allowed her to become the quality improvement champion for the group. Dr. McClay received her DNP in adult/gerontology acute care from the University of Arizona and has remained active in research and project development, with several peer-reviewed publications. Her research focus is on improving the bedside experience through supporting and implementing healthy work environment standards. In her spare time, she loves to take road trips around the country searching for wonderful, locally influenced artisan chocolates.

Nursing Home Administration

Eighth Edition

Michael Mileski, DC, MPH, MHA, MSHEd,
LNFA, FACHCA
Rebecca McClay, DNP, MS, ACNPC-AG,
CCRN-CMC-CSC, TCRN, NPD-BC

 SPRINGER PUBLISHING

Springer Publishing Company, LLC
11 West 42nd Street, New York, NY 10036
www.springerpub.com
connect.springerpub.com

Acquisitions Editor: David D'Addona
Compositor: diacriTech

ISBN: 978-0-8261-4846-9
ebook ISBN: 978-0-8261-4847-6
DOI: 10.1891/9780826148476

SUPPLEMENTS:
Instructor Materials:
Qualified instructors may request supplements by emailing textbook@springerpub.com
Instructor's Manual ISBN: 978-0-8261-4848-3

22 23 24 25 26 / 5 4 3 2 1

Library of Congress Cataloging-in-Publication Data
LCCN: 2022904287

Contact sales@springerpub.com to receive discount rates on bulk purchases.

Printed in the United States of America by Hatteras, Inc.

Gone are the days of yesterday's nursing facility.
COVID-19 has changed our lives forever.
Today our halls are filled with heroes.
This book is dedicated to all those we have loved and lost.

Contents

Preface

This textbook will help you become an effective nursing facility administrator. You will gain the knowledge, skills, and ability to work through issues to help you transition into a successful career.

More than 50 years of the authors' collective experience, research, and knowledge have been included in this book. The authors also have nearly 50 years of experience in the classroom teaching long-term care administration, healthcare administration, nursing, anatomy and physiology, pathophysiology, and other science-based courses. One does not need to be a clinician to be a successful administrator; however, it has proved quite helpful in the case of the authors.

The eighth edition is fully updated in all areas. The current National Association of Long Term Care Administrator Boards (NAB) Domains of Practice, effective July 2022, are presented throughout the book as they correspond to the chapter text. Being entirely up-to-the-minute has proved to be an impossible task in the era of COVID-19; however, at the time of publication, the text is as cutting-edge as our knowledge will allow. A list of Web Resources with the most up-to-date information is provided at the end of the text.

An important area of consideration in your career is that we speak many different languages in long-term care. The Centers for Medicare & Medicaid Services (CMS) speaks its own language, not reflective of current literature. The medical field speaks a wholly different language. Those who bill services for you need to speak in two languages, *International Classification of Diseases, Ninth Revision (ICD-9)* and *ICD-10*. Honestly, none of these align very well, but it will be your job as the administrator to bridge and facilitate communication for your team. Additionally, *ICD-11* has been introduced into the mix, and when it is implemented in the United States, it will certainly cause more confusion in this area. The CMS often runs many years behind the most current information. For example, the CMS requires an ESRD (end-stage renal disease) diagnosis for the start of Medicare for a patient with ESRD. The problem is that we no longer call ESRD by that name. Today, ESRD is chronic kidney disease (CKD)—Stage 5. If you were to bill for medical care under ESRD, most likely, you would not get paid. If you were to submit CKD—Stage 5 to the CMS, the resident would not have dialysis coverage. This lack of uniformity is the way of the world currently.

We leave you with a challenge—*"know more than your surveyors, know as much as your nurses."* Such knowledge can quickly get you out of some tight spots with surveyors and help you interact much more effectively with your resident care staff.

PART 1: LEARNING HOW TO MANAGE THE HEALTHCARE ORGANIZATION

Part 1 introduces the student to the concept of the nursing facility administrator being the leader of the facility. Management styles are discussed, and how to think as a manager is introduced. Management as an art is presented, and the essential functions required of every administrator are discussed in depth. The information presented in this section directly relates to the administrator-in-training (AIT) experience. The lessons from Part 1 should allow the student to have a mastery of nursing facility basics and gain a clear understanding that administrators are ultimately responsible for everything that happens under the roof.

PART 2: UNDERSTANDING THE DEPARTMENTS AND MANAGING HUMAN RESOURCES

Part 2 introduces the many departments of the nursing facility and their function. The student will realize that each department is dependent on the others. The facility is a giant think tank filled with experts in their fields. Leveraging these individuals' experiences and knowledge will allow the administrator operational success. The nursing facility is a symbiotic organism that constantly changes and needs continual nurturing.

PART 3: LEARNING TO MANAGE THE ORGANIZATION'S FINANCES

Part 3 examines the financial role of the administrator. The nursing facility administrator must be an expert in finance, billing, budgeting, financial documents, and accounting. The administrator must have a sizable economic vocabulary and a firm understanding of leveraging it for the operation's success.

PART 4: LEARNING THE CONTINUUM OF LONG-TERM CARE

Part 4 discusses the framework of federal, state, and local laws. Fitting into this continuum is the daily work of the administrator. The administrator must be aware of Medicare, Medicaid, and other laws to be successful. A central point of understanding is that laws change frequently. Staying ahead of the curve through forecasting and monitoring the changes is an important consideration.

PART 5: BUILDING YOUR RESIDENT CARE SKILLS

Part 5 provides fundamental clinical aspects within the facility. Many administrators do not believe this is essential knowledge, as nursing handles this facility area. This is a flawed assumption. The administrator must understand a level of medical information to identify good care versus inadequate care. This chapter goes into depth to provide a basic medical vocabulary and understanding of the body's systems. This section aims to convert the Greek and Latin your nurses and doctors use into understandable English.

PART 6: PUTTING THE SYSTEMS TOGETHER

Part 6 provides a cursory set of developed policies and procedures on which a facility can operate. The section is provided mainly to allow the new administrator to correlate policy with regulation. Federal regulation numbers are supplied throughout the section to explore further.

Successfully administering a nursing facility is one of the most complex and challenging tasks one can undertake, and one of the most rewarding professional commitments available in the healthcare field. The nursing facility administrator and the director of nursing are uniquely responsible for the quality of care and quality of life of the residents/patients and staff in their facility.

You are about to embark on a lifestyle in which those entrusted to you depend on you and your knowledge to run a successful facility. You are becoming part of a very elite group of nursing facility administrators. Always do your best to ensure the highest quality of care. Despite this being the most highly regulated part of the healthcare industry, you can be amazingly successful with your diligence, knowledge, and perseverance. You can be as successful as you choose to be in this field. Do not let anything stop you from reaching the apex of the profession.

CASE STUDIES

Many of the concepts discussed in the text are illustrated in case studies. These case studies enable you to apply the concepts presented throughout the reading. Many of these cases are based on actual events. The case studies presented throughout the sections have culminating wrap-ups at the end of the part.

WHAT WOULD YOU DO?

These cases are provided at the end of each part to allow for a freeform discussion in the classroom. Answers are not provided here. These could easily be used as a basis for online or face-to-face discussions. The goal is for students to delve into their beliefs and biases and find solutions to problems. They also allow the professor to tease out information and guide further understanding of the administrator's role in handling facility problems. Overall, there are no right or wrong answers here, only a framework for great discussion.

Michael Mileski
Rebecca McClay

List of Figures

List of Tables

Instructor Resources

Nursing Home Administration, Eighth Edition, includes quality resources for the instructor. Faculty who have adopted the text may gain access to these resources by emailing textbook@springerpub.com.

Instructor resources include:

- Instructor's Manual
  - Suggested Learning Activities
  - Section Summaries
  - Case Studies With Discussion Questions and Suggested Answers
  - Discussion Questions
  - Multiple Choice Questions With Answers and Rationales
  - What Would You Do? Scenarios

PART 1

Learning How to Manage the Healthcare Organization

1.1 MANAGEMENT FUNCTIONS

Section Concepts

- *Ways to conceptualize your role as an administrator*
- *The many facets of the administrator role*
- *What administrators "do" in a facility*

Consider as the Administrator . . .

- *Why is managing a facility such a complex task?*
- *Considering the many definitions of management, how would you define your role in the facility?*

NEW POSSIBILITIES WITHIN THE NURSING FACILITY SETTING

NAB DOMAIN 4A1: ORGANIZATIONAL STRUCTURES (E.G., DEPARTMENTS, FUNCTIONS, SYSTEMIC PROCESSES); 4A3: ORGANIZATIONAL BEHAVIOR (E.G., ORGANIZATIONAL CULTURE, TEAM BUILDING, GROUP DYNAMICS); 4A4: LEADERSHIP PRINCIPLES (E.G., COMMUNICATION, STYLES, MENTORING, COACHING, PERSONAL PROFESSIONAL DEVELOPMENT)

Nursing facility administration takes place within the continuum of long-term care. We are faced with unique challenges and opportunities today, as we see many changes in technology, record keeping, and best practices. We can do more in the current environment than we ever have before due to technology and how we are leveraging electronic health records (EHRs) to provide higher levels of care. We are seeing many new devices to diagnose, assist with, and monitor our residents' health concerns. This new technology, coupled with best practices for care, allows for capacities to improve chronic disease management, quality of life, longevity, and many other unique possibilities in the nursing facility setting.

Tremendous changes have altered the landscape of the care we can give within a nursing facility. New and constantly changing legislation such as the Health Information Technology for Economic and Clinical Health Act (HITECH Act) has moved nursing facilities' abilities forward so they can leverage new technologies and EHRs to provide improved care. Technology has truly changed our environment and will continue to do so as time passes. We will continue to see new and innovative ways to provide care more effectively and efficiently. Technology has become the vehicle by which we will blend the continuum of care (Topol, 2015).

Technology, legislation, and improved care practices have created a unique opportunity for nursing facilities to deliver complex care we previously could only imagine. These trends affect most facility functions, including the administrator's role, acuity levels, nursing skill levels, medical director roles, business office roles, nutritional management, and physical, occupational, and speech therapies. Some of the many ways these new trends create new opportunities for the nursing facility industry are explored throughout this text.

The long-term care continuum is now the largest segment of the healthcare industry. In this textbook, you will learn how the health industry functions and how to be a successful administrator in the long-term care field. The focus is on you and your career as a long-term care administrator. To be a successful long-term care administrator requires that you acquire several skills. We begin Part 1 by teaching you how to become an effective manager of long-term care organizations. After gaining the management skills required to direct a healthcare organization effectively, you will build skills in managing people (the human resources function; Part 2) and learn how the many departments within the nursing facility function. You will then learn how to manage a healthcare organization's finances (Part 3).

However, to effectively manage a nursing facility, one must understand the larger environment—the continuum of healthcare—within which the nursing facility functions as a key player. In Part 4, you will gain the skills to understand the continuum of long-term care and the broader healthcare system within which long-term care functions.

In Part 5, you will learn how to care for residents. Part 6 puts it all together. The administrator is the individual expected to harmonize everything in a nursing facility. You will find that all roles are equally—and crucially—important for the success of a nursing facility, the health of the residents, the satisfaction of families and staff members, and the needs of all community stakeholders.

The healthcare managerial skills you learn in this textbook apply equally to all healthcare organizations. Once you have mastered managing a skilled nursing facility, it is an easy step to manage other long- and short-term health organizations. This mastery is due to the myriad of regulations. Understand that managing a nursing facility is the most complex managerial position anywhere in healthcare. No matter what type of healthcare organization one is managing, good decision-making is the critical ingredient for success.

The Skilled Administrator

The skilled administrator of a nursing facility is the person capable of organizing the resources and finances available to best meet the needs of the residents. In accomplishing this, the administrator makes innumerable decisions throughout their day.

Management is decision-making (Hitt et al., 2017; Robbins & Judge, 2019). Ultimately, what the administrator does for the nursing facility is make decisions about what needs to happen in the facility and when it should happen while being cognizant of the effects of these decisions on the operation (Chies, 2021; Robbins & Judge, 2019; Singh, 2016).

Although there is an exhaustive amount of literature describing management theory, the field tends to return to a basic set of activities as the best explanation of what managers do (Chies, 2021; Hitt et al., 2017; Robbins & Judge, 2019).

The manager's tasks are as follows:

- Planning
- Organizing
- Staffing
- Directing
- Coordinating
- Reporting
- Budgeting

To apply this to the nursing facility, this is what an administrator does:

Plans. Decides what needs completing and makes a set of plans to accomplish it.

Organizes. Decides after the plan is made how to structure a suitable organization to implement the plan and put it into action. The plan will include the staff, materials, or other requirements necessary to execute it successfully.

Staffs. Attempts to find the right person for each defined job.

Directs. Provides direction (preliminary training and ongoing supervision) through communication to each employee to learn and understand expectations.

Budgets. Projects costs and establishes categories with dollar amounts for each.

Forecasts. Projects trends and needs that the facility management must meet in the future.

Evaluates. Judges the extent to which the organization accomplishes its goals (usually set by corporate).

Controls quality. Takes steps to ensure that goals are accomplished and that each job is done as planned (Robbins & Judge, 2019).

Innovates. Leads the staff to develop new ideas that enable the facility to enhance its attractiveness to the community served.

Markets. Ensures that the facility successfully attracts and admits, to the extent feasible, the persons it seeks to serve.

Coordinates. Takes the ultimate responsibility for everything going on in a facility and works with the correct staff to be successful in this area.

The nursing facility administrator is responsible for ensuring that all these activities are accomplished by the facility. Ensuring that forecasting, planning, organizing, staffing, directing, evaluating, controlling, innovating, and marketing become accomplishments is providing leadership to the facility.

The Two Basic Values

An approach to leadership of particular value in the nursing facility setting is leading by walking around (LBWA). LBWA allows the administrator to ensure that facility resources and finances are successfully utilized to meet the needs of the residents (Singh, 2016). This is a part of the quality assurance process set by the facility, corporate, and payers, such as the Centers for Medicare & Medicaid Services (CMS). In this textbook, our focus is on how to manage by walking around, ensuring two primary values: (a) acceptable quality of care for residents and (b) acceptable choices for residents (Welch & Welch, 2015). LBWA and management by walking around (MBWA) are relatively synonymous terms. *MBWA* was a term coined by Peters and Waterman (2006), which LBWA is mostly based on, but has some negative connotations due to its perception as a "managing" and "controlling" process of employees.

Another explanation of the manager's function is that "management is getting things done through other people" (Hitt et al., 2017; Robbins & Judge, 2019). A staff member who becomes a manager may or may not continue to give direct care but does assume new duties that are entirely managerial. The new manager is no longer directly responsible for doing specific work, such as resident care, but ensures that such care occurs successfully throughout the day. For example, when a nurse who has been giving direct care to residents becomes the director of nursing, this new job entails supervision of other employees to provide the residents' nursing care. This distinction is critical when, typically, the director of nursing becomes the licensed administrator.

According to another group of management theorists (Hitt et al., 2017), the general manager (such as a nursing facility administrator) performs five functions:

- Planning for future operations
- Designing and administering decision-making structures (organizing)
- Developing human resources and capabilities (staffing, directing)
- Supervising current operations (controlling)
- Representing and holding an organization responsible for its various constituencies, the most important are the residents, corporate, and the CMS

The administrator's job is to ensure that the appropriate employees do the tasks of the organization at an acceptable level of quality (Hitt et al., 2017; Robbins & Coulter, 2018). Many volumes exist regarding managing because it is one of the more complex tasks in modern society. What administrators do can be visualized by asking three questions:

- **Where are we now?**
- **Where do we want to go?**
- **How do we get there?**

A DETAILED LOOK AT WHAT MANAGERS/ADMINISTRATORS DO

We have described in very general terms what administrators do. What is involved in forecasting, planning, organizing, staffing, directing, evaluating, controlling, innovating, and marketing? Consider the following essential functions of a manager:

Forecasting (projecting trends into the future). The administrator forecasts the economic, social, and political environment expected for the facility and the resources that will be available to it.

Planning (deciding what is to be done). The administrator decides what will be accomplished, sets short- and long-term objectives, and then decides on the means to achieve them (Chies, 2021; Krupp & Schoemaker, 2014).

Budgeting (deciding acceptable costs). All facilities must operate on plans that are translated into budgets that are realistic yet functional.

Organizing (deciding the scheme of the organization and the staffing and resources it will require). The administrator decides on the structure the organization will take, the skills needed, and the staff positions and their duties and responsibilities. Organizing includes coordinating work assignments, specifically the departments' interrelationships and their workers (Konopaske et al., 2018; Robbins & Judge, 2019).

Staffing (the human resources function). The administrator attempts to find the right person for each defined job.

Directing (providing daily supervision employing good communication, people, and skills). The administrator provides day-to-day supervision of subordinates, makes sure that subordinates know expectations, and helps the staff improve their skills. In short, the administrator explains what needs to happen, and the employees make it occur. The daily reality in the nursing facility is much more complex, of course.

Evaluating (comparing actual to expected results). The administrator determines how well jobs were completed and what progress is occurring to achieve the organization's goals as stated in its policies and plans.

Controlling Quality (taking necessary corrective actions). The administrator revises policies, procedures, and plans of action and takes necessary personnel actions to achieve the facility's goals. Over time, the administrator writes many "plans of correction" for corporate and the many agencies that survey the facility.

Innovating (an effective administrator is always an innovator). The administrator develops new ideas, combines old ideas to form new ones, searches for useful ideas from other fields and adapts them, and acts as a catalyst to stimulate others to be creative.

Marketing (identifying and attracting the persons to be served). The administrator ensures that the facility identifies the group(s) of persons to be served and successfully attracts (to the extent marketplace realities will allow) and serves the residents it seeks.

These are the essential functions of administrators. Understandably, administrators do much more than what is described here. However, if forecasting, planning, organizing, staffing, directing, evaluating, controlling, innovating, and marketing are not successfully accomplished, a nursing facility administrator's minimum leadership responsibilities have not been fulfilled. The skilled long-term care administrator can provide leadership that accomplishes each of these tasks in a manner that meets the facility's financial, resident care, corporate, and surveyors' needs and requirements.

Tom Peters and Robert Waterman, contemporary management theorists, advocate a simple four-part scheme of management's role: care of customers, constant innovation, turned-on people, and leadership (Cole & Kelley, 2020; Peters & Waterman, 2006). They observe that in both the for-profit and not-for-profit sectors, sustained superior performance depends on two things: (a) taking exceptional care of residents in the facility via superior service and superior quality of care and (b) constant innovation.

They also observe that financial control is vital, but one does not sell financial control (Peters & Waterman, 2006). One can sell a quality service or product (i.e., excellently cared-for residents). A facility seldom sustains superior performance merely by having all the beds full; the superior facility sustains itself through innovation to serve residents and promote market development. Effective management of a budget is simply an expectation, as this function does not produce a deliverable item that others can see or touch. A nursing facility becomes superb by the success of all its operations overall. Successful operations allow for visualizing how the facility serves the residents, families, and community stakeholders.

Peters (2014) advocates a management model based on what he calls a "blinding flash of the obvious." This encompasses things such as giving every employee the space to innovate, at least a little; answering the phones and resident call buttons with common courtesy and timeliness; doing things that work (giving quality care); listening to residents and families and asking for their ideas and then acting on them; soliciting staff input and then, as appropriate, implementing it; and wandering around: with residents, staff, suppliers, visitors, and inspectors. Most would argue that these are all commonsense items or simple people skills. However, if this were the case, all employees would practice these things.

Consider as the Administrator . . .

- *If Peters is correct about the "blinding flash of the obvious," then why is it so difficult to achieve the obvious?*

To achieve Peters's blinding flash of the obvious in the nursing facility environment, the administrator typically must cultivate good people skills (i.e., communicate successfully with both residents and staff) to achieve excellence in service to the facility residents and their significant others. You are setting off into a profession that focuses on many things, including excellent people skills. Building those skills is imperative for your success.

1.1.1 LEVELS OF MANAGEMENT

Section Concepts

- *How to distinguish upper-, middle-, and lower-level managers*
- *How important line and staff functions are in the daily operations of a facility*

Consider as the Administrator . . .

- *If it is "so easy" to distinguish these three levels of management, why is it so difficult for you to enforce these levels?*

UPPER-LEVEL MANAGEMENT

The upper-level manager is responsible for the facility's overall functioning, normally interacting directly with the board of directors and/or owners and multiple inspectors. This person is responsible for formulating policies that are applied to the entire facility. A nursing facility administrator is an excellent example of upper-level management (Hitt et al., 2017). It is the upper-level manager who is often charged with assigning responsibilities to middle- and lower-level managers. The administrator assigns the work but does not perform the management tasks. Ensuring that middle- and lower-level managers are accountable for their duties is the responsibility of the upper-level manager.

MIDDLE-LEVEL MANAGEMENT

Middle-level managers report to upper-level managers and at the same time interact significantly with lower-level managers. An excellent example in the nursing facility is the director of nursing, who reports to the facility administrator and has managers—for example, nursing supervisors and charge nurses—reporting to them (Hitt et al., 2017; Singh, 2016).

As the name implies, this staff member interfaces with upper- and lower-level managers. The middle-level manager typically does not make policies affecting the entire facility, as the facility administrator does. However, the middle-level manager does make decisions on policies for managers reporting to them. The middle-level manager must have good communication skills to deal successfully with the facility's administrator, the lower-level managers, and the line staff.

Some nursing facility chains allow local facility administrators wide latitude in decision-making, so the local administrator functions primarily as an upper-level manager. In other chains, decision-making is more centralized in the corporate offices. Some dimensions of the local administrator's role more nearly resemble that of the middle-level manager.

LOWER-LEVEL MANAGEMENT

As a rule, lower-level managers have direct supervisory responsibilities for the staff who do the actual work; for example, the nurse's aide who physically takes care of the resident in the room. A nursing supervisor or a charge nurse is an excellent example of lower-level management in a nursing facility. At this level, managers deal directly with those at the middle level but not with administrators at the upper level. That is, they are expected to conduct their business through the channel of their middle-level managers.

If the charge nurse wants a change in a policy, they discuss the matter with the nursing supervisor, who will bring it to upper-level managers' attention, should this be desirable. The middle-level manager might also make a policy decision without consulting upper-level management, such as changing the bathing schedule to accommodate an additional workload due to increased occupancy.

Management decisions in nursing facilities are, of course, noticeably more complicated than the simple establishment of the lower, middle, and upper levels of management. The presence of several professions (e.g., physicians, nurses, physical therapists, dietitians) causes decision-making in nursing facilities to be a complex and often delicate task. The environment also dictates that upper- and middle-level managers have direct relationships with lower-level management and line staff.

1.1.2 LINE–STAFF RELATIONSHIPS

NAB DOMAIN 4A3: ORGANIZATIONAL BEHAVIOR (E.G., ORGANIZATIONAL CULTURE, TEAM BUILDING, GROUP DYNAMICS); 4A4: LEADERSHIP PRINCIPLES (E.G., COMMUNICATION, STYLES, MENTORING, COACHING, PERSONAL PROFESSIONAL DEVELOPMENT)

Consider as the Administrator . . .

- *Why is it difficult to keep the line–staff distinctions in the facility? Who keeps these lines blurred?*

Line–staff relationships constitute a second important concept in understanding management functions (Hitt et al., 2017; Robbins & Coulter, 2018). A person whom the administrator empowers to make decisions for the organization is said to have line authority. A person is said to have a staff role if they are advisory to the manager and do not have authority to make decisions for the organization.

A LINE POSITION

The administrator must assign to other employees some of the decision-making authority to accomplish the organization's work. Such employees are line managers. They are empowered to make decisions on behalf of the administrator. The director of nursing is a line position. Therefore, decisions by the director of nursing have the same force as if the administrator made them. The administrator remains responsible for all decisions made on their behalf by persons to whom they delegated decision-making authority.

A STAFF POSITION

A staff position, on the other hand, is an advisory role. None of the administrator's decision-making authority is delegated to persons in staff positions. An accountant in the business office is an example of a staff position (Singh, 2016). Persons who are paid consultants, such as a local pharmacist or a registered dietitian, hold staff positions (Singh, 2016). These persons are expected to advise the administrator or appropriate others in the facility on what to do. However, the administrator has given them no authority to make decisions on behalf of the facility.

Smaller nursing facilities typically do not employ a person eligible for registration by the American Dietetic Association as their food services director. Consequently, to meet federal regulations, they hire such a person as a consultant periodically. Although the consulting dietitian may be a better-trained person, if the nursing facility administrator allows this consultant to give direct orders to the food service director, lines of authority in the facility may become confused and staff morale will suffer. In actuality, however, matters are slightly more complicated. Only a person eligible for registration by the American Dietetic Association may designate diets as prescribed by physicians. In this case, the consultant makes decisions for the facility that an unqualified food service director cannot make.

Alternatively, in a very large facility, the administrator might hire a specially trained geriatric nurse practitioner to advise the administrator or the director of nursing, on nursing functions in the facility. This nurse would typically have no authority to ask or order anyone to do anything in the facility, but can only make decisions surrounding residents' care.

It is the director of nursing to whom power and authority to make nursing decisions are delegated, and they are enabled to make decisions on behalf of the administrator in the nursing area. The director of nursing can hire and fire, assign work, and give whatever orders are needed to make the facility's nursing activities function because the line authority to do so has been delegated to that employee.

If, for example, the administrator permitted the geriatric nurse practitioner, to whom a staff role had been assigned, to tell the director of nursing what to do or give orders to nurses on the halls, the director of nursing's authority would be undermined. The director of nursing and nursing staff would be understandably confused about the director of nursing's role. Confusion would leave staff not knowing who is managing whom, and there would be no clear line of leadership authority easily determined.

Again, life in the nursing facility is seldom so uncomplicated. Chains operate a large number of nursing facilities in the United States with corporate staff who often visit or are assigned to assist a facility for a short period. Technically, these corporate representatives may be there only to advise, but facility staff are hardly free to ignore such "advice." Some chains expect their corporate staff to function merely as consultants to the local facilities they visit; other chains want them to function as if they exercised line authority in their area of expertise while in one of that chain's facilities. Alternatively, when the facility functions smoothly, the corporate representative might be comfortable with a "take it or leave it" approach to the advice given. However, in times of crisis, that same representative might exercise direct line authority in the day-to-day operation of that facility.

COMMON PITFALLS IN PRACTICE

- New administrators are often not informed enough about the field. You need to begin to ensure you stay informed, up to date on current events, and "in the know." Subscribe to industry magazines (e.g., *McKnight's*), get involved in professional organizations (e.g., the American College of Health Care Administrators [ACHCA]), and begin to get to know your future colleagues.
- New administrators often find themselves in the position of "being friends" with their staff, thus violating the different levels of management. Keeping your professional life separate from your personal life is a best practice toward success.
- It is important to understand and abide by the line–staff relationships in any facility. Know these relationships and work with them for a good amount of time before you make any change. These relationships are the "politics" of a facility.

CASE STUDY

The Nurse Consultant Arrives at The Laurels Nursing Facility

It is early Tuesday morning. Ms. Monday, the nursing consultant from the regional office of The Laurels chain, arrives at the request of the administrator to consult with the director of nursing. It is expected that Ms. Monday will begin spending 4 hours per month in the facility for the next several months. The day nursing supervisor informs Ms. Monday and Ms. Smith, the

(continued)

administrator, that the director of nursing just called in sick and said to tell Ms. Monday to proceed without them. Ms. Monday, on an approving nod from Ms. Smith, proceeds.

After studying a dozen or so patient charts, Ms. Monday becomes upset. The charts show that the PRN medications (i.e., medications prescribed by physicians that nurses may administer on an as-needed basis as judged by the nurse) are not properly documented considering the CMS's interest in medications as a quality indicator. Furthermore, having arrived early, Ms. Monday compared the breakfasts served against the diets of the five insulin-dependent diabetic patients on one wing. The required diets were not followed.

At 11:00 a.m., Ms. Monday announces that at the 3:00 p.m. change of shift, she wants to meet with the nursing supervisors and charge nurses from the day and evening shifts. At the 3:00 p.m. meeting, Ms. Monday informs the nursing supervisors that beginning tomorrow, the supervisors are to instruct the charge nurses to develop procedures to implement the new policy Ms. Monday has written out for handling PRN medications.

Ms. Monday also instructs the nursing supervisors to tell each charge nurse that beginning with tomorrow's breakfast, the charge nurses are to personally supervise the kitchen personnel in the main kitchen as they assemble food trays for the five diabetic patients.

Ms. Monday leaves a lengthy memo for the director of nursing explaining that she has put two new policies into place, arguing that they are more in line with what the nursing facility inspectors will demand.

On her way out, she stops by the administrator's office and gives her a copy of the memo. Ms. Smith reads the memo, nods approvingly, and compliments Ms. Monday on how she is taking hold.

As Ms. Monday leaves, the administrator thinks, "This is great, we finally have someone who will come in and tell those nurses what to do so that the inspectors will stay off my case."

About a week later, the director of nursing tells the administrator to either prohibit the nurse consultant from establishing policies for their nursing staff or accept the director of nursing's resignation.

Ms. Smith wonders what has upset the director of nursing and whether it might not be a good idea to let them resign if they will be a disruptive employee.

Ms. Smith picks up the phone, calls her regional administrator, and tells them that she plans to let the director of nursing go.

- *As the regional administrator and direct supervisor of Ms. Smith, what would you do in this situation? What would you say to Ms. Smith?*

We turn now to a more detailed discussion of some of the activities and skills involved in the management functions. We will begin to further explore some of the complexities of these functions.

1.2 FORECASTING

Section Concepts

- *The importance of forecasting and how critically important it is to the success of a facility*

Consider as the Administrator . . .

- *How can you begin to sense trends in the field?*
- *What do you need to be doing now so that you can predict the future based on facts?*

Managerial success belongs to those who successfully prepare for the future. In the nursing facility industry, the future belongs to administrators who can anticipate and successfully prepare for rapid change.

TREND ANALYSIS

Few would have expected the profound changes in long-term care after the Omnibus Budget Reconciliation Act (OBRA) passage in 1987. This groundbreaking legislation entirely changed how facilities were viewed and regulated. OBRA was arguably the most significant change to the industry in history. Today, amendments to OBRA, new laws, and other changes have the industry in an incredible (and constant) period of change (Zelman et al., 2020). Today's administrators are expected to keep abreast of developments in all areas and make changes based on what they anticipate is coming next.

Forecasting involves trend identification and analysis. Clues to the future are present in trends that the alert administrator can observe (Krupp & Schoemaker, 2014). The skill needed in forecasting is accurately predicting the future implications for the nursing facility of new trends to which the current environment may offer clues. For example, the CMS instituted "pay for performance" initiatives in acute care, the effects of which also impact nursing facilities. It has become imperative to ensure that the highest levels of care are provided to admissions from hospitals to prevent their return to acute care (Mileski et al., 2017). The CMS has also begun Nursing Home Value-Based Purchasing Demonstrations in several states (CMS, 2020) with the intention of offering incentive payment awards to nursing facilities that have the highest quality measures. Alert administrators in states using other reimbursement approaches can estimate how this method may be adopted in their states and make contingency plans to adapt if this occurs.

One apparent certainty is that conventional perceptions of the nursing facility's roles will be challenged in the American healthcare system. In the past, developments occurred more incrementally, at a slower pace. Forty years ago, administrators had the luxury of making long-range projections during a period of relative stability in the healthcare industry under less limited Medicare and Medicaid reimbursements from the federal and state governments. In today's world, the rate of transformation in the healthcare field is exponential. Change is often so rapid that it is ever more challenging to predict the nursing facility industry's shape, even from year to year. We see continual change as Congress, states, and the CMS modify, sometimes radically, the inspection procedures and the reimbursement rules.

THE CHANGING CORE

Consider the following. Every 10 years, one fourth of all current knowledge and accepted practices in healthcare and other industries become obsolete. The life span of new technologies decreases each year. Estimates are that people younger than 25 years of age can expect to change careers every decade and jobs every 4 years, either by choice or because the industry in which they work will disappear and be replaced by others yet unimagined. The "core" business of the nursing facility of the late 21st century may be entirely different from the one in the second decade of the 21st century (Krupp & Schoemaker, 2014; Robbins & Coulter, 2018).

Nursing facility administration is in a new and unpredictable world, an arena in which we have not played before. The rules will be different, especially in our current COVID-19–focused world. The game itself is changing—the nursing facility we went to work for 5 years earlier may have changed entirely. Everything is moving faster in the health field. New technologies are replacing current technologies ever faster. What the nursing facility administrator needs to know to act effectively is changing. The CMS is rapidly moving to an electronic system for monitoring resident care, processing surveys, and reimbursing the facility for the care given. The shape of the final system is unknown. Relying on the "tried and true" is dangerous because what worked yesterday is no longer true today. Nursing facilities that continue to rely on conventional formulas for success will miss opportunities for new markets and find themselves in the backwash of the healthcare industry as it metamorphoses into constantly new permutations.

The truth is that for the first time in human history, the capacity exists to provide more expensive and effective healthcare than any nation, including the United States, may be able to afford. The roles possible for hospitals, nursing facilities, multiunit senior housing, assisted living facilities, home health agencies, managed care organizations, and other providers are endless. They will remain up for the taking for the next few decades as society struggles to absorb healthcare costs and technologies.

CHANGE ITSELF

Change at a laser-fast pace will continue (Krupp & Schoemaker, 2014). Humankind's cumulative knowledge seems to be increasing exponentially. In the health sciences field, this may be occurring even more rapidly than in the economy as a whole. The U.S. Congress's Office of Technology has warned that the development rate is too fast for the proper monitoring of the effects and will threaten the foundations of even the most secure American businesses. The nursing staffs in long-term care facilities are experiencing culture shock. Thirty years ago, these nurses were working at a lower technological level than hospital nurses. Today, nursing facility nurses are busy learning high-tech skills to be able to treat the subacute care residents. We see increases in the acuity of nursing facility residents yearly. Almost as soon as rules are established, they become obsolete.

Survival in the nursing facility industry will depend on forecasting the future and learning entirely new ways of thinking, behaving, motivating, and communicating in the nursing facility. It will also depend on the ability and willingness to change, something both owners and staff do with great reluctance.

COMMON PITFALLS IN PRACTICE

- When administrators do not know enough about the field, it becomes very difficult to forecast anything. Always be on top of current events!
- Do research on your community. You cannot possibly forecast anything if you are unaware of the community's needs, which are in a state of continuous change.

1.3 PLANNING

1.3.1 WHY PLAN?

Section Concepts

- *How to perform planning for a facility*
- *How planning is a means of coping with uncertainty*
- *Steps in the planning process*
- *How to utilize a plan*

Consider as the Administrator . . .

- *Why is it so difficult for you to plan for the facility?*

NAB DOMAIN 4A2: ORGANIZATIONAL CHANGE MANAGEMENT; 4A4: LEADERSHIP PRINCIPLES (E.G., COMMUNICATION, STYLES, MENTORING, COACHING, PERSONAL PROFESSIONAL DEVELOPMENT)

AN INTEGRATED DECISION SYSTEM

The purpose of planning is to provide an integrated decision system that establishes the framework for all facility activities based on the administrator's change forecast. Plans, in essence, are statements of the organizational goals of the facility.

A MEANS OF COPING WITH UNCERTAINTY

Plans are a means of coping with the future's uncertainty (Hitt et al., 2017; Robbins & Coulter, 2018). All organizations must deal with the outside world to survive. Inevitably, events beyond the nursing facility's control will shape the range of options available to the facility and set the context within which it will be obliged to function (Krupp & Schoemaker, 2014).

A plan predicts what the facility's decision-makers believe they must do to cope with the future. A carefully developed plan makes it possible to compare what happens to what was expected to happen. The plan may then be altered to achieve the set goals when external conditions change.

STRATEGIC PLANNING

NAB DOMAIN 4B2: STRATEGIC BUSINESS PLANNING (E.G., NEW LINES OF SERVICE, SUCCESSION MANAGEMENT, STAFFING PIPELINE)

To survive and prosper, the nursing facility must engage in strategic planning (Robbins & Coulter, 2018). *Strategy* comes from the Greek word *strategos*, referring to a general (the administrator's) grand design behind a campaign or battle. *Strategic management* is the conception and implementation of the pattern or plan that integrates the facility's primary goals, policies, and action sequences into a cohesive whole (Noe et al., 2019). It is the process of analyzing the facility's competitive position, developing the strategic goals, devising a plan of action, and allocating the resources that will best achieve those goals (Noe et al., 2019).

The strategic plan can be developed, implemented, and evaluated by the administrator and the staff. This plan in each local facility implements the mission, values, and goals established by the board of directors, which oversees the facility operations. Each facility's strategic plan must be endorsed (approved) by the governing body (Welch & Welch, 2015).

Break-It Thinking

It is essential to have a plan. Sometimes it is even more critical to abandon it! Today change is coming at such a fast pace that today's innovations are tomorrow's outworn models. There is a common observation that "if it isn't broken today, it will be tomorrow!" The nursing facility administrator in the current millennium is faced with multiple new technologically based possibilities.

Take medication administration, for example. The average number of prescriptions for persons aged 65 and older is four (Charlesworth et al., 2015). In nursing facilities, it is often double or more of that number. Today, technology is beginning to have huge effects on medication usage and medication error rates. Technologies such as EHRs, electronic prescribing, computerized physician order entry, and clinical decision support systems are changing how medications are prescribed and utilized. These systems can combine resident information, diagnoses, drug utilization, and a myriad of other information, which can help reduce prescription error and other problems such as unwanted side effects for each resident's drug protocol (Topol, 2015). The facility's decision-makers cannot know what new healthcare monitoring opportunities will evolve but can make a conscious decision to include these new monitoring opportunities as they come about.

1.3.2 STEPS IN PLANNING

Section Concepts

- *The three phases of planning:*
  - *Phase 1—Deciding what ought to be done*
    - *Governmental permissions*
    - *Analyzing competition*
    - *Factoring for the economy*
    - *Accounting for the market*
  - *Phase 2—Setting short- and long-term goals*
  - *Phase 3—Deciding how to achieve the objectives*
- *How to use plans in the real world*

Consider as the Administrator . . .

- *Is a plan a means to your success? If so, what must you do to ensure success as you work up a plan?*

PHASE 1: DECIDE WHAT OUGHT TO BE DONE

NAB DOMAIN 3B: REGULATORY COMPLIANCE; 4A6: PROFESSIONAL ADVOCACY AND GOVERNMENTAL RELATIONS

Few people have the opportunity to plan for an organization from its very outset. Typically, in a nursing facility, an individual is hired as the administrator of an already operating facility. For illustration, however, let us follow the planning process that might occur in the creation of a new nursing facility.

Suppose that the regional vice president asks an administrator of a midsized publicly traded for-profit chain of nursing facilities to evaluate a medium-sized community (about 50,000 residents) to recommend or advise against building a nursing facility there. Assume that sufficient funds are available if the decision is favorable. The assumption is further made that, if a facility is built, the person doing this assessment will serve as its initial administrator.

This individual must appraise the current competitive, economic, and political environment in that community. We will not attempt to provide a complete checklist for arriving at an assessment of a community, but the major planning considerations might include the following factors.

Governmental Permissions

Numerous governmental bodies must grant permission to build a facility. Zoning requirements, building codes, and local fire codes must be met. If a certificate of need or similar governmental permission to build a new nursing facility legislation exists, the likelihood of obtaining this is an early consideration. Will approval of all required federal, state, and local government permits be forthcoming (Hitt et al., 2017; Singh, 2016)? What is the political climate in the town? Is the proposed nursing facility likely to be welcomed, or if not, would permits probably be delayed, disapproved, or interpreted so strictly that costs rise unacceptably?

The facility will work with numerous governmental groups throughout its existence. Governmental relations are essential to the facility. The government's purposes are the same as the facility's purposes: to provide high-quality care to all residents. Rather than an adversarial relationship, the facility should seek a cooperative and positive working relationship with the various governmental agencies that oversee the facility's day-to-day actions.

Competition

What is the level of unmet need for nursing facility beds in the community and its surroundings? How many competitors are there? What are the competitors' present and projected bed capacities? Is there enough unmet bed need to expect that a new nursing facility would fill up sufficiently quickly and maintain the desired level of occupancy over an extended period of at least 5 or, preferably, 10, years? What expansion plans do the present facilities have? Are other competing nursing facilities apt to be built over the next 3 to 5 years? In many communities, assisted living facilities are being built beyond capacity to absorb. Are licensed and/or unlicensed multiunit senior living facilities whose residents will want to "age in place" (thus avoiding admission to a nursing facility) being built? What is known about local hospitals? Are they likely to enlarge, shrink, or stay the same? Are hospitals themselves in the process of opening long-term care beds or expecting to do so? What is known about local home healthcare agencies? Is it probable that they will aggressively siphon off patients who might currently be candidates for nursing facility placement? Is there an active hospice agency (Halter et al., 2017)? Will there be competition, or is a cooperative effort possible, placing selected hospice patients in the proposed nursing facility?

Economic Considerations

Are the expected residents apt to have the present and future income to keep the occupancy level high and with the desired mix of residents? Based on the company's projected daily charges for care, would the facility, if built, be competitive with daily charges by its competitors? Will the community and its surrounding area maintain or improve its economic condition over the next several years? What are the public and third-party reimbursement trends in this community and state? Can your company build a facility and charge competitive prices based on present and anticipated reimbursement trends for nursing facility care?

> **NAB DOMAIN 2A: FINANCIAL MANAGEMENT; 2A5: REVENUE AND REIMBURSEMENT (E.G., PDPM, PDGM, ACOs, HMOs, MEDICAID, PRIVATE PAYORS); 4A2: ORGANIZATIONAL CHANGE MANAGEMENT**

What are the trends among third-party payers in this community? Are health maintenance organizations, preferred provider organizations, and similar third-party reimbursement groups, such as health insurance companies, hiring case managers to place persons in nursing facilities and control their lengths of stay and types of care? Are these case managers placing patients at favorable negotiated rates based on acuity levels of care needs in this community? Is it possible to negotiate bed-hold contracts with other providers such as hospitals or health maintenance organizations that would guarantee payment for a specified number of the facility's beds, whether occupied or not? To what extent are Veterans Affairs patient contracts available in this community?

Market Considerations

The evaluator must visualize the desired roles of the proposed nursing facility in this environment. A needs assessment for the proposed facility must be conducted. Unmet need, however, is not the sole criterion. The company may seek to create new markets for nursing facility care not currently existing in that community as, increasingly, the nursing facility census is made up of a profile of several types of residents. The long-term resident is only one of several types of residents for which a facility might be planned. Nursing facility care is now more frequently characterized by niche marketing. Facilities commonly offer Medicare-funded rehabilitative care and other identifiable, increasingly specialized types of care for subacute conditions, ventilator care, Alzheimer's disease, wound care, behavioral care, and numerous others as a niche (Singh, 2016).

PHASE 2: SET SHORT- AND LONG-RANGE OBJECTIVES

Let us assume that a decision to build a new 100-bed facility was made. The next step is to develop broad goals, objectives, and plans that will direct the efforts. A broad goal might be to build, in keeping with the community's architecture, in a location convenient to the local hospital.

From a set of broad goal statements such as these, more specific objectives and plans can be developed. A short-range objective (Hitt et al., 2017; Robbins & Coulter, 2018) might be set to have a 100-bed facility in operation within 18 months and, as a long-range objective, a new wing of 60 additional beds within 10 years.

PHASE 3: DECIDE ON THE MEANS TO ACHIEVE THE OBJECTIVES

The next logical step is to translate broad planning goals into practical efforts on a more detailed basis. At this stage, allowable cost levels are determined, detailed plans for the building are drawn, and the building site is purchased.

The planning process has moved from the general to the specific: from broad goals to architectural plans detailed enough to direct every person connected with the project. In this way, broad goals are translated into specific and complex behaviors for everyone who takes part in realizing these goals, resulting in the project's culmination.

PLANNING FOR NEXT YEAR

We have used planning for a new facility as an example because this demonstrates the entire planning process. Most planning is of shorter range (done for the next year). As a practical matter, this planning is usually accomplished when the next fiscal year's budget (next 12 months) must be developed.

Once plans have been crystallized, the next step is to put them into effect to make them operational. Plans are given an organizational form in this fashion. The form depends on the administrators' perceptions of that structure and organizations' behavior in general.

PLAN TO CHANGE YOUR PLANS

No matter how carefully we plan, at any moment, circumstances can change. The three primary sources of residents today may be entirely different tomorrow. Perhaps this is why administering a nursing facility will remain challenging: Nothing is ever stagnant in the healthcare field.

Consider teaching people how to prepare mentally for difficult rock climbing. Looking up the mountain from the bottom, one mentally constructs a plan to reach the top. Once the climb begins, however, the view becomes different. Other, more promising routes to the top begin to appear. So, one changes the route. Mountain climbers come to expect that no matter how well they plan from the bottom of the mountain, they can count on running into the unexpected on the ascent. To those who enjoy finding new ways and improving current modes of doing things in the nursing facility, this is an exciting prospect, an opportunity for creativity. Nursing facility administrators who learn to deal with the unexpected, even to thrive on it, will endure in the profession. The unexpected often offers rich opportunities for successful innovation (Krupp & Schoemaker, 2014).

Successful nursing facility administrators can assume that they will meet new people once they begin to implement any plan, receive new information, learn new developments, and see possibilities about which they could not have known at the outset. The unexpected is uncontrollable. In today's nursing facility, uncertainty and surprise from both the public and private sectors are normal. What can be controlled is one's attitude toward the unanticipated. If one accepts that change is integral to living, one can look forward to it and be ready to take advantage of the new opportunities. Accepting the inevitability of changes is an attitude that will serve the administrator well.

In today's technologically driven world, be an early adapter: Embrace each new technology available to staff to improve resident care as it becomes available, not just when required by the government or when requested by the resident's family (Topol, 2015).

COMMON PITFALLS IN PRACTICE
- Despite most facilities being a part of a corporation, it is possible to have some input to planning. Corporate does not necessarily know your local community. You are the local expert on this and can provide invaluable information, driving the success of your facility.
- Plans are made to be broken. Understand that even the best-laid plans fail—therefore, you plan for this failure in your planning to begin with. If your plan does not change during the time you are implementing it, you are most likely doing something incorrectly!

(continued)

- Most administrators never meet their competitors, never visit their facilities, and know nothing about what is happening around them. Consider this your challenge to go against: Get out of your facility, meet other administrators, see other facilities, and learn about your community.

CASE STUDY

The Needs Assessment

Evaluate your urban area (or the nearest large town) for The Laurels chain owners to place a new nursing facility.

Phase 1. What governmental permissions will be needed; for example, zoning, building codes, local fire codes, and certificate of need?

- Competition: What is the level of unmet need in (your city/town)? What are present and projected bed capacities in the competitive area? At what rate could a facility be expected to fill? At what level should the facility operate in the near term, long term?
- Patient mix: What mix could be expected? What are the economic trends of the community, the area of competition?
- What role, roles, niche, etc., would any facility you recommend fill?

Phase 2. Set short- and long-range objectives for The Laurels owners. What size, style, and so on of the facility should be considered?

- What means will be needed? For example, what building site, cost levels, and so on?

Phase 3. Develop a preliminary budget recommendation to The Laurels owners.

1.4 ORGANIZING

Section Concepts

- *How organizations function*
- *The systems and subsystems that make up an organization*
- *Inputs, throughputs, outputs, policies, feedback, and control that are parts of each organization*
- *How to identify systems*
- *The characteristics of systems*

Consider as the Administrator . . .

- *Is it possible for you to understand an organization as complex as a nursing facility?*
- *Are there instances where systems do not work? If so, what do you do about it?*

NAB DOMAIN 2C: HUMAN RESOURCES; 2C9: HUMAN RESOURCE POLICIES (E.G., DRUG-FREE WORKPLACE, DISCIPLINE, JOB CLASSIFICATION, PHOTOGRAPHY AND VIDEO, SOCIAL MEDIA USAGE, MOBILE PHONE USAGE); 4A: LEADERSHIP

Organizing is a method of ensuring that the work necessary to achieve a goal gets broken down into segments, each handled by one person (Hitt et al., 2017; Robbins & Coulter, 2018). There must be no duplication of work. Efforts are directed toward accomplishing the goal by dividing the work up so that one person can do each job and to provide a means for coordinating the jobs done by different people—the managers' task.

Descriptions are written for each job. A job list for each position usually includes the following:

- The objectives (result to be accomplished)
- The duties and authorities of the position
- Its relationship to other positions in the organization
- A prepared organizational manual containing all job descriptions and several charts

One way to effectively organize the right jobs and the right workers consists of answering the following questions:

- What does the worker do? (worker functions)
- How does the worker do it? (methods and techniques)
- What aids are necessary? (machines, tools, and equipment)
- What is accomplished? (products, services produced)
- What knowledge, skills, and abilities are involved? (qualifications)

Organizing is the first step in the implementation of a plan. It is the process of translating plans into combinations of money, materials, and people.

All administrators organize their facilities according to some theory of organization. Their understanding of the organization is reflected in their day-to-day and year-to-year direction. For some administrators, this is a very thoughtful process; for others, it is relatively superficial. Nevertheless, all of them apply their concept of the organization through their behavior in daily decision-making.

SYSTEMS

Organizations are systems of interactions among the three available inputs: people, materials, and money (Hitt et al., 2017; Robbins & Coulter, 2018).

A great deal of literature exists from recent decades about systems theory. This literature appeared after World War II and has paralleled the development of computer applications to management tasks. The systems concept is primarily a way of thinking about the task of managing any organization. It offers the manager a framework for visualizing the internal and external environment of the organization (Singh, 2016).

A system is defined as an organized or complex whole, an assembling or combining of things or parts forming a complex or single whole (Cole & Kelley, 2020; Robbins & Coulter, 2018). Stated more simply, the idea of systems helps us figure out how things are put together. How, for example, do all nursing facility departments relate to each other, the community, and the rest of the world that affects them (Robbins & Coulter, 2018; Robbins & Judge, 2019)?

Systems theory is a tool for making sense of our world by clarifying the organization's interrelationships. The administrator uses systems theory to determine the relationship between the facility and the larger outside community.

1.4.1 DESCRIPTION OF THE ORGANIZATION AS A SYSTEM

Section Concepts

● *How to think about the facility as a conglomeration of systems and subsystems*

Consider as the Administrator . . .

● *Are there any organizational functions that cannot be broken down into subsystems? If so, why is this of concern for you as an administrator?*

NAB DOMAIN 4A1: ORGANIZATIONAL STRUCTURES (E.G., DEPARTMENTS, FUNCTIONS, SYSTEMIC PROCESSES)

Systems descriptions vary from entirely nonmathematical to highly sophisticated mathematical models demanding specially trained personnel and computers (Hitt et al., 2017; Robbins & Coulter, 2018). The model we present does not require quantification, although numerical weights could be given to each of its elements.

OVERVIEW

In Figure 1.1, we illustrate a systems model that may be useful to the nursing facility administrator in the daily management of the facility. This model consists of the following elements: inputs, processor, outputs, control, plans of action, feedback, and environment.

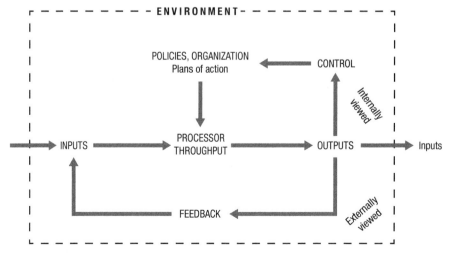

FIGURE 1.1 Simplified systems model.

Organizations such as nursing facilities use inputs to get work done, resulting in outputs that can be the desired outputs or the undesired/unintended outputs. The residents, their families, and other stakeholders evaluate the quality and acceptability of outputs and then react, and the facility receives feedback. The outputs are also evaluated by the administrators and compared to what was sought. Suppose the results, or outputs, do not conform to the organizational policy and action plans. In that case, the administrator takes control (plans of correction) to bring the outputs into line with those planned. All these activities occur within the organization's constraints by the external environment (Cole & Kelley, 2020).

INPUTS

NAB DOMAIN 2A: FINANCIAL MANAGEMENT; 2B: RISK MANAGEMENT; 2C: HUMAN RESOURCES

The inputs to any organization can be described as three elements: money, people, and materials. Inputs are elements the facility administrators can change and use to their advantage. Inputs are the resources available to the organization. The administrator and staff holding line authority, such as the department and area heads, must decide how to allocate available resources so that they are optimized effectively. Allocating and optimizing resources and programs is a stewardship skill. To allocate resources is to divide resources among the various competing possible uses of those resources. Optimizing resources is allocating resources with the result that the most effective possible use of these resources is achieved.

How Can Inputs Be Increased?

A primary concern of the system's administrator is how inputs can be renewed and increased. To accomplish this, organizations take in resources (Hitt et al., 2017; Robbins & Coulter, 2018). Just as the human body must have oxygen from the air and food from the environment, the nursing facility must always draw renewed energy supplies from other institutions, people, and the material environment.

As residents are rehabilitated and return home or die, more residents must be admitted into the facility for it to continue functioning. As the food is consumed in the dining rooms, more food supplies must be brought in so that the facility's work (caring for residents) may continue. As employees leave for other jobs, new staff must be recruited. As the month's cash income is spent paying the facility bills, more revenue from residents must be brought in.

PROCESSOR

The processor is the work the organization accomplishes. Organizations transform the energy (inputs) available to them, just as the human body converts starch and sugar into heat and action. The nursing facility cares for residents. Work is accomplished. Inputs are reorganized (e.g., food supplies are blended into recipes for the next meal). This process is sometimes called throughput. It is the actual work that the organization performs (Hitt et al., 2017; Robbins & Coulter, 2018).

The nursing facility takes its inputs (staff, money, materials) and reorganizes them into active caring for residents. In essence, nursing facilities take money resources from residents and other sources and use those funds to hire staff and provide materials needed (buildings, beds, food, syringes, tissues, etc.) to provide resident care.

OUTPUT

NAB DOMAIN 1A: QUALITY OF CARE; 1B: QUALITY OF LIFE; 1B8: CARE RECIPIENT (AND REPRESENTATIVE) SATISFACTION; 3B3: CERTIFICATION AND LICENSURE REQUIREMENTS FOR THE ORGANIZATION; 4B1: MISSION, VISION, AND VALUE STATEMENTS; 4B5: PUBLIC RELATIONS AND EXTERNAL STAKEHOLDERS (E.G., HOSPITALS, REFERRALS SOURCES, LOCAL COMMUNITY, DONORS)

The work that nursing facilities do (caring for residents) is the output, the product of the organization's work. The organization exports some products (services) to the environment. The output can be good care or "bad" care. The surveyors visit primarily to identify inadequate care and verify plans of correction. They are there to assist in ensuring that only "good" care is happening.

Nursing facilities produce services for residents. This service may take many forms, such as day care as the output for an adult day program, mobility as the output of a physical therapy program, self-feeding as the output of a restorative feeding program, meals served to senior citizens in the community, and so forth. Nursing facilities can and do provide an increasing variety of outputs.

Output Evaluation by the Facility's Stakeholders

The facility's outputs are evaluated by its stakeholders: the persons and groups that are the exchange partners. These are the suppliers, the employees, bank creditors, visiting regulators, advocacy groups, and other healthcare providers. It is the administrator's job to help communicate the mission, vision, and values (MVVs) to them. Each of the stakeholders needs to be continually educated about the facility's contributions. Hospitals need to learn the values and care vision of the facility for its residents. Suppliers such as contractors delivering food to dietary or providing pest control services need to buy into the facility's values and mission. Physicians in the community need to share the facility's vision for resident care; this will encourage referrals to the facility and make physicians positive about providing care to their patients in the facility.

Some of the ways the facility can educate its stakeholders include:

- Providing information on respite care
- Holding fundraising events for local not-for-profit organizations
- Educational seminars for the public on such matters as Medicare and Medicaid
- Classes for persons providing care to family members at home
- Becoming a local Meals on Wheels center

A conscious program effort to identify, foster, and maintain positive relationships with key stakeholders will serve the facility well. Suppose a positive relationship exists with the dietary food contractor. In that case, the contractor will make sure the facility receives priority for food delivery in emergencies, such as hurricanes or ice storms. The facility can help educate the local hospital discharge workers on such matters as facility admission requirements, such as having physician's orders for each resident immediately before or at admission.

Stakeholders must also be educated by the facility staff on regulatory requirements and standards of care. Few physicians read the Federal Requirements and Guidelines to Surveyors rules and regulations governing resident rights and the Minimum Data Set (MDS) requirements for periodic care evaluations.

The most direct stakeholders in the facility are the care recipients and their support network. The residents' families and friends are vitally important to the facility's reputation in the community. It is useful to invite family members and other support persons to participate in feedback sessions about the quality of care being received. An implemented policy of responding to every support network member's suggestions and ideas will benefit the facility. Care evaluation forms can be kept available in the reception area and given to visitors as they arrive or leave the facility.

Similarly, the stakeholders continually evaluate and judge the work: the output of the facility. The stakeholders hear what the community thinks about the facility and can provide valuable feedback to the facility for use in its decision-making.

CONTROL OF QUALITY

Control is discussed at greater length in the following. To explore the systems diagram in Figure 1.1, control is described only briefly here. Control is the most essential tool available to administrators in the process of keeping the organization on course. Control is the corrective action taken after the evaluation of outputs by the organizational decision-makers. The intended output may not have been achieved.

In the nursing facility, the administrator exercises control of quality by comparing the actual care given to residents and the actual output with the care called for in the organizational policies and plans of action. This is at the very heart of what administrators do. Just as important, every nursing facility administrator is responsible for comparing the ultimate financial results with the expected financial results.

Controlling quality is the process of asking if the work accomplished (actual output) by the facility is up to expected standards and, if not, taking corrective actions to remedy the problem (Hitt et al., 2017; Robbins & Coulter, 2018). Here we are discussing the actual standards the organization has established for itself through its policies and plans of action.

Several "standards of care" exist for nursing facilities. Among them are the federal requirements for care and the standards imposed by each state for a license to operate.

POLICIES AND PLANS OF ACTION

To illustrate the system configuration we use, let us simply refer to policies and plans of action as the guidelines the administrator uses to compare the output against the expected. As the arrows in Figure 1.1 indicate, the administrator uses the organization's policies (broad statements of goals and procedures) and plans of action, which are the more specific procedures designed to govern the implementation of the policies (Robbins & Coulter, 2018).

Numerous organizations are geared to set policies and impose plans of action for nursing facilities in the United States. This has been a response, in part, to the financing of nursing facility care by the CMS and OBRA itself.

Congress imposed detailed operating regulations, called requirements, on facilities prepared to accept Medicare patients. At the request of Congress, individual states have also issued very specific sets of policies and detailed requirements for facilities that wish to serve Medicaid patients. Many state surveyors leave little room for the exercise of discretion, while others have allowed a more permissive hand.

Nevertheless, there are many areas in which nursing facilities must develop and implement their own policies and plans for action. One such area is food services. Every facility develops policies by which it hopes to control the quality of food served to its residents.

To summarize, administrators compare the results obtained with the results expected and then take steps to reorganize the inputs and/or reorganize the processor (the work itself) to more nearly achieve the desired standards (Krupp & Schoemaker, 2014).

FEEDBACK

Feedback is a form of control, but feedback is used here to refer to the external responses to the output ("good" or "bad" resident care provided, etc.) by the nursing facility.

Nursing facility outputs have many dimensions, such as providing long-term, short-term, subacute, or rehabilitative care to patients hospitalized before returning home.

Resident Council Feedback

Feedback from residents and their families represents a key source of evaluative help for the administrator and staff. Many nursing facilities have resident councils, and many have family groups as an additional form of feedback to the facility. Typically, the social worker assumes the primary responsibility for maintaining an active resident council.

Regulatory Feedback

Inevitably and systematically, members of the community and other individuals, such as state inspectors, complaint investigators, and ombudspersons, evaluate the results of nursing facility efforts to provide quality care to residents. Several decades ago, congressional feedback to the nursing facility industry resulted in the considerable reshaping of the industry's inputs when these lawmakers established the requirements then called the Conditions of Participation.

OBRA, which contained Medicare and Medicaid reforms, imposed even more stringent requirements. Laws passed by Congress and subsequent regulations prescribe how nursing facilities must configure inputs (e.g., sufficient staff hours per patient day, square feet of floor space per patient, and like issues). Consequently, the potential freedom to determine operating policies is reduced. It is frequently asserted that the nursing facility industry is one of the most heavily regulated, coming in a close second place to nuclear power plants. However, in more recent days, it appears that nursing facilities may have surpassed nuclear power regulations.

External Feedback

External feedback to an industry is typically not manifested in such powerful and influential terms as stringent federal and state regulations. Hospitals, for example, are lightly regulated by comparison to nursing facilities. The feedback is normally expressed through community reactions about the quality of work (outputs) being produced, such as the following:

- Word-of-mouth evaluations
- Newspaper articles, radio, and television commentary
- The reputation enjoyed by the facility's staff that leads potential employees to consider it a desirable or undesirable place to work
- The number of potential residents applying for admission to the facility
- The willingness of hospital discharge workers to refer patients to a facility

The reader can add to the list. All these elements constitute what is referred to in Figure 1.1 as the environment.

ENVIRONMENT

The environment consists of all relevant external forces that affect the nursing facility.

Defining the Environment

Defining one's organization's relevant environment is perhaps the most complex and least apparent aspect of viewing organizations as systems. The environment consists of opportunities and constraints. One way to conceptualize this is to ask two questions:

1. Does it relate meaningfully to my objectives? If so, it is an opportunity.
2. Can I do anything about it? If not, it is a constraint.

If the answer to the first question is yes and to the second question is no, it is a constraint in the relevant environment. If the answer to both questions is yes, it is an opportunity for the facility.

From the systems perspective, the entire world is interconnected in one large network. The challenge is to identify the aspects of the external world that now affect or may eventually affect the facility in its attempt to achieve objectives, such as serving residents and making a profit. This is the first step in the management process: forecasting.

The environment, then, is both a set of constraints within which the facility must operate and a set of opportunities that the facility's administration may seize (Hitt et al., 2017; Robbins & Coulter, 2018).

Some easily recognizable constraints in a nursing facility's environment might include the following:

- Federal, state, and local regulations
- The number of other facilities operating in the area
- The availability of qualified applicants for positions to be filled in the facility
- The availability of foods at affordable prices

- State and federal Medicare and Medicaid practices and reimbursement policies
- Availability and costs of money
- Inflation or deflation rates

Some recognizable opportunities might include the following:

- The increasing availability of managed care contracts for individual residents at negotiated rates
- The opportunity to offer "higher tech" services
- The opportunity to identify and serve niches in care needs
- The unprecedented increasing number of frail older adults who will need nursing care
- Pressures for the increased number of beds due to the aging of the "baby boomer" population explosion that followed World War II (these persons, born between 1945 and 1963, constitute one of the largest populations entering nursing facilities)

1.4.2 IDENTIFYING SYSTEMS

Section Concepts

- *How different employees have different points of view on systems*

Consider as the Administrator . . .

- *Who defines the systems by which a facility operates? How much of this do you control?*

NAB DOMAIN 4A1: ORGANIZATIONAL STRUCTURES (E.G., DEPARTMENTS, FUNCTIONS, SYSTEMIC PROCESSES)

The outputs of one system usually become the inputs for the next system (Hitt et al., 2017; Robbins & Coulter, 2018); an example is the set of relationships among hospitals, nursing facilities, home health agencies, and hospice providers.

Hospital patients who no longer need acute care and who need facility-based nursing care (the outputs of the hospital) can become the nursing facility's inputs—new-resident admissions. A rehabilitated nursing facility resident who no longer needs facility-based nursing care but requires follow-up home care (the nursing facility output) becomes the home health agency's input or perhaps the hospice agency's.

We have been using the nursing facility as an entity to illustrate the systems concept. We could have selected another level of function within the facility, for instance, the department of nursing.

WHO DEFINES THE SYSTEM?

A system and what composes it are left entirely to the discretion of the person who describes or analyzes it. This may be one of the subtler concepts in systems theory. The fact is that the user decides what to designate as a system for their purposes.

The CMS, which pays 80% to 90% of all nursing facility bills in the United States, defines "the system" as the MDS and the changing requirements that come with it, such as the Patient Driven Payment Model (PDPM). The chief executive officer of a large nursing facility chain always considers the several hundred facilities as the system. The individual nursing facility administrator may conceive of the departments operating in the facility as the system. The maintenance department manager may consider their department as the system.

One of the systems concept's virtues is that it is almost infinitely adaptable to the needs of the individual user. Anybody can define any set of interrelationships as the system for purposes of description or analysis. All of us use systems analysis in our everyday thinking about the interrelationships of things around us. The systems theory and model described here is an analytic tool that the administrator can use to solve organizational problems as they arise.

We see constant change in the landscape of what the "hot button" items are when it comes to F-tag citations nationwide. It seems that COVID-19 has entirely changed what is getting cited and how often. As of March 2021, the top 10 F-Tags were as follows:

- F0884—Reporting to National Health Safety Network (NHSN)
- F0880—Infection prevention and control
- F0886—COVID-19 testing—Residents and staff
- F0689—Free of accidents hazards/supervision/devices
- F0684—Quality of care
- F0580—Notify of changes (injury/decline/room, etc.)
- F0883—Influenza and pneumococcal immunizations
- F0885—Reporting—Residents, representatives, and families
- F0686—Treatment/services to prevent/heal pressure ulcers
- F0609—Reporting of alleged violations (Finck-Boyle, 2021)

1.4.3 ADDITIONAL CHARACTERISTICS OF SYSTEMS

Section Concepts

- *How one system becomes an input for another system*
- *How organizations grow and maximize their basic character*
- *Why organizations resist change, become increasingly complex, and are difficult to predict*

Consider as the Administrator . . .

- *What information do you need to be able to predict future trends in the field?*

Social science researchers have identified several characteristics of systems that the reader may find useful as analytic tools.

Each system's output furnishes the stimulus for repeating the cycle (Robbins & Coulter, 2018). In nursing care facilities, the successfully cared-for resident (the desired outcome of the nursing facilities efforts) furnishes the source of more inputs:

other persons apply for admission to the facility to replace the departing resident. The new resident brings renewed energy in the form of a renewed source of continuing income to the facility and thereby furnishes a renewal of the facility's capacity to continue to pay employees and provide services.

The administrator can view the nursing facility as a dynamic system the essence of which is the cycle of activities (providing care to residents, making sufficient income) for which they are responsible.

ORGANIZATIONAL GROWTH

Nursing facilities and similar social organizations can grow indefinitely.

Scientists speak of the entropic process, a universal law of nature that all organisms move toward death (Hitt et al., 2017). All of us, for example, realize that one day we will die because one or more of our vital systems come to a halt.

In sharp contrast, a nursing facility or chain not only does not have to die but can keep on growing, with no time constraints, as long as it receives more energy from the environment than it consumes. In this way, organizations can be said to acquire negative entropy.

Organizations tend to try to grow—not in every case, of course, but in general. Organizational theorists have called this the tendency of organizations to maximize the ratio of imported to expended energy. An organization's growth rate within specific ranges is dramatic if it exists in a medium that makes available unrestricted amounts of additional inputs. The significance for administrators is that organizations, unlike people, are not subject to disintegration if they can keep adding to their resources and that organizations, like people, tend to try to grow. At one time, American hospitals added vastly to their expensive equipment and procedures because Congress had made virtually unlimited resources available through reimbursement for whatever they chose to charge under Medicare. In more recent years, Congress has been progressively limiting what it will reimburse hospitals and has even put forth policies that punish underperforming facilities. Growth may be qualitative (better care) or quantitative (a larger patient census or more facilities being added to the chain).

MAXIMIZING BASIC CHARACTER

Another important aspect of organizations is that as they grow, they attempt to accommodate the world around them to meet their own needs (Hitt et al., 2017; Robbins & Coulter, 2018). For example, in planning for an extended care system, the nursing facility associations place themselves at the heart of the system. On the other hand, the American Hospital Association envisions the American healthcare system with hospitals at its core. The insurance companies are similarly convinced of their strategic importance at the very center of such a system. Each type of care provider maximizes its fundamental character and views itself as the "center of the world." This mindset is often used as a strategic advantage by these organizations.

MAINTENANCE FUNCTIONS: "ATHEROSCLEROSIS"

Once in place, organizations become creatures of habit and develop a tendency to resist change. There can be a strong effort to keep the current relationship pattern with others from changing at all. Sometimes this is called organizational hardening of the arteries (atherosclerosis; Halter et al., 2017). Organizations that have become set in their ways will try to maintain the status quo through several devices:

1. Any internal or external situation that threatens to force a change in the organization is countered by employees seeking to retain their old patterns and modes of operation (Robbins & Coulter, 2018; Robbins & Judge, 2019). For example, a nursing facility faced with a "disruptive employee" agitating for change will terminate the relationship with the employee (Hitt et al., 2017).
2. Administrators, when confronted with external changes that might affect the organization, will try to ignore them. For example, if their resident census declines while it increases in nearby facilities, the tendency will be to find excuses rather than examine if other facilities offer better services.
3. Resisting change, many organizations will attempt to cope with external forces that might force them to change by acquiring control over them. For example, if a nursing facility chain loses patients to a competing freestanding group of facilities, the chain might attempt to acquire those other facilities rather than remedy its own situation (Hitt et al., 2017; Robbins & Coulter, 2018).

Nursing facilities and nursing facility chains can fall from leading to trailing the pack. How can this happen? A Massachusetts Institute of Technology study on productivity attributes this possibility to "a deep reservoir of outmoded attitudes and policies" at most organizations (Dertouzos et al., 1989).

Rapid and unanticipated changes are a permanent fixture of the managerial landscape of today.

WE HAVE ALWAYS DONE IT THIS WAY

Once firmly in place, systems, policies, procedures, plans, organizational approaches, and assumptions become the facility's standard operations, its "sacred cows." They are sacrosanct because it has "always" been done this way. They are created by the training received in nursing, medical, or physical therapy school. In this way, creativity is stifled, and competitive strength is weakened. Today, anything that remains unchallenged or untouched for very long can become the sacred cow of tomorrow.

Sacred cows are difficult to round up for a variety of reasons. For many adult children, putting their mother or father in physical restraints so they will not fall is one such sacred cow despite all the research evidence showing that restraints do not stop falls and that wearing restraints makes injuries worse when someone does fall while wearing them.

Sacred cows may be untouchable because the state inspectors want operations done the federal and state way or are the administrator's unique concerns or relate to one department's closely guarded turf.

You cannot move fast if you are following a herd of sacred cows. Electronic trails represent people trying to keep tabs on other people. All this occurs even though the real purpose of systems as we have described them previously is to empower, not control, people and to liberate staff to experiment with new ways to meet resident needs, not to tie them down. The nursing facility industry is full of sacred cows: federal, state, and local officials; physicians; registered dietitians; the residents' children; and a host of other well-meaning individuals see to that. However, it is up to us to use published best practices to begin changing these ideas. Considering all this, we should briefly mention two other characteristics of organizations.

ORGANIZATIONS GROW INCREASINGLY COMPLEX

New organizations tend to be simple at their start and then become increasingly complex as they grow. The human personality is similar. As infants, we have few perceptions. As we grow, we begin to build ever more complex and complicated perceptions of the world around us. The personality we develop is a system with no physical boundaries. A social organization such as a nursing facility is also a system with no physical limitations (Hitt et al., 2017; Robbins & Coulter, 2018; Robbins & Judge, 2019).

Just as the human personality becomes progressively more sophisticated, social organizations move toward the multiplication and elaboration of roles with greater specialization of functions. For example, the mom-and-pop nursing facilities are nearly extinct today and have given way to increasingly more extensive and more sophisticated facilities offering medically complex, highly computerized services.

The organization of American medicine provides another illustration. In the 1800s, 80% of all American physicians were general practitioners. Only a few were specialists. Today, we see a significant change in this area and a change that continues further. General practitioners are in a class of their own, referred to as primary care specialists. The rest of the physicians are made up of specialists in their fields. We see a further compounding of this field using "physician extenders," such as nurse practitioners and physician assistants. These fields have seen a significant change, with doctorally trained nurse practitioners (Doctors of Nursing Practice [DNPs]) having full practice rights in many states today (with the numbers thankfully increasing).

The process of nursing facilities grouping into increasingly larger and competing chains (i.e., multiplication and elaboration of roles) has multiplied the number of possible management jobs available to persons interested in such a career. Middle-level and upper-level positions are now available for licensed nursing facility administrators in corporate management offices.

Nursing care is growing more complex. Long gone are the days of custodial residents in nursing facilities. These residents often seek placement in assisted living or independent living facilities today. Nursing facilities have become a true step-down from acute care. We care for residents today who would have been hospital patients a few years ago. We have seen increasing complexity every year, and many facilities are providing ventilator care, specialty wound programs, and in-house dialysis, all things we would not have even considered in this environment previously.

ORGANIZATIONS ARE DIFFICULT TO PREDICT

There need not be a single strategy for an organization to achieve an objective. We have argued that organizations are dynamic systems of social interactions. Because the situation is volatile, there is low predictability (Hitt et al., 2017; Robbins & Coulter, 2018).

An organization can reach its goals from different starting points and by a variety of routes. If, for example, a small, financially weak chain wanted to take over a financially more robust and larger chain, there are many possible alternatives. They could try to compete more successfully, thus weakening the larger chain and making it more susceptible to takeover. They could raise enough venture capital to buy out the larger group (Hitt et al., 2017). They could arrange to be taken over by an unrelated corporation with considerable liquid assets, thereby enabling them to buy the currently more robust and larger chain.

The top 10 list of nursing facility chains has changed rapidly over the past several years. Predictability is equally low in many fields, for example, hospitals, the assisted living industry, multiunit senior housing, the home healthcare industry, and health maintenance organizations, to mention a few.

COMMON PITFALLS IN PRACTICE

- You will find that the process for making positive change has many bumps in the road. Finding those in the facility who are against your change can be your best defense for making that change. It is your job as the administrator to help them see the reasons for your change and to help get them to understand why the change needs to occur.
- The "we've always done it this way" mentality is prevalent in every facility. Nobody likes to change—and you can use this to your advantage. Make employees part of this change process. Include everyone in the facility in your organizing and allow them to help you make positive change instead of working against you.
- New administrators often make incorrect assumptions in that "they are right." Whereas this might be true in certain cases, seeking feedback from everyone you can is the easiest way to assert change in a facility. The more people feel that they have been heard, the more people will be willing to be a positive force for you.

1.5 STAFFING

Section Concepts

- The definition of staffing and its role in the facility

Consider as the Administrator . . .

- How do you know when you are hiring the right person for the right job?
- Do we have the luxury of holding out for that "right" employee to come along anymore?

NAB DOMAIN 2C2: SELECTION AND HIRING PRACTICES (E.G., EEOC, INTERVIEWING, ADVERSE IMPACT, PROTECTED CLASSES, OCCUPATIONAL QUALIFICATIONS); 2C4: ORGANIZATIONAL STAFFING REQUIREMENTS AND REPORTING (E.G., PBJ)

Staffing is hiring the right person for the right job in an organization. It is one of the most challenging tasks the administrator and their department managers face because it is seldom possible to predict from an interview and recommendations how a person will work out on the job. The number of variables is almost infinite, and many of them are difficult to recognize beforehand. Factually, many poorly qualified candidates are skillful at presenting themselves well in initial interviews.

Staffing patterns of nursing facilities are more prescribed than for most other healthcare institutions. The scrutiny around staffing results from federal requirements and/or state regulations, which carefully delineate qualifications for each type of staff position and require minimum staffing (or, in the judgment of the surveyors, sufficient staffing) in nearly every area of the facility. Many states have clear expectations and staffing ratios; many others do not. The administrator must have a mastery of these ever-changing regulations.

The success of the nursing facility depends directly on adequate staffing. Nursing care merely is providing care for residents. The interactions between residents and staff determine the quality of life in the nursing facility. Physical facilities are essential, but once they are in place at a minimally adequate level, the resident's satisfaction with the facility varies directly with their satisfaction with the staff's performance.

The administrator may choose to delegate the coordination of the hiring process to a human resources director or assign it to the individual department managers (typically) with the administrator's advice and consent.

COMMON PITFALLS IN PRACTICE

- Ensure that you are doing your best to hire the right person for the job. Do not hire simply because someone applied and they are qualified for the job. This might seem to be what you need at the time but often backfires later.
- Administrators often do not attempt to develop relationships with their staff. You need to operate on a first-name basis. Know your staff and a bit about their personal lives. Ask about their children, their continuing education, or other things you know about them. This "humanizes" you and shows that you care as the administrator.

1.6 DIRECTING

Section Concepts

- *The purpose and functions of policies in a facility*
- *Differences between policies and procedures*
- *How to think about the art of decision-making*

- *Understanding the different types of leadership and knowing which to use when*
- *How change is a part of our daily work and how change affects the facility*
- *Definitions of power and authority, sources of power, and constraints on power*
- *Communication skills and the levels of communication that exist in the facility*
- *Organizational values and norms*

Consider as the Administrator . . .

- *Might it be better for a facility to not have its own policies?*

NAB DOMAIN 4A1: ORGANIZATIONAL STRUCTURES (E.G., DEPARTMENTS, FUNCTIONS, SYSTEMIC PROCESSES); 4A3: ORGANIZATIONAL BEHAVIOR (E.G., ORGANIZATIONAL CULTURE, TEAM BUILDING, GROUP DYNAMICS); 4A4: LEADERSHIP PRINCIPLES (E.G., COMMUNICATION, STYLES, MENTORING, COACHING, PERSONAL PROFESSIONAL DEVELOPMENT)

Directing is the process of communicating to employees what is to be done by each of them and helping them accomplish it. An earlier step, organizing, included breaking down the work necessary to achieve the organizational goals into work assignments that one person can handle. Directing is an aspect of the organizational activity in which the actual work gets completed.

Several important management concepts will be included under this heading:

- Policymaking
- Decision-making
- Leadership
- Power and authority
- Communication skills
- Organizational norms and values
- Additional related concepts

Directing involves referencing each of these key concepts to arrive at the goal of a successful program.

1.6.1 POLICYMAKING

Section Concepts

- *How policies are developed and used in the facility*
- *Differences between policies and procedures*

Consider as the Administrator . . .

- *Is there such a thing as too many policies?*
- *Can having too many or too specific of policies backfire on you?*

NAB DOMAIN 3B: REGULATORY COMPLIANCE; 4A5: GOVERNANCE (E.G., BOARD OF DIRECTORS, GOVERNING BODIES, CORPORATE ENTITIES, ADVISORY BOARDS)

The governing body for the facility sets the mission and goals. The facility administrator's and upper-level staff's role is to develop, implement, monitor, and evaluate policies and procedures that comply with the directives of the governing body. The governing board may, for example, set services primarily to persons experiencing various forms of dementia such as Alzheimer's disease as the mission. A goal could be to establish facilities in which the resident population is at least 90% persons with dementia. It is the job of the facility's upper-level staff to develop, implement, and evaluate policies that staff can follow to achieve the service mission. Policies would be established for admissions specifying the criteria for admission to the facility. The governing body's role is to set broad policies such as these. The facility's role is to write and implement more specific policies and procedures to implement the mission.

NAB DOMAIN 3B: REGULATORY COMPLIANCE; 4A1: ORGANIZATIONAL STRUCTURES (E.G., DEPARTMENTS, FUNCTIONS, SYSTEMIC PROCESSES)

The administrator's ultimate goal is to design a program in which every member of the organization makes the same decisions given the same set of circumstances. This action is the ultimate purpose of policies and procedures. To this end, the administrator attempts to persuade the entire staff to precisely carry out their responsibilities as the administrator would like them to.

PURPOSE AND FUNCTION

The administrator cannot be everywhere at once, 24 hours a day, throughout the facility (Cole & Kelley, 2020). However, the administrator can make policies that direct employees' activities everywhere in the facility 24 hours a day. These policies function to communicate what the management expects in any situation on the job.

It is, of course, neither possible nor desirable to establish policies for every conceivable situation. However, a person can provide guidelines or policies that become the framework within which the employee decides what to do in each case requiring action on behalf of the nursing facility. Policy is a verbal, written, or implied comprehensive guide that sets up boundaries, supplying the general limits and direction in which managerial action will occur.

Policies are used to help keep decisions within the planners' areas because they provide for some consistency in what employees decide in specific situations, usually under repetitive conditions. Policies reveal the facility administrator's intentions concerning the behavior of employees, residents, and the public in the future. Policies are set before the need for employee knowledge arises. Two illustrations may be useful.

Management cannot know when, where, or even if a fire will break out in the facility. By developing a complete set of procedures for personnel to follow in case of fire, the administrator can communicate—before the occasion arises—precisely what each employee in the facility must do if a fire should occur. This policy would be included in a more comprehensive manual of disaster procedures for personnel to follow in many different disaster situations.

The use of clinical pathways has become quite popular in the era of increased interest in quality improvement. A clinical pathway is a tool that nursing personnel can utilize to make decisions. A popular tool in nursing facilities is the Interventions to Reduce Acute Care Transfers (INTERACT) program that guides a nurse through the decision-making process to ensure that all potential considerations have been taken before seeking out the authorization of the physician to transfer a resident to the hospital. The tool provides a flow sheet style format of yes/no and if/then statements to allow a nurse to make an appropriate and consistent decision on discharge.

DEFINING POLICIES AND PROCEDURES

The reader may have noticed the use of the word "procedures" in the earlier discussion rather than "policies." Writers in the field of management use the terms *policies*, *procedures*, and *plans of action* to indicate the movement from generalized statements of intention (policies) to a specific spelling out of the method and then to a step-by-step (procedures) plan of action for implementation.

It may be useful to think of the following set of concepts, which moves from the general to the specific, setting forth behaviors the manager wishes the employees to exercise.

EXAMPLES OF POLICIES AND PROCEDURES

Fire Preparedness

General goals or objectives may be stated for the facility. In the area of fire preparedness, it might be "to have our facility employees completely prepared to take appropriate action in case of fire." The administrator might then draw up a general policy statement indicating that the head of the housekeeping department would develop a step-by-step plan of action based on Life Safety Code requirements for every department to follow in case of fire. This plan is a set of procedures, a highly detailed plan of specific actions that each employee would be expected to follow in case of fire.

Notice that at each level, the degrees of freedom within which decisions could be made are reduced. The head of housekeeping could develop various configurations for employee responsibilities, but by the time the individual employee became involved, the degrees of freedom had nearly vanished. The responsibility in the case of fire had moved from the general goal or policy of fire preparedness to a detailed set of instructions or procedures to be followed to the letter. "The moment you hear the fire alarm, proceed immediately to Station J on the blue wing and report to the nurse in charge" is an example of a procedure.

Food Preparation

The owners might set a policy goal of offering an outstanding selection of first-quality food to the facility's residents. It becomes the responsibility of each progressively lower level of management to implement this policy. The food service director must take this communicated policy or goal and develop a series of procedures for the kitchen staff's decision-making that result in the actual service of an outstanding selection of first-quality food to the residents.

General policies are developed at each level of management. Typically, the amount of specificity increases at each lower level. The food service manager may, for example, announce a policy to the food service supervisor responsible for salads that there be a sufficient variety with specified proportions of crisp fresh lettuce every evening. The supervisor may then write out a step-by-step set of procedures for the kitchen worker who prepares salads.

The salad worker's set of steps start at 4:00 p.m. each afternoon, beginning, perhaps, with removing the lettuce from the refrigerator, is an example of a set of procedures. The broad policy of excellence in food service promulgated by the administrator has now been translated into individual steps for the salad worker in the kitchen to follow at 4:00 p.m. each afternoon to ensure crisp lettuce is served each evening. Sounds simple but ask the residents. Too few nursing facilities succeed in serving a good variety of salads with crisp lettuce. Interesting salads 365 days a year is but one of hundreds of complex tasks that must be successfully accomplished every 24 hours. Additionally, a simple recipe for chocolate-chip cookies could be considered a set of procedures.

Insertion of a Peripheral Device

A policy statement regarding peripheral devices might read as follows: "It is the policy of this facility to permit nurses to insert peripheral devices only after 20 hours of specialized training and certification by the director of nursing that the nurse has qualified."

A procedure statement regarding insertion of a peripheral device and administration of continuous solution might read as follows:

1. Verify physician's orders. Verify resident identity. Check for allergies.
2. Compare the label on the solution with the order.
3. Wash hands.
4. Assemble the equipment and supplies.
5. Inspect the solution and container.
6. Close the flow clamp on the tubing.
7. Attach the administration set to the fluid container. Hang on the intravenous (IV) pole.
8. Prime the IV therapy tubing by squeezing the drip chamber to fill half full; open the flow clamp until the tubing is primed; close the flow clamp.
9. Explain the procedure to the resident; position the resident.
10. Apply a tourniquet to the extremity (optional).
11. Select catheter insertion site, cleanse the site with antimicrobial swab; start at the center of the site, use a circular motion moving outward.
12. Repeat with an antimicrobial swab. Allow to completely dry on the skin for at least 30 seconds.
13. Don gloves.
14. Place the thumb below the intended venipuncture site; gently draw the skin toward you.
15. For a wing-tipped needle, hold the needle by the wings, with the bevel up, at 45° angle to the skin surface, penetrate the skin surface, lower the angle of the needle almost parallel with the skin, and pierce the vein. Observe for blood return; release the tourniquet if one has been applied. Secure wings with tape.

16. Attach IV tubing or extension set if used for intermittent infusion. Start solution at a slow rate.
17. Observe for signs of infiltration at the venipuncture site.
18. Cover the venipuncture site with a transparent dressing. Make a small loop with infusion tubing and secure it with tape.
19. Check and regulate flow rate according to physician's orders.
20. Place label on dressing, indicating the following: date and time, type, length and gauge, and nurse's initials.
21. Discard used equipment appropriately.

Documentation

Record the procedure in the resident's medical record. Include the following:

- Type, length, and gauge of device
- Date and time of insertion
- Site of insertion
- Resident's response
- Number of attempts
- Type of dressing applied
- Solution and rate of administration
- Nurse's initials/signature

TWO CASES ON THE POWERFUL ROLES POLICIES CAN PLAY

CASE STUDY (AN ACTUAL CASE)

Man Dies After Nurses Forget to Turn on Respirator

A small town in Pennsylvania—Only the comforting sound of their footsteps and the swishing of their white uniforms could be heard as the nurse and the respiratory technician made their rounds at the local nursing facility. It was about 4:20 a.m. when the pair entered room 125, the coroner's report said.

The registered nurse stood on the left side of the patient's bed next to his respirator, across from the respiratory technician, as they began clearing the 65-year-old patient's breathing passages, the report said.

Irritated by a "disturbing" abnormal noise produced by the respirator, the nurse turned off the machine and continued the suctioning work, the report said. When the women finished, they left the room.

At 4:40 a.m., an alarm on a pump began ringing in the patient's room. The nurse returned and found the patient unresponsive. She also noticed the respirator was still off. She frantically turned the respirator on and called 911, but it was too late. Attempts to revive the patient failed. At 5:30 a.m., the self-employed auto mechanic was declared dead, the victim of what the coroner called a "therapeutic misadventure."

The patient's wife and son still find it hard to accept his death. "We just keep thinking about it all the time," his wife said. "It was the lousiest thing anybody could do."

(continued)

Officials at the nursing facility and other health professionals are more matter of fact.

"When you're dealing with health, you're dealing in a business where human beings are providing service to other human beings," said a spokeswoman for the chain, which runs several hundred nursing facilities. "And that means that tragic errors sometimes do occur."

A spokesperson for the American Hospital Association said, "Unfortunately, humans do make errors from time to time. Recently there seems to be a rash of them. It certainly raises questions."

What can be inferred about this chain management's attitudes toward the following:

1. *Marketing*
2. *Chain/facility policy enforcement*
3. *Quality control*
4. *Patient care policies*
5. *Sacredness of life*
6. *Patient rights*

CASE STUDY

New Jersey Woman in Legal Fight Over Feeding Tube Dies

A small town in New Jersey—A woman whose family asked the U.S. Supreme Court to be allowed to disconnect her life-sustaining feeding tube after she had spent 7 years in a coma-like state died Friday morning in a hospital.

The woman, 32 years of age, died at a local hospital 2 weeks after her family had won the right to have her feeding tube removed, hospital officials said.

"The family is feeling a sense of relief and release and joy that she is finally free," said the pastor who had counseled the family and will conduct a memorial service for her Sunday. "There were no second thoughts."

Citing the family's desire for privacy and recent Health Insurance Portability and Accountability Act (HIPAA) requirements, hospital officials and family spokespeople would not say when the tube had been removed or disclose the exact cause of death.

A group called Coalition for Life, which had opposed the state supreme court's right-to-die decision that allowed the removal of the tube, said in a statement that the woman's death "indicates a callous disregard of the sacredness of life."

The woman was several months' pregnant when she was involved in an auto accident. During surgery to remove the dead fetus after the accident, she went into a coma-like state.

(continued)

Until July, she had lived at a local nursing facility, where officials had refused to allow the feeding tube to be pulled, although relatives had contended that the woman had said she would not want to be kept alive by artificial means (given the coma, there was, therefore, no way for the patient, upon admission, to be afforded the opportunity for a living will required by the Patient Self-Determination Act).

The woman was moved to the hospital in July, a month after the New Jersey State Supreme Court ruled that the feeding tube could be removed. Despite the ruling, the nursing facility and family continued their battle, taking the case to the U.S. Supreme Court, which refused to interfere.

What can be inferred about this facility owner's attitudes toward the following:

1. *Marketing*
2. *Chain/facility policy enforcement*
3. *Quality control*
4. *Patient care policies*
5. *Sacredness of life*
6. *Patient rights*

FURTHER CONSIDERATIONS

Policies serve as general statements or understandings that guide or channel subordinates' thinking as they make decisions. Policies limit the area within which a decision is to be made and seek to ensure that each decision will be consistent with the overall objectives. Policies tend to decide issues beforehand by establishing the framework and scope of the actions.

The decisions made at each level of management establish the framework for decision-making at each successively lower level of management, generally with progressively less and less discretion to do so. However, each management level does participate in the policymaking process, and policies are made at every level of management. Policy is made by persons at upper, middle, and lower levels of management within the nursing facility. Defining *policymaking* is complicated by this fact.

When do policies become procedures? Sometimes these are separated by a fine line, which is hard to distinguish. Generally, a policy is a statement that contains some degree of freedom, some further need for interpretation. Procedures are step-by-step instructions on how a specific task is to be carried out.

A CAUTIONARY NOTE

NAB DOMAIN 4B1: MISSION, VISION, AND VALUE STATEMENTS

Most healthcare facilities write their policies and procedures well enough. Every facility needs to individualize its mission and achieve it by developing appropriate policies and procedures to achieve its goals.

However, it is important to note that if a facility's policy or procedure sets a higher standard than the state or federal requirements, the facility will be held to that higher standard on both federal and state surveys and in courts of law. The federal government has done a remarkably detailed and excellent job of setting the appropriate policies for nursing facilities in the United States over the years. Facility policies should conform as closely as possible to federal and state guidelines. Even so, most corporations and facilities write their own policies and procedures.

1.6.2 MAKING A DECISION

Section Concepts

- *Why decision-making is difficult to define, and why it is more of an art than a science*
- *What makes up successful decision-making*

Consider as the Administrator . . .

- *What is a decision for you in the facility? How many decisions do you believe you will make on a given day?*
- *What makes a "right" decision versus a "wrong" decision?*
- *Who decides if a decision was the right one in a facility?*

NAB DOMAIN 2B3: ETHICAL CONDUCT AND STANDARDS OF PRACTICE

Although *decision-making* can be synonymous with *managing*, it is difficult to define. "Deciding" can be the focal creative psychic event in which knowledge, thought, feeling, and imagination are fused into action (Hitt et al., 2017; Robbins & Coulter, 2018). A universally helpful formula for decision-making does not exist. Inevitably, we are left with an imprecise definition of the process. Even so, administrators do make numerous decisions every day.

Making the "right" decision in each situation is often difficult. It is the nursing facility administrator's job to ensure that all employees make the right decisions for the organization as often as possible (Robbins & Coulter, 2018).

A successful manager can, on balance, make enough right decisions for the organization and no disastrously wrong ones.

Successful Decision-Making: Enough Right Decisions

In the nursing facility's day-to-day world, decision-making translates into successfully implementing corporate, federal, and state policies and procedures. The successful nursing facility administrator will achieve successful inspections from the many entities whose policies and procedures the nursing facility must implement. An inspection by the CMS (the federal and state surveyors) that results in few or no deficiency citations (e.g., only level A deficiencies, which are defined as isolated [involving few residents] and no actual harm with potential for minimal harm) signals that the facility has a successful administrator—making enough right decisions (Krupp & Schoemaker, 2014).

Unsuccessful Decision-Making: Disastrously Wrong Decisions

An example of disastrously wrong decision-making would be for an inspection by the CMS to result in deficiency citations revealing patterned bad decisions (level K) or widespread bad decision-making (level L) resulting in immediate jeopardy to resident health or safety. Citations for deficiencies at levels K and L can be disastrous since the facility is typically given notice that Medicare/Medicaid certification will be terminated within 30 days if deficiencies are not satisfactorily corrected.

> **NAB DOMAIN 2B3: ETHICAL CONDUCT AND STANDARDS OF PRACTICE; 2B4: COMPLIANCE PROGRAMS; 3B1: FEDERAL HEALTHCARE LAWS, RULES, AND REGULATIONS; 3B3: CERTIFICATION AND LICENSURE REQUIREMENTS FOR THE ORGANIZATION**

The nursing facility administrator is expected to make decisions ethically. Although ethical decision-making is expected in all walks of life, it takes on special meaning for the administrator in a long-term care setting. The administrator is expected to make decisions about staff matters that maximize staff well-being. Honesty in dealing with the many contractors is expected. Most important, the nursing facility administrator is the support person of last resort for the facility's residents. The administrator's job is to advocate for the resident, to ensure that the resident's well-being is the cornerstone of each decision affecting residents. Advocating for residents may sometimes put the administrator at odds with the owners, the staff, the physician, or the resident's family.

Ethical practices throughout the facility are the administrator's responsibility, especially among all caregiving staff.

COMMON PITFALLS IN PRACTICE

- Many administrators have never read the policies under which their facilities operate. You cannot possibly manage people or enforce policies and procedures if you, yourself, do not know them.
- Policies and procedures are what you will be measured by when it comes time for state or federal surveys. Making sure your employees are following policy simply makes your life much easier during the survey.
- Many administrators do not really pay attention to survey concerns until they are in their annual survey window. This is a mistake. Make every day a survey-ready day!

1.6.3 LEADING

Section Concepts

- *Definitions of leadership*
- *Leadership by walking around/wandering around*
- *How to ride the waves of change in today's nursing facility*
- *The continuum of leadership styles*
- *Distinguishing among upper, middle, and lower leadership functions*
- *Three levels of leadership skill requirements*

Consider as the Administrator . . .

- *What is your personal leadership style? What do you do if it is not a match for your facility?*
- *What are the downsides to leadership by walking around?*

NAB DOMAIN 4A: LEADERSHIP; 4A4: LEADERSHIP PRINCIPLES (E.G., COMMUNICATION, STYLES, MENTORING, COACHING, PERSONAL PROFESSIONAL DEVELOPMENT)

Organizations that thrive over an extended period (years) depend on influential leaders—persons who have foresight combined with an ability to guide the organization to take advantage of the opportunities the future successfully offers (Singh, 2016).

THE GREAT LEADERSHIP THEORY OF HISTORY

Just as a satisfactory description of "deciding" is elusive, so is a sufficient description of leading. There are, however, those who propose the "great leadership theory of history," suggesting that history is "made" or measurably influenced by individuals who become leaders. Whatever one might think of their accomplishments, Alexander the Great, Genghis Khan, Confucius, Joan of Arc, George Washington, Abraham Lincoln, Margaret Sanger, and Winston Churchill seem to have assumed leadership roles that affected the course of history.

Leadership in the business world seems to be no less crucial to the success of organizations. Thomas Watson, Sr., and Thomas Watson, Jr., provided leadership to an organization, International Business Machines Corporation (IBM), that came to dominate the computer world during their tenure because this father and son had the foresight (successfully predicted the future) combined with an ability to guide the organization to successfully take advantage of the opportunities offered by the future. A hospital administrator, William McWhorter, was given responsibility for 103 hospitals that the Hospital Corporation of America believed to be irreversibly unprofitable (industry dogs). Nevertheless, through his leadership skills, he surprised everyone, and these hospitals became both profitable and significant leaders in the hospital industry. Recent leaders can be characterized by Jeff Bezos (Amazon), Bill Gates (Microsoft), Elon Musk (PayPal/Tesla), Richard Branson (Virgin), Steve Jobs (Apple), Herb Kelleher (Southwest Airlines), and a bevy of other amazing individuals who were able to push themselves to the limits and take their businesses where nobody had ever conceived previously.

The leadership provided to the nursing facility by the administrator, director of nursing, and other department managers is no less critical to the success or failure to thrive of each nursing facility (Halter et al., 2017). Understand, the nursing facility administrator needs to emulate those leaders discussed earlier, as this is truly where your success lies.

THE ADMINISTRATOR AND THE DIRECTOR OF NURSING THEORY

There is scant research literature to prove the assertion that leadership by the administrator, director of nursing, and department heads is key to any nursing facility's success. Even in the absence of such data, there is a broad consensus among the industry observers, especially the federal and state inspectors, that quality care in a nursing facility does depend on its administrators to exercise sound leadership skills. Inspectors usually try to visit a nursing facility within 6 months after a change in the administrator or director of nursing, believing that leadership (or lack of it) from these administrators directly affects the quality of care in a facility. When IBM's leadership changed after 60 years under the Watsons, the giant lost its leadership position. IBM had ridden the wave of change for 60 years with them at the helm.

When the Watsons led IBM, it usually was ranked in *Fortune* magazine's annual survey of America's Most Admired Corporations as #1. More recently, out of the 500 rated companies, IBM had dropped from the most admired corporation to one of the least admired corporations! Leadership counts. The Watsons inspired IBM to decades of greatness with a vision. Vision, it seems, also matters. More recently, IBM leaders have developed and implemented a vision of IBM becoming the service leader in the computer industry, and, to some extent, IBM has regained its place as one of several moderately successful industry leaders but not as the industry leader. IBM has had to nearly re-create every part of its business to get to its current success level.

Through forecasting, planning, organizing, staffing, directing, evaluating, controlling quality, innovating, and marketing decisions, the administrator, provides leadership to the nursing facility. There are various leadership styles (e.g., democratic, authoritarian, or laissez-faire; Robbins & Coulter, 2018).

LEADERSHIP BY WALKING/WANDERING AROUND

One effective style is LBWA. When walking around and observing such things as staff interaction with residents and with families, volunteers, and other employees, one can personally evaluate the quality of care being rendered. Walking around is also an opportunity to see if the residents have any problems and physically inspect the building and equipment.

LBWA provides an opportunity for the staff to speak with the administrator informally. It allows time to observe what is going on and let the team know the administrator is interested in them, the residents, and the facility. LBWA is not new to the nursing facility setting. In many nursing facilities, each shift is expected to make "rounds," reporting on each resident's condition over the preceding 8 hours. These observations are how nursing keeps informed of and anticipates care needs for the coming shift.

Through LBWA, the administrator receives a daily update on the facility's real world—in the rooms, hallways, departments, loading dock, and restrooms. This positions the administrator to uncover problems before they become significant issues (e.g., the NO SMOKING sign has fallen, or staff is smoking next to the oxygen cylinders). Administrators who do not take the initiative to keep informed about facility affairs daily often become involved in an ineffective management style known as firefighting. Once minor issues become major issues, the administrator must spend much time putting out large fires instead of stopping them from starting.

In making daily "rounds," the administrator can listen and observe, gaining raw impressions of what is happening in the facility, sensing how things are going. Do you think not enough time is available to get the paperwork done, meet all the other administrator requirements, and still make time to walk around the facility each day, sensing its pulse? Sam Walton, the Walmart Corporation originator, visited every one of his stores at least once a year when he had 18 stores. Later, when he owned more than 800 stores, he was still visiting each one at least once a year, riding cross-country with Walmart truck drivers and having donuts at 3:00 a.m. He thought the checkout clerk (read: certified nursing assistant [CNA]) to be the most important employee. Until his death, every checkout clerk knew that sometime each year, Mr. Sam might be the next customer waiting in the checkout line, observing how the customer ahead of him was being treated!

The future does not just happen—leaders like Sam Walton and the local nursing facility administrator dream it, shape it, sculpt it!

Effective Delegating

An effective leader knows how to delegate line authority to the appropriate department and other facility managers. The administrator must empower middle-level managers (the department heads) to make the appropriate decisions for the facility. With the authority to make decisions on behalf of the facility comes the inevitability of making mistakes. The effective administrator does not overrule middle-level managers unless harm could result. The administrator's job is to empower middle-level managers to make necessary decisions on behalf of the facility, mistakes, and everything that comes with that responsibility.

WALKING YET MAINTAINING THE CHAIN OF COMMAND

Wandering around the facility talking with residents, visitors, and staff appears to violate the traditional chain of command. The administrator is there to hear it firsthand and to communicate firsthand. One administrator who used LBWA took lots of notes on scraps of paper but never told people down the line what to do or change. The administrator never corrected on the spot but did promise to get back to the resident, visitor, or employee in a few days. The administrator then discussed each situation with the department head and charted with them a course of action to resolve any problem. And after a few days, the administrator would check with the resident, visitor, or employee to see if the appropriate action had been taken, practicing what is called "visible management" (Robbins & Coulter, 2018).

LBWA's basic benefits are listening (finding out what's happening on the firing line), teaching (communicating the facility's values), and facilitating. Through LBWA, the administrator can ease employees' work by asking questions, finding out what is frustrating the staff, and then running interference and knocking down small hurdles for them. Only the facility that pays excessive attention to details can achieve excellence in resident care. Quality of care is staff paying attention to the details that lead to excellent care as they emulate their administrator.

CHOOSING TO LEAD

Deciding on one's approach to leading is one of the more essential decisions managers ever make. Leading an organization can be compared to riding the waves of change. The time to change is when you do not have to. Change happens easily when you are on the crest of a wave, not when you are in the trough. In the world of healthcare delivery administration, the surf is up! Waves of change are coming from the government, third-party payers, and the residents and their families.

The best surfers (nursing facility administrators) are not necessarily the best swimmers (best management theoreticians). The best surfers are persons with the following mindset.

Riding the Wave of Change

Passion rules. Catching and riding a wave is simple, but many give lip service to the art. They have the correct equipment, stylish outfits, and the right jargon but spend most of their time on the beach talking about surfing. The best surfers spend their time out in the water, rough or calm, looking for the next wave. They are committed to surfing, body, mind, and spirit.

No dare/no flair. Good surfers constantly push their limits, continuously trying new moves, going for bigger and bigger waves. They know that no two waves are ever the same, so each one is ridden a little differently. Keeping ahead of the wave involves taking risks, constantly challenging yourself and those around you.

Expect to wipe out. For every successful ride, there will likely be two or three wipeouts. Sand is part of every surfer's diet. A changing ocean with its dynamic wave patterns and shapes is a source not of fear but of challenge that provides the thrill of surfing. Successful surfers know that if they do not wipe out several times each day, they play it too safe to keep improving.

Do not turn your back on the ocean. Surfers know that they are dealing with an environment beyond their control. They understand that uncertainty and unpredictability are part of the game. They respect the ocean and its power, never taking it for granted. They never turn their backs on the ocean.

Keep looking "outside." The outside waves are those on the horizon. It is essential to pay attention to the wave closest to you and to what is coming. First, there may be a bigger and better wave coming in on the horizon. Second, the wave on the horizon may crash over you as you come up for air after riding the wave closest to you.

Move before it moves you. Surfing is forecasting and planning for the future. You must begin moving while that big wave is still on the horizon, or it will surge by you, leaving you in its trough.

Never surf alone. It is not intelligent to tackle the complexities of life alone. One needs backup help when emergencies arise. By pooling their knowledge and insights, surfers can learn about and get more exotic spots and trade tips and techniques that work. It is beneficial to have a friend along to "talk story" with as you navigate the complexities of the nursing facility operations. Having someone share your hopes, dreams, and frustrations leads to more creativity, joy, and effectiveness.

The future is coming at us like enormous waves of change in set after set, and they are getting bigger. The surf is up in the hospital industry, the assisted living industry, the life care communities, the multiunit senior housing industry, the home healthcare industry, and the managed care industry. The future belongs to those who decide to ride, to those who welcome the unexpected.

"Business as usual" in the long-term care industry is over. Success in today's world depends on understanding where the industry is heading, having a vision of the future, and developing the capacity to implement change as an ongoing aspect of managing a facility. Facilities that resist change and continue to function in isolation may survive but will not thrive in this 21st century.

FIRE IN THE HEART

To be a successful nursing facility administrator over a sustained period of years requires that one be excited and passionate about the profession. Top performers in all fields have one quality in common: passion. Their drive and enthusiasm are what distinguish them. As numerous executive recruiters have observed, the thing that makes the difference between a good manager and an inspiring, dynamic leader goes beyond competence. It's passion. That is the single quality that will lift a person head and shoulders above the rest.

Passion brings a complete commitment to one's work: physical, emotional, and mental. It sustains the successful administrator through the outrages of regulations and an abusive public image of the field. Passion is contagious. An administrator who is enthusiastic about the work can inspire excitement in the nurses and nursing assistants. Knowledge of the field, competence, and experience make them a good manager, but a greater commitment gives one the necessary edge to provide the leadership required in today's nursing facility.

Of course, passion is not a scientifically measurable component of nursing facility administration, but management is not yet exactly a science. What the nursing facility administrator needs is a fire in the heart for continuously improving the quality of each resident's daily life.

A Continuum of Leadership Styles

NAB DOMAIN 4A1: ORGANIZATIONAL STRUCTURES (E.G., DEPARTMENTS, FUNCTIONS, SYSTEMIC PROCESSES); 4A3: ORGANIZATIONAL BEHAVIOR (E.G., ORGANIZATIONAL CULTURE, TEAM BUILDING, GROUP DYNAMICS); 4A4: LEADERSHIP PRINCIPLES (E.G., COMMUNICATION, STYLES, MENTORING, COACHING, PERSONAL PROFESSIONAL DEVELOPMENT)

There is a continuum of leadership styles that can be characterized by seven possible positions along the continuum, from manager-centered to employee-centered leadership. Several dimensions are portrayed in Figure 1.2. Under manager-centered leadership, the manager retains a high degree of control and uses authority extensively.

Manager-Centered Leadership

Position 1. The manager simply makes the decision and then announces it (autocratic style; Konopaske et al., 2019; Robbins & Coulter, 2018).

Position 2. The manager attempts to convince the employees of the value of the decision made.

Position 3. The manager presents ideas and invites questions, in effect engaging the employees actively in the decision-making process.

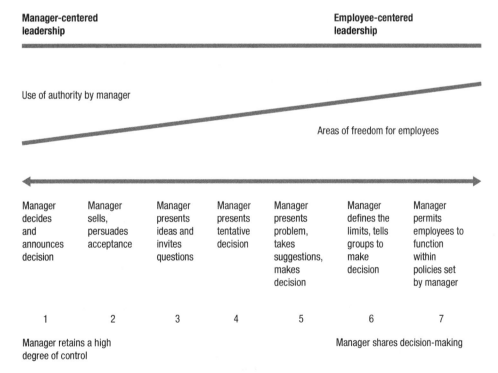

FIGURE 1.2
Range of decision-making strategies open to the manager.

Employee-Centered Leadership

Position 4. The manager presents a tentative decision, subject to change. Here the employees are further involved in the decision-making process itself.

Position 5. The manager presents the problem requiring a solution, invites suggestions, and then makes the decision.

Position 6. The manager permits the subordinates to make the decision and function within limits defined by the manager (laissez-faire leadership style; Robbins & Coulter, 2018).

DECIDING HOW TO LEAD

At least the following three levels of considerations should be examined by the administrator selecting the leadership style for a particular situation.

First level. Forces in the administrator:

- Their own values
- Their confidence in the department heads
- Their own feelings of security or insecurity

Second level. Forces in the employees:

- The facility administrator can permit greater freedom to department managers who:
    - Require independence (e.g., the director of nursing)
    - Are ready to assume responsibility for decision-making (are professionally licensed)
    - Are interested in the problem and consider it important (take resident care seriously)
    - Understand and agree with the mission statement/goals of the facility
    - Have the necessary knowledge and experience (e.g., the RN who comes with 2 years of intensive care experience)
    - Are prepared and expect to make decisions (e.g., a trained, licensed physical therapist)

Third level. Forces in the organization:

- Expectations of the organization's management (a position taken by a corporation or the board)
- Ability of subordinates to function as a group (eight competent department heads who have worked together for 3 years versus five new and three continuing department heads)
- The problem itself (excessive medication errors or excessive in-house acquired pressure injury rates cannot be permitted)
- Time constraints (e.g., plans of correction for deficiencies all have correction dates)

THREE LEVELS OF LEADERSHIP SKILL REQUIREMENTS

We have already discussed three management levels: upper, middle, and lower levels, each with its skill requirements. Figure 1.3 shows three different levels of leadership skills.

The upper-level manager. The nursing facility's upper-level administrator is primarily responsible for creating and changing the organization's structure.

The middle-level manager. The head of dietary, the head of housekeeping, or other department heads are responsible for developing more specific policies that interpret administration policy implications for their departments.

The lower-level manager. The charge nurse who supervises a specific group of nurses/nursing assistants is responsible for applying the policies provided by the director of nursing to the hour-by-hour care given.

As Figure 1.3 suggests, different skills are needed at the three distinct levels of management.

Upper-level management's job. The chief administrator must understand how the organization accommodates the external environment and how all the subsystems function within the nursing facility itself.

Middle-level management's job. The middle-level manager is responsible for implementing the administration's policies by devising ways to put them into action within the facility. This level of management translates the broader institutional policies by developing more specific ones to control employee behavior. The administrator, for example, may set a goal of preventing acquired pressure injuries. The middle-level manager must understand how the subsystems of the organization fit together to achieve such overall goals. They have the difficult task of representing to upper-level management the needs of those supervised. To function effectively, middle-level managers must realize that they are the conduit through which action travels in both directions.

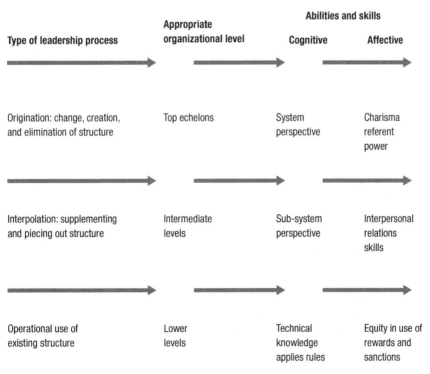

Type of leadership process	Appropriate organizational level	Abilities and skills	
		Cognitive	Affective
Origination: change, creation, and elimination of structure	Top echelons	System perspective	Charisma referent power
Interpolation: supplementing and piecing out structure	Intermediate levels	Sub-system perspective	Interpersonal relations skills
Operational use of existing structure	Lower levels	Technical knowledge applies rules	Equity in use of rewards and sanctions

FIGURE 1.3
Three levels of skill requirements for managers.

Lower-level management's job. Lower-level managers guide employees according to the established policies of the facility. The rules must be thoroughly understood and applied evenhandedly to all employees under their direction to accomplish this. One vital key to effective leadership at the lower level is the sense the employees have of their manager's advocacy for the employees they supervise. It is not enough to be their advocate, however; the manager must be their effective spokesperson.

Any level can write management procedures; in most cases, procedures are written by both middle-level and lower-level managers.

CHARACTERISTICS OF THE EFFECTIVE LEADER

An effective leader is a person who does the following:

- Mediates and tempers the organizational requirements to the needs of persons in a manner that is organizationally enhancing (the facility assists employees having family crises through unplanned time off and other support, not just because the Family and Medical Leave Act requires it).
- Promotes group loyalty and personal ties (working for the facility becomes a personally satisfying experience).
- Demonstrates care for individuals (knows each employee by name and something about that employee's interests).
- Relies on referent power (respect from employees and residents) rather than the power of legitimacy and sanctions alone (Chies, 2021; Robbins & Coulter, 2018).

A successful leader is a person who is keenly aware of relevant forces in the situation, understands themselves and the individuals with whom they deal, and can behave appropriately in individual situations, making decisions when needed and sharing the decision-making when appropriate.

The successful leader is neither strong nor permissive, but rather is endowed with a strong "instinct" (gut-level feeling) for determining appropriate personal behavior and capable of acting accordingly.

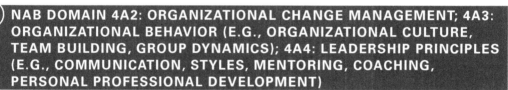

NAB DOMAIN 4A2: ORGANIZATIONAL CHANGE MANAGEMENT; 4A3: ORGANIZATIONAL BEHAVIOR (E.G., ORGANIZATIONAL CULTURE, TEAM BUILDING, GROUP DYNAMICS); 4A4: LEADERSHIP PRINCIPLES (E.G., COMMUNICATION, STYLES, MENTORING, COACHING, PERSONAL PROFESSIONAL DEVELOPMENT)

Day-to-Day Leadership Requirements

In the daily administration of a typical long-term care facility, the administrator will face various situations with differing leadership needs. Recognition of appropriate leadership behavior for any specific situation is a valuable insight; the capacity to behave in differing leadership styles is an accomplishment of a high order indeed. Much of the flexibility the administrator can exercise in distinctive leadership styles depends on how comfortable they are in wielding power and authority in the facility's management. The administrator is the facility's lead problem-solver. Problems arise hourly in a nursing facility. The main job of management and staff is to solve the problems by making appropriate decisions while delivering quality care to the residents. Problem-solving is the process of analyzing and interpreting information/data. All information must be evaluated as to the information source's validity, and appropriate interpretations must be thought through.

Complete information is seldom available in problem-solving situations. The administrator and staff will develop skills in sensing the point at which sufficient data are available to make appropriate decisions for the organization. The ability to think critically about matters is a lifelong skill-building process. Being able to think critically is to be able to do the following:

- Recognize problems, to find workable means for meeting those problems.
- Understand the importance of prioritization and order of precedence in problem-solving.
- Gather and marshal pertinent (relevant) information.
- Recognize unstated assumptions and values.
- Comprehend and use language with accuracy, clarity, and discernment.
- Interpret data, to appraise evidence and evaluate arguments.
- Recognize the existence (or nonexistence) of logical relationships between propositions.
- Draw warranted conclusions and generalizations.
- Put to the test the conclusions and generalizations at which one arrives.
- Reconstruct one's patterns of beliefs based on wider experience.
- Render accurate judgments about specific things and qualities in everyday life.

Looking Ahead: Dually Focused Leadership

The effective leader must focus on both the current situation and the anticipated changes that will affect the facility. In their book, *Winning the Long Game*, authors Steven Krupp and Paul Schoemaker write that in times of crisis and change, when people are confused about what to do, ordinary leadership must rise to the level of strategic leadership. The trick, they believe, is to deliver short-term results while securing long-term viability. Especially in uncertain times, facilities must tilt more toward strategic leadership than toward operational excellence.

Strategic leaders need two perspectives: outside/in and future/back. *Outside/in* means starting with the external marketplace when addressing problems without getting wrapped up by internal organizational issues. *Future/back* means that strategic leaders use their long-term vision to guide their short-term decisions flexibly when playing the long game.

If strategic leaders are to thrive and play the long game, they need six elements critical for effective strategic leadership: anticipate, challenge, interpret, decide, align, and learn. Mastering just a few of these skills is not enough. The more uncertain the environment becomes, the more Krupp and Schoemaker believe a leader needs the following six disciplines in combination because they possess self-reinforcing qualities when deployed as an interdependent leadership system.

Anticipate. Strategic leaders are constantly vigilant, honing their ability to anticipate by scanning the environment for signals of change. They develop and maintain an external mindset. How quickly do you spot vague threats and opportunities on the periphery of your business (Krupp & Schoemaker, 2014)? The paradox is that the more humility we have about our ability to make predictions, the more successful we can be in winning the long game.

Challenge. Strategic leaders question the status quo. Open a window to let in the fresh air and look in the mirror. Are you comfortable with conflicting views and differences in opinion? How often do you question your own and other people's assumptions (Krupp & Schoemaker, 2014)?

Opening the window is the practice of understanding outsiders' perspectives, to see complex issues in context. Looking in the mirror is the practice of deep self-reflection, whereby leaders confront outmoded beliefs, faulty assumptions, and stubbornness in themselves and others (Krupp & Schoemaker, 2014).

Interpret. Strategic leaders amplify signals and connect multiple data points in new and insightful ways to make sense of complex, ambiguous situations. Can you pick up on cues to distinguish anomalies from leading indicators of change? What are you not seeing or hearing? We begin by recognizing the facts and then "re-cognizing," or rethinking, them to expose their hidden implications. Leaders get blindsided not so much because they aren't receiving signals but because they aren't exploring alternative interpretations or getting locked into one piece of the puzzle (Krupp & Schoemaker, 2014).

Decide. Strategic leaders seek multiple options to ensure flexible decision-making. They don't get prematurely locked into simplistic yes/no choices. How often and how quickly must you make tough calls with incomplete information? Exploring options means having the wisdom, cool-headedness, and perspective to consider all the alternatives available. Showing courage means demonstrating the fortitude to commit to the right solution and, if that solution proves ineffective, critically stepping back to reconsider (Krupp & Schoemaker, 2014).

Align. Strategic leaders engage stakeholders to understand change readiness, manage differences, and create buy-in. They are adept at finding common ground. This requires active outreach. Good communication is key. Do you regularly engage your managers' direct reports in decisions that affect their work? Where do you stand with the people you need to influence (Krupp & Schoemaker, 2014)? Here, problems are now interconnected, and this changes issues. More people need to be involved in the decision-making.

Learn. Strategic leaders continuously reflect on successes and failures to improve performance and decision-making. When was the last time you admitted you were wrong—in public?

Leaders must make their moves when the future is still ambiguous. If an organization is continually learning, then everyone is primed for change and ready to move in a different direction when needed (Krupp & Schoemaker, 2014,).

Charismatic Leadership

Although the administrator cannot consciously choose charismatic leadership, it is worth mentioning here (Robbins & Coulter, 2018). This quality has been described by Max Weber (Cole & Kelley, 2020) as a magical aura with which people sometimes endow their leaders. It appears when a group has an emotional need for a person who, they feel, will make the right decision for them. The acts of charismatic leaders are typically unexamined. Their followers do not scrutinize their actions as they would those of their immediate supervisors. Charisma is not an objective assessment by the followers and typically requires a psychological distance between the followers and the leader (Konopaske et al., 2018). When charisma is assigned to a leader, the power and authority of the organization are enhanced.

COMMON PITFALLS IN PRACTICE

- You do not get a choice in the matter. If you take the job as an administrator, you have become the leader in charge of a multimillion-dollar healthcare facility, and you are responsible for the lives of everyone who lives under your roof. Embrace your job as a leader; do not shy from it.
- When an administrator fails to take the leadership role, they are giving permission for someone else to take up that mantle. When this happens, it is very difficult to be successful or to drive change.
- Quickly understand that you may not get to choose your leadership type. This is often dictated by the facility and the situation you have undertaken. Be fluid in your approach and do what you must to ensure success.

CASE STUDY

After the Seminar: A New Leadership Style for The Laurels

The Laurels Nursing Facility administrator returned from a seminar on employee participation convinced that she should share leadership of the facility equitably among the department managers.

At the staff meeting the following week, Ms. Smith told the department managers that beginning that week, all department heads were to be fully responsible for all aspects of running their respective departments. Under this new policy, each department head was given the final say in all matters affecting their department.

The department heads were pleased with their new power and responsibilities. They felt this was a show of confidence by Ms. Smith, the administrator, in their abilities to manage.

After about 3 weeks under the new policy, arguments began to be heard among the departments.

Matters came to a boil when the head of dietary refused to implement the director of nursing's new food service policy. Under this policy, dietary personnel, in addition to the previous responsibility of delivering the hot-food carts to nursing, were to be fully trained in inpatient feeding techniques; that is, they must feed the patients and then return the carts to the kitchen.

The director of nursing reasoned that under this policy, the kitchen staff would handle the entire process, leaving the nursing personnel more time to do "real nursing." "Let the kitchen staff see how poorly the residents take to the usually cold, usually untasty, sometimes unrecognizable food here!" she thought. The staff development coordinator for the facility, at the request of the director of nursing, trained and "certified" the dietary personnel as feeders.

(continued)

The first morning under the new policy, the food carts were delivered by the kitchen personnel to the nursing wings at 7:30 a.m., but as usual, the kitchen employees, although newly trained in feeding, returned immediately to the kitchen. At 9:30 a.m., no patient/resident had received breakfast.

Matters were further complicated by the head of housekeeping's announcement that housekeeping personnel no longer participated in mopping up after incontinent patients. Under the new policy, housekeeping personnel were responsible only for mopping the floors on a scheduled basis. Often, patient "puddles" remained on the floor for several hours until the scheduled mopping occurred.

A staff meeting was scheduled for 2:00 that afternoon by Ms. Smith. Ms. Smith believed that despite these minor incidents, she had done an excellent job implementing democratic leadership following the definition she had been given at the seminar: "encouraging maximum feasible participation by others in organizational decisions, ensuring that decisions are made at the lowest level in the organization believed competent to make any particular needed decision."

"Surely," Ms. Smith thought, "these department managers are capable of making these decisions."

She wondered aloud to herself why employee participation did not seem to be working. She wondered whether to take back the authority she had delegated to the department managers or let the department managers fight it out until they reached a mutual agreement.

She thought she would probably just let them fight it out. "After all," she reasoned to herself, "they are all competent professionals."

That noon the regional administrator chanced to come by. At lunch, Ms. Smith brings the regional administrator up to date on this situation.

- *As the regional administrator, what would you do or say to Ms. Smith about being informed of this situation?*

1.6.4 POWER AND AUTHORITY

Section Concepts

- *The different types of power—legitimate, reward, punishment, referent, and expert*
- *Power comes from both inside and outside a facility*
- *The power of the administrator is constrained*
- *Communication itself is power*
- *Systems of communication, and barriers to communication*
- *The power of subgroup allegiances*

Consider as the Administrator . . .

- *What is your actual power in a facility as the administrator?*
- *What constraints exist on your power in the facility? Outside the facility?*

Power is the ability to control the behavior of others. A person has power when they can make other people do what they want them to do. Several writers call this the ability to motivate someone to do something they would otherwise not do (Cole & Kelley, 2020; Robbins & Coulter, 2018). The administrator of a nursing facility can order employees to act to implement the facility's goals as expressed in the policies and plans.

One dictionary gives 14 definitions for the word *power*. An additional half-dozen synonyms indicate that *power* denotes the inherent ability or the admitted right to rule, govern, determine, control, regulate, restrain, and curb. Power is a complex concept in our culture and the workplace.

The administrator has the power (from the board or the ownership) to tell employees what to do and expect them to do it. It is well known that although an organization theoretically provides equal legitimate power to all administrators at the same level, the administrators do not, in fact, remain equal.

For example, a board of directors controlling five nursing facilities, in theory, delegates equal authority to the administrators to act on its behalf in the five facilities. Some of these five administrators might have firm control over employee behavior, while others might be having difficulty convincing employees to do what they request. Why?

RECIPROCITY

Power is a reciprocal relationship. The board of directors or the owners can confer power on the administrator, but the employees and residents must accept that power as permissible if it is to be meaningful. This does not imply disrespect or chaos. The concept of authority or power is more complicated than announcing that power has been given to the administrator by the board or the owners.

Writers have identified at least five types of power: legitimate, reward, punishment (coercive), referent, and expert (Robbins & Coulter, 2018). Considering this, administrators need to be familiar with these types of power and their applications.

Legitimate power. This describes authority given to a particular position and is associated with the person's role in the organization (Robbins & Coulter, 2018). Organizations expect each person to yield to the appropriate authority. The administrator has more legitimate power than the director of nursing and so forth. When employees or residents respond to legitimate power, their actions are motivated by the manager's level or position, not by any personality, knowledge, or other characteristics of that person.

Reward power. The fact that reward is the second type of power is testimony to the mundane reality that employees do not always respond correctly. Administrators are given reward power to induce or persuade employees or residents to do what the administrator asks. If not, certain desired approval(s) may be withheld (Robbins & Coulter, 2018). For example, if the administrator has the authority to give a 15% year-end cash bonus to the three supervisors who have best achieved the facility's goals (translate: those who most often responded acceptably to the administrator's instructions), then they have reward power.

Punishment power. Sometimes known as coercive power, the employee believes that a manager has the ability (and inclination) to punish unacceptable behaviors. The ultimate punishment power is firing the employee, but there are many intermediate, less drastic means. The employees who do not observe the manager's rules for functioning in the facility may receive a written warning, a copy of which is placed in the human resources file. The use of punishment power usually is a last resort—used after other types of power have failed. An extensive use of punishment power leads to distrust and fear (Robbins & Coulter, 2018)—circumstances not conducive to quality resident care.

Referent power. Power to influence is often based on liking or identifying with another person. When the employees like the administrator and identify with them, they are more apt to do what the administrator wishes. Referent power exists to the degree employees and residents identify with the administrator. This is both simple and powerful. Employees who do not admire an administrator or do not identify with them are more difficult to control; that is, it is harder to make them do their work as the organization wishes.

Expert power. Power can derive from recognition by the employees and residents that the administrator is very skillful, has had considerable training, and is quite knowledgeable in the field of nursing facility administration. For the nurse, this acknowledgment comes from the RN license, and, for the physician, the license to practice medicine (Chies, 2021).

POWER FROM OUTSIDE THE ORGANIZATION

It is important to note that expert and referent power, as present in the facility, add to the power of organizationally given rewards and punishments because the organization cannot confer expert and referent power. There is an increase in the amount of power or control exerted over the personnel and residents, and it is a constant factor in increased organizational performance.

Conferring expert and referent power rather than power based on punishment achieves organizational goals. This substitution can mean fewer harmful, undesired, or unintended organizational consequences. Promoting referent power is a more robust action than giving power based on rewards and punishment or executive directives alone. Remember, the administrator's task is to motivate the organization's members to achieve the organization's goals.

Expert and referent power is available to all members of the staff. Referent power depends on personal and group characteristics and is conferred by peers (persons at the same level) in the organization. Peer influence is often more readily accepted than influence from superiors. If, for example, one of the nurses is particularly skillful in creating a cheerful atmosphere in the facility, their leadership through referent power gives the nursing facility greater control over the quality of life achieved.

THE ADMINISTRATOR'S POWER IS REAL

Administrators do have power over other people's lives. The chief administrator's power is potentially "irresponsible," not based on the use of power in any decision or the administrator's motives. Often, those affected by administrative decisions (the employees, residents, their significant others, even the board or owners) have little or no direct input in the making of some decisions (e.g., when to finally tell an employee that the cumulative effect of their behaviors renders them unfit to work at that facility). This lack of input can be especially true when most of the power is centralized to the administrator. However, there are limitations to the administrator's power.

THE ADMINISTRATOR'S POWER IS CONSTRAINED

As we discuss elsewhere, nursing facilities typically have complex authority chains with several professional groups present within the facility: physicians, nurses, dietitians, physical therapists, and other specialties. All these groups have professional organizations and loyalties that influence their behavior in the nursing facility. They have "authority" within their own professional spheres.

The facility administrator's authority is constantly constrained or limited by the influence of medical, nursing, and other professions over the behavior of its physicians, nurses, nutritionists, and other professionals within the facility. Professional groups are often governed more by licensing boards and professional standards than by the nursing facility's policies or goals, such as physicians and the medical board and nurses and the nurse practice act and enforcement board. It is important to know these professional boards and licenses dictate when conflict over roles or activities arise within the facility. It is not that the administrator has little or insufficient control. Instead, the administrator must remember the presence of professional group controls may constrain the professional. The administrator cannot ask licensed professionals to violate the law or go against their scope of practice as prescribed by licensure, even if facility regulations might dictate otherwise.

The task of achieving control over professional employee behavior is a complicated one, requiring tact and ingenuity on the administrator's part.

COMMON PITFALLS IN PRACTICE

- Many new administrators do not understand their place in the facility. Put simply, "you're it." All decisions, all changes, all of everything comes from you. This is truly power. Embrace this power and the position. Work within the constraints of the facility you run.
- Power without humility is a fallacy.
- There is a big difference between power and attitude. Those with power with good attitudes do very well in the facility. Always remember, attitude flows from the top. Make your attitude what you want those around you to embrace and emulate.

CASE STUDY

The Owners' Directives

In a confidential memo to the administrator, the owners noted that the facility had lost money on its Medicaid residents over the past 24 months and received several deficiencies. They directed that the following should be effective as soon as practicable:

1. When the Medicare/Medicaid certification and/or state inspection teams were anticipated, corporate would provide five extra nursing staff for a time period (no more than about 4 months total) prior to the inspection to improve the staff/resident ratio and to fill in any gaps in the facility information to pass the inspection.
2. Over the next 6 months, the proportion of Medicaid residents was to be systematically reduced by 10% after determining that the facility is unable to give the needed level of care believed required by various Medicaid applicants.
3. The administrator was to increase the previous year's average number of Medicare days for each Medicare resident, taking as near full advantage as possible of the 100 days coverage for each Medicare resident because these patients have the highest reimbursement scores.
4. The previous year's daily raw food costs per resident were to be reduced from $6.00 to $5.75 per day.
5. To save money, the administrator was to reduce the full-time staff by using more pools and establishing additional part-time positions, thus reducing ongoing overhead.

- *What are the administrator's options?*
- *How should the administrator respond to each of these directives?*

1.6.5 COMMUNICATION SKILLS

Section Concepts

- *Effective communication has many barriers to it being successful*
- *In the facility, environmental norms and values may be the most valuable assets in the facility*

Consider as the Administrator . . .

- *Do you accept the idea that communication = information = power?*
- *Can you as the administrator give employees real power and keep the facility in compliance?*

NAB DOMAIN 2C: HUMAN RESOURCES; 2C12: EMPLOYEE SATISFACTION, ENGAGEMENT, AND RETENTION; 4A: LEADERSHIP; 4A3: ORGANIZATIONAL BEHAVIOR (E.G., ORGANIZATIONAL CULTURE, TEAM BUILDING, GROUP DYNAMICS); 4A4: LEADERSHIP PRINCIPLES (E.G., COMMUNICATION, STYLES, MENTORING, COACHING, PERSONAL PROFESSIONAL DEVELOPMENT)

Directing is the process of communicating the organizational objectives to the staff, residents, and their significant others. Communication is the exchange of information and the transmission of meaning.

Communication is essential for the survival of any social system. The administrator's skill in communicating what is to be accomplished and how it is to be carried out is pivotal to achieving the facility's plan. Unless the plans of action are successfully communicated to the staff, the plans have no likelihood of being accomplished.

The steps in the communication process are that (a) someone initiates it, (b) it is transmitted from its source to its destination, and (c) it has an impact on the recipient. If a message does not have its intended impact on the recipient, communication has not taken place.

COMMUNICATION = INFORMATION = POWER

Communication is the transmission of information. Information provides a sounder basis for judgments, giving the well-informed person power. The withholding of information is also a form of power since the person with the knowledge is in a superior position to make decisions. Good communication requires active listening, which is listening with (a) intensity, (b) acceptance, (c) empathy, and (d) a willingness to assume responsibility for understanding the speaker's complete message (Robbins & Coulter, 2018).

SYSTEMS OF COMMUNICATION

Organizations have two overarching communication processes: the formal and the informal. And the information in communication may travel in directions social scientists describe as upward, downward, and horizontally.

The formal communication process follows the formal organizational structure of the nursing facility. The administrator may send memoranda to the department managers, or the department managers may send them to their staff.

The informal communication process exists in nearly every organization. The social groups within the facility define the informal communication process. Chatting in the lounge is informal communication; however, important information is often present in such casual conversation.

Communication flow is important to a functioning organization. Upward communication flows from subordinates up the organizational hierarchy to the next level. Communication from upper-level management to lower-level staff is a downward flow. Horizontal communication is information flowing between peers or persons of equal rank or status (Robbins & Coulter, 2018).

Communicating is at the heart of the management process. The closer a person gets to the organizational center of control, the more pronounced the emphasis is on exchanging information. Administrators make decisions on processed information and share those decisions with other members of the organization.

Communicating is an art that managers must master. Communications between administrators and personnel are full of subtleties and shades of meaning. Most communication also has numerous levels of purpose and function and is essential to building a relationship. Any act of communication may answer a question at the moment, but it has different meanings for the persons involved. Managers need to be aware that there are many barriers to full, clear communication. Seldom does any single communication have only one level of meaning (Robbins & Coulter, 2018).

BARRIERS TO COMMUNICATION

Agenda carrying. Each person carries their own agenda(s) into every communication situation, centered on individual concerns and life experiences. Perceptions serve as filters of communication and are unique to each receiver.

Selective hearing. Individuals tend to listen to what they want or expect to hear, thereby filtering out the unpleasant and receiving only selective messages. A nursing supervisor may wish to communicate to an aide dissatisfaction with one aspect of the aide's performance. To soften the effect, the supervisor may first praise the employee for some other work. The employee may hear the praise and effectively screen out the criticism.

Differences in knowledge levels. Persons who have only incomplete knowledge about a topic may process information quite differently from persons who may be more knowledgeable. Degrees of sophistication vary among listeners, and the "information" they process from a single communication may differ significantly.

The filter effect. The manager may receive messages reflecting what the employees believe the manager wants to hear. It is not easy to give bad news to a superior when one already knows such information is not welcome. Ancient Greek literature recounts multiple examples of messengers being killed after bringing bad news to the king. The implications of this reaction are demonstrated in many organizational members.

It seems that no matter how frequently administrators insist they want to hear bad and good news, the employees filter the information toward the known bias of the next level(s) of management. When several management layers exist to filter unwelcome news, upper management may receive little accurate information (another good reason for the administrator to manage by walking around and listening in the hallways!).

Subgroup allegiance. Each one of the subgroups in the organization (nurses, housekeepers, residents on a hall) demands allegiance from its members. Within each group, tangible and intangible rewards are given, so communication is interpreted within each subgroup's goals and needs rather than from the view-point of the organization (Robbins & Coulter, 2018).

- People communicate far more with members of their own subgroup than with any other persons (e.g., the nurses have difficulty in learning what the nurses' aides are thinking and feeling).
- People prefer to communicate with someone of higher status than themselves (the aides prefer to talk to the nurses).
- People try to avoid communicating with those lower in status than themselves (the nurses prefer to talk to the doctors, not to the aides except when instructing them).
- People will communicate with those who will help them achieve their goals— higher-status persons have the power to create either gratifying or depriving experiences.
- People communicate with those who can make them feel secure and avoid those who make them anxious.

Status distance. The nursing facility staff is composed of a broad range of professional and nonprofessional groups (Robbins & Coulter, 2018). At the top of the status ladder is the physician whose orders determine most nursing facility activities. Numerous health professionals at the mid-level are present in the facility: advanced practice registered nurses (APRNs), RNs, licensed practical nurses (LPNs), several types of therapists (e.g., physical, occupational, and recreational), dietitians, pharmacists, physician assistants, and others. Toward the lower end of the status ladder are the nurse's aides and housekeepers, few of whom have any formal training. It is difficult for lower-level employees to communicate upward. The administrator must be aware of these many groups' status sensitivities and be capable of successfully fostering the needed communication among all of them.

Language barrier. Doctors and nurses speak "medicalese." The pharmacists speak yet another language, and the physical therapists have their own jargon (Robbins & Coulter, 2018). In short, given the great variety of professional specialists who must by regulation be employed or retained as consultants, the nursing facility administrator and the staff who deal with them have a complicated task in ensuring that resident care is not compromised through miscommunication among these occupations.

Self-protection. Persons often fail to communicate information that might reflect poorly on them, their friends, or the organization (translated: the administrator should ensure that the accident report accurately portrays what occurred).

Information overload. The abundance of information flowing in the facility (as many as 100-plus separate forms) may produce an information overload that results in the staff's compromised ability to distinguish among communications requiring prioritizing and attention. Bad news travels fast. Good news hardly travels at all.

Others. The administrator must bear in mind that all communication is multidimensional, needing appropriate interpretation to be of use.

In sending out a memorandum to employees or engaging in any communication, the administrator must consider that its effect depends at least on the following:

- Feelings and attitudes of the parties toward each other
- Expectations
- How well the organization meets the subordinate's needs—if the nursing facility is supportive, the employee receiving administrative communications may be less defensive and more problem oriented, that is, readier to absorb the communication and comply with the organization's request

COMMON PITFALLS IN PRACTICE

- A large part of communication is the attitude with which it is imparted. Be positive. Be team oriented. Be appropriate.
- When one works with wood, they quickly learn the idea to "measure twice, cut once," meaning to ensure you are correct before you move forward. Make sure that what you are communicating is what you want your people to hear. Coming back to change it later creates confusion and delay.
- Many new administrators are "afraid" to communicate with others. They have not mastered public speaking or interacting with others. Now is your time to correct this concern if it is yours. Find your local Toastmasters chapter, get involved.

1.6.6 ORGANIZATIONAL NORMS AND VALUES: CODE OF ETHICS AND STANDARDS OF PRACTICE

Section Concepts

- *The role of norms and values in the operation of a facility*
- *How to connect roles to norms*
- *Soft versus hard*
- *Dreams, visions, goals, and how they need the administrator to happen*
- *The concepts of efficiency and effectiveness*
- *The history of management services*

Consider as the Administrator . . .

- *How do you know if your ethics are "right" when it comes to decision-making?*
- *Can one be efficient but not effective?*
- *Where do values and norms come from? Were these learned at home during childhood? In school? At university? Why does this matter?*

NAB DOMAIN 2B3: ETHICAL CONDUCT AND STANDARDS OF PRACTICE; 2C9: HUMAN RESOURCE POLICIES (E.G., DRUG-FREE WORKPLACE, DISCIPLINE, JOB CLASSIFICATION, PHOTOGRAPHY AND VIDEO, SOCIAL MEDIA USAGE, MOBILE PHONE USAGE); 2C12: EMPLOYEE SATISFACTION, ENGAGEMENT, AND RETENTION

EFFECTIVE RELATIONSHIPS: DEVELOPING LOYALTY TO FACILITY GOALS

Administering a nursing facility is a complicated process. We have discussed some of the administrator's difficulties as they attempt to lead employees in required tasks. One of the impediments to accomplishing this is that the organization can never count on the individual employee's undivided attention. This division of attention is called partial inclusion or the segmental involvement of people in the job role.

LIMITATIONS ON EMPLOYEE PARTICIPATION

The nursing facility defines behaviors that require only a portion of a person's 24-hour day. The facility asks that employees perform the tasks or roles prescribed for them, which were agreed upon on hiring, during each shift. However, the whole person must be considered in the work situation (Robbins & Coulter, 2018). Often the employee is asked to set aside the nonjob aspects of life while at work. This request is a depersonalizing demand, which most employees find difficult to accomplish, so informal "organizations within the organization" develop to defend personal identity. Separating outside life from work activities is further complicated by technology, from which many employees must "unplug" when they come to work each day.

The result is that people behave less as members of the nursing facility and more in terms of compromising their many commitments. For example, when asked about the sources of satisfaction from their jobs, employees often rate their interpersonal relationships with their fellow employees as an essential aspect of their work. Associating with the residents follows, with the nursing facility's goals and values tending to be somewhat low on the list of employee motivations. Administrators and supervisors engage in a constant struggle to gain employee loyalty and dedication to the facility's goals.

There is yet another important limitation to employees' full participation. People tend to define the facility based on their experience with a particular organization section. This narrow perception is another reason why upper-level administrators who collect information only from their immediate subordinates may never know the full scope of what is taking place. Each administrator must do their best to actively know each employee, their name, and a little about their situation. When the administrator does this, it allows the administrator to become a "real person" in the employee's eyes.

People tend to exaggerate their importance to the organization. Loyalties develop to the work area rather than to the whole facility, a potential source of conflict among departments. Each employee group, shift, or specialty also creates an additional filter for perceptions and loyalty.

Job descriptions and definitions are essential to enable staff to accomplish necessary work and behaviors associated with the organization's objectives. Roles are standardized patterns of required behavior (Robbins & Coulter, 2018). The nurse's aide has very clear organizational expectations for their 8 hours on the job, as does each employee. Clear communication of expectations is essential for each task to be performed.

NAB DOMAIN 2B3: ETHICAL CONDUCT AND STANDARDS OF PRACTICE

Connecting Roles to Norms

To build loyalty, organizations try to match roles and persons, filling them with the organization's norms or values.

Professional standards for nurses and nurse's aides are norms, behavior patterns to which all members of the group are expected to adhere. Respecting the HIPAA rights of residents would be an example of such a norm. Another example is Sam Walton, the founder and past owner of Walmart, who exemplified this by standing in a checkout line in each of his Walmart stores each year and constantly teaching and reinforcing an important norm: Ensure that checkout is a pleasant experience, thus stimulating the customer to feel favorable toward Walmart.

Norms are justified by values, which are more generalized statements about the behavior expected from staff members. Values furnish the rationale for the normative requirements. Treating all residents with respect for their rights as persons is an example of a broad value statement, justifying the more specific norm that nursing personnel should respect each resident's privacy. For Sam Walton, building customer loyalty and repeat business might be the general value under which he established a pleasant checkout experience as a norm to be enforced.

System norms and values are attempts to connect employees with the system to remain within system values while carrying out their role assignments. Norms and values furnish "cognitive road maps" (ways to think about the organization and its goals). Norms help personnel adjust to the system.

Nursing facilities' norms and goals revolve around providing the highest quality of life achievable for residents. Under Tag F550, the federal government defines this as treating each resident with respect and dignity and caring for each resident in a manner and in an environment that promotes maintenance or enhancement of their quality of life, recognizing each resident's individuality. The quality-of-life citation is easily one of the top 10 citations annually. This standard of care involves assisting residents to be well groomed and dressed appropriately, promoting independence in dining, allowing private space and property, speaking and listening respectfully, and focusing on the individual's communication.

Ethics are values or norms that guide behavior. A facility administrator is expected to be an ethical person who follows professional health personnel's standards of practice. The American College of Health Care Administrators (ACHCA; the nursing facility administrators' professional organization) has adopted an ethics code based on intent, actions, and professionalism (Exhibit 1.1). Each state licensing board or agency publishes standards of practice and sets the ethical behavior expectations for nursing facility administrators licensed in that state.

EXHIBIT 1.1 American College of Health Care Administrators (ACHCA) Code of Ethics.

Code of Ethics

American College of Health Care Administrators

PREAMBLE: The preservation of the highest standards of integrity and ethical principles is vital to the successful discharge of the professional responsibilities of all long-term health care administrators. This Code of Ethics has been promulgated by the American College of Health Care Administrators (ACHCA) in an effort to stress the fundamental rules considered essential to this basic purpose. It shall be the obligation of members to seek to avoid not only conduct specifically proscribed by the code, but also conduct that is inconsistent with its spirit and purpose. Failure to specify any particular responsibility or practice in this Code of Ethics should not be construed as denial of the existence of other responsibilities or practices. Recognizing that the ultimate responsibility for applying standards and ethics falls upon the individual, the ACHCA establishes the following Code of Ethics to make clear its expectation of the membership.

Expectation I
Individuals shall hold paramount the welfare of persons for whom care is provided.
PRESCRIPTIONS: The Health Care Administrator shall:
• Strive to provide to all those entrusted to his or her care the highest quality of appropriate services possible in light of resources or other constraints.
• Operate the facility consistent with laws, regulations, and standards of practice recognized in the field of health care administration.
• Consistent with law and professional standards, protect the confidentiality of information regarding individual recipients of care.
• Perform administrative duties with the personal integrity that will earn the confidence, trust, and respect of the general public.
• Take appropriate steps to avoid discrimination on basis of race, color, religion, sex, pregnancy, sexual orientation, citizenship status, national origin, age, physical or mental disability, past, present or future status in the U.S. uniformed services, genetics or any other characteristic protected under applicable law.

PROSCRIPTION: The Health Care Administrator shall not:
• Disclose professional or personal information regarding recipients of service to unauthorized personnel unless required by law or to protect the public welfare.

Expectation II
Individuals shall maintain high standards of professional competence and personal conduct.
PRESCRIPTIONS: The Health Care Administrator shall:
• Possess and maintain the competencies necessary to effectively perform his or her responsibilities.
• Practice administration in accordance with capabilities and proficiencies and, when appropriate, seek counsel from qualified others.
• Actively strive to enhance knowledge of and expertise in long-term care administration through continuing education and professional development.
• Demonstrate conduct that is in the best interest of the profession.

PROSCRIPTIONS: The Health Care Administrator shall not:
• Misrepresent qualifications, education, experience, or affiliations.
• Provide services other than those for which he or she is prepared and qualified to perform.
• Conduct themselves in a manner detrimental to the best interest of the profession.

(continued)

EXHIBIT 1.1 American College of Health Care Administrators (ACHCA) Code of Ethics (*continued*).

Expectation III
Individuals shall strive, in all matters relating to their professional functions, to maintain a professional posture that places paramount the interests of the facility and its residents.
PRESCRIPTIONS: The Health Care Administrator shall:
• Avoid partisanship and provide a forum for the fair resolution of any disputes which may arise in service delivery or facility management.
• Disclose to the governing body or other authority as may be appropriate, any actual or potential circumstance concerning him or her that might reasonably be thought to create a conflict of interest or have a substantial adverse impact on the facility or its residents.

PROSCRIPTION: The Health Care Administrator shall not:
• Participate in activities that reasonably may be thought to create a conflict of interest or have the potential to have a substantial adverse impact on the facility or its residents.

Expectation IV
Individuals shall honor their responsibilities to the public, their profession, and their relationships with colleagues and members of related professions.
PRESCRIPTIONS: The Health Care Administrator shall:
• Foster increased knowledge within the profession of health care administration and support research efforts toward this end.
• Participate with others in the community to plan for and provide a full range of health care services.
• Share areas of expertise with colleagues, students, and the general public to increase awareness and promote understanding of health care in general and the profession in particular.
• Inform the ACHCA Standards and Ethics Committee of actual or potential violations of this Code of Ethics, and fully cooperate with ACHCA's sanctioned inquiries into matters of professional conduct related to this Code of Ethics.

PROSCRIPTION: The Health Care Administrator shall not:
• Defend, support, or ignore unethical conduct perpetrated by colleagues, peers or students.

Justification of the Facility: "Soft" and "Hard"

NAB DOMAIN 4B1: MISSION, VISION, AND VALUES STATEMENTS

Another contribution of organizational norms and values is the moral or social justification for the nursing facility's activities. This focus is often put in the form of a mission statement for the facility, defining the facility's purposes and values. The mission statement often appears at the front entrance and often at the front of the human resources handbook—it becomes the first impression the visitors and prospective employees have of the facility's purposes.

When nursing facilities are attacked in the newspapers or subjected to public criticism, staff members look to their administrators to reaffirm the facility's worth, enabling them to feel good about themselves and the work they perform there.

The administrator demonstrates what is important, the values that guide staff's day-to-day behavior, how they behave, and what they give attention to. If the administrator constantly moves around the facility, ensuring that each resident is getting quality care and enjoying a high quality of life, the employees will probably follow suit. Likewise, if the administrator concentrates instead on getting the paperwork done, meeting regulations, and saving money, that is where the staff's attention will focus. To develop pride in the facility and enthusiasm for its works is the goal of people management. The most successful administrators are those who are hands-on.

When it comes to achieving long-term success with personnel, soft is hard. Quality care and high quality of life are soft, but the administrator must be uncompromising and implacable in implementing them (hard). Administrators care deeply about and respect their staff and residents. Yet, they must enforce a "no excuses" environment when it comes to resident care. The successful administrator is tough on values and tender in support of staff who try to implement those values.

Dreams, Vision, and Goals

NAB DOMAIN 4B1: MISSION, VISION, AND VALUES STATEMENTS

Another way to conceptualize values, norms, and roles is to equate them to dreams/ visions, goals, and behaviors, respectively. Employees are more motivated by and able to accept a vision or ideal held by the facility. A dream or vision is a motivating abstract or belief. A nursing facility administrator's dream or vision could constantly improve residents' and staff's daily life experiences in the facility. Specific goals, such as having a full activities program, are secondary to the dream. Goals give employees specific targets to shoot for and provide feedback, but goals must be guided by something larger—a dream or vision that inspires. Dreams, then, can become goals with wings. Each goal is a step toward a dream.

Most nursing facility corporations publish mission statements that resemble a list of goals more than a vision or dream (e.g., "We seek to be the provider of choice for each community in which we have a facility"). While fine for the corporate level, this is not very motivating to the nursing assistants in their day-to-day struggles to provide care. Goal statements from the corporate level seldom motivate. Many local facilities have corporate goal statements in large print on well-designed posters on the walls, but these may not be their own goals. Corporate-generated goal statements are subject to the not invented here (NIH) phenomenon. Each facility must generate its own vision of what it is seeking.

A major nursing facility chain has a corporate vision that can motivate all employees if the highest management level stands behind it: "whatever it takes." The corporation promises to assist every employee in giving the best quality of care possible to their residents by the corporate commitment to assist each employee, no matter what it takes at the corporate level. If each employee believes they will be supported in their individual effort to improve residents' and staff's daily lives, each employee can participate in the dream.

The most significant issue with mission, vision, and value (MVV) statements is that many facilities have them, but they are never again shared with employees after the first day on the job. We see these concepts stressed during orientation but quickly forgotten when not implemented in practice. Instead, employers should embody these MVV statements daily to keep their staff on task, reminding them why they are there and what should be important to them throughout the day. Companies that stress the MVV can often deliver on those promises.

WHY ORGANIZATIONS NEED ADMINISTRATIVE LEADERSHIP

NAB DOMAIN 4A1: ORGANIZATIONAL STRUCTURES (E.G., DEPARTMENTS, FUNCTIONS, SYSTEMIC PROCESSES); 4A2: ORGANIZATIONAL CHANGE MANAGEMENT; 4A3: ORGANIZATIONAL BEHAVIOR (E.G., ORGANIZATIONAL CULTURE, TEAM BUILDING, GROUP DYNAMICS); 4B1: MISSION, VISION, AND VALUES STATEMENTS

Once all the plans have been developed and staff hired and trained, why doesn't the organization just run smoothly? Although there are several dimensions to any answers to this question, we discuss a few that are especially relevant.

All organizational designs are imperfect (Hitt et al., 2017; Robbins & Coulter, 2018). Differences between the organizational chart, the written policies, and the organization's actual functioning are common. The new worker often turns to the group's members to learn job requirements as implemented rather than adhering to their onboarding instructions.

Actual behavior, the organization's true functioning, is infinitely more complex, inconclusive, and variable than the plan. An illustration of this is organizational sabotage. Any worker who wants to sabotage the facility can do so by merely following organizational law to the letter—doing what is formally stipulated, no more and no less.

Nursing facilities, like all organizations, need administrative leadership to cope with the constantly changing external environment that requires internal adjustments (Krupp & Schoemaker, 2014). For example, with three new assisted living facilities and a new residential hospice center open in your area, your facility occupancy rate drops from 92% to 72%; organizational leadership is required.

Organizations also need leadership to accommodate the changes constantly occurring within the organization. Employees retire or find work elsewhere, the needs of staff and residents change, conflicts develop, physical systems break down, and decisions to repair or replace are required.

Change is here to stay. To meet current challenges, an organization must adapt constantly. Whether one feels one has reached the top or is still climbing, one cannot stay still. The old saying "if it isn't broken, don't fix it" needs to be changed to "if you don't fix it all the time, it will break." This constant evaluation and adjustment is the cycle of quality assessment and performance improvement.

1.6.7 RELATED CONCEPTS

Section Concepts

- *Corporate culture and its daily influence on the facility*
- *Management concepts*

Consider as the Administrator . . .

- *If you run a facility that is highly effective but barely efficient, can you survive?*

We turn now to several additional concepts worth reviewing in any consideration of attempts by administrators to direct the efforts of the organization.

CORPORATE CULTURE

Corporate culture is the overall style or atmosphere of a facility. The corporate culture governs how people relate to each other in the organization; for example, "this is how we do things in this facility." Corporate culture is vital to the organization's survival. For the nursing facility to have the best chance of succeeding, it needs a stable staff (low turnover), with all staff members participating in the facility's culture and taking personal responsibility to make the corporate culture a daily reality. In a sense, the CNAs (the certified nursing assistants who deliver most of the hands-on care in the facility) may be the key staff members in implementing the corporate culture.

DELEGATION

The concept of delegation is permitting decisions to be made at the lowest possible level. Such authority is given to middle-level and lower-level managers, allowing them to make decisions for the organization as appropriate. The essential issue is the determination of the nature of the decisions to be made at whatever level (Robbins & Coulter, 2018).

Delegating can be both beneficial and disadvantageous. At optimum operation, delegation channels decision-making to staff members who are best informed and most skilled to make a particular decision or set of decisions. The negative aspect of this practice is that because the managers have only a partial view of the organization, they consciously or unconsciously may make decisions to maximize their area of the organization to the detriment of the holistic facility. The nursing facility is a living, breathing entity in which all parts must operate in perfection as if it were an orchestra.

Ultimately, responsibility cannot be delegated. The chief administrator is held accountable for the acts of all persons working under facility auspices.

UNITY OF COMMAND

The concept of unity of command emphasizes the importance of each person being accountable to only one supervisor (Hitt et al., 2017). It is functionally difficult for any employee to answer to two managers, and the facility must be organized to ensure this relationship.

SPAN OF CONTROL

How many immediate subordinates with interrelated work should a manager supervise? This balance has been a point of contention for decades (Konopaske et al., 2018). The British World War I general Sir Ian Hamilton insisted that six was the maximum span of control (Hitt et al., 2017). Others have proposed different numbers. Decisions by several state governments illustrate this issue, as they have expanded operations to the point that perhaps 100 persons were reporting directly to the governor. This structure created a practice in which no one was supervising these 100 persons. Several states regained control of employees by reconstructing their organizational pattern to include a department of human resources to whose supervisor most of the former 100 reported, leaving perhaps a dozen persons reporting directly to the governor. In the last analysis, the administrator must be confident that each employee has adequate supervision.

SHORT CHAIN OF COMMAND

This principle asserts that there should be limited management levels between the chief administrator and the rank and file (Hitt et al., 2017). Certainly, for the communication purposes of upper-level management, this seems a good principle to follow. It minimizes the number of interpreters through whom information for upper-level managers must be sifted.

BALANCE

Advocates of the principle of balance assert that there is a need for continual surveillance to maintain harmony among the following:

- Size of the various departments
- Standardization of procedures and flexibility
- Centralization and decentralization services (Cole & Kelley, 2020)
- Span of control and short chain of command

MANAGEMENT BY OBJECTIVES

This approach emphasizes setting specific, jointly developed goals with a defined time for goal achievement and performance feedback. The theory is to create a process of participation beginning with the lowest levels of workers whose recommendations are constantly moved upward until the final selection of the goals to be implemented is made by upper management (Singh, 2016).

Management by objectives (MBO) was first put into practice (under this rubric) by Lyndon B. Johnson. As president of the United States, he wished to gain meaningful control of the largest bureaucracy under his management, now known as the Department of Health and Human Services (DHHS). He utilized MBO to do just this and successfully brought oversight to the DHHS.

Although MBO, in theory, meaningfully involves lowest level employees/managers in recommending organizational goals, the real effect is to shift power upward. This shift occurs because upper-level managers make the final choice among (and modify if necessary) recommendations from the lower levels.

MANAGEMENT INFORMATION SYSTEMS

NAB DOMAIN 3A5: INFORMATION SYSTEMS INFRASTRUCTURE (E.G., CONFIGURATIONS, DATA SECURITY, TECHNICAL CONTROLS)

The phrase "management information systems" (MIS) originally came into the literature as a description of computer-based information processing for managers in making their decisions. MIS is the study of how the organization communicates and processes information to maximize the effectiveness of management and further the organization's objectives (Cole & Kelley, 2020; Singh, 2016).

MIS's point is that the manager needs a constant rationalized and organized flow of information to make appropriate decisions. Developing an MIS is as simple as:

1. Determining one's need for information
2. Identifying the sources of information
3. Deciding on the amount, form, and frequency of information needed
4. Choosing the means of information processing
5. Implementing the system

MANAGEMENT BY EXCEPTION: PRIORITIZING AND MANAGING TIME

NAB DOMAIN 4A3: ORGANIZATIONAL BEHAVIOR (E.G., ORGANIZATIONAL CULTURE, TEAM BUILDING, GROUP DYNAMICS)

Every day the manager receives numerous verbal and written reports that usually contain routine information about the functioning of the facility. A way managers can effectively use their time is by giving attention to exceptions to the plan. If the census, the number of meals served, or their costs are within the plan, there may be no need for action. There are multitudes of detailed tasks being accomplished acceptably by the staff every day. What merits the administrator's attention are the exceptions to the policies and plans of action initially established for the organization.

The budget is one of the more useful tools for spotting exceptions. Getting information about the amount of money that has been spent in the last period is a reasonably exact control on measurement services (Cole & Kelley, 2020). If any department is spending within the agreed-on budget, there may be no need for the administrator's attention. Whenever a departmental budget falls short or exceeds the amounts allocated to it, the administrator should give attention to the exception and take whatever steps may be necessary to bring expenditures back within the budgeted limits. Nursing having to hire unexpected numbers of "pool" nurses (nurses hired by the day from an agency that supplies temporary nursing help) for weekends, for example, is a frequent cause of budget overage. However, too little expenditure by nursing or food service might be as much a cause for alarm as too great an expenditure. In the first case, the facility might be short on the required number of nursing personnel hours per day; in the second case, the quality of food being purchased and prepared might be unsatisfactory.

Management by exception does not mean that the routine and within-specification behaviors of the facility remain unexamined. It is the routine behaviors of the organization that are examined for deviations from the norm.

The effective administrator prioritizes available time. The goal is to ensure that the facility functions as desired at all levels. How to ensure this can be problematic. The staff managers must manage their time in ways that result in the facility's tasks being performed appropriately. The director of nursing must not spend most of their available time on the floor assisting other nurses. The nursing director's role is to keep the facility's total functioning in mind when deciding how to spend the time available.

PROJECT MANAGEMENT—PERT/CPM

Project management is a currently emerging field, including many different certifications and methods. In fact, there are individuals who specialize in project management as professionals. Project (program) evaluation review technique (PERT) and critical path method (CPM) are examples of project management control tools that show the relationship among the activities that make up a project. The renovation of a wing of a facility, for example, can be mapped out with time estimates for completion of each necessary step: the critical path facilitating resource allocation.

CONCEPTS OF EFFICIENCY AND EFFECTIVENESS

Efficiency is producing the desired effect with a minimum of effort, expense, or waste. Efficiency can be measured by the ratio of effective work to the energy expended in producing it. In systems terms, this simply means getting the maximum outputs with the minimum inputs.

Effectiveness is the power or ability to bring about the desired results. A nursing facility that sets a goal of achieving excellence in resident care and then does so is effective. However, efficiency does not guarantee the excellence of patient care. The facility may, for example, be employing a large number of nurses and aides to accomplish excellence in resident care. Yet, studies in human resources reveal that when more people than needed are placed on a work shift, the quality of care is not necessarily improved and is often decreased. The staff may simply divide the required work to lighten the load for everyone or take more frequent breaks and not give additional attention to the residents. In this case, the too heavy staff/resident ratio may lead to both inefficiency and ineffectiveness. This mismatch is often created when staff do not understand their roles, assignments, or what they are supposed to be doing, resulting in confusion and care delay.

The solution is to assign the optimum number of staff known to be needed to provide excellent care to a specified number of residents and manage their time to optimize the amount and quality of work. In this way, the manager achieves both efficiency (the desired effect with a minimum of effort, expense, waste) and effectiveness (the desired results). Given enough resources and appropriate consultation, almost any nursing facility administrator can achieve effectiveness. What is essential today is to be both effective and efficient.

1.6.8 HISTORY OF THE CONCEPT OF MANAGEMENT

Administrators have been managing organizations, large and small, for thousands of years. Some 5,000 years ago, the Sumerian civilization (Iran and Iraq of today) developed a script to control business accounts. Archaeologists have found clay tablets recording business transactions from that ancient time. We have records of Cheops, the Egyptian king who built the Great Pyramid around 2900 BCE. We know that this monument covered 13 acres and employed 100,000 laborers for 20 years and that 8,368 lower-, middle-, and upper-level managers administered the project (Robbins & Coulter, 2018). In ancient Greece, music was used to govern motions in the production lines.

In the fifth century BCE, Plato reports in *The Republic* a dialogue between Socrates and a Greek general about the extent to which management is a transferable skill. The general, it seems, was incensed that the Athenian Assembly had just appointed as the commander in chief of the army the Athenian chorus manager, who had shown himself to be an excellent fundraiser and chorus director. Socrates argued that if the man could run the chorus well and raise the necessary revenue, he could also be a good general. Fifteen upper-level executives of a major U.S. automaker more recently expressed the same view of their own ability to manage almost anything during a 15-month study of their skills. Managers' opinions of their capabilities have not changed much over the last 5,000 years.

SCIENTIFIC MANAGEMENT

By the 1800s, the early scientific management movement was underway in England as an outgrowth of the Industrial Revolution. The managers at Soho Foundry of Boulton, Watt and Co. were concerned with market research and forecasting, planned site location, machine layout study, production standards, planning, standard components, cost controls, cost accounting, employee training, work-study programs and incentives, and employee welfare (Robbins & Coulter, 2018).

During that epoch, management literature began appearing, but there was little recognition of the principles of management we have discussed. The West's current management philosophy seems to have evolved from four schools of thought, although various writers further refine them.

HUMAN RELATIONS MANAGEMENT

At the end of the 19th century, a group of writers who believed management could be an exact science emerged. They focused on the physical activities involved in production. Frederic Taylor (Robbins & Coulter, 2018) researched a Philadelphia machine shop, demonstrating with time and motion studies that work done by as many as 450 shovelers at Bethlehem Steel could be accomplished with as few as 150 persons, provided they received instructions to improve their effort. Frank Gilbreth's time and motion studies are well known. Henry Gantt developed his now widely used Gantt chart, with its task and bonus plan and standard hour concept (Cole & Kelley, 2020; Robbins & Coulter, 2018).

Early in the 20th century, Henri Fayol identified management "universals": to plan, to organize, to command (tell others), and to coordinate (control) services (Cole & Kelley, 2020; Robbins & Coulter, 2018). Fayol thus developed one of the earliest formulations of a general theory of management. The "process school" members, such as Fayol and James Mooney, focused on departmentalization, coordination, and organizational form—the issues we have discussed under "organizing."

During the 1920s and 1930s, a group of theorists led by Elton Mayo described management as consisting primarily of human relations skills. According to them, successful organizations fulfill the employees' economic needs and the organization's social and psychological needs (Cole & Kelley, 2020).

Sponsored by the National Research Council, Mayo conducted several experiments at the Hawthorne manufacturing plant to determine the effect of illumination (improved lighting) on output (Cole & Kelley, 2020; Robbins & Coulter, 2018). He found that production rose for the experimental group when illumination was increased. But the control group also produced more, although it had no increase in lighting. Illumination was then reduced to the barest minimum in both groups, yet their production continued to rise, the apparent reason being the increased attention they were given by the managers (Robbins & Coulter, 2018). His experiments convinced Mayo that human factors exercise the most powerful influence on employee behavior because of the workers' need to participate in social groups. He concluded that besides meeting production requirements, work arrangements must meet the employee's need for social satisfaction on the job. Unfortunately, the "behavioral school" experienced a low predictability rate.

COMPUTERS AND MANAGEMENT: THE INFORMATION TECHNOLOGY ERA

NAB DOMAIN 3A5: INFORMATION SYSTEMS INFRASTRUCTURE (E.G., CONFIGURATIONS, DATA SECURITY, TECHNICAL CONTROLS)

Technology Infrastructure

Various names are applied to management theory emerging after World War II. Its major focus has been systems theory using mathematical quantification. This statistical evaluation level is made possible by the development of computers capable of processing enormous quantities of complex data. Some members of the management "science schools" believe that almost everything can be quantified. However, the problem remains that people assign the mathematical weights to each factor quantified, and then others must interpret for themselves the meaning they attach to the quantified results (Robbins & Coulter, 2018).

Computers are a vital part of our daily operations. We utilize computers at the facility level to provide care, keep track of medication administration, physician and nurse charting, financial reporting, MDS processing, care planning, and many other required daily duties. We also use these same computers to analyze all the data that have been input into them to identify problem areas requiring attention, as an early notification system and quality improvement. These same computers are used at the corporate level to ensure that business progresses effectively at the facility level and identifies quality improvement opportunities, especially when comparing facilities. This assists in ensuring regulatory compliance and high-quality care are achieved in all facilities of the chain.

Managing is an exceptionally complex, multidimensional task not yet fully understood by the social sciences. However, much has been learned that can be useful to the nursing facility administrator in their efforts to ensure a caring environment while running the nursing facility as a good business operation.

Today, nursing facilities also use technology and the internet to market, drive admissions, develop relationships, and connect to the industry, vendors, and other stakeholders. We can find best practices within the input of a few keystrokes to assist in the provision of care. We can identify suppliers and other stakeholders who are willing to work with us in any area imaginable. Computers and the internet have truly changed how daily business is completed at the nursing facility.

The use of computers is simply a requirement for the facility. Our staff will interface with computers and technology on a minute-by-minute basis in providing care. Our facilities will be reporting that same information to those tasked with managing it. Much of that same information is reported to state and federal entities for oversight. We utilize computers for billing insurance, Medicare, and Medicaid. We interact with computers of other entities to credential our clinical and medical staff. Everything we do in a facility is somehow touched by computer technology, and the more we embrace new technology as it comes, the easier our abilities to provide care will be.

> **NAB DOMAINS 2B11: HEALTHCARE RECORD REQUIREMENTS (E.G., CONFIDENTIALITY, DISCLOSURE, SAFEGUARDING, HIPAA, HITECH); 3A5: INFORMATION SYSTEMS INFRASTRUCTURE (E.G., CONFIGURATIONS, DATA SECURITY, TECHNICAL CONTROLS)**

The safeguarding of databases that contain both resident information and facility information is an ongoing concern. Hackers are increasingly becoming more effective in their efforts at breaching databases. At a minimum, every computer and user in the facility needs to have proper credentials to log in, many times with dual-factor authentication or other more stringent means of protection. Despite our best efforts, we see routine breaches by skilled hackers. Cryptology, computer security, information technology security, cloud security, and points of access remain major challenges. Eternal vigilance is the price of minimizing the chance that the facility's or its residents' information is breached, and even this is not enough in some circumstances. Security of residents' medical records is of particular concern, as explicit and extensive rules cover it under HIPAA and the HITECH Act (covered in Part 4 of this book).

The administrator must manage the information processed by the facility and maximize the use of technology systems to facilitate information flow that allows each worker to accomplish expected work.

Utilizing Social Media

> **NAB DOMAIN 2C9: HUMAN RESOURCE POLICIES (E.G., DRUG-FREE WORKPLACE, DISCIPLINE, JOB CLASSIFICATION, PHOTOGRAPHY AND VIDEO, SOCIAL MEDIA USAGE, MOBILE PHONE USAGE)**

Social media can be thought of as the web-based interaction among people in which they create, share, and exchange information and ideas in virtual communities and networks. Social media use mobile and web-based technologies to create interactive platforms through which individuals and communities share, co-create, and discuss ideas. The facility may wish to have a blog on its website for idea discussion. The facility can utilize social media as a marketing tool by giving the facility a presence on the web. Today, care must be given to ensuring resident privacy on the myriad of available social sites. This privacy must stem from the facility level and must extend to employees and their use of smartphones and other handheld technology and to families and visitors with the same technology. We live in a time in which it is very difficult to maintain even our own personal privacy, and with cameras and video recorders as part of nearly every phone on the planet, we need to be more vigilant than ever.

COMMON PITFALLS IN PRACTICE

- Employees respect administrators who are not only a part of the facility but also interact with the facility. Your office is a place where you go to meet with people. Otherwise, answer those emails and get on the floor. BE VISIBLE, be known!
- You may be the administrator, but your job is, in large part, being a relationship manager as well. Any stakeholder (resident, family, vendor, community, hospital, etc.) requires a great relationship with you. Your time in building relationships is an investment in your success and your future.
- Mission, vision, values, dreams, goals—these are not only things communicated during new-employee orientation. They need to be lived and embodied in your actions daily. When employees see this as important to you, it becomes important to them as well.

1.7 COMPARING AND CONTROLLING QUALITY

Section Concepts

- *Requirements for effective control of quality*
- *How to diagnose organizational quality*
- *Benchmarking*
- *Total quality management (TQM) and quality assurance*
- *Common quality terminology*

Consider as the Administrator . . .

- *Quality is an important thing. Do you think you can actually control it?*
- *Quality to one person may be defined differently for another. Is it possible to meet the quality expectations for every person and every family? Should you even attempt to do so?*

NAB DOMAIN 1B3: CARE RECIPIENT BILL OF RIGHTS AND RESPONSIBILITIES

NAB DOMAIN 4A2: ORGANIZATIONAL CHANGE MANAGEMENT

NAB DOMAIN 4A4: LEADERSHIP PRINCIPLES (E.G., COMMUNICATION, STYLES, MENTORING, COACHING, PERSONAL PROFESSIONAL DEVELOPMENT)

Because all organizational designs are incomplete, the quest for quality is frustratingly elusive, both in industry and in healthcare settings. The nursing facility's quest for quality is especially challenging because of the facility's organizational complexity and, often, limited resources. However, technology has helped level the playing field for each facility and has provided them with specific resources to utilize or general resources to access provided by other entities.

EVIDENCE-BASED PRACTICES

The federal government is increasingly involved in establishing clinical practice guidelines for caregiving in the nursing facility setting. These clinical practice guidelines represent what is believed to be best practices in caregiving. Studies on modalities of care that appear to yield consistently good results with patients over time create the base of such guidelines. Typically, panels of experts are appointed who together agree on guidelines. Guidelines such as these are being introduced into the federal guidelines to surveyors' instructions. Often such guidelines employ checklists that, if followed, minimize unwanted effects or down-level caregiving. An example of this type of instrument would be the INTERACT tools available for use and download.

Even so, or perhaps because of this circumstance, maybe the most valuable functions managers perform for the facility are comparing (evaluating) and controlling the quality of facility outputs. Comparing is judging the extent to which actual results of the facility's efforts achieve the outcomes proposed in the plans. Controlling quality follows comparing, and then taking the steps necessary to adjust the policies and plans of action to achieve stated goals more satisfactorily.

One problem in controlling quality is that it obliges the manager to take sometimes unpleasant corrective actions to keep the facility on target. These actions may involve advising staff members that the work result is not suitable or informing department managers that the actual outputs (levels of performance) are unsatisfactory. Managers often find this an awkward business and avoid acting in the hope the situation will correct itself or that the problem will disappear on its own. But matters usually get worse and require attention for a solution.

1.7.1 SOME REQUIREMENTS FOR EFFECTIVE CONTROL OF QUALITY

Section Concepts

- *The control of quality in the facility is both complex and complicated with many dimensions to consider*

Consider as the Administrator . . .

- *How can you determine when you have effective control of quality?*

We discuss several of the current methods used for controlling quality, such as the Deming method, benchmarking, reengineering, and various continuous quality improvement (CQI)/total quality management (TQM) services.

There are at least nine conditions that any method for effective control of quality should observe:

1. Translate goals into policies and plans of action that are clearly stated, known, and measurable.
2. Identify appropriate measurements. If the wrong measurements to compare actual to expected outputs are used, no quality control system, however sophisticated, can truly inform and manage quality.
3. Set limits to deviations from the goal/policy/plan of action. The manager must have predetermined and known outside limits for each output (quality goal) being controlled.
4. Disseminate information to the appropriate staff in a useful form. It must be timely, easily understood, and unambiguous so that the employee cannot use a lack of clarity as a pretext for nonconformity.
5. Management action, following set policies, must be taken when limits are exceeded, or quality is not achieved. The policies must be known to the managers responsible for controlling outputs. Clear statements of policies are crucial for influencing staff members to take corrective actions when needed.
6. Corrective actions must be taken. An effective system of rewards and punishments is needed to encourage managers to take required corrective actions. When middle- and lower-level managers sense any softening in the administrator's determination to enforce the quality control policies, there will be a simultaneous softening of the quality control effort.
7. Systematic evaluation and a renewal of control measures account for any changing organizational goals (as expressed in new or modified plans of action). Regular review and responses to changes in the organization's external or internal environments are required. Middle- and lower-level managers may interpret portions of the quality system being discarded as evidence that the entire quality control system is no longer in force (Cole & Kelley, 2020). Eternal vigilance is the price of a quality control system that remains effective over an extended period.
8. Functional and valued quality control mechanisms must be supported by each management level if they are to remain effective. If the staff responsible for enforcing quality controls do not feel that the measures are acceptable and productive, excuses will be found not to rely on them.

9. Keep limitations of the scope and capabilities of the quality control system itself constantly in mind. They are, as we shall see in the following discussion, never perfect. It is not possible to devise an organizational quality control system that does not need the good judgment of concerned employees to arrive at an interpretation of what the organization "really wants" in any situation (Hitt et al., 2017; Robbins & Coulter, 2018).

1.7.2 DIAGNOSING ORGANIZATIONAL QUALITY

Section Concepts

- *How to diagnose an organization as a necessary skill of the administrator*
- *Deming's approach to ensuring quality in an organization*
- *Benchmarking*
- *TQM/CQI*
- *The concept of structure–process–outcome used to assist in evaluating the quality of care*
- *How to judge quality in a facility*
- *Common acronyms and definitions used in quality assurance*

Consider as the Administrator . . .

- *Who defines quality? Is quality the same for you as the administrator as it may be for residents, families, or stakeholders?*

NAB DOMAIN 2B5: RISK MANAGEMENT PROCESS AND PROGRAMS; 2B6: QUALITY IMPROVEMENT PROCESSES (E.G., ROOT CAUSE ANALYSIS, PDCA/PDSA); 3B6: CENTERS FOR MEDICARE AND MEDICAID SERVICES (CMS) QUALITY MEASURES; 3B7: QUALITY ASSURANCE AND PERFORMANCE IMPROVEMENT (QAPI); 4A2: ORGANIZATIONAL CHANGE MANAGEMENT

In caring for their patients, physicians base their treatment on their medical diagnoses, which they interpret from the patient's presenting symptoms. In the same way, administrators are organizational diagnosticians who manage the nursing facility by using judgments based on their interpretation of presenting organizational symptoms. Physicians diagnose and treat patient illness much like administrators diagnose and treat organizational illness or organizational pathologies. Organizational pathology is the study and diagnosis of what is believed to be a problem adversely affecting the nursing facility (Robbins & Coulter, 2018).

In this section, we compare organizational care concepts to diagnoses. Three diagnoses that affect us all also affect organizations:

- Atherosclerosis (narrowing and hardening of the arteries, allowing less blood to flow)
- Aortic stenosis (a stiffening of the main blood vessel supplying the body, reducing the amount of blood reaching the limbs)

- Congestive heart failure (CHF; a progressive reduction of the heart's ability to pump enough blood), which often leads to peripheral vascular diseases (reduced blood flow to the limbs)

Organizations suffer from similar pathologies (disease processes), reducing their effectiveness and ability to function.

Managers have always sought to achieve quality control in their organizations, but this remains one of the more elusive aspects of successful management. Several studies have demonstrated quality indicators for nursing facilities in the past, and we continue to discover new areas based on technology.

The CMS has sought to measure and improve quality measures through data collection and assessment using its developed forms, which collect residents' physical, clinical conditions and abilities. The quality measures change from time to time. The CMS is currently focused on the following quality measures:

Short-Stay Quality Measures

- Percentage of short-stay residents who were rehospitalized after a nursing facility admission
- Percentage of short-stay residents who have had an outpatient emergency department visit
- Percentage of residents who newly received an antipsychotic medication
- Changes in skin integrity postacute care: pressure ulcer/injury
- Percentage of residents who made improvements in function
- Percentage of residents who were assessed and appropriately given the seasonal influenza vaccine
- Percentage of residents who received the seasonal influenza vaccine
- Percentage of residents who were offered and declined the seasonal influenza vaccine
- Percentage of residents who did not receive, due to medical contraindication, the seasonal influenza vaccine
- Percentage of residents who were assessed and appropriately given the pneumococcal vaccine
- Percentage of residents who were offered and declined the pneumococcal vaccine
- Percentage of residents who did not receive, due to medical contraindication, the pneumococcal vaccine (CMS, 2021)

Long-Stay Quality Measures

- Number of hospitalizations per 1,000 long-stay resident days
- Outpatient emergency department visits per 1,000 long-stay resident days
- Percentage of long-stay residents who received an antipsychotic medication
- Percentage of long-stay residents experiencing one or more falls with a major injury
- Percentage of long-stay high-risk residents with pressure ulcers
- Percentage of long-stay residents with a urinary tract infection
- Percentage of long-stay residents who have or had a catheter inserted and left in their bladder
- Percentage of long-stay residents whose ability to move independently worsened

- Percentage of long-stay residents whose need for help with activities of daily living has increased
- Percentage of residents who were assessed and appropriately given the seasonal influenza vaccine
- Percentage of residents who received the seasonal influenza vaccine
- Percentage of residents who were offered and declined the seasonal influenza vaccine
- Percentage of residents who did not receive, due to medical contraindication, the seasonal influenza vaccine
- Percentage of residents who were assessed and appropriately given the pneumococcal vaccine
- Percentage of residents who were offered and declined the pneumococcal vaccine
- Percentage of residents who did not receive, due to medical contraindication, the pneumococcal vaccine
- Percentage of long-stay residents who were physically restrained
- Percentage of long-stay low-risk residents who lose control of their bowels or bladder
- Percentage of long-stay residents who lose too much weight
- Percentage of long-stay residents who have symptoms of depression
- Percentage of long-stay residents who got an antianxiety or hypnotic medication (CMS, 2021)

The CMS has made quality indicators available to the public at https://www.medicare.gov/care-compare/. These indicators include those pertaining to the following types of providers: doctors and clinicians, hospitals, nursing facilities (including rehab services), home health, hospice, inpatient rehabilitation, long-term care hospitals, and dialysis providers.

THE W. EDWARDS DEMING APPROACH TO ENSURING QUALITY IN ORGANIZATIONS

Consider as the Administrator . . .

- *To what extent is Deming's work applicable to the facility? Can you use everything that Deming suggests?*

Dr. Deming, a management theorist, was not "discovered" in the United States until his appearance on a 1980 television documentary titled *If Japan Can...Why Can't We?* This led to the immediate broad popularity of Deming and his theories in this country. Dr. Deming lectured on his 14 points and seven deadly organizational diseases to enthusiastic American corporate executives, even while wheelchair-bound, until a few weeks before his death at the age of 93. His 14 points and seven deadly organizational diseases, along with their potential application to the nursing facility industry, are explored in the following (Robbins & Coulter, 2018). Deming's theories are very focused on the manufacturing industry; however, they are easily applied to the nursing facility.

Deming's 14 Points

1. *Create and publish to all employees a statement of the aims and purposes of the organization. The management must constantly demonstrate its commitment to this statement.* He argued that the role of the corporation, rather than making money, is to stay in business and provide jobs through innovation, research, constant improvement, and maintenance. The nursing facility chain's goal, then, is to stay in business and to provide jobs. This is to be accomplished through innovation (discovering current healthcare needs and foreseeing future healthcare needs), research (finding how effective current care is and finding new ways to give better care), constant improvement (of the experience of being a resident in their facilities), and maintenance (keeping everything in working order).

2. *Learn the new philosophy, top management, and everybody.* Do not tolerate poor caregiving and sullen service to residents. Mistakes and negativism in approaching residents and other staff are not acceptable.

3. *Understand the purpose of inspection for improvement of processes and reduction of cost* (focus on the resident's daily experience, not on nursing summaries and plans of care). Mass inspection means inspecting the product as it comes off the line or at major stages—defective products are thrown out or reworked, which means paying twice, paying employees to give less-than-quality care, and then paying them to correct poor care (preventing pressure injuries is easier and less expensive than curing them), and this does not lead to corrective actions. Quality, he argues, comes not from inspections but from the improvement of the process. Keep focused on improving the caregiving process, not on the quality of the nurses' notes or doctors' orders but rather on achieving an improved level of care; that is, stay focused on improving the residents' daily experiences.

4. *End the practice of awarding business based on price tag alone.* Buying the lowest-priced item often means buying low quality. The goal should be to identify a single quality supplier for any one item in a long-term relationship (e.g., food vendors). The goal should be good, dependable quality over a long period, consistently good food supplies, medical supplies, physical therapy, pharmacy supplies, and the like.

5. *Improve constantly and forever the system of production and service.* Management's job is to look for ways to reduce waste and improve quality continually; for example, do not use expensive medicine cups as water cups while doing medication rounds.

6. *Institute training.* Too often, nursing assistants, LPNs, and even the directors of nursing learn their job from workers who were never appropriately trained. Workers are forced to follow poor instruction sets and cannot do their jobs because no one told them how.

7. *Teach and institute leadership.* The nursing supervisor's or department head's job is not to tell nursing assistants what to do or to punish but to lead (i.e., help employees do a better job) through learning by objective methods to find out who needs individual help (i.e., sort out the nursing assistants whose work is not in an acceptable range). This level of involvement will pay significant dividends in safer resident care and reduce risks at a facility.

8. *Drive out fear.* Create trust. Create a climate for innovation. Create an atmosphere in which employees feel secure enough to ask questions, take positions, admit errors, and learn by them, not get out the "whiteout" or write an erroneous incident or accident report.

9. *Optimize toward the company's aims and purposes the efforts of teams, groups, and staff areas.* Facility staff often compete or have goals that conflict: nursing versus dietary, nursing versus housekeeping (who cleans up the spill?), dietary versus activities (who is responsible for the residents' afternoon bingo?).

10. *Eliminate exhortations for the workforce.* Deming believed these communications emphatically urging an employee to do something never helped anybody do a good job; instead, they allowed people to put up their own slogans.

11. *Eliminate numerical quotas for production.* Instead, learn and institute methods for improvement. Eliminate management by objective (MBO). Instead, learn the capabilities of processes and how to improve them. Numbers take account only of numbers, not quality or methods. Quotas usually guarantee inefficiencies and high costs. Most CQI programs set numerical quotas in nearly every departmental area. Employees become focused solely on attaining these quotas. Achieving the numerical goal becomes the employees' goal and focus, not improving residents' daily experiences. Deming agrees that the "goal" of quotas is laudable but notes that they become ends in themselves, and the employee will "meet the quota" at any price, regardless of the damage to the facility (e.g., the nurse determined to pass medications at or below the prescribed error rate, disregarding a small crisis that needs managing during the medication pass).

12. *Remove barriers that rob people of pride in their work.* People are eager to do a good job and become distressed when they cannot perform well due to misguided supervisors, faulty equipment, or defective materials. Often there are too few nursing hours per resident day to permit the nursing assistants or the rest of the staff to make Mrs. Jones's experience that day a good one; for example, the proverbial "we're working short today" answer to numerous resident requests. Somehow, avoid using nursing pool personnel. They don't know the residents and, all too often, don't care.

13. *Encourage education and self-improvement for everyone.* Both management and the staff will have to be educated in the new methods, including teamwork and statistical techniques.

14. *Take action to accomplish the transformation.* Like most others who prescribe quality improvement programs, Deming emphasized a need to involve top management in any quality improvement effort but stressed that it takes both managers and workers for success.

Deming's Seven Deadly Diseases

1. *Lack of constancy of purpose.* Keep the focus on staying in business, including long-range plans, not making dividends next quarter, or paying good dividends this year. The workers need to feel that the corporation is preparing for the future and will stay focused on giving quality healthcare.

2. *Emphasis on short-term profits.* Don't worry about paying a dividend.
3. *Evaluation by performance, merit rating, or annual review of performance.* These, Deming felt, destroy teamwork and nurture rivalry. Performance ratings can build fear if not done carefully, leaving people despondent, bitter, beaten, and encouraging management turnover.
4. *Mobility of management.* Job hoppers don't understand the facility and are not there long enough to follow through on long-term changes needed for quality and productivity (e.g., three directors of nursing in 1 year, three administrators in as many years).
5. *Running a company on visible figures alone.* The most important statistics, Deming argued, are unknown and unknowable, for example, resident satisfaction. Point: A nursing facility's staff achievements cannot be defined by numbers alone.
6. *Excessive medical costs.* What more should be said on this issue?
7. *Excessive costs of warranty, fueled by lawyers who work on a contingency fee.* Successful malpractice suits against nursing facilities continue to raise the price of required insurance.

Deming's diagnosis for corporations cannot be directly generalized to all companies. Deming was prescribing corrections to organizational illnesses he felt existed in the United States. Essentially, he was pointing to excesses—good ideas originally that were taken too far or became mindless rules. What's right and what's wrong with organizations change over time, resembling the swings of a pendulum, as did Deming's list of deadly organizational diseases. But enduring messages are there for the U.S. industry and individual nursing facilities—powerful reminders of how difficult it is for the facility to keep the residents' importance constantly in focus. Others have other diagnoses and have written their own prescriptions to assist organizations to achieve and maintain quality. The CMS certainly has, and the CMS-prescribed ways of operating the facility dominate every participating facility's daily actions.

BENCHMARKING

Benchmarking is a management tool by which an organization seeks to improve its business practices by comparing them with other organizations' best practices (Robbins & Coulter, 2018). The Westinghouse Corporation uses benchmarking as a quality control tool within its Total Quality Improvement Process to identify best practices, wherever they exist, and implement and communicate those practices throughout Westinghouse to improve competitive performance and preserve core competencies (Brigham & Houston, 2019).

A Five-Step Description

Benchmarking studies other corporations' very best practices and seeks any better practices as sufficient to justify a benchmarking effort. This can be accomplished in five steps:

1. Deciding what to benchmark
2. Forming a team
3. Identifying benchmark partners
4. Collecting and analyzing the benchmarking information
5. Implementing the new methodology

Benchmarking is a measuring process resulting in comparing performance measures, but it also describes how superior performance is attained. The practices that lead to exceptional performance are called enablers. Benchmarking, then, results in two types of outputs: (a) measures of comparative performance and (b) enablers, the theory behind the more successful process being benchmarked.

A Four-Step Description

Benchmarking can also be done as a four-step process:

1. Select and define the process to be studied. What should we benchmark? Whom should we benchmark?
2. Gather as much information as possible about the process, then communicate with the organization being benchmarked through telephone surveys, written questionnaires, and/or on-site visits.
3. Analyze the information gained to determine the magnitude of the performance gap and identify the process enablers that facilitated the performance improvement at the organization chosen as a benchmark.
4. Adapt, improve, and implement the benchmarked process in one's own organization.

For example, most major nursing facility chains strive to serve a predominantly private-paying and Medicare-eligible clientele. One chain has consistently achieved this to a far greater extent than most. Chains that, despite their goals, have a low census of private-paying and Medicare residents might seek to "benchmark" the successful chain; that is, study and learn the process by which that one chain achieves its desired resident mix noticeably more successfully than the rest.

Benchmarking against other businesses is a common practice seen in healthcare today. Comparisons of nursing facility operations to Walmart or Disney World's efficiency can help identify success examples that we can implement.

Deming warned that it is a hazard to copy blindly. He believed in adapting over adopting and that understanding the theory behind the benchmarked process is more likely to lead to successful extrapolation. Successful process enablers that result in a high private census tend to reflect a specific business environment and corporate culture. Those specific environmental or cultural elements may or may not function well in a different organization, even one seeking to raise its private-paying census. Every facility has original inputs resulting in a specific culture, people, residents, community, and employees. No one policy, procedure, or way of doing things is effective everywhere.

TOTAL QUALITY MANAGEMENT/CONTINUOUS QUALITY IMPROVEMENT

The earliest quality and quality control publications, which led to the current TQM literature, have been attributed to Walter A. Shewhart at Bell Telephone Laboratories in the 1920s. An extensive literature on TQM has emerged since that time.

Definitional Difficulties

TQM is challenging to precisely define because it is a philosophy of total organizational involvement toward improving all aspects of service quality. No single set of steps has gained broad acceptance as the TQM methodology. However, most follow the ideal of Deming's fifth point: "Improve constantly and forever the system of production and service." This view supports quality production from the source instead of depending on costly inspections and retrograde solutions.

Quality at the Source

NAB DOMAIN 2B5: RISK MANAGEMENT PROCESS AND PROGRAMS; 2B6: QUALITY IMPROVEMENT PROCESSES (E.G., ROOT CAUSE ANALYSIS, PDCA/PDSA); 3B6: CENTERS FOR MEDICARE AND MEDICAID SERVICES (CMS) QUALITY MEASURES; 3B7: QUALITY ASSURANCE AND PERFORMANCE IMPROVEMENT (QAPI); 4A3: ORGANIZATIONAL BEHAVIOR (E.G., ORGANIZATIONAL CULTURE, TEAM BUILDING, GROUP DYNAMICS)

To achieve total quality, responsibility for high-level service or products lies with the producing workers. This worker commitment is sometimes called quality at the source. In this scheme, the quality departments are focused on training employees in quality control and implementing the quality control concepts throughout the organization. Employee empowerment in decision-making, the use of teams in the organization, individual responsibility for services, and customer service are characteristics of most TQM effort services (Cole & Kelley, 2020).

Continuous Quality Improvement

TQM uses the scientific method and customer to improve organizational systems. Quality improvement should include evaluating every aspect within an organization—its services, products, suppliers, business procedures, management systems, and human resources. Continuous improvement is a process of continuously striving to exceed customer expectations. Problems within an organization are organizational process problems, not problems of individuals within the organization, and then are improved through processes using TQM approaches. Continuous improvement in resident care is required to address resident balance, specific needs of individuals, and response to health interventions and care (Topol, 2015). Data-driven technology-savvy customers (the residents and their loved ones) will demand that the quality of care reflects individualized care and healthcare breakthroughs almost immediately.

Section Concepts

● *Daily life in the facility is controlled using structure–process–outcome*

Consider as the Administrator . . .

● *Who defines the outcome? Is an outcome the same in every possible situation? Should you expect the same every time, or should you expect variation?*

STRUCTURE–PROCESS–OUTCOME

When the nursing facility industry began to assume its present size and shape, quality measurements primarily focused on structure, such as an adequate physical plant, proper equipment, sufficient trained staff, and enough income. The perception was that Medicare, Medicaid, and state nursing facility inspectors should ensure that these "structure inputs" required for good care were in place (Hitt et al., 2017). However, the quality of care remained unsatisfactorily low.

Process

Federal and state inspectors expanded their focus to include both structure and process. The evaluation of structure measures the capacity to give resident care, while process evaluation measures how well resident care is provided. Inspecting for process ensures that all the organizational arrangements to accomplish the required work are in place. This set of processes is what the systems model described as the processor. For example:

● Is each MDS appropriately filled out?
● Is a well-developed, individualized plan of care in place for each resident?
● Are all the resident assessment protocols triggered by the MDS appropriately filled out and being followed?

Outcome

Even after measuring for both structure and process, Congress ruled through the Nursing Home Reform Act that inspectors must focus not only on structure (capacity to give care) and process (the giving of care) but also caregiving outcomes. The outcome is the third part of our systems model discussed earlier and is the result of the efforts made, measured by impacts on the nursing facility resident. Outcome focuses on measuring whether residents enjoy a high quality of life, have full enjoyment of the Patient's Rights established by Congress, and receive high-quality nursing and medical care.

One of the approaches surveyors use is to look at outcomes first. Only if outcomes appear deficient will the surveyors examine the processes by which the facility is giving care. If both outcomes and processes appear unsatisfactory, the surveyors will investigate the caregiving structures that are in place.

Examples of the federal requirements set by Congress for the quality of care include:

1. Each resident must receive, and the facility must provide, the necessary care and services to attain or maintain the highest practicable physical, mental, and psychosocial well-being, in accordance with the comprehensive assessment and plan of care.

2. A resident's abilities in activities of daily living do not diminish unless circumstances of the individual's clinical condition demonstrate that diminution was unavoidable. This reasoning includes vision and hearing, urinary incontinence, range of motion, mental and psychosocial functioning, nasogastric tubes, accidents, nutrition, hydration, special needs, unnecessary drugs, weight loss, and medication errors.

3. Regarding pressure injuries, a resident who enters the facility without pressure injuries does not develop any pressure injuries unless the individual's clinical condition demonstrates that such injuries were unavoidable.

NAB DOMAIN 2B5: RISK MANAGEMENT PROCESS AND PROGRAMS; 2B6: QUALITY IMPROVEMENT PROCESSES (E.G., ROOT CAUSE ANALYSIS, PDCA/PDSA); 3B6: CENTERS FOR MEDICARE AND MEDICAID SERVICES (CMS) QUALITY MEASURES; 3B7: QUALITY ASSURANCE AND PERFORMANCE IMPROVEMENT (QAPI)

ESTABLISHING AND JUDGING QUALITY IN THE NURSING FACILITY

Nearly every nursing facility in the United States has a mission statement with its accompanying goals for resident care quality and resident life. Local facilities often self-determine their mission statement, with quality goals carefully spelled out in the facility's policy and procedures.

Whose Quality Goals Matter?

Ultimately, the CMS (formerly the Health Care Financing Administration) sets the American nursing facility's quality goals for daily life. Administrators seldom judge their success or failure by corporate or facility standards. Instead, administrators' feelings about success or failure are dictated more by the CMS's quality standards embodied in the Federal Requirements and Guidelines to Surveyors. The CMS survey determines whether the facility is deficiency-free at least annually. A facility that is not deficiency-free may receive civil money penalties of large sums (sometimes in the hundreds of thousands of dollars) through CMS rulings. The CMS requires that its quality judgments (survey results) be displayed prominently for all who visit the facility to see and posts survey results on the web for everyone in the world to see. Additionally, each facility's survey results are posted on the CMS's Care Compare website.

The practical reality is that the CMS's judgments become, for most facilities, both the de jure (by law) and de facto (by practice) quality standards for U.S. nursing facilities. And suppose the surveyors are especially concerned about their findings.

In that case, they can put the facility on a "fast track" to decertification, which ends Medicare and Medicaid eligibility *and* prohibits new admissions until the CMS is satisfied with the facility's plan for correcting the deficiencies. Given the razor-thin operating margins of most facilities, the inability to admit new residents, even for a short time, can induce traumatic economic woe.

THE FEDERAL QUALITY ASSURANCE PROCESS: UNDERSTANDING AND ACCESSING FEDERAL REQUIREMENTS

NAB DOMAIN 3B6: CENTERS FOR MEDICARE AND MEDICAID SERVICES (CMS) QUALITY MEASURES; 3B7: QUALITY ASSURANCE AND PERFORMANCE IMPROVEMENT (QAPI)

Nearly all federal requirements for nursing facilities are available on the CMS website, https://www.cms.gov. The nursing facility administrator can access and download necessary CMS information, regulations, survey preparation tools, and interpretive guidelines from this website.

Quality Measures

Quality measures vary from year to year as the CMS alters quality goals to improve performance over time. The focus areas and continuously updated administrative tools are available on the CMS Nursing Home Quality Initiatives website. A significant portion of this site provides tools surrounding the MDS 3.0, an essential document for each resident, impacting nursing facility and swing-bed care.

Daily Update Information for the Administrator

In addition to frequent visits to the websites, as mentioned earlier, the administrator may choose to receive daily update information via email by signing up for the email lists at the CMS and similar websites.

SOME COMMON ACRONYMS AND DEFINITIONS OF TERMS ASSOCIATED WITH ASSESSING RESIDENTS AND SETTING THE PAYMENT LEVEL FOR EACH MEDICARE/MEDICAID RESIDENT

CFR (Code of Federal Regulations). The federal Congress passes laws for which implementing rules are written and enforced. These are the Federal Requirements and Guidelines to Surveyors.

OBRA (Omnibus Reconciliation Act). A law that enacted reforms in nursing facility care and provided the statutory authority for the MDS.

CMS (Centers for Medicare & Medicaid Services; formerly the Health Care Financing Administration. The federal agency that administers the Medicare, Medicaid, and Child Health Insurance Programs.

SOM (State Operation Manual). The title given to the current requirements and surveyors' guidelines. The current edition can be downloaded from the CMS website: https://www.cms.gov

PDPM (Patient Driven Payment Model). A case-mix group (CMG) reimbursement model focused on clinically relevant factors, rather than volume-based services or RUG-IV codes. Reimbursement is calculated through CMG scores, not the number of therapy minutes which drove RUG-IV reimbursement. Information is included below on RUGs and associated terms as RUG-IV reimbursement is still used by insurance companies and other entities outside the CMS.

PPS (Prospective Payment System). A payment system developed for Medicare for skilled nursing facilities, which pays facilities an all-inclusive rate for all Medicare Part A beneficiary services. Case-mix determines payment classification using a defined system (RUG-IV or current version).

RUG-IV or Current Version of the RUG. A resident classification system that identifies the relative resource use for providing care to different types of residents in nursing facilities based on their resource use.

A hierarchy is used in the RUG methodology to classify an assessment and matching conditions and services. There are more than 40 reimbursement categories. The RUG-IV version includes seven resident groups, ordered from highest to lowest: extensive services, rehabilitation, special care, clinically complex, impaired cognition, behavioral problems, and reduced physical functions. These categories vary from time to time.

RAI (Resident Assessment Instrument). The designation for the complete resident assessment process mandated by the CMS, including the comprehensive MDS, resident assessment protocols (RAPs), and care planning decisions.

Case Mix. A measure of the intensity of care and services used by a group of residents in a nursing facility. "Case" refers to the overall data collected and used regarding an individual. "Mix" describes the combination of variables (observations) used for classifying an observation according to distinctive characteristics based on a dependent variable. So the mix includes things such as time or costs.

Case Mix Index. Weight, or numeric score, of each RUG-IV (or current RUG version) group, which reflects the relative resources predicted to be necessary to provide care to a resident. The higher the case mix index (weight), the greater the resource requirements are for the resident. Payment to the facility is made monthly for each resident based on the facility's case mix index.

MDS (Minimum Data Set). A core set of screening, clinical, and functional status elements, including common definitions and coding categories that form the foundation for the comprehensive assessment for all residents of long-term care facilities certified to participate in Medicare and/or Medicaid.

RAPs (Resident Assessment Protocols). A problem-oriented framework for organizing MDS information and additional clinically relevant information about an individual's health problems or needs. Checking certain boxes or combinations of boxes on the MDS form triggers the requirement for that resident's care plan to address condition(s) identified as needing special attention.

MDCN (Medicare Data Communication Network). The secure connection used to transmit MDS data to each state's repository. A user ID and password are issued for each person who requires access to the CMS MDS intranet.

QIS (Quality Initiative Survey). The CMS survey process working toward performing facility surveys on laptops using wireless technology. This conversion will enable immediate communication between surveyors throughout the survey process.

MDS Completion Date. The date at which the RN assessment coordinator attests that all portions of the MDS have been completed.

FEDERAL STANDARDS: MINIMUM OR MAXIMUM?

The literature and federal surveyors describe the federal requirements as minimum standards. However, the standards were only minimums when first established. Now, after 50-plus years of intense federal CQI efforts, if all federal standards are achieved, remarkably high quality of care is achieved. It is an ongoing process. MDS 1.0 was followed by MDS 2.0, followed by MDS 3.0 with CQI, RUG reimbursement changing to PDPM, and many more changes to come as our population grays (Singh, 2016). Federal standards and their enforcement will continue to evolve, and administrators need to remain aware of the changes.

COMMON PITFALLS IN PRACTICE

- Quality is a lifestyle. You do not simply fix something and forget it. Quality is like a garden. You tend to it, you weed it, you fertilize it, you care for it, and it produces high-quality produce. When we forget these steps, we see quality diminish quickly.
- You will have noticed many different tools to address quality. Choosing only one is a mistake. You learn many methods so you can pull the right tool out at the right time. Use all the tools in your toolbox!
- New administrators often believe that they have no say-so in their quality measures or their Five-Star rating. It is imperative that you learn how to work with these numbers and what positive things you can do that will allow you to drive change. All these numbers and measures rest solely in your office.

1.8 INNOVATING

Section Concepts

- *Innovation is a skill necessary to the survival of the administrator*

Consider as the Administrator . . .

- *How do you acquire the skill of innovation? What can you begin to do now to help you in your future career?*

NAB DOMAIN 4A2: ORGANIZATIONAL CHANGE MANAGEMENT

The effective manager is always an innovator. Innovating is bringing new ideas into the way an organization accomplishes its purposes.

The process of innovating is bringing organizational changes based on the administrator's study of the changes in the organization and the environment. Innovating is an act of leadership (Cole & Kelley, 2020). It is the manager's role to be the sensor for external and internal changes that will impact the organization's well-being (Hitt et al., 2017; Robbins & Judge, 2019).

The manager is not necessarily the innovator but does have the task of ensuring that innovation occurs within the organization. To best achieve this goal, the manager should encourage interdisciplinary development of the change, including new ideas, combining old ideas into new ones, borrowing or adapting ideas from other fields, or stimulating others to develop innovations (Hitt et al., 2017).

Maintaining focus on the residents and their families/significant others increases awareness of the residents' changing needs. Nearly all staff have connections with residents and their families/significant others. Practical innovation from staff requires them to become outwardly focused adaptive sensors, listening and adapting to changing needs. Employee empowerment to observe and communicate any changes or needs of residents and the facility acknowledges their importance to the organization.

WELCOMING INNOVATIONS AND ORGANIZATIONAL CHANGE

NAB DOMAIN 1C4: TELEMEDICINE (E.G., E-HEALTH); 2B11: HEALTHCARE RECORD REQUIREMENTS (E.G., CONFIDENTIALITY, DISCLOSURE, SAFEGUARDING, HIPAA, HITECH); 2B12: SECURITY (E.G., CAMERAS, MONITORING SYSTEMS, LOCKS, STAFF LOCATION REPORTING); 3A5: INFORMATION SYSTEMS INFRASTRUCTURE (E.G., CONFIGURATIONS, DATA SECURITY, TECHNICAL CONTROLS); 4A2: ORGANIZATIONAL CHANGE MANAGEMENT; 4A3: ORGANIZATIONAL BEHAVIOR (E.G., ORGANIZATIONAL CULTURE, TEAM BUILDING, GROUP DYNAMICS)

Change Is Hard Work

The effective manager has difficulty setting specific long-term objectives because the external environment changes continually, and organizational strategies must constantly adapt. The more explicit a strategy statement is, the more difficult it is to persuade the employees to turn to different goals when needs and conditions change (Chies, 2021). This resistance is often paired with the rebuttal, "we have always done it that way." Instead, instilling the idea that we, as an organization, are always adaptive to needs supports required changes (McClay et al., 2021).

Consider as the Administrator . . .

- *Is imprecision a value you should use as an administrator? Can you leverage imprecision to succeed?*

Values in Imprecision

Goals or objectives are communicated over time through a consistent pattern of operating decisions. We also advise guarding against a degree of specificity in goal and policy statements that discourages changes.

All the forces that tend to lead to organizational resistance to change are formidable enemies of the manager who must introduce changes to keep the facility in tune with the environment. The nursing facility administrator must keep policies precise enough to guide employee decisions and at the same time continually introduce change into the facility—not an easy task.

Innovating

A nursing facility's staff will innovate only when the administrator intentionally introduces changes in the organization and encourages others to do the same. *Innovation* is the process of finding new solutions to creating a good quality of life for residents and staff. Not all innovations will work. To continue promoting staff suggestions and accountability, the administrator must encourage and praise changes that fail and those that succeed. Staff buy-in is key to success in this area.

Innovation requires constant awareness of new requirements, new employment trends, new benefits, and new resident activities. To be innovative is to respond flexibly to changes in the environment. Most organizations fight innovation. Hospitals fought against creating birthing suites until women arranged deliveries outside the hospital in homelike suites. The same situation occurred in nursing facilities that fought against making private rooms, in-room bathrooms, and fine-dining areas or focusing on culture change. These responsive facilities are the future and are much more competitive than older models of facilities from the 1950s and 1960s.

Rearranging Nursing Duties

A Washington, D.C., facility, faced with difficulties finding nurses and pressures on nurses' time to perform administrative functions, tried replacing the charge nurse with an assistant administrator. Initially, this person made out the nurse assistant assignments; ensured that supplies and linen were available to the nursing assistants and the nurses; resolved any logistical problems with transportation, dietary, and housekeeping; and coordinated any immediate and long-term maintenance and housekeeping needs for the unit. This new employee made rounds daily or more often, ensuring that residents' needs were met and that nurse's aides were following nursing directives (i.e., walking, turning, and repositioning residents as required). This freed nurses to concentrate more on resident assessment, medication administration, and care conferences. In this case, everyone won. The facility enabled the more expensive nurse time to be devoted to good nursing care; the residents' quality of care and level of satisfaction were improved by a unit manager who was practicing LBWA.

The American health insurance industry grew out of an innovation developed by a hospital administrator in Texas. Faced with a drastically reduced cash flow during the Depression because patients had little money, a hospital administrator devised a plan to create a regular cash flow to the hospital. For 50 cents a month, Baylor University Hospital offered up to 14 days of prepaid hospital care per year to schoolteachers who still received an income from public taxes. The teachers bought the idea, and U.S. health insurance was born.

The innovators tend to be survivors of change. The future belongs to those organizations that are successful in constantly innovating over time. The years of the 21st century hold promise to innovators in the nursing facility industry.

Success today requires that, compared to your competitors, you be:

- More creative
- More customer-focused
- More cost-conscious
- More employee-aware
- More focused on culture change and "new ways" of doing business

It falls to the administrator to identify organizational change needs and lead the necessary initiatives to implement change.

Books and Smartphones

In his book *The Patient Will See You Now*, Eric Topol compares the impacts of the smartphone to those of Gutenberg's printing press. Both inventions did the following:

- Spurred innovation
- Caused an explosion of knowledge
- Increased the power of the individual
- Became the basis of social networks
- Spread ideas
- Spurred creativity
- Marked immense cost reductions
- Archived knowledge (Topol, 2015)

Today's administrator needs to constantly look for opportunities like these to leverage to provide better care for their residents.

New Medical Technologies

The two major mobile operating systems—Google's Android and Apple's iOS—have facilitated the unprecedented development of apps affecting not only medicine and science but also finance, energy, retail, transportation, and everyday life.

There is one significant difference between the printing press and smartphone adoption. It took more than 400 years for 10 million books to be printed, and it took 13 years (2005–2013) for 1.25 billion smartphone device shipments, which have connected the globe through the internet. Today, using the smartphone camera and text messaging, one can screen for skin cancer anywhere in the world if there is internet access. This shift to technology includes the nursing facility (Topol, 2015, p. 52). Whether commercially available or in development, wearable wireless sensors can be placed on the nursing facility resident to capture physiologic data on a smartphone. These data include blood pressure, heart rhythm, respiratory rate, oxygenation, the oxygen concentration in the blood, heart rate variability, cardiac output, cardiac stroke volume, galvanic skin response, body temperature, eye pressure, blood glucose, brain waves, intracranial pressure, and muscle movements (Topol, 2015). The applications for mobile health solutions have exploded in past years as baby boomers have become more comfortable using technology (Kruse et al., 2017). We continue to see specific apps that can provide information in real time from a user's smartphone directly to the doctor, who then can make immediate decisions based on the information provided (Mileski et al., 2017). This information can be used for treatment purposes or to provide direct intervention, including dispatching an ambulance to a location matching the user's phone's GPS signal.

A smartphone microphone can quantify lung function components, analyze a voice to gauge mood, even diagnose Parkinson's disease or schizophrenia. Nurses in the facility can digitize residents' breath to measure many compounds such as nitric oxide or organic chemicals to track lung function. We have telemedicine interventions today which will allow a resident in a nursing facility room to be seen by a doctor, hundreds or thousands of miles away from them, using electronic versions of the same tools they would be using if they were in person (Kruse et al., 2020; Mileski et al., 2017).

The Hospital in a Handheld

Beyond this, imaging now done in hospitals, such as magnetic resonance, CT, nuclear scanning, and ultrasound, are being developed or used via handheld devices usable by facility nurses. These nurses, skilled in the use of such devices, can perform the physical examination of the eyes, ears, neck vessels, heart, lungs, abdomen, and similar organs and transmit this information to the hospital or other medical caregiver directly from the devices and into the electronic medical records systems of the facilities.

The Residents' Children and the Government

Technological innovations allowing nurses to perform healthcare procedures traditionally available only in the hospital setting are reshaping the face of healthcare in the 21st century. Through the smartphone, these new capabilities are increasingly available to the residents' children. If the facility does not adopt technologies as soon as possible, be assured residents' children will. When the resident develops pneumonia, a new urinary tract infection, or shows symptoms of an impending stroke, the facility must diagnose before the children do. Failure by the facility to do so will imperil resident health and expose the facility to multiple lawsuits.

If not motivated to deliver state-of-the-art medicine by resident family preference, be sure that the federal government will eventually force the issue. The Affordable Care Act focused sharply on creating a national and individual patient database that would include timely diagnosis of health conditions changes. Together, the government and the children are forcing nursing facilities to embrace state-of-the-art care.

Who Will Thrive?

Nursing facilities that thrive in this new technological environment will be the early adopters of these new opportunities to improve care quality through early adoption. Many of the newly constructed facilities we see today are fully online, offering electronic medical records, real-time pharmacy records, online resident portals providing information to families, in-room TVs with capabilities of video chat, and many other technical features. Eventually, this will become the norm, but until that time comes, these facilities will thrive as they provide a much higher/different level of service than their competitors.

A Glance at the Future of Innovations in Healthcare

We are truly living during a fantastic time in medicine. We are witnessing what technology and research can genuinely produce. Most recently, surrounding the COVID-19 pandemic, we have seen never-known mRNA vaccines being produced to protect our employees and residents. We have seen gene therapy being used to cure diseases of a genetic nature. Technology has brought us to a time when open-heart surgery is commonplace. That same technology has us doing that same surgery through a keyhole opening in the chest, in many cases using robotic-assisted surgery. New ultrasound technologies can potentially break apart plaques in the brain to alleviate Alzheimer's symptoms. And the list goes on. We will continue to see unbelievable changes in the medical world throughout our lifetimes.

COMMON PITFALLS IN PRACTICE

- It is important to realize that change is inevitable. Just over 50 years ago, *Star Trek* was on TV showing us the future and what it held with handheld communicators. Thirty years ago, that handheld communicator was better known as a cellular phone and its use was widespread. Around the same time, personal computers were becoming commonplace. Today, we have mated the cellular phone and the computer with what you are most likely carrying around in your pocket—the smartphone. Today's smartphone has exponentially more power and memory than the original computers. We have gone further to marry this technology to the medical field, and you can use it to see a doctor, monitor your health, or make medical records entries from around the world. This is all because someone chose to innovate. Change is coming. Do not get left behind by it. Embrace the change!
- All ideas (even bad ones) started somewhere. Do not hide your ideas. Get them out there! You might be the next Steve Jobs or Bill Gates. They are innovators. You can be as well!

1.9 MARKETING THE LONG-TERM CARE FACILITY

1.9.1 THE TURN TO MARKETING

Section Concepts

- *Without marketing, a facility will most likely close its doors*
- *The federal government and surveyors are among your most important customers*

- *An understanding of the forces leading to the intense competition among facilities*
- *How healthcare marketing is evolving*

Consider as the Administrator . . .

- *How involved should the administrator be in marketing the facility? Should they be in the field? Or should they only be at the facility improving services to improve care and perceptions?*

NAB DOMAIN 4B4: BUSINESS DEVELOPMENT (E.G., SALES, MARKETING, PARTNERSHIPS, ACOs, CONTRACTS AND AGREEMENTS, NEGOTIATIONS)

One might ask why the nursing facility administrator should be concerned with marketing? Due to the graying of the baby boomers, the proportion of Americans who will need nursing facility care is expected to increase yearly, at least through the middle of the 21st century. Resident waiting lists exist in some facilities due to the simple lack of beds in specific communities, which places more and more pressure on hospitals to rapidly discharge acute care patients to nursing facilities and/or, increasingly, home health agencies for periods of subacute and managed care (Singh, 2016). However, many factors are developing that may threaten high occupancy rates, despite the community's need for services.

NAB DOMAIN 4B4: BUSINESS DEVELOPMENT (E.G., SALES, MARKETING, PARTNERSHIPS, ACOs, CONTRACTS AND AGREEMENTS, NEGOTIATIONS)

FORCES LEADING TO COMPETITION

Narrowed Profit Margins

A nursing facility's ability to survive economically is affected by an increasing variety of pressures, such as federal and state reimbursement policies, the types of services offered by the facility, and resident payment sources. Over the past decades, government regulators who pay for the care of Medicare and Medicaid residents in nursing facilities have sought ways to narrow the margin of facility profit to achieve mandated government cost savings.

Simultaneously, facility costs have increased in meeting the additional regulatory requirements under the nursing facility reform act and subsequent amendments. Such bills as the Americans with Disabilities Act, the Family Medical Leave Act, and the more rigorous universal precaution requirements (increased even greater due to COVID-19) all add to often unreimbursed costs to the provision of care. Increasing human resources costs, particularly as the level of acuity increases, for personnel such as nurses threaten profitability. We have seen an increasing lack of available nurses, leaving many facilities to turn to contract nursing, with costs often triple or more than that of one employee. This nursing situation can prove to be a significant cost drain to a facility already operating dangerously close to margins.

Reduction of Federal Influence in Shaping the Product Mix

Product design in nursing facilities, that is, the mix of services and business activities, has been heavily influenced by the Medicaid and Medicare agencies' product and price decisions. The states' Medicaid offices' payment policies and Medicare claims authorities are predominant influences on prices charged and services offered in the industry (Hitt et al., 2017).

Survival of the average facility may depend on the administrator being able to find a niche—to identify and successfully market the facility's offerings to defined groups of persons who need the emerging types of services now available. We see specific examples of this across the country where facilities cater to certain types of residents: behavior-based facilities, male/female sex offender facilities, facilities that cater to those released from prison, facilities that take those residents unable to be placed elsewhere, and many other niches we continually identify in the field.

Consider as the Administrator . . .

- *If the CMS is under pressure to lower costs, what pressure will this place on you as an administrator? What new issues will this cause for you?*

Always Mess With Success

The most cogent reason to turn to marketing the nursing facility is that if you don't mess with your success, your competitor will. Conventional wisdom has advised don't mess with success. It is easy to be blinded by one's short-term success. Whenever a facility feels it has achieved premier status as the best caregiver in the community, whenever it starts taking its success for granted, it will lull itself into complacency and slack off (Krupp & Schoemaker, 2014). However, better outcomes are associated with lauding success then moving forward toward the next goal. Change must occur for success to happen continually.

Good Isn't Good Enough

Good-enough nursing facilities (public opinion notwithstanding) abound. Simply doing a good job of marketing the facility will not yield the edge necessary to succeed in today's pressure-packed healthcare marketplace. Good only places you with the rest of the pack. Facilities must find things that make them stand out from others and capitalize on them. Innovators win in this business, and others simply get left behind.

1.9.2 THE "MARKETING" OF HEALTHCARE

Section Concepts

- *Healthcare marketing is a recent development*
- *Six steps in marketing a facility*
- *Marketing a facility is marketing an intangible service*

Consider as the Administrator . . .

- *Consider "healthcare" advertisements you have seen online. How are these different from advertisements for regular products? Is there a difference you need to be leveraging?*

How does the "consumer" of facility services make the decision to choose a facility? Several years ago, the U.S. Supreme Court ruled illegal any self-imposed restrictions by health and other professionals against advertising services or prices that result in keeping the public ignorant of or inhibiting the free flow of commercial information. As a result, over recent decades, professional health services' marketing has become an increasingly accepted practice. This perception was taken a step further in recent times during the Trump administration, during which price transparency became a requirement for healthcare providers.

HEALTHCARE PROVIDERS BEGIN TO MARKET

Hospitals have turned to marketing because the occupancy rates across the United States have fallen for several years.

Hospitals compete to increase occupancy rates, introduce standalone emergency departments, outpatient surgery, other service centers, nursing facilities, hospice services, and home health agencies for patients, attempting to distinguish themselves from their competitors. Many have worked on cornering the entire market in their service areas.

Competition occurs when two or more organizations seek to serve the same individual or group in an exchange process. An exchange requires (a) at least two parties, (b) that each party is offering something the other values, (c) that each party is capable of communicating and delivering what is valued, and (d) that both are free to accept or reject the offer.

Competition for patients among public, not-for-profit, and for-profit hospitals is a new experience. In the face of assisted living facilities and home health agencies increasingly siphoning off residents who, until recently, would have entered a nursing facility, administrators of nursing facilities are similarly encountering a need to "market" their services. This siphoning has caused intriguing marketplace issues where hospital patients are placed in less-than-appropriate situations due to marketing. We see subacute patients going to a rehabilitation hospital or long-term acute care instead of skilled nursing, where they could be equally cared for (at a lesser cost). We are also witnessing patients leaving the hospital only to be placed in less than adequate facilities for their level of care, often due to better marketing efforts by those providers.

DEFINITION OF MARKETING

The American Marketing Association defines *marketing* as the process of planning and executing the conception, pricing, promotion, and distribution of ideas, goods, and services to create exchanges that satisfy both individual and organizational objectives. The nursing facility is in the business of marketing services.

The spread of marketing to hospitals and nursing facilities was inevitable due to lowered occupancy rates and increasingly marginal net income due to reduced reimbursement rates. Marketing is currently regarded as central to health services administration. It is the effort to improve the interaction between the organization's goals and the persons whose needs the organization seeks to serve (Singh, 2016).

Why is it increasingly necessary to pay special attention to the "fit" between the nursing facility's goals and the "needs" of the persons it seeks to serve? To ensure that the facility will stay in business! Also, to ensure that the placement is appropriate and that the chosen facility is doing more good than harm.

The steps in marketing are as follows:

1. The audit
2. Market segmentation
3. Choosing a market mix
4. Implementing the plan
5. Evaluating the results
6. Control

These steps mirror management steps.

MARKETING AS MANAGERIAL THINKING

Marketing employs the management techniques we have discussed and recommended, using a vocabulary explicitly developed for the field of marketing. The purposes of marketing are to identify and satisfactorily serve the community's institutional nursing facility needs. Marketing is a useful additional vocabulary, another way of thinking about how the nursing facility can successfully identify and satisfy an expanding array of healthcare needs (Robbins & Coulter, 2018).

As a variation on managerial thinking, marketing focuses sharply on the idea that success for the facility depends on bringing about a voluntary exchange of values (services) with the target persons.

END TO THE PRODUCTION ORIENTATION

Over 50 years ago, healthcare providers' focus was on designing a quality hospital or nursing facility, correctly assuming that building a facility would lead to it filling with patients. This thinking defines *production orientation*, which holds that the facility's task is to deliver care that the health professionals know is good for the residents and that the sales task is to stimulate potential residents' interest in what the facility has decided to offer. This attitude is "seller's market" thinking. There is nothing further from the truth today. Administrators fight for each resident for whom we are privileged to provide care.

SPECIAL CONTEXT OF NURSING FACILITY MARKETING

Local families want people they know and to whom they can entrust their parents' care. The administrator who is visibly active and creates a community presence can create an atmosphere of trust through such networking.

The nursing facility faces two unique challenges: (a) the requirement to maintain a societal marketing orientation and (b) public ambivalence toward the nursing facility itself. In the societal marketing orientation, the nursing facility's primary task is to determine the needs, desires, and best interests of residents and configure the facility to deliver satisfactions that preserve and enhance the well-being of the residents, families, and community.

Residents, both short- and long-term stay, may wish to be allowed to remain in their beds, to avoid exercise, and to eat only foods they can taste (typically foods high in sugar; Kane et al., 2018). But society has determined through the development of nursing facility regulations that residents must be urged to get up each day, dress and move about the facility to maintain blood flow, exercise when feasible, practice good oral hygiene, and eat the balanced diet mandated by the federal and state regulations. Thus, the nursing facility is obligated to encourage residents to engage in behaviors society has determined are in the residents' best interest, sometimes contrary to the individual resident's preference. We have become regulatorily bound to doing so and thus are in a challenging position of providing care to residents who often do not want it. It is up to us to help them receive the care they deserve instead.

Nursing facility marketing often faces public ambivalence, presenting a specific challenge and often creating a problem area. Most people do not want to consider a nursing facility alternative to living to a healthy and robust old age with all senses and capabilities intact, staying in their own homes. Marketing a vision of the typical nursing facility resident with three to four chronic illnesses requiring. a physician's care, six or more medications daily, a limited ability to perform daily living activities, and a need for 24-hour-a-day nursing care is exceedingly difficult. There is much more avoidance involved in public feelings toward the care in nursing facilities than toward hospitals, based on perceived outcomes of hospital discharge being healed and returning to active community life. Sadly, however, the mentality surrounding nursing facilities is that they are the places where the old go to die. Perhaps this was the case at one time, but we have come a very long way from this pre-OBRA world. Entering new marketing areas must be done with great forethought. An improperly analyzed niche can become a new cost center rather than the hoped-for new profit center.

1.9.3 DEVELOPING A MARKETING STRATEGY

Section Concepts

- *To survive, a facility needs an aggressive marketing strategy*
- *A niche market might be required of a facility for it to be successful*

Consider as the Administrator . . .

- *Can niche marketing backfire on the facility?*
- *Can you market a niche without providing the financial outlay necessary to cater to them once they are in the facility?*

NEED FOR A MARKETING STRATEGY

NAB DOMAIN 4A2: ORGANIZATIONAL CHANGE MANAGEMENT

NAB DOMAIN 4B2: STRATEGIC BUSINESS PLANNING (E.G., NEW LINES OF SERVICE, SUCCESSION MANAGEMENT, STAFFING PIPELINE); 4B4: BUSINESS DEVELOPMENT (E.G., SALES, MARKETING, PARTNERSHIPS, ACOs, CONTRACTS AND AGREEMENTS, NEGOTIATIONS); 4B5: PUBLIC RELATIONS AND EXTERNAL STAKEHOLDERS (E.G., HOSPITALS, REFERRALS SOURCES, LOCAL COMMUNITY, DONORS)

Organizations must continually adapt to changes within and outside the organization (Krupp & Schoemaker, 2014). An adaptive organization systematically monitors the external environment and revises its mission, strategies, and objectives to take advantage of emerging opportunities.

A constantly evolving marketing strategy is needed because continuous changes occur in the demographic, technologic, regulatory, economic, political, reimbursement, and social environment, leading to changing demand for nursing facility services. Marketing plans need to continually respond to new competition, new client demands, and changing values.

Competition for potential nursing facility clients is increasing. Hospitals are showing an increased interest in converting empty acute care wings to nursing facility–type beds on the acute care side. Some hospitals are even building new nursing facilities on their grounds or nearby to create a new revenue stream. From another perspective, home healthcare agencies are increasingly providing sophisticated nursing care such as IV feeding in the patient's home—previously performed chiefly in hospitals and only a few nursing facilities. Thus, acute care patients may increasingly go directly home, bypassing the nursing facility. Then, there are assisted living facilities bursting onto the scene that promise to let their residents "age in place" (read: never have to go to a nursing facility). Some assisted living facilities are now serving sliding-scale diabetics (difficult-to-treat diabetics) previously served by nursing facilities. Also, large and often unregulated multi-unit senior housing facilities are being built that can also let their residents "age in place" by bringing home healthcare workers to these facilities.

A marketing strategy includes selecting a target market or markets, choosing a competitive position, and developing a compelling marketing mix to reach and serve the identified customers (Cole & Kelley, 2020; Hitt et al., 2017; Robbins & Coulter, 2018).

A market is all the persons who have an actual or potential interest in using the facility's services. A facility may select among several market coverage strategies. It may concentrate on one market or market segment; for example, it may choose to serve only Medicaid residents (called market concentration). The facility may decide to offer only one service for all markets (product concentration), for example, serving only Alzheimer's patients regardless of their funding source. The facility may opt for a market specialization by serving a specific market segment, such as persons who need rehabilitative care and are expected to return home within a specified brief period. Or it may prefer to work in several product markets, for example, to serve both Alzheimer's and other brain-damaged persons of all ages (selective specializations; Chies, 2021).

CREATING NEW MARKETS, NEW NICHES

It is useful to distinguish between market sharing and market creation. Persons using the market-share mentality focus on how they can attain a desired share of the present market. Market creators are those who attempt to create a new market. We saw the advent of the ventilator unit in many nursing facilities in past days to create a new long-term care market. We see wound units, dialysis units, short-term-to-home units, and many other varied opportunities that enterprising administrators undertake today. Survival for both individual facilities and nursing facility chains is becoming increasingly tied to specializing in market niches in which one can gain a reputation for excellence, to keep census at the needed levels.

WHICH NICHE?

In recent years, niche marketing has taken new twists. Both assisted living facilities and nursing facilities have begun offering home care services to seniors in the community in the hope that those served will choose to move to the facility offering the home care services when a higher level of care is eventually needed. This both offers new revenue centers for facilities and markets to a niche in the community that might become full-time in-facility clients.

The number of dedicated HIV/AIDS beds is about 2,000—a fraction less than 1% of all beds in the United States.

The number of hospice patients in the United States grew from 52,000 in 1992 to 105,000 in 2000, to more than 1.55 million in 2018, a trend expected to continue (National Center for Health Statistics, 2005; National Hospice and Palliative Care Organization, 2020). Not surprisingly, more than 66% of hospice patients are 75 years of age and older (National Hospice and Palliative Care Organization, 2020).

Finding and establishing niches must be done carefully: What may be a great marketing tool may be cost-prohibitive in practice. Many administrators have found that, although high, ventilator reimbursements barely cover the increased costs of service!

STEPS IN DEVELOPING A MARKETING STRATEGY FOR THE FACILITY

Section Concepts

- *The steps in developing a marketing strategy in a facility*
- *How a facility is in the business of marketing services*
- *How consumers make decisions on a facility*
- *Effective marketing tools*

Consider as the Administrator . . .

- *If your facility does not have a marketing plan, are you going to be successful? Or is your facility on the road to ruin?*

NAB DOMAIN 4B5: PUBLIC RELATIONS AND EXTERNAL STAKEHOLDERS (E.G., HOSPITALS, REFERRALS SOURCES, LOCAL COMMUNITY, DONORS)

Step 1: The Audit

As indicated earlier, the first step in developing a marketing strategy is the audit. Auditing is the process of identifying, collecting, and analyzing information about the external environment. Those marketing human resources typically characterize a market as potential, available, qualified, served, and penetrated. The potential market is all the persons who express some level of interest in a defined market offer. Removing persons who are interested, but unable to pay, defines the available market, that is, persons who have the interest, the funds, and access to the market offering. The qualified available market is those persons who have interest, financial means, access, and quality, for example, meet the requirement for 24-hour-per-day nursing care. The served market is that part of the qualified available market the facility tries to attract to the facility. The persons who are admitted to or served by the facility constitute the penetrated market—the persons consuming the services offered.

It is necessary to estimate the extent of demand for a service the facility might offer. Total market demand is the total volume of services that would be bought by a defined available number of persons in a specific geographic area in a defined period in a stated marketing environment under a specific marketing program. Market forces suggest the number of services the facility could expect to be purchased under such a specific marketing plan.

In forecasting future demand, the facility can examine three categories: (a) uncontrollable environment factors such as the economy, technological changes, reimbursement formula changes, and broad changes in the healthcare system (such as the emergence of managed care); (b) new competition from other providers (e.g., new facilities, new services, and new marketing budget); and (c) intraorganizational factors (such as the condition of one's facility, possible new services, and promotional efforts programs). Forecasts may be based on what people say they will do, are doing, and/or have done in the past.

Step 2: Market Segmentation

Market segmentation is using the audit information to divide the potential persons served into identifiable subgroups. Subgroups may be longer term residents and shorter term residents who come for rehabilitation and then return home or groupings such as private-pay patients and public-pay patients. Furthermore, a nursing facility chain might segment the market it seeks by geography, for example, region of the country, urban/rural, density, and/or climate. Markets can be segmented by demographic characteristics such as age, family size, sex, educational level, occupation, or religion. Psychographic social classes can be used (e.g., lifestyle and personality). Persons who are by nature gregarious and thrive on extensive personal interactions, for example, are good candidates for application to life care communities. In addition, behavior tendencies can be used to segment markets; benefits sought (e.g., a life care community benefit set), user status (within age limits and able to pay), and readiness stage (e.g., persons above a certain age, retired, and actively seeking a caregiver) all identify market segments (Hitt et al., 2017).

Step 3: The Market Mix

Determining the market mix consists of deciding what types of residents to approach and in what proportions. Most facilities find it useful to identify specific groups of persons being sought to serve. This is more feasible and necessary in urban settings than in rural areas where choices of whom to serve may be more limited by geography and income.

Most facilities will consciously choose a product mix, that is, the set of all product lines and items they intend to offer. A product line in the nursing facility setting is a set of services within the product mix that are closely related due to functional similarity, for example, being made available to the same type of persons or marketed through the same channels. A facility may choose to serve a combination of heavy-care patients from the local hospital who can expect to return home or die shortly as one group, plus another group of persons who enter as light-care patients expected to remain in the facility for the foreseeable future. A product item is a distinct unit within a product line that is distinguishable by purpose in some other characteristic. The facility may, for example, within the heavy-care group, especially solicit persons being fed intravenously or needing tracheostomy care.

Step 4: Implementing and Evaluating the Plan

Implementing the marketing plan is the process of managing organizational behaviors and outreach activities to attract residents with the identified characteristics in the proportions desired.

Creating awareness among potential consumers that the services exist, assisting them in deciding, and ensuring that they are satisfied with the quality of services provided by the facility is the process of marketing implementation. An ongoing evaluation of the effectiveness of the marketing efforts is necessary as well.

Steps 5 and 6: Evaluation and Control

Once the marketing effort is operational, it is necessary to devise ways to measure the results and take corrective action to ensure that the desired results are achieved.

THE MARKETING OF SERVICES

Nursing facilities are primarily in the business of marketing services. A service is an activity or benefit that one person can offer to another, which is intangible and does not result in ownership of anything. Services have four characteristics that differentiate them from durable goods (e.g., cars or TV sets): intangibility, inconsistency, inseparability, and inventory.

The Characteristics of Services

Intangibility. Services cannot be touched, sat in, or driven like a car: They are intangible. Potential residents cannot directly experience the healthcare that they expect to receive before entering the facility. However, nursing facilities can make services appear more tangible (e.g., a TV advertisement portraying attentive care being given to a resident at the facility).

Inconsistency. Marketing services differs from marketing tangible goods such as automobiles because the quality of service can be inconsistent from day to day or even shift to shift. Quality that endures over time can be built into a car through consistent assembly line procedures and quality checks, but the service received at the hands of the nurses or nursing assistants on any given day can vary widely depending on the mood of the employee (Singh, 2016).

Inseparability. The third characteristic of marketing services is that the consumer cannot separate the service from the deliverer or the setting in which the service is given. The nursing facility may be giving excellent nursing care, but if the bathrooms smell bad and are dirty, the residents' and visitors' perceptions of the facility, including their perceptions of quality of nursing care, are affected. The services received and the service provided are inseparably linked in the consumer's mind.

Inventory. Idle production capacity (i.e., the presence of an unoccupied bed in a healthcare facility) is the fourth characteristic of service marketing. Inventory-carrying costs of empty nursing facility beds is high: Empty beds may cost as much as 70% of the costs of occupied beds due to fixed and semi-variable costs.

Often, if a nursing facility carefully proportions the number of subsidized and private-pay residents, it can provide better accommodations and services for both. This balance is important because in many states, the public reimbursement rates are at or below costs, forcing providers to subsidize publicly paying patients by shifting these costs to the bills of private-pay patients.

CONSUMER DECISION-MAKING

Consumer decision-making is typically characterized as follows:

1. Problem recognition
2. Information search
3. Alternative evaluation
4. Purchase decision
5. Postpurchase evaluation

or as

1. Need arousal (trigger factors, such as a hospital episode)
2. Information gathering

3. Decision evaluation
4. Decision execution
5. Postdecision assessment

The decision for a person to enter a nursing facility is often a complex one shared by several participants. The decision-making unit may consist of the following:

- *The initiator.* The daughter, for example, suggests looking into nursing facility care
- *The influential friend.* For instance, acquaintances already in local nursing facilities or who have convalesced in one
- *The decider.* The person or persons who ultimately force some part of the decision, for example, the daughter who decides she cannot provide the new level of care needed
- *The buyer.* The person or persons who will pay the bills if the resident is not the payer
- *The user.* The person who will be the new resident or nursing facility service user (Hitt et al., 2017; Singh, 2016)

Consumer decisions are based on their perceptions of whether the service provided by the nursing facility will meet their needs. Research suggests that physicians typically have a significant influence on patient decisions. Recommendations from local physicians can provide the facility with a sustainable advantage. Hospital discharge planners are an essential group whose image of the facility and communication can also provide a competitive edge program (Konopaske et al., 2018).

Consider as the Administrator . . .

- *How effective is the CMS Nursing Home Compare website? How effective is the Five-Star system? Does the Five-Star system simply penalize a facility for having a bad day?*

EFFECTIVE MARKETING TOOLS

A personal tour through the building that includes meeting staff and residents is one of the most effective marketing tools available to the facility. During the visitor visits, the potential client or clients, usually the children or close friends of the prospective resident, are gathering impressions on which they will make judgments of the facility. Often, subliminal perceptions become the key factor. Subliminal perceptions are factors the decision-maker is not consciously aware of, such as the facility's general appearance, the absence of odors, the friendliness of the staff, and the appearance of the residents.

Numerous ways of creating a positive image for the facility in the community are available. Developing a community advisory board, hosting neighborhood open houses, publicizing enthusiastic families and volunteers, and cosponsoring community events such as local arts festivals are but a few of the avenues available to facilities.

ADVERTISING

Many facilities have begun advertising their services. Advertising consists of non-personal forms of communication conducted through paid media with a clear sponsorship program. The purpose of advertising is to motivate the target audience to move through the following buyer-readiness states toward actual use of facility services (Cole & Kelley, 2020; Konopaske et al., 2018; Singh, 2016):

- Cognitive advertising (aware that the facility is available)
- Effective advertising (favorable image of facility when comparing it to alternatives)
- Behavioral advertising (conviction; e.g., ask a physician to "place mother there")

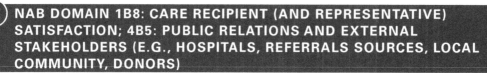

NAB DOMAIN 1B8: CARE RECIPIENT (AND REPRESENTATIVE) SATISFACTION; 4B5: PUBLIC RELATIONS AND EXTERNAL STAKEHOLDERS (E.G., HOSPITALS, REFERRALS SOURCES, LOCAL COMMUNITY, DONORS)

Marketing the facility begins before admission. The facility exists to serve the customer. It is crucial to think of residents as the facility's customers in the same way a hotel or a restaurant thinks of the customer. The facility is, de facto, the residents' temporary or permanent home. The staff may be thought of as persons hired to meet these customers' needs on an ongoing basis. Public relations are a lifeline of the facility. Good relations with the local news outlets will benefit the facility in inevitable times of crisis. Policies must be established as to what staff members may give press interviews. Generally, all staff are required to refer press persons to the administrator.

COMMON PITFALLS IN PRACTICE
- The idea that marketing is not the job of the administrator is purely false. Sure, you might get out into the field into the thick of it all and market. However, understand that every thought, every decision, and every interaction you have all day long is marketing. Make sure that all these are on the level and moving the facility to where you want it to be.
- Many new administrators think that marketing is not important. This is far from the truth as your facility needs "heads in the beds" to remain successful. This takes marketing. Nobody knows about a restaurant that is hidden somewhere that does not advertise. They will quickly fail. The same goes for your facility. You must have market share and provide market value. People must know you and what you are selling!

1.9.4 MARKETING CONCERNS

Section Concepts

- *Remuneration of any kind is unacceptable when it comes to marketing*

Consider as the Administrator . . .

- *Agreements and understandings which are in place between providers often are potentially skirting legality when it comes to these laws*

NAB DOMAIN 2B3: ETHICAL CONDUCT AND STANDARDS OF PRACTICE

NAB DOMAIN 4B4: BUSINESS DEVELOPMENT (E.G., SALES, MARKETING, PARTNERSHIPS, ACOs, CONTRACTS AND AGREEMENTS, NEGOTIATIONS)

Marketing is an essential part of any facility's success; however, as with everything, there are considerations surrounding marketing that one needs to be acutely aware of. First and foremost, understand that marketing is a relationship game. You build relationships with others, they build relationships with you, and you make a decided effort to work with those you have relationships with. Put more simply, people remember what is in front of their faces. For many years, it was an industry standard to shower potential referral sources with pens, pads of paper, and other marketing tchotchkes. At one point, it was also considered acceptable to take your referral sources to expensive lunches, provide box seats to baseball games, or even send certain individuals who were prime sources on lavish trips to Hawaii or Mexico. Marketing was a "pay to play" situation. Fast-forward from there to the 1970s and many different incantations of laws later, we are left with today's anti-kickback statutes (AKSs) and Stark laws.

FEDERAL ANTI-KICKBACK STATUTES

The federal AKSs prohibit the exchange or offer of exchange of anything of value to induce (or reward) the referral of business that is reimbursable by federal healthcare programs (Anti-Kickback Statutes, 2020). Examples of such kickbacks include financial incentives for referrals, free or low rent office space, excessive compensation for medical directorships, waiving copayments, providing "extra" free services, questionable cost sharing by hospice companies, and a myriad of other considerations that boggle the ethical mind.

The CMS holds the belief that such kickbacks have led to the overutilization or inappropriate utilization of healthcare services. There is also some evidence to show that medical decision-making can become corrupted in such situations and that patients are steered from what they need to what/whom decision-makers have relationships with. As such, there are potential penalties of up to $25,000 per occurrence, jail time, and full exclusion from Medicare and Medicaid programs for life (Anti-Kickback Statutes, 2020).

PHYSICIAN SELF-REFERRAL LAWS (STARK LAWS)

These laws cover a particularly touchy area when it comes to the medical field, and that surrounds who owns what. Many physicians have interests in medical facilities, hospitals, nursing facilities, and other entities that exist within the medical field. The Stark laws are set up to prohibit physician self-referral of Medicare or Medicaid patients to an entity that provides healthcare services if the physician (or their family) has a financial relationship with said entity (Stark Laws, 2020). There are significant penalties associated with this law (not unlike AKS); the entity in question can be denied payments, forced to refund monies paid, or be levied civil penalties of up to $15,000 per occurrence, and there is the potential of having to pay back three times the improper payment, as well as exclusion from the Medicare and Medicaid programs and further civil penalties of up to $100,000 per occurrence for each identified scheme breaking the law (Stark Laws, 2020).

COMMON PITFALLS IN PRACTICE

- If you think a deal is too good to exist, it probably is. Be very wary in getting into deals with other providers to "help" each other.
- Ignorance of AKSs and Stark laws does not make breaking them acceptable. These are laws that consist of thousands of pages. It is highly suggested that you become very familiar with them.

CASE DISCUSSIONS

The Nurse Consultant Arrives at The Laurels Nursing Facility

This case illustrates the uses and abuses of line/staff authority—and the blurring often created by corporate staff behaviors.

Ms. Monday, the chain consultant, had no authority to do any of the things she did. She had no authority to meet with the nursing supervisors and charge nurses. She had no authority to issue procedures or a new policy for the PRN medications.

Ms. Monday set up a violation of the infection control rules. Nursing staff in the dietary area supervising food tray staff creates cross-contamination.

The administrator should have been upset with both the administrator's authority and the director of nursing's authority being usurped by the corporate staff visitor, Ms. Monday. The administrator simply capitulated to the corporate staff person taking the administrator's line authority away.

The director of nursing had a reasonable case for threatening to resign. The corporate nurse had come in, taken charge, overruled, and embarrassed the director of nursing. Here the director of nursing is simply stating to the administrator that she must be given clear line authority over nursing staff if she is to be effective. It would be foolish of the administrator to let this director of nursing go.

Man Dies After Nurses Forget to Turn on Respirator (An Actual Case)

Oh, for a checklist! The nurses had no checklist, or if they did, they failed to use it. This clearly was a preventable death. All the nurses needed was a list of items to check before they exited the treatment phase of a resident on a life support machine. Checklists, and the need for them, are discussed in the text. A facility without checklists (procedures) for staff to follow is not doing even a minimum job on risk management.

What can be inferred about this chain's attitude toward:

(continued)

1. Marketing: None. The attitude purveyed is we give it a college try, and if it works (good care is given), fine; if not, that's OK too! After all, we're all just humans.
2. Chain/facility policy enforcement: We do what we can, but we don't take policy enforcement very seriously.
3. Quality control: We don't worry much about quality control; after all, you must expect mistakes to occur now and then.
4. Patient care policies: We have them, but we don't pay much attention to them.
5. Sacredness of life: It's not very sacred. You must expect tragic errors to happen here.
6. Patient rights: We do the best we can, but don't expect too much.

Of course, the chain may simply have been following its lawyers' advice to admit nothing and act like nothing preventable had happened!

New Jersey Woman in Legal Fight Over Feeding Tube Dies

Who won this case? The facility won! The facility kept the woman on a life-sustaining feeding tube for 7 years. The facility refused, citing its own policy not to remove feeding tubes. The family had won the right to have the tube removed but not the right to overrule facility policy, which prohibited removing feeding tubes if death would be the result. The family was so furious they tried to get the U.S. Supreme Court to rule that the facility must remove the woman's feeding tube. By refusing to interfere, the U.S. Supreme Court affirmed the facility's right to have and enforce its policy that no feeding tube will be removed if that removal will result in a resident's death.

This, of course, is a very complicated case. Seven years in a coma-like state is a very long time and very expensive taxpayer burden. The facility and the family are debating the right-to-life issue. The patient's rights are also at issue, as is the question of how to assert patient rights for persons unable to state their wishes.

What can be inferred about this facility's attitudes toward:

1. Marketing: A mixed message here. This facility is indirectly informing the public that its policy is to maintain and preserve all residents' lives regardless of the apparent quality of life being experienced by a patient. Message: If you want to go where the medical staff will remove life-sustaining measures, such as a feeding tube, go to another facility, a hospital, or your own home. The facility seems happy to be marketing itself as a place where resident's right to life is preserved.
2. Facility policy enforcement: All the way to the U.S. Supreme Court! That's a powerful commitment to one's policy position. This facility must have spent several hundreds of thousands of its own dollars to defend its right to make and enforce its policies.
3. Quality control: Absolutely! The facility felt that quality care meant preserving all life entrusted to it. Any compromise was unacceptable to the facility policymakers.

(*continued*)

4. Patient care policies: In contrast to the "Man Dies After Nurses Forget to Turn on Respirator" case discussed earlier, this facility cares passionately about enforcing its patient care policies.
5. Sacredness of life: Clearly, this facility felt that life is sacred. The facility policymakers believed that the family, in this case, had no right to require the facility to remove a life-sustaining feeding tube.
6. Patient's rights: This facility felt that all patients had an absolute right to life, whatever its "quality." This, of course, raises the right-to-die issue, which has been so hotly debated in the United States.

This case demonstrates the complexities of end-of-life decisions, the right of a facility to enforce its policies, and the importance of residents (all of us!) having a living will. Had this woman had a living will, would all this acrimony have been avoided? In this case, probably not.

After the Seminar: A New Leadership Style for The Laurels

This case, of course, was written to illustrate the principles presented in the text.

The regional administrator might respond as follows to Ms. Binz on being asked for his thoughts:

"Ms. Binz, you do not seem to understand that equals cannot be expected to coordinate equals. That's not the way organizations work. Your job as an administrator is to create and lead a team of department heads. You are the team leader. It is not feasible to give each department head the final say in all matters affecting their department."

"It is not surprising that dietary and nursing are squabbling about job descriptions for their respective departments. It is usual for any one department to try to maximize its well-being at the expense of other departments."

"Did it occur to you that both your staff development coordinator and your director of nursing seem not to understand the concept of cross-contamination? Trained nurse's aides are the appropriate persons to feed residents in their rooms. That is a nursing function, not a dietary function by the usual definition of *dietary duties*."

"If the director of nursing has such a poor attitude toward dietary's abilities to provide tasty and timely food, there are important issues you should tell me you are addressing!"

"I'm not surprised, although I am dismayed that you let it happen, that no resident had been fed at 9:30 a.m. due to the disputes between dietary and nursing. What have you done to avoid this in the future?"

"What do you mean housekeeping won't clean up spills and puddles! That's their job. It's every staff member's job: You find it, it's yours. Keeping the facility floors safe and dry is everyone's responsibility. 'Puddles' are an all-hands operation for all staff members."

"Ms. Binz, you do not seem to understand that the lowest level in the organization for organizational decisions affecting the entire facility stop in your office. You are the person who must create a team that delivers quality care and maximizes

(continued)

choices for residents. Department managers cannot 'fight it out' without affecting the quality of resident care and likely destroying the facility's ability to provide safe care. That's not the way power works! Your department heads may be competent professionals. But you can know ahead of time that departments will normally seek to maximize their own well-being, often at the expense of other departments. You don't seem to understand how organizations behave, Ms. Binz!"

The Owners' Directives

This case illustrates how pressures at the corporate level can directly affect the local facility administrator. Constraints abound for the local nursing facility administrator.

1. Corporate probably owns some hospitals where it is customary to add staff and prepare the facility for The Joint Commission inspection, which is scheduled by and paid for by the hospital several months in advance. This kind of pre-inspection period and staffing assist is not normally available to the nursing facility administrator. Nursing facility administrators can guess, if the 12- to 15-month inspection has not occurred for 10 months, that an inspection will come in the next 2 to 5 months. But to know in advance an exact date is a misdemeanor. Nursing facility records are so carefully reviewed that the surveyors review staffing for the entire period being covered by an inspection. Any recent bulking up of staff will be noticed.
2. Systematically reducing one's Medicaid residents is a difficult position for the facility. Claiming that the facility is unable to give the needed level of care believed required is looked upon with suspicion by the surveyors and by the local hospital discharge planners. Every facility is expected to take its proportionate share of Medicaid residents—usually an informal understanding in a community of providers.
3. Yes, many facilities have increased the number of Medicare residents in recent years in response to profitable levels of reimbursement for Medicare admissions. But one must be very careful not to provide more days of care than are objectively justifiable under Medicare rules. Pushing the limit on care permitted under Medicare can be a dangerous game. Such behaviors are now easily monitored via computer models used to reimburse for care given.
4. Reducing an already low daily raw food budget will likely draw negative feedback from the residents.
5. Using more pools is believed, in the end, to be more expensive than using regular staff due to the increased level of risk involved in having outside staff who are unfamiliar with the residents.

Corporate is often responding more to cash flow for the corporation than to the well-being of any one facility. It is the administrator's job to walk a careful line between corporate-stated interests and what the administrator may believe to be in the best interest of the residents and the individual facility.

WHAT WOULD YOU DO?

You are the administrator of a 180-bed facility, and you are confronted by a family member who tells you that your care and services are substandard. The family member tells you that your sheets are scratchy, your food is not fit for a dog to eat, and your services are pathetic for those who live there.

You are presented with a list from the family member that includes the following:

- All meals are to be prepared by a French chef.
- Thread count for sheets is expected to be no less than 1,000.
- Daily massage therapy services are to be provided to their loved one as part of your per diem.
- Each therapy (physical therapy, occupational therapy, and speech therapy) needs to see their loved one daily as that "is what they are for" despite no need for any of the therapies.
- Call bells are not to be used with their loved one. Your staff is expected to be at the beck and call of the resident and should be standing at attention in the room to meet their needs.

1. What would you do from here?
2. Are the expectations of this family in line with federal standards?
3. Do you have to meet any of these outlandish requests?
4. How do you make this family member happy, or is this an impossible task?

REFERENCES

Anti-Kickback Statutes, 42 U.S.C. § 1320a-7b. (2020). https://public-inspection.federalregister.gov/2020-26072.pdf

Brigham, E. F., & Houston, J. F. (2019). *Fundamentals of financial management* (15th ed.). Cengage Learning.

Centers for Medicare & Medicaid Services. (2021). *Quality measures.* https://www.cms.gov/Medicare/Quality-Initiatives-Patient-Assessment-Instruments/NursingHomeQualityInits/NHQIQualityMeasures

Charlesworth, C. J., Smit, E., Lee, D. S., Alramadhan, F., & Odden, M. C. (2015). Polypharmacy among adults aged 65 years and older in the United States: 1988-2010. *Journals of Gerontology: Biological Sciences and Medical Sciences, 70*(8), 989–995. https://doi.org/10.1093/gerona/glv013

Chies, S. (2021). *Pratt's long-term care: Managing across the continuum* (5th ed.). Jones & Bartlett.

Cole, G. A., & Kelley, P. (2020). *Management theory and practice* (9th ed.). Cengage Learning.

Deming Institute. (2015, November 19). *If Japan can, why can't we?* [Video]. YouTube. https://www.youtube.com/watch?v=vcG_Pmt_Ny4

Dertouzos, M. L., Lester, R. K., & Solow, R. M. (1989). *Made in America: Regaining the productive edge.* MIT Press.

Finck-Boyle, J. (2021, March 3). *Top 10 survey citations—March 2021.* LeadingAge. https://leadingage.org/regulation/top-10-survey-citations-march-2021

Halter, J. B., Ouslander, J. G., Studenski, S., High, K. P., Asthana, S., Supiano, M. A., & Ritchie, C. (2017). *Hazzard's geriatric medicine and gerontology* (7th ed.). McGraw Hill.

Hitt, M. A., Ireland, R. D., & Hoskisson, R. E. (2017). *Strategic management: Concepts and cases: Competitiveness and globalization* (12th ed.). Cengage Learning.

Kane, R. L., Ouslander, J. G., Resnick, B., & Malone, M. (2018). *Essentials of clinical geriatrics* (8th ed.). McGraw Hill.

Konopaske, R., Ivancevich, J. M., & Matteson, M. T. (2018). *Organizational behavior and management* (11th ed.). McGraw Hill.

Krupp, S., & Schoemaker, P. (2014). *Winning the long game.* Public Affairs Press.

Kruse, C., Fohn, J., Wilson, N., Patlan, E. N., Zipp, S., & Mileski, M. (2020). Utilization barriers and medical outcomes commensurate with the use of telehealth among older adults: Systematic review. *JMIR Medical Informatics, 8*(8), e20359. https://doi.org/10.2196/20359

Kruse, C. S., Mileski, M., & Moreno, J. (2017). Mobile health solutions for the aging population: A systematic narrative analysis. *Journal of Telemedicine and Telecare, 23*(4), 439–451. https://doi.org/10.1177/1357633X16649790

McClay, R., Natividad, J., & Mileski, M. (2021). Changes to a shift reporting sheet on a critical care unit—Nurse perceptions and lessons learned. *Journal of Multidisciplinary Healthcare, 14*, 381–387. https://doi.org/10.2147/JMDH.S289384

Mileski, M., Kruse, C. S., Catalani, J., & Haderer, T. (2017). Adopting telemedicine for the self-management of hypertension: Systematic review. *JMIR Medical Informatics, 5*(4), e41. https://doi.org/10.2196/medinform.6603

National Center for Health Statistics. (2005). *Health, United States, 2005.* Author.

National Hospice and Palliative Care Organization. (2020). *NHPCO facts and figures.* Author.

Noe, R. A., Hollenback, J. R., Gerhart, B., & Wright, P. (2019). *Human resource management: Gaining a competitive advantage* (11th ed.). McGraw Hill.

Papadakis, M. A., McPhee, S. J., & Rabow, M. W. (2021). *Current medical diagnosis & treatment 2021.* McGraw Hill.

Robbins, S. P., & Coulter, M. (2018). *Management* (14th ed.). Pearson.

Robbins, S. P., & Judge, T. A. (2019). *Organizational behavior* (18th ed.). Pearson.

Singh, D. A. (2016). *Effective management of long-term care facilities* (3rd ed.). Jones & Bartlett.

Stark Laws, 42 U.S.C. § 411. (2020). https://public-inspection.federalregister.gov/2020-26140.pdf

Topol, E. (2015). *The patient will see you now: The future of medicine is in your hands.* Basic Books.

Welch, J., & Welch, S. (2015). *The real-life MBA.* Harper Collins.

Zelman, W. N., McCue, M. H., Glick, N. D., & Thomas, M. S. (2020). *Financial management of health care organizations: Introduction to fundamental tools, concepts, and applications* (5th ed.). Jossey-Bass.

PART 2

Understanding the Departments and Managing Human Resources

What You Will Learn in Part 2

- *How the typical nursing facility is organizationally structured*
- *The scope of responsibilities and basic information about these functional areas:*
  - *The administrator's office*
  - *Medical and allied health functions*
  - *Patterns of physician care*
  - *Dental care*
  - *Foot and eye care*
  - *Pharmacy services*
  - *Physical therapy/occupational therapy/speech therapy*
  - *Laboratory and other diagnostic services*
  - *Nursing services*
  - *The business office*
  - *Medical records*
  - *Admissions*
  - *Dietary*
  - *Social services*
  - *Activities and recreation*
  - *Housekeeping/laundry/maintenance*

2.1 ORGANIZATION OF THE NURSING FACILITY AND ITS STAFF

Section Concepts

- *The myriad of staff that makes up a successful nursing facility*
- *The complexity of the number of individuals required for a facility to operate*
- *The number of different types of workers you as the administrator will be expected to oversee*

Consider as the Administrator . . .

- *What resources are available to the administrator to ensure that all the functional areas work as a single team?*

COMPLEXITY OF THE STAFF'S ORGANIZATIONAL TASKS

NAB DOMAIN 4A1: ORGANIZATIONAL STRUCTURES (E.G., DEPARTMENTS, FUNCTIONS, SYSTEMIC PROCESSES)

The goal of total quality management (TQM) is that human resources in every unit arrive at a level of daily performance reflecting a passion for quality (Hitt et al., 2017; Johnson & Sollecito, 2020; Robbins & Coulter, 2018; Spath & Kelly, 2017). This goal is easier to state than achieve. The multitude of regulations to be obeyed can seem overwhelming due to the rules and regulations that are constantly evolving. Probably only partly in jest, it has been stated that the nursing facility industry was the second-most regulated industry, with nuclear power being first. That position is not true. Nursing facility industry regulations have surpassed those of the nuclear power industry—and they keep growing.

As regulations continue to proliferate, the average nursing facility administrator must increasingly act as a resource and overall facility expert who depends on department heads and their staff to be the experts in their specific area. One of the essential aspects of the administrator's job is knowing where to find the necessary information and providing that information in a timely fashion to their staff.

NAB DOMAIN 2A: FINANCIAL MANAGEMENT; 2C4: ORGANIZATIONAL STAFFING REQUIREMENTS AND REPORTING (E.G., PBJ)

The decision on how to staff a nursing facility depends on many variables. An overarching consideration is the level of medical complexity of care to be delivered. Changes in a facility's case mix will typically result in altered staffing patterns. The admission of several medically complex residents may lead to employing an additional experienced RN and retraining most of the floor nurses. The admission of several lighter-care residents may call for additional aides rather than an additional RN. Certain states also have minimum staff-to-resident ratios that are required. In this chapter, we present options in organizational forms and a staffing pattern that the administrator of a 100-bed facility with an average level of intensity might consider.

ORGANIZATIONAL PATTERN FOR A 100-BED FACILITY

Figure 2.1 shows the organizational pattern and staffing levels for a 100-bed facility suggested in the federal government regulations.

Various Configurations

In actual practice, these 17 "departmental" areas can be, and routinely are, given different titles and combined variously. Nevertheless, however configured, these areas must be accounted for in the typical nursing facility organizational plan.

In Figure 2.1, each position within the 17 departments or functional areas (e.g., admissions) is depicted, along with the number of its staff and whether they work full-time or part-time.

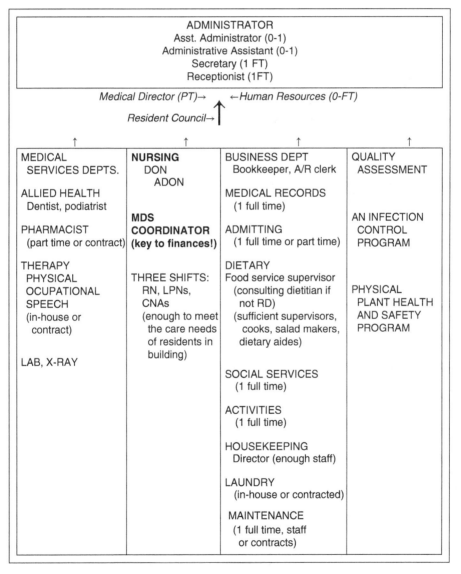

FIGURE 2.1 Organizational pattern for a 100-bed facility.
ADON, assistant director of nursing; CNAs, certified nursing assistant; DON, director of nursing; LPNs, licensed practical nurses; MDS, Minimum Data Set.

Emergence of the "Minimum Data Set" Coordinator

In recent years, the Minimum Data Set (MDS) coordinator role has become central to both the nursing facility's quality of care and reimbursement for care. With the recent advent of the Patient Driven Payment Model (PDPM) by the Centers for Medicare & Medicaid Services (CMS), this role has become even more critical. The MDS is the federal effort to define and control the quality of care within nursing facilities that are Medicare and/or Medicaid certified.

The upper area in Figure 2.1 reflects the administrator, their immediate staff, and advisory roles (indicated by italics) of the medical director and resident council. The first column includes the medical and allied health professionals essential to the facility (e.g., physicians, dentists, pharmacists, occupational and physical therapists). The nursing service, with its three shifts, is the second column. Areas in the third column are also necessary to function as a facility (e.g., the business office, dietary, social services, activities, housekeeping, maintenance). In the final column are activities mandated by federal requirements.

Consider as the Administrator . . .

- *Suppose this one person, the MDS coordinator, "controls" both the facility's financial reimbursement and the perceived quality of care. What should be the relationship between the MDS coordinator and the administrator?*

Workable Variations

Numerous workable variations on the model exist. In this one, line authority is given to the administrator leading to the several functional areas or departments. The administrator has responsibility, directly or indirectly, for all the functions of the facility.

A variant of this model, more suited to a larger facility of perhaps 200 residents, is to group several of these functions under middle-level managers who report to the administrator. One such arrangement is to appoint several middle-level managers who are directors of:

- Resident services (e.g., volunteers, transportation, barbers, beauticians)
- Administrative services (e.g., admissions, business office, clerical staff, human resources)
- Therapy services (e.g., physical, occupational, speech therapy)
- Nursing services (all nursing activities)
- Supportive services (housekeeping, laundry, maintenance)
- Dietary services

The more common model is depicted in Figure 2.1, where all department heads report directly to the administrator. In the typical 100-bed nursing facility, the administrator will have eight or nine department heads reporting directly to them.

We turn now to consider the organizational work to be accomplished by each department and consider their staffing requirements.

COMMON PITFALLS IN PRACTICE
- Many new administrators do not believe they need to know how to work with an MDS or what the MDS coordinator does—this is a mistake in the highest regard.
- The administrator is responsible for *all* employees, vendors, and contractors who work in their facility. Understand how to manage all these individuals.

2.1.1 THE ADMINISTRATOR'S OFFICE

Section Concepts

- *Everything starts and stops—and is controlled—by the administrator's office*
- *The administrator holds the welfare of the resident as a direct part of their position*

Consider as the Administrator . . .

- *Your entire staff looks to you for cues on how to do their jobs. How can you as the administrator ensure you are giving the right cues at the right times to your staff?*

NAB DOMAIN 1B8: CARE RECIPIENT (AND REPRESENTATIVE) SATISFACTION; 3B1: FEDERAL HEALTHCARE LAWS, RULES, AND REGULATIONS; 3B3: CERTIFICATION AND LICENSURE REQUIREMENTS FOR THE ORGANIZATION

The administrator is responsible for ensuring that all work is accomplished according to policy at an acceptable level of quality.

To summarize, consider the following as an initial description given in a random order of priority. The following are the charge of the administrator:

- Ensure a satisfactory quality of care and life for residents and staff
- Advocate for the residents and, as needed, staff and the facility
- Monitor and control all the subsystems in the facility
- Develop and manage the budget
- Manage the interface between the facility and its many stakeholders
- Monitor and manage the human resources functions
- Coordinate or ensure coordination of the work of all departments and functions in the facility
- Lead and provide stimulus daily to activities that implement the facility's goals and mission
- Forecast and lead the facility to a successful future

- Assist all staff and residents to understand the nature and value of change
- Interface with owners, inspectors, ombudspersons, third-party insurers, hospitals, fire departments, and the myriad of other persons, groups, and functions necessary for the survival of the facility
- Communicate with staff, residents, and other vital parties
- Empower department heads and staff to accomplish their work
- Facilitate the functioning of the facility by walking around and similar management approaches
- Set the tone for the facility in matters of dress, taste, compassion, and concern by word and behavior
- Settle territorial and jurisdictional disputes among staff, residents, and owners
- Meet providers' certification and licensing requirements
- Demonstrate empathy

The effective administrator does whatever it takes to have effective control of resident care in the facility. In recent years, facility administrators have utilized some variation of a daily department head meeting. Some call it "stand up" and meet for plus or minus 10 minutes each morning, some call it "stand up" and sit down for plus or minus 30 minutes each morning and review every resident, and others meet with department heads only once a week or less often.

In addition, the administrator is, more than anyone else in the facility, responsible for resident rights. Resident rights are a very large portion of today's federal regulations, ranging from F550 to F586. These 36 very specific regulations are important areas of the administrator's purview and require daily oversight in most cases. Any one of these regulations being out of compliance for the facility can cause significant issues. This group of regulations traditionally has anywhere from 10% to 15% noncompliance nationwide and must be a constant concern for the administrator.

Table 2.1 demonstrates other areas of general concern to the administrator. Intriguingly, these areas have changed as a result of COVID-19; however, there is still some commonality to the citations. We might postulate that once some normality returns, the types of citations will change back to the "old normal"; however, at this point, that would be a difficult conclusion to draw.

TABLE 2.1 Top 10 Cited F-Tags

F0884	Reporting to the National Health Safety Network
F0880	Infection control and prevention
F0886	COVID-19 testing—residents and staff
F0689	Free of accident hazards/supervision/devices
F0684	Quality of care
F0580	Notification of changes (injury/decline/room/others)
F0883	Influenza and pneumococcal immunizations
F0885	Reporting—residents, representatives, and families
F0686	Treatment/services to prevent/heal pressure ulcers
F0609	Reporting of alleged violations

Source: Adapted from Finck-Boyle, J. (2021). *Top 10 survey citations—March 2021*. LeadingAge. https://leadingage.org/regulation/top-10-survey-citations-march-2021

EMPATHY

NAB DOMAIN 1B2: PERSON-CENTERED CARE AND COMPREHENSIVE CARE PLANNING

Empathy is the ability to identify with the feelings, thoughts, or attitudes of another. Aging is often associated with progressive losses of functions and the ability to cope effectively. The administrator must empathize with the residents their losses and concerns about needing 24-hour-a-day nursing care. Beyond this, the administrator must ensure that the staff builds skill in putting themselves in the place of the residents to appreciate residents' experiences better. This concept is often communicated through workshops where staff is put "in the shoes" of a resident by different ways of emulating disease processes using tools that mimic diseases; for example, petroleum jelly–coated glasses to emulate macular degeneration. Demonstrating empathy is a daily need in the nursing facility setting.

NAB DOMAIN 3B1: FEDERAL HEALTHCARE LAWS, RULES, AND REGULATIONS; 3B3: CERTIFICATION AND LICENSURE REQUIREMENTS FOR THE ORGANIZATION; 4A1: ORGANIZATIONAL STRUCTURES (E.G., DEPARTMENTS, FUNCTIONS, SYSTEMIC PROCESSES); 4A3: ORGANIZATIONAL BEHAVIOR (E.G., ORGANIZATIONAL CULTURE, TEAM BUILDING, GROUP DYNAMICS)

It is the administrator's role to understand and enforce, throughout the facility, the many certifications and licensing requirements required to be a health service provider. Most staff in the facility and the facility itself must meet certification and licensing requirements. Initially, the facility must receive CMS certification as a nursing facility to provide services and receive Medicare and Medicare reimbursement. Most states, counties, and cities require business licenses to operate a facility. In addition, most staff must be certified or licensed. Certification or licensure is required for RNs, licensed practical nurses (LPNs), and nurse's aides. Allied health providers, such as physical therapists, occupational therapists, and speech therapists, used by the facility must be licensed. The podiatrist and other health caregivers must be licensed. The pharmacist must be licensed. Persons who provide laboratory and different types of diagnostic services must be licensed or certified. The dietician must be licensed. The head of dietary must be certified or meet specific requirements. The social services staff and activities staff must be licensed. In addition, persons such as those providing pest control must be licensed. In short, most persons employed directly or indirectly as subcontractors for services the facility provides, such as transportation to appointments, must be either certified or licensed. It is the administrator's task to ensure that all such persons are trained, certified, and licensed before providing healthcare through the facility; thus, the need for proper credentialing for everyone who provides care at any level, whether the facility directly employs them or not.

ASSISTANT ADMINISTRATOR/ADMINISTRATIVE ASSISTANT

An assistant administrator has line authority to represent the administrator, can make decisions on their behalf, and is usually assigned some area to oversee. An assistant administrator is often licensed as a nursing facility administrator. On the other hand, an administrative assistant has no line authority, cannot make decisions for the facility, and does not represent the administrator except in an information-gathering or information-processing manner. The administrative assistant is a staff position.

In the typical nursing facility of 100 beds, there tends not to be enough "organizational room" for an assistant administrator; 300 or more beds would call for an assistant administrator. The appointment of an assistant administrator and administrative assistant depends on the personality of the administrator.

As a rule, the administrator has several advisory persons or groups. The medical director and resident council often fit into this slot. Other consultants, such as the pharmacist, podiatrist, or dentist, and any other advisory committees might appear here. The administrator's office is responsible for keeping on file the original of several types of information, for example, reports of the state facility inspection teams, department reports, and other essential documents.

COMMON PITFALLS IN PRACTICE

- New administrators may not feel comfortable enough in all these areas from their first day in the office. Pick an area, improve yourself on it, and then move on to the next area. As time goes by, you will become a quick master of all the areas discussed here.
- Many administrators (new and old) operate without the surveyor in mind. Make *every* day a survey-ready day. This way, you are never blindsided by a wayward survey.

2.1.2 MEDICAL AND ALLIED HEALTH FUNCTIONS

Section Concepts

- *Knowing your medical staff and how they operate can make your job an easier one*
- *Finding providers and maintaining relationships is crucial for all types of medical providers—physicians, dentists, podiatrists, optometrists, pharmacists, laboratories, and others*

Consider as the Administrator...

- *Should you have a working relationship with all your medical staff?*
- *Will you need to correct your medical staff or educate them on regulatory concerns?*

NAB DOMAIN 1A9: MEDICAL DIRECTOR; 1C6: DENTAL AND ORAL CARE SERVICES; 1C7: HEALTHCARE PARTNERS AND CLINICAL PROVIDERS (E.G., MD/DO, NURSE PRACTITIONER, PSYCHIATRIST, PODIATRIST, DENTIS)

NAB DOMAIN 2B7: SCOPE OF PRACTICE AND LEGAL LIABILITY; 2C5: STAFF CERTIFICATION AND LICENSURE REQUIREMENTS

NAB DOMAIN 2C6: PROFESSIONAL DEVELOPMENT (E.G., MAINTENANCE OF CREDENTIALS, CONTINUING EDUCATION)

PATTERNS OF PHYSICIAN CARE

As a rule, the typical 100-bed facility does not require the services of a full-time medical director. The medical director is typically paid a contractual monthly fee to provide medical supervision. It is desirable to have the medical director be a member of the American Medical Directors Association (The Society for Post-Acute and Long-Term Care Medicine; https://paltc.org), which keeps the facility medical director updated with federal guidelines and current geriatric clinical practice.

THE OPEN MEDICAL STAFF

The predominant pattern for nursing facilities of approximately 100 to 200 beds is to allow any physician licensed to practice in the state to admit residents to the facility and provide their medical care while they reside there. No one can reside in a nursing facility without physician admitting orders and continuing physician supervision. This open medical staff arrangement is often made under an independent contractor agreement between the physician and the nursing facility. Under this pattern, the part-time medical director tries to ensure that the medical needs of the residents are met as they arise. The medical director often substitutes for the personal physician who fails to visit the patient on a timely basis or perform the annual physical required by federal or state regulations.

People prefer to talk with those of equal rank; thus, a vital role played by the medical director is to visit on a peer basis with physicians who are not meeting the actual care needs or making the required visits to patients in the facility. Because there is usually no organized medical staff, the medical director advises the facility administrator concerning the quality of its physician and nursing care and assists the director of nursing (DON) to ensure that a good quality of resident care is delivered. The medical director may or may not admit and care for residents in the facility but typically does so for some of them. This patient load has the functional value of allowing the medical director to be visible in the facility while seeing those patients. The medical director has specific duties to the facility under F841, including the implementation of resident care policies and the coordination of medical care in the facility. There is a significant focus on the medical director ensuring that medical care is given according to current standards of practice.

THE CLOSED MEDICAL STAFF

An organized medical staff is a closed group of physicians who provide all the primary care to the patients. A second model of medical direction is the *closed medical staff*. This structure means that only physicians who have been approved by the organized medical staff of the facility may admit or treat its patients. Initially, the board or governing body appoints one or more physicians to organize a medical staff, elect a medical director, and write bylaws to govern the medical care given in that facility, functioning much like an organized hospital medical staff.

Closed medical staffs are more feasible for larger facilities of perhaps 300 or more residents. In this situation, the physicians, usually five or six for a facility of 500 to 600 residents, divide care of the residents. Numerous variations are possible. A closed medical staff has several advantages. One physician can always be on duty (or immediate call) and attend to residents needing medical care whose assigned physician is not immediately available. Some or all of the physicians may work full-time, but most work part-time. Continuous care is thus available, and because the staff physicians have some economic dependency on the facility, the administrator has available the required services. With the open staff model, gaining conformity of medical services on a timely basis as mandated by the federal (and state) requirements can be a time-consuming task.

MEDICAL STAFF CONCERNS

New medical director requirements issued in the Federal Requirements and Guidelines to Surveyors increase the physicians' burden to take a more active role in the nursing facility. The cause for concern regarding this burden is related to the dwindling numbers of physicians in the United States. In 2003, 736,211 active doctors of medicine were professionally active and potentially available to serve as a medical director (Health, 2005). Today, that number is down to 535,601 (Statista, 2021), including all eligible physicians (MD and DO). Reasons for this net loss are outside the scope of this text; however, it has brought a focus on ways to replace those physicians with other highly qualified providers. One way to do this has been using nurse practitioners (NPs). Nursing facilities using NPs to provide care to their residents enjoy lower hospitalization rates, timelier responses to resident issues, timelier comprehensive assessments toward their MDSs, higher staff morale, and higher resident satisfaction rates (Mileski et al., 2020). Since the COVID-19 pandemic, we are seeing a push by NPs holding doctoral preparation (Doctor of Nursing Practice [DNP]) toward full practice rights instead of acting only as "mid-level" practitioners or "physician extenders." Many states have granted DNPs full practice authority (26 states and Washington, D.C., as of this writing). The number of states is expected to continue to grow as the physician crisis continues. This change is currently a congressional action item in many states.

Consider as the Administrator . . .

- *Would you rather have a closed or open medical staff for your own facility?*

COMMON PITFALLS IN PRACTICE
- A good relationship with your physicians and providers is essential to your success. Develop that relationship beginning on your first day in a facility.

2.1.3 DENTAL CARE

Dental care is a significant, often neglected, aspect of services delivered in the nursing facility. Local dentists typically do not own the portable equipment—costing $10,000 to $15,000 and more—needed to give dental care inside a nursing facility (Halter et al., 2017). Beyond a dental practitioner lacking equipment is perhaps the discomfort about functioning outside their office and the complex medical histories of patients whose medical records are a few inches thick. Finally, the dentist is reimbursed at approximately half the standard office fee, if that. Many Medicaid residents do not have dental benefits as a direct part of their state coverage. These states often have alternative ways to fund dental care for these residents; however, this process often takes months to get approved, all while the residents are suffering from dental issues.

The need for routine dental care does not change because one enters a nursing facility. Yet no one in the typical facility is trained in oral care. The mouth is not included in any significant way in the nursing curriculum, and physicians do not focus on the mouth.

Formerly, most current residents in nursing facilities had dentures. The introduction of fluoride and other dental care technologies after World War II has resulted in increasingly larger proportions of residents having teeth rather than dentures. It has been estimated that as few as 5% of residents arrive with dentures, thus presenting a full mouth of teeth needing care. For any residents who do have dentures, using an inexpensive denture label kit will simplify life for the residents and staff of the facility.

Solutions to difficulties surrounding dental care vary, but successful ones will likely include the appointment of a dental director in a structure similar to a part-time medical director, with a similar monthly retainer fee. This dentist will make monthly visits, perform needed care, and third-party bill payers for the provided care.

It is customary for the dental director to assist the facility in hiring a dental hygienist who will make monthly rounds on residents and train the nursing staff to observe and meet oral needs. One approach is to train oral-care aides; these are regularly employed nurse's aides who assume responsibility for maintaining residents' daily oral healthcare in the facility. Sadly, we see a decrease in this practice due to decreasing reimbursements (as this is an uncovered service) and reduced numbers of staff to become oral care aides overall.

Consider as the Administrator . . .

- *Is refusing to brush one's teeth or allowing one's teeth to be brushed a resident right?*

COMMON PITFALLS IN PRACTICE
- Dental care is often difficult to obtain for residents, especially in a small town. Finding providers to work with you is crucial to your success and your residents' health.

2.1.4 FOOT AND EYE CARE

There is a need for a *podiatrist*—a physician concerned with the care of the ankle and foot. Podiatric care includes clipping of toenails for diabetics and others and caring for ailments, such as corns, bunions, and other foot conditions.

Routine visiting providers, such as podiatrists, become more necessary as the nursing facility population becomes less able to leave the facility to make healthcare visits. The podiatrist may arrange their work area in a room or even a secluded hallway monthly and provide care to a large portion of the residents over a morning or afternoon. There are approximately 18,000 practicing podiatrists in the United States. However, despite the nursing facility being a major professional focus for a podiatrist because there are multiple clients in a single location, finding podiatrists willing to practice within the nursing facility due to reimbursement and regulatory issues can be complex.

Eye care needs are similar to those for teeth and feet. As the nursing facility population's mobility becomes more and more restricted, arrangements for periodic visits by a local optician are also a routine healthcare need. Many nursing facilities rely on large optical provider chains to see residents as travel office equipment costs are high for individual providers.

COMMON PITFALLS IN PRACTICE
- A lack of podiatry or eye care providers in your area is not a reason to neglect providing these services. Finding ways to provide these services often requires some innovation on the part of the administrator.

2.1.5 PHARMACEUTICAL SERVICES

The consulting or the facility pharmacist is responsible, at a minimum, for ensuring the following:

- All medications are available as ordered
- All medications are within expiration date and properly labeled and handled
- All reorders and stop orders are implemented
- Each resident's medications are reviewed monthly for possible adverse reactions and/or interactions
- Appropriate pharmacy policy and procedures are followed

Typically, medications are kept in locked medication rooms. Controlled substances are kept under double lock in medication rooms. Each medication room has very specific guidelines which must be conformed to by the facility.

The consulting pharmacist is responsible for reviewing the drug regimen, including observing medication passes and recording and reporting drug error rates and any other problems observed. Although the federal requirements require the consultant to report to the attending physician and the DON, the administrator would be wise to stipulate the need for the pharmacist also to keep them fully informed (Halter et al., 2017). Reporting is often accomplished with meetings throughout the day or during an exit meeting performed by the consulting pharmacist.

Besides receiving the required reports, the administrator can talk with the pharmacist, nurses, physicians, and residents to learn how the system functions and identify any success barriers. If drug reorders are not arriving on time, the nurses will be ready to share this information with the administrator. If the residents are not getting the medicines they believe they depend on, they will be quite willing to report it. But in this, as in every such case, both the resident and staff must be queried.

As more facilities utilize electronic medical records, we see massive changes in the administration and documentation of medications. The prudent use of such a system quickly allows the administrator and the DON to see missed medication doses, questionable use of PRN medications, and other means of quality improvement.

COMMON PITFALLS IN PRACTICE
- Many administrators assume that clinical staff will oversee the medication area. This is often correct; however, it is important to realize that you are still responsible for those employees. The pharmacy, the storage of drugs, and consultant reports are easily overlooked by otherwise overburdened clinical staff members.

2.1.6 PHYSICAL THERAPY/OCCUPATIONAL THERAPY/SPEECH THERAPY

Section Concepts
- *Therapy is a huge need in skilled nursing and often why residents seek out placement*
- *High-quality services are required to remain competitive in the market*

Consider as the Administrator . . .
- *Is the concern with providing therapy services under PDPM as important as it was during Resource Utilization Group (RUG) reimbursement?*

NAB DOMAIN 1A6: REHABILITATION AND RESTORATIVE PROGRAMS

A facility of 100 residents may or may not have in-house physical, occupational, and speech therapy services. There has been an ongoing debate over whether to employ therapy providers in-house or hire an outside therapy contractor. As it stands today, it seems that utilizing therapy contractors is more cost-effective since there is little or no "downtime" for outside physical therapists who also bill more effectively for reimbursement services provided. These contracted providers are there to provide therapy and are not expected to participate in other facility functions. These providers often have a director of rehabilitation whose main job is to interface with the facility instead of individual therapists doing so.

The number of physical therapists active in the United States is around 265,000 today. The number of occupational therapists is about 132,000. The number of speech therapists is approximately 120,000. The number of available therapists has increased over the past several years, likely due to higher Medicare reimbursement rates driving the need for these therapists.

These therapists' work is not fully accomplished unless the nursing and other staff are involved in helping the residents achieve the desired level of function in their activities of daily living and not merely during the therapy period. Thus, cooperation between the specialized rehabilitative staff and the regular staff who are doing "habilitative" therapy for the residents all the time is needed. This cooperation must be physical and reflected in the documentation provided by everyone—therapists, nurses, and aides alike. Inconsistent documentation can quickly affect the MDS and reimbursement.

A method of bridging the potential gap between the therapist's work and the nursing staff is to establish a restorative nursing program, usually undertaken by a nurse or highly qualified aide specialized in this area. The restorative team works directly with both the therapy staff and the nursing staff to ensure that efforts by the therapists are successfully integrated into the activities of daily living of the residents.

The administrator may want to ensure that a rehabilitative team approach is being implemented. This study can be accomplished by studying one or two residents' rehabilitation plans and then casually observing the extent to which the involved staff members are implementing them.

COMMON PITFALLS IN PRACTICE

- We often see "no therapy" on the weekends or for new admissions that occur late on Friday or the weekend itself. This is a common area of complaint and serious concern in customer service.

2.1.7 LABORATORY AND OTHER DIAGNOSTIC SERVICES

Section Concepts

- *Providing quality laboratory and diagnostic services is becoming more important today as the acuity of residents increases*

Consider as the Administrator . . .

- *How involved do you need to be in procuring diagnostic services and receiving timely results?*
- *Can the lack of timeliness of your lab cause regulatory concerns for your facility?*

NAB DOMAIN 1C5: DIAGNOSTIC SERVICES (E.G., RADIOLOGY, LAB SERVICES); 2B13: CONTRACTED SERVICES (E.G., ROLES, RESPONSIBILITIES, OVERSIGHT, BACKGROUND CHECKS)

A physician's order is required for laboratory and x-ray or other diagnostic services. These may be on the premises or contracted for in a local hospital or private office. Portable x-ray and additional diagnostic services are generally available on an on-call basis to provide services when a fall or other event occurs in which a resident might have been injured. Quick turnaround for these services is often imperative to avoid unnecessary hospitalizations for residents who have had a change in condition. Unnecessary admissions, and more specifically readmissions, are a significant quality improvement focus for facilities due to cost and resident health complications (Mileski et al., 2017).

With the advent of electronic health records and increased internet use in healthcare, we have seen a much faster turnaround on results for most laboratory tests. Today, a stat x-ray can be taken at the facility and sent digitally to a radiologist for reading. Results are often obtained within 15 minutes or less—faster than a trip to the hospital in an ambulance. X-ray staff can remain until the reading is complete in case there is a need for further imaging studies. Laboratory studies are still hampered by the transport and processing of the samples by qualified personnel. However, we are seeing increased use of real-time testing by laboratories that have equipment on-premises (or nearby) to provide quick turnarounds on lab results, which are delivered via an internet portal and often directly to the physician of record.

Time sensitivity is essential in the modern provision of care. Technology has enabled us to provide much better care in a much quicker fashion than we ever have before. We will continue to see tremendous changes as time passes in this area.

The U.S. Department of Health and Human Services passed a rule in 2014 that allows residents or their representatives direct access to laboratory reports. This ruling has resulted in more accessible reports but also higher scrutiny of them. The administrator must have a general understanding of reading a lab report, as families and residents will have questions regarding results. Try your hand at a few of these sites to help your knowledge along:

- Lab Tests Online. (2021). *Deciphering your lab report.* https://labtestsonline.org/articles/how-to-read-your-laboratory-report
- U.S. National Library of Medicine. (2021). *How to understand your lab results.* https://medlineplus.gov/lab-tests/how-to-understand-your-lab-results/
- Whitlock, J. (2020). *Understanding common blood tests and what they mean.* https://www.verywellhealth.com/understanding-common-blood-tests-and-what-they-mean-3156935

COMMON PITFALLS IN PRACTICE
- Lab services are often considered to be an "additional service" offered by the facility. This is incorrect; they are a *crucial and required* service in the facility as this information can be used for treating acute issues for your residents instead of sending them to the hospital for an inappropriate visit.

Consider as the Administrator . . .

- *If you had your choice, would you want to offer in-house lab services in your facility?*

2.1.8 NURSING SERVICES

Section Concepts

- *Nursing is the largest department of the facility, and the one that requires the greatest amount of administrator oversight*
- *The number of areas included under nursing are voluminous, and compliance in each one is necessary for success*

Consider as the Administrator . . .

- *Do you need to have clinical acumen as the administrator? Or can you simply allow the nurses to operate without your understanding of what they do?*

NAB DOMAIN 1A: QUALITY OF CARE; 1B: QUALITY OF LIFE

The nursing service has, among others, the following responsibilities:

- Providing nursing care to residents as ordered by the physician
- Completing the MDS, any required protocols triggered by the MDS, and creating, implementing, and updating the comprehensive plan of care
- Administering medications to the residents
- Keeping patient records
- Monitoring residents for changes in condition and notifying the responsible physician; in short, serving as the physician's eyes and ears on a 24-hour basis
- Achieving optimal quality of care and quality of life for residents
- Ensuring that every resident is functioning at the highest possible level
- Playing a coordinating role with other staff (e.g., ensuring that planned physical therapy, activities, physician office visits, and the like take place)

In short, nursing is involved in a myriad of activities and occurrences. These activities and occurrences include assessments; wound care; starting IVs; tube feeding; oxygen therapy; range of motion; toileting; feeding; counseling; friendship; comfort; ambulation; transfer; assistance with the activities of daily living; changing briefs and sheets; turning patients; the use of assistive devices; bathing; toileting; dressing; ambulating; cleaning up spills; washing hands; room tidiness; ice water; hospice; discharge planning; recruiting; training; disciplining; evaluating staff; interfacing with the other departments; observing universal precautions; interfacing with physicians, pharmacists, and numerous other healthcare professionals; counseling; reassuring families and significant others; coping with volunteers; cooperating with the police and the fire department; doing infection control; working short; conducting in-services; charting, charting, charting; bowel and bladder programs; fire safety;

disaster preparedness; answering call bells; checking on the residents hundreds of times each day; participating in lengthy care planning sessions; afternoon and evening snacks; getting food substitutes from dietary; settling battles among residents; coping with Alzheimer's and other extensive dementias; learned helplessness; death and dying; emergencies; morticians; endless admissions; lost clothing, lost teeth, lost jewelry; running out of bed pads; hazardous waste rules; inspectors from everywhere for days at a time; electrical outages; failing equipment; room transfers; roommate dissatisfaction; refusal to eat; broken bed rails; restraint issues; missing oxygen tank wrenches; snippy staff; arrogant physicians; dissatisfied residents; troublesome visitors; unresponsive pressure injuries; unresponsive medical directors; the on-call nurse or physician who does not return calls for 45 minutes; overflowing linen bins; broken wheelchairs; epidemics among staff and residents; out-of-uniform staff; missing name tags; wandering patients; pool (contract) personnel who do not know or do not care; misplaced charts or files; emergency carts that were used and not restocked; constant phone calls; late lab reports; physicians who do not sign orders or visit on a timely basis; global pandemics—and this is only the tip of the iceberg. Nursing is the quintessential embodiment of the reality that if it can happen, it will.

With this myriad of duties, it is not surprising that some things do not get done as acceptably as desired. As one might assume, although most nursing duties are successfully carried out, success in achieving acceptable levels in performing comprehensive assessments and care plan documentation remains problematic. Additionally, qualified personnel's accuracy of assessments has always been a problematic area when it comes to compliance. The DON, by most state regulations, is required to be an RN. State nursing board regulations do generally not allow an LPN to supervise RNs or perform assessments requiring RN-level training. A large portion of federal regulations, F635 through F646, F655 through F661, F675 through F680, F684 through F700, and F725 through F732 are all areas that are focused on nursing services. There are also many other regulations that are included in other areas with a nursing focus. The necessity for high-quality nursing services to be provided is clear.

NAB DOMAIN 1A1: MEDICAL AND NURSING CARE PRACTICES

The nursing profession is one that is highly concerned with ethical principles and appropriate actions by those who practice. This is very similar to what we saw as expected by administrators in Part 1. In fact, the code of ethics for nurses is an amazingly detailed document that is produced by the American Nurses Association (ANA) and serves as a compass for the actions of nurses in the profession.

The ANA Code of Ethics is available here: https://www.nursingworld.org/coe-view-only

Elopement

NAB DOMAIN 1B4: CARE RECIPIENT SAFETY (E.G., FALL PREVENTION, ELOPEMENT PREVENTION, ADVERSE EVENTS); 2B7: SCOPE OF PRACTICE AND LEGAL LIABILITY

Elopement is defined as "when a resident who is cognitively, physically, mentally, emotionally, and/or chemically impaired wanders away, walks away, runs away, escapes, or otherwise leaves a caregiving facility or environment unsupervised, unnoticed, and/or prior to their scheduled discharge" (National Institute for Elopement Prevention and Resolution, 2021). Another term sometimes used is *critical wandering*, which refers to any person with dementia who wanders away from their caregiver or controlled environment (Algase et al., 2007). Elopement or wandering is of particular importance to nurses caring for patients with Alzheimer's disease or dementia. It is estimated that more than 60% of people with Alzheimer's will wander at some point during the course of the disease (Alzheimer's Association, 2021).

The following are possible causes of wandering in older adult patients:

- Memory loss
- Physical needs (e.g., toileting, hunger)
- Social needs, searching for friends or family
- Insomnia
- Side effects from medication
- Disorientation, unfamiliar surroundings
- Attempting to fulfill former habits or obligations

Interventions to prevent wandering include the following:

- Consult family members to determine if there is a history of patient wandering
- Orient patient to unit and surroundings
- Secure the unit and facility
- Be watchful and vigilant of patients with dementia and Alzheimer's
- Determine whether wandering represents unmet needs
- Provide diversional activities
- Consider environmental changes (e.g., exit doors positioned near staff work areas, painting exit doors the same color as surrounding walls)
- Consider technological approaches, for example, alarm bracelets, facility-wandering systems

Elopement prevention is critical to good care. Once an elopement occurs, the facility must notify all appropriate local authorities and possible sources of help in locating the resident. An elopement usually involves a report to (and visit from) state regulatory as well. Typically, both the local fire department and police department will combine to mount an effective search.

Subacute Care Nursing (Today's Norm)

When nursing facilities admit subacute care patients, nurses must be proficient in tasks often considered to be within the expertise of hospital nurses. High-tech nursing skills are expected by stakeholders today, especially on skilled nursing units. Among these skills are the administration of IV medications through IV ports, implanted ports, or midline catheters; advanced wound care; administration of high-level antibiotics; enteral/parenteral feeding; nasopharyngeal aspiration; tracheostomy aspiration; insertion and replacement of suprapubic catheters; and a myriad of other services that are considered out of the scope of the nursing facility a mere 10 years ago.

NAB DOMAIN 1B12: PAIN MANAGEMENT

Pain management is a very significant area of focus today for the facility, as many residents are in some type of pain on admission or throughout their stay. Pain management requires excellent documentation and a large degree of nursing judgment. Pain management is a very large area of focus by surveyors today, as a lack of pain management leads to a decreased quality of life for our residents and many other complications that may otherwise be eliminated if pain were being adequately managed.

Some basic principles of pain management include the following:

- Pain is entirely subjective for each resident.
- Each resident has a different pain threshold/tolerance. Therefore, the "same pain" is different for everyone who experiences it.
- Pain is often expressed by facial expression, body habitus, or other means other than verbalization.
- Residents often have multiple sources of pain based on multiple chronic disease processes occurring simultaneously.
- Long-term care residents are at an increased risk for drug interactions because of their health status and medication usage.
- Pain is a common symptom as a resident nears the end of life, as many chronic and age-related conditions have pain associated with them.
- The resident's self-report of pain is the single most reliable indicator of pain. The gold standard measure of pain used by most hospitals and nursing facilities is to ask the resident how much pain is being felt at that moment on a scale of 1 to 10, with 1 being *no pain* and 10 being *unbearable pain*. There are also specific evidence-based pain scales available for nonverbal residents for staff to use that allow consistent and quantified judgment of pain.
- All long-term care staff and residents' families share in the role of pain management.
- Pain often increases from zero to an intolerable level when care is being provided to residents.
- Everyone caring for the resident must know to recognize and report pain.

It is essential to understand that many types of pain are described in the literature. Types or categories of pain often are specific to certain disease processes. For example, cancer pain is classified as somatic, visceral, and neuropathic (Bast et al., 2017). There is also acute pain, chronic pain, nerve pain, musculoskeletal pain, central pain, diabetic pain, regional pain, and a myriad of others to confound and make treatment and identification difficult overall. When considering pain in general, it is important to understand basic principles surrounding it, how to simply identify it, and what to do about it once you do.

Treatment of Pain

F697, §483.25(k), Pain Management—Pain Management is found and is commonly cited in facilities. It is common to "undertreat" pain in all healthcare settings, not just nursing facilities. Key elements of noncompliance in this area include failing to provide pain management to a resident experiencing pain, providing pain management at a level less than the current standard of practice, or not providing pain management per the resident's care plan. There is seemingly minor information in the literature on why this noncompliance occurs—or the resulting undertreatment of pain.

Rules of Thumb, Commonsense Rules

- Lowest dose, simplest route.
- Simplest agent to ameliorate the pain. If this fails, only then seek to add additional agents.
- Stay ahead of the pain. It is easier to stay out of pain than to get out of pain. Using long-acting medications or continual dosing with PRN medications for breakthrough pain is often the most effective method of pain control.

As the acuity of residents increases with time, the necessity for pain management will increase as well. Ensuring nursing staff is adequately prepared and educated on pain management, pain assessment, and appropriate pharmacology is crucial to appropriate resident care.

AVERAGE NURSING HOURS PER RESIDENT DAY

NAB DOMAIN 1A5: ACTIVITIES OF DAILY LIVING (ADLs) AND INSTRUMENTAL ACTIVITIES OF DAILY LIVING (IADLs); 2C4: ORGANIZATIONAL STAFFING REQUIREMENTS AND REPORTING (E.G., PBJ)

Federal regulations are somewhat nebulous in this area, as each facility has different needs. Some facilities provide services to a very subacute population; others serve niche markets, such as ventilator units, dementia-specific care units, behavior units, or other various needs. Each of these niches does not require the same level of staffing; as such, it is not necessarily defined by federal regulation. Nursing facilities must provide 24-hour licensed nursing services that are sufficient to meet the nursing needs of each of its residents. Some states (such as California) have specific requirements for the number of nursing hours per day. Specific regulations such as these have backfired to a certain degree, as facilities may not need that number of staff, or they are not able to find that number of staff to hire to meet the regulatory requirement. Nursing staff typically account for 70% or more of all nursing facility employees.

Quality of Resident Life

There are unwritten dimensions to caring performed by the nursing service. It is not possible, and perhaps not desirable, federal efforts notwithstanding, to set them all down, for many nursing acts that increase the quality of life cannot be fully spelled out in policy statements. The quality of life enjoyed is directly proportional to the quality of the effort given by the nursing staff.

Dr. William Thomas's Eden Alternative movement should cause alarm bells to sound. Dr. Thomas observes that most nursing facility resources are spent on the war against disease when the real need is to address loneliness, helplessness, and boredom. The typical current nursing facility is the creation of government regulations founded on a hospital model. Edenizing is the process of combining nature, hope, and nursing facilities. A nursing facility can be more nearly a human habitat when it is "Edenized," that is, when it has birds, cats, dogs, fish, rabbits, chickens, children, plants, and gardens to walk in. The Eden concept emphasizes intergenerational contact (Thomas, 1996).

More recently, efforts have been made to deinstitutionalize the nursing facility setting by replacing long halls with small clusters in which 8 to 10 residents can form a community. In this design, a floor of a building might be divided into four distinct living areas or clusters, with each area having a dining and recreation area. In this way, residents feel they are living in small face-to-face communities with the opportunity to know and interact in ways difficult to achieve in the traditional nursing facility with long hallways of 30 to 40 residents and centralized nursing stations. This design has become known as the *Green House approach* (Cohen et al., 2016).

NURSE AVAILABILITY

Although there seems to be a chronic shortage of good nurses, the total number of active RNs increased from 1.2 million in 1980 to more than 2.98 million in 2020 (U.S. Bureau of Labor Statistics, 2021). Of these, 9.34% of nurses work in nursing care facilities, 11.35% in home health, 30.9% in acute care, and the rest in various other settings.

We see numbers of LPN/LVNs in the workplace as well. As of 2020, there are more than 676,000 in the workplace (U.S. Bureau of Labor Statistics, 2021). Of these, 13.02% of licensed practical/vocational nurses work in nursing care facilities, 5.65% in home health, 5.66% in continuing care retirement communities and assisted living, and the rest in various other settings.

INCREASING DEPENDENCE ON THE NURSING ASSISTANTS

Despite increasing numbers of nurses in the workforce, most nursing facilities today find themselves at a loss to fill all necessary positions with RN or LVN/LPN staff. These increasing numbers are too small to fill the need for more qualified nursing staff to provide direct care due to the onslaught of baby boomers entering the care system. As a result, we find more staff are needed to "extend" the ability of nurses to provide care to residents, and we are doing this through the use of nursing assistants.

The nursing facility population is heavily dependent on the nursing staff, especially the nursing assistants. The five essential activities of daily living are as follows:

1. Eating
2. Dressing
3. Toileting
4. Bathing
5. Transferring (e.g., from bed to chair or bed to toilet)

These areas are often highly time-consuming for nurses to perform, which takes away from their ability to provide care elsewhere in the facility. The use of certified nursing assistants can fill this area of necessary care to residents, freeing nurses to prioritize their time for work requiring licensed nursing care (such as medication passes, treatments, and assessments).

Consider as the Administrator . . .

- *If faced with a choice, would you rather have more RNs and fewer nurse's aides or more aides and fewer RNs?*

Organizational Interdependencies

Organizational interdependencies exist between nursing and virtually every other area within the facility. Nursing is dependent on dietary, housekeeping, laundry, maintenance, the business office, the social worker, and the allied health professionals, to mention a few examples. For nursing to do its tasks properly, nearly every other department and functional area within the organization must also be performing its tasks. No department in the facility can exist or be successful without the successful operation of the others. There must be synchrony among all departments for a facility to operate well.

Staffing

 NAB DOMAIN 2A: FINANCIAL MANAGEMENT; 2C4: ORGANIZATIONAL STAFFING REQUIREMENTS AND REPORTING (E.G., PBJ)

Two or three nursing shifts, 24 hours a day, 365 days a year, offer a staffing challenge. The proportional ratios among RNs, LPNs, aides, and even geriatric NPs will vary with the staffing philosophy of the facility administrators and the patient profile. As acuity level increases in many facilities, the proportion of professionally trained nurses increases. Permanently assigning nurses and nursing assistants to residents can lead to improved care by enabling holistic care and becoming personally involved in and vested in their duties. Research has demonstrated that this permanent (or consistent) assignment also resulted in happier and more empowered staff and higher resident satisfaction ratings with fewer complications for residents. However, in practice, permanent assignment is difficult to enact due to turnover, callouts, and other staffing concerns outside the administrator's control.

Conversely, there is also much discussion that rotating staff is healthier for the employee and the work environment. Changing assignments seems to help with staff burnout, dealing with the same problematic concerns permanently for staff, decreasing the potential for staff-to-resident abuse, callouts, turnover, and a myriad of other situations. There is much more research to support the consistent assignment versus the empirical data to support constant change.

Administrative Observations

Just as the DON is expected to make daily resident rounds, the administrator may emulate nursing. The administrator must decide to what extent they wish to receive daily reports on admissions, discharges, changes in resident conditions, accidents, incidents, transfers, deaths, and the like as part of their information system. The reports are not a satisfactory substitute for the administrator's observation, as they learn by wandering around and observing what is taking place in the facility. Also, one must be on the scene to be the coach, energizer, and communicator of one's vision for the facility.

COMMON PITFALLS IN PRACTICE

- Many new administrators do not place enough focus on nursing and often are left in the dark as to what is occurring within the department. Take part in clinical meetings, Medicare meetings, care plans, and other actions so you have a clear understanding of what is happening in your facility.
- A clear focus needs to be placed on employee satisfaction for nursing staff. Know your staff, show them you appreciate them.
- The night shift needs to know the administrator as much as the day shift. Your facility is mainly staffed by nursing employees at night. Make the time to get to know them and their work quality.

2.1.9 THE BUSINESS OFFICE

Section Concepts

- *The business office and medical records work in concert with each other to ensure documentation is correct for billing*
- *The business office has many different functions in the facility*

Consider as the Administrator . . .

- *How much of a business office manager do you need to be?*
- *How important is it to facility success that you have an efficiently and effectively operating business office?*

NAB DOMAIN 2A: FINANCIAL MANAGEMENT

In a typical 100-bed facility, one full-time and often an additional part-time employee staff the business office. Briefly, the business office:

- Keeps financial records
- Manages accounts receivable and accounts payable
- Maintains vendor files
- Assists in monitoring the budget

- Prepares the payroll
- Acts as the human resources department
- Keeps required records and makes financial reports
- Deals with third-party payers, Medicare, Medicaid, and others
- Safeguards and controls resident funds
- Often acts as a receptionist and answers the telephone

KEY ROLE FOR THE BUSINESS OFFICE: CENTERS FOR MEDICARE & MEDICAID SERVICES ACCURACY

Neither the MDS coordinator nor the team members who sign their portions of the MDS are necessarily business/reimbursement-oriented. As the CMS now bases Medicare and Medicaid payments on the boxes checked on the MDS, nearly two thirds of the total revenue of the average nursing facility depends on which boxes are checked. This process is essential as scores from the six categories of the case-mix adjusted components for PDPM (physical therapy, occupational therapy, speech therapy, nontherapy ancillaries, nursing) set reimbursement. The business office must regard the MDS scores as a matter for complete understanding and careful attention to correctness of resident assessments for business purposes, just as the nursing, social services, dietary, and other staff must master the MDS to ensure competent resident care.

Receptionist, Secretary, and Advisory Functions

In the typical 100-bed facility, the bookkeeping, secretarial, clerical, and reception functions are variously combined. Generally, the facility secretary works in the administrator's office, in an area shared with the receptionist/telephone operator/manager. The receptionist needs to know all the employee application procedures if applicants are to feel welcome. The receptionist needs to be in the communication loop. The receptionist is key to satisfaction and relationships. It is an ugly scene if relatives visit at 11:00 a.m. and the receptionist cheerily asks, "Are you here to see Uncle Don?" and the family informs her that he died an hour earlier. "Oh, I'm sorry, I didn't know." Often, due to the size of facilities, reimbursement, and other factors, the use of receptionists or secretaries is not perceived. It is not uncommon for these functions to be absorbed by business office staff.

The Facility's Window to the World

The business office, with its several functions, becomes the facility's window to the world. First telephone contacts are typically received here; many first-time visitors are served here. First impressions always count. If the person contacting the facility by phone or in-person receives a positive impression, much has been gained. This "front office" is responsible for the facility's customers: first-time callers, family members, friends, surveyors, physicians, job applicants, emergency medical services (EMS) team members, delivery persons, and volunteers, to mention a few. The front office staff is a valuable marketing tool. Phones must be answered promptly;

visitors must feel that their needs are important and immediately addressed. These are vital and complicated tasks that must be completed successfully if the facility is to thrive. Protocols for answering phones, receiving visitors, and attending to the needs of whoever walks through the front door are an important part of facility policies. Answering phones via a "three-ring" protocol is not an uncommon expectation in the facility (i.e., the phone is answered professionally in no more than three rings).

2.1.10 MEDICAL RECORDS

Section Concepts

- *The facility tends to operate around the information that medical records collect and attend to.*
- *Electronic records are slowly taking over the industry, and medical records will become an even more important function in the facility as we move forward.*

NAB DOMAIN 1A8: CLINICAL AND MEDICAL RECORDS AND DOCUMENTATION REQUIREMENTS (E.G., STORAGE, RETENTION, DESTRUCTION)

A full-time employee must, by federal requirements, be assigned to keep the medical record service up to date. Usually, this function falls to a ward clerk or other staff member assigned to specific areas of the facility. We have seen some change in this area as more and more facilities are moving to electronic health records from paper ones. Facilities are required to keep a high volume of records. Among the most important is the medical record. If medical records are not complete and current, federal and state inspectors will typically issue a directive to correct the condition within a specified period. Increasingly, medical records compliance requires a full-time person, often with appropriate credentials, to work with medical records. These credentials may include a Registered Health Information Technician or Registered Health Information Administrator—both credentials administered by the American Health Information Management Association. Put quite simply—documentation matters. The better the facility's documentation, the fewer the citations, the lesser the risk, and the easier the quality improvement.

MEDICAL RECORDS GOING FORWARD

Despite many facilities today still adhering to paper records where possible, much of what we do in the facility must be done electronically. Soon, facilities will be left with no choice but to go entirely electronic. These electronic records will soon mimic what we would see in acute care with nurses' notes and physicians' notes, all lab work, full radiographs, and the potential for integration with records from previous facilities or hospital visits. This technology will allow for a much better picture and full details on which decisions can be made surrounding the resident's care.

COMMON PITFALLS IN PRACTICE

- Effective administrators are very well versed in business office and medical records functions, knowing a facility cannot be successful without either center being efficiently or ethically run.

2.1.11 DIETARY DEPARTMENT

Section Concepts

- *The dietary department has very essential functions in the health of the resident; however, it is also a center of satisfaction and quality experience for the resident*

Consider as the Administrator . . .

- *Can you successfully run a facility with bad food?*
- *How much a part of life and dignity is good food served well?*

NAB DOMAIN 1A4: NUTRITION AND HYDRATION (E.G., SPECIALIZED DIETS); 1B15: FOODSERVICE (E.G., CHOICE AND MENU PLANNING, DIETARY MANAGEMENT, FOOD STORAGE AND HANDLING, DINING SERVICES)

THE FOOD STANDARD

Food is an essential ingredient in the quality of resident life. Satisfaction with the facility is as often influenced as much by the food as by the quality of nursing care. Some families feel that they may not have enough medical background to judge the adequacy of nursing care, but most do consider themselves experts in the matter of food. Tasty food is important to a satisfactory quality of life. Hospital food, eaten for a relatively short time, can be tolerated. Nursing facility food, consumed for extended periods, sometimes forever, is subject to much greater scrutiny by residents and their families/significant others.

MENU CYCLE

Typically, a set of menus is designed to cover a period of perhaps 4 weeks during which major items on the menu are not repeated. Thus, over a year, the same menu cycle will repeat 12 times. Seasonal variations can help minimize repetition. A registered dietician reviews these menus as part of their consulting work with the facility in most cases. Many administrators also have specific resident food councils to meet surrounding menu approval to reduce complaints and concerns.

The Food Standard: Can It Be Met?

The dietary manager in the typical nursing facility (one with 70% Medicaid, 15% Medicare, 10% private pay, and 5% other) is permitted to spend about $4.50 to $6.00+ per day for raw food costs. This figure is often referred to as a PPD (per patient day), and nearly everything in a typical facility is budgeted using a PPD multiplier. The typical life care community (with almost 100% private pay) spends $14.00+ per day for raw food costs. The daily cost of raw food per patient can be calculated as:

Per resident day cost × Census = Total food cost (per)

Food budget PPD: $4.50
Census: 100
Days in a month: 30
Days in a year: 365
$4.50 × 100 = $450 per day
$4.50 × 100 × 30 = $13,500 per month
$4.50 × 100 × 365 = $164,250 per year

FOOD INVENTORY

NAB DOMAIN 2A9: SUPPLY-CHAIN MANAGEMENT (E.G., INVENTORY CONTROL)

The administrator must closely monitor food inventory; however, this is delegated to the dietary/food service manager who is accountable for inventory. Computer software is available, allowing a perpetual inventory showing the quantity of each item of food and supplies is on hand. However, there is a need for physical observation of this inventory. Running out of food, supplies, or the means to prepare food is incomprehensible.

Consider as the Administrator . . .

- *What would be your policy about providing meals to employees? Would you provide meals free, at a reduced cost, or for actual cost?*

Food Production

A nearly infinite range of choices is available, ranging from cooking and serving all items for each meal to precooking some items that are then chilled or frozen (par-cooking) to purchasing precooked food, which is then assembled and served. Each facility's choices will be influenced by the cost-effectiveness of the combinations of methods chosen. There are tradeoffs among each of the options. Purchasing precooked food that is assembled and served can be the most expensive method and often leaves the facility with too little control over food additives such as the excessive salt often used in such prepackaged foods. However, for a pureed diet, this added expense is usually offset by resident satisfaction. There are prepared pureed dietary foods available that look and taste like the actual food item (pureed corn looks like corn, hamburger looks like a hamburger patty) instead of a scoop of the food that was run through a food processor.

Food Intake, Therapeutic Diets

Specialized Diets

Food intake and plate waste must be documented for each resident. The physician determines whether the resident receives a regular diet or a special/therapeutic diet. As choosing which food to eat and how much to eat is one of the few choices left to residents, therapeutic diets may lead to residents refusing to eat the food prescribed. Types of therapeutic diets include the following:

- High fiber or low fiber
- Dietetic diets with a prescribed balance among fats, proteins, carbohydrates, and sugar substitutes
- High carbohydrate or low carbohydrate
- Clear or full liquid
- Pureed or mechanical soft

Although the nation's nursing facilities maintain good nutritional status for residents a fair share of the time, we still see many citations written for F800 through F814. Many reasons could be postulated for this; however, it does appear that a more realistic raw-food budget for the nation's facilities would help with some of these concerns.

BASIC PRINCIPLES OF NUTRITION

NAB DOMAIN 1A4: NUTRITION AND HYDRATION (E.G., SPECIALIZED DIETS); 1B15: FOODSERVICE (E.G., CHOICE AND MENU PLANNING, DIETARY MANAGEMENT, FOOD STORAGE AND HANDLING, DINING SERVICES)

The Well-Balanced Diet

The dietary choices in the nursing facility setting must meet several standards. The U.S. Department of Health and Human Services and the U.S. Department of Agriculture publish guidelines specifying such goals as sufficient fruits and vegetables in adequate variety each day; 3 or more ounces of whole-grain products; 3 cups daily of fat-free milk or equivalent; and similar requirements. The daily menu for each resident must be prescribed by the resident's attending physician in consultation with the registered dietitian hired by the facility.

NUTRITIONAL ASSESSMENT

Aging Changes

Aging is characterized by the loss of some body cells and reduced metabolism in others. These conditions cause loss of bodily function and changes in body composition. Adipose tissue stores usually increase with age, and they centralize, leaving a "large belly" appearance in older adults. Lean body mass and bone mineral contents typically decrease with age.

A person's protein, vitamin, and mineral requirements usually remain the same as they age, whereas the caloric needs of older adults decrease. Decreased activity may lower energy requirements by about 200 calories per day for men and women aged 51 to 75 years, 400 calories per day for women older than 75 years, and 500 calories per day for men older than 75 years.

Other physiological changes that can affect nutrition in an older adult patient include the following:

- Decreased renal function, causing greater susceptibility to dehydration and formation of renal calculi
- Loss of calcium and nitrogen (in patients who are not ambulatory)
- Decreased enzyme activity and gastric secretions
- Decreased salivary flow and a diminished sense of taste, reducing the appetite and increasing consumption of sweet and spicy foods
- Decreased intestinal motility

Resident History

Disabilities, chronic diseases, and surgical procedures (e.g., gastrectomy) commonly affect a resident's nutritional status; therefore, they should be appropriately recorded in the resident history. Drugs or substances taken by the resident for a medical condition may also affect nutritional requirements. For example, mineral oil, which many older adults use to correct constipation, may impair gastrointestinal absorption of vitamin A.

Some common conditions found in older adults can affect nutritional status by limiting the resident's mobility. These disorders include degenerative joint disease, paralysis, and impaired vision (from cataracts, glaucoma, or macular degeneration).

Gastrointestinal complaints, especially constipation and stool incontinence, commonly occur in older patients. A decrease in intestinal motility characteristically accompanies aging. Constipation may also be related to poor dietary intake, physical inactivity, or emotional stress. Constipation may also occur as a side effect of certain drugs. Laxatives, another substance commonly used by older adult patients, cause rapid food transport through the gastrointestinal tract and subsequent decreased periods of digestion and absorption.

Measures used to assess a patient's nutritional status include the following:

- Common sense
- Consideration of factors that place any resident at nutritional risk
- Dietary history
- Your objective data (keeping their limitations in mind)
- Monitoring the resident's intake

The dietary department's influence extends more than 24 hours a day. The availability of bedtime snacks, or midnight snacks for insomniac residents, is as much a part of the facility's ambiance as the availability of continuous nursing services. This department is heavily interactive with nursing services (e.g., refreshments at social activities) and most other departments. The food service depends on other departments such as laundry for linens and maintenance to keep the kitchen functioning. Some facilities utilize outside vendor contracts for food service. In this situation, the head of dietary may be an employee of the food service contractor rather than the facility.

The administrator can monitor food services in several ways. Daily random walks through the kitchen, eating with residents in the dining hall, and assisting with feeding in resident rooms and dining rooms (if suitably qualified) are productive ways to monitor food services. Getting and eating a tray under circumstances similar to those experienced by the resident can be very enlightening.

The dietary department has a vast array of critical functions, including achieving the nutritional diet prescribed by the physician and developed by the registered dietitian, ensuring tasty food at the right temperature, doing nutritional assessments, monitoring weight gains and losses, monitoring input and output, providing food substitutes as requested, catering for facility functions and its many visiting groups, and maintaining the dietary area according to cleanliness standards.

Consider as the Administrator . . .

- *Very few residents may choose to eat a "well-balanced diet" . . . is this okay?*

Typically, the dietary department hires cooks, cook's helpers, and dietary aides. Generally, dietary aides deliver food to the hallways or living areas. The nurse's aides distribute the food, monitor its consumption, and pick up the trays at the end of the meal. Suppose a facility does not employ a registered dietitian. In that case, it must contract with a registered dietitian who assists and directs the planning and use of menus and recipes, monitoring nutrition-related resident problems, and developing dietary policies. This person also makes recommendations for the operations of the kitchen.

Recent culture changes have led to more user-friendly dietary interactions for residents. Before typically breakfast was served about 8:00 a.m., lunch at or near noon, and supper about 5:30 p.m. Few residents appreciate conforming their lives to such an institutional regimen. More recently, facilities are moving to a five-meal schedule with a continental breakfast around 7:30 a.m., a substantial brunch around 11:00 a.m., a snack of beverages and high-calorie items served around 2:00 p.m., and a regular dinner around 6:00 p.m., followed by a late evening snack. Menu cycles are essential to extended-stay residents. While a hospital and a hotel generally have a 1-week menu cycle before the same foods are served again, it is better not to repeat the same menu for perhaps a month in the nursing facility and tie foods to the seasons. Eating is one of the most important pleasures available to residents.

FOOD SAFETY

NAB DOMAIN 1B15: FOODSERVICE (E.G., CHOICE AND MENU PLANNING, DIETARY MANAGEMENT, FOOD STORAGE AND HANDLING, DINING SERVICES)

Numerous standards apply to food sanitation and safety. In addition to national food safety standards, the local health department sanitarian will inspect the facility and typically give the facility a score. Residents and families pay special attention to the facility sanitation score. Any score below 97% or 98% is cause for concern.

While the typical administrator will keep all food safety standards in mind, improved awareness comes from routinely carrying and using a food thermometer to check for items such as the following:

- Are foods being cooked to the correct internal temperature: 165°F for poultry; 160°F for pork and ground meat; and 145°F for lamb, veal, and beef?
- Are food holding temperature standards being achieved: are cold foods kept below 40°F and hot foods above 140°F? (Temperatures between 40°F and 140°F allow undesirable bacteria to thrive.)
- Are leftover foods being quick-cooled and refrigerated within 2 hours?
- Are the refrigerators kept no warmer than 40°F?
- Are the freezers maintaining the food at 0°F or lower?
- Are the kitchen employees leaving washed items on racks to air dry, so water does not pool? (Wiping can cause cross-contamination.)
- Do steam tables maintain hot foods at 140°F or above?
- Steam tables are not to be used for warming food.
- Cold tables must maintain food at 45°F or lower and should not be used to refrigerate food.

Presentation

Appetite depends on presentation as well as tastiness. Facilities must strive to present food to residents in the same manner as a good restaurant. Color and texture matter. Temperature matters. Hot food hot and cold food cold are expected at the point of service. The days of simply dropping off a tray of food in front of a resident are long gone. Today, many facilities have a fine dining service at each meal or at least once a day where fine china and glassware are used. Many newer facilities have dining rooms that are set up to mimic fine restaurants or even favorite restaurants in the town where the facility is located. Meal service is more than eating. Meals are a social occasion, an activity, and a place where adults meet for interaction.

COMMON PITFALLS IN PRACTICE

- Many complaints come because of meals, yet many administrators have never tasted the food being served from their kitchens. Taste the food (even the pureed). Find out if it is of a high-enough quality. When you know this, you can better address food-quality concerns.
- Many consider eating one of the few luxuries of life left for our residents. Be a part of the dining process. Circulate among the residents, talk with them, and find out suggestions or ways to improve the dining process.

2.1.12 SOCIAL SERVICES AND ADMISSIONS

Section Concepts

- *Admissions is a very detailed process as it is steeped in regulation*
- *Social services is often leaned on as the route for communicating with administration*
- *Both of these areas are highly concerned with customer service*

Consider as the Administrator . . .

- *How involved should you, as the administrator, be in admissions?*
- *Can the administrator act as a social worker, or should this be left to the professionals instead?*

ADMISSIONS

NAB DOMAIN 1A11: TRANSITION OF CARE (E.G., ADMISSION, MOVE-IN, TRANSFER, DISCHARGE, AND MOVE-OUT); 1B8: CARE RECIPIENT (AND REPRESENTATIVE) SATISFACTION; 1B16: SOCIAL SERVICES PROGRAMS

In states where first-come first-served rules do not exist, the person or persons in charge of admissions influence the facility's case mix. Often a person with a social work background is employed as the admissions coordinator. On certain occasions, one employee heads both admissions and social work. However, it is more common for one person to provide oversight for admissions and marketing and the social worker to provide separate duties to the facility. Sometimes, the DON does admissions.

In most cases, the admissions process is shared jointly by the DON and the admissions director. Admissions profoundly affect the facility's workload, atmosphere, and ability to achieve its goals and provide appropriate care. Who is admitted from where and with what care needs and reimbursement rates are the lifeblood of the facility.

The admissions person(s) must find, screen, process, facilitate, and manage case mix, keeping financial, light versus heavy care, and goodwill of the hospital discharge planners, managed care, or other source elements all balanced. The admissions person(s) are significant promoters of the facility, marketing to all the relevant world (e.g., hospital discharge planners, the local physicians, third-party payers, managed care organizations, workers' compensation insurance, insurance companies, and the like). Outreach to these stakeholders and relationship building is an expectation that can build admissions and community presence.

Admission Records

The social worker is often responsible for ensuring that the incoming resident's medical records are available at admission and that current physician's orders for the resident are available. Physician orders must certify the need for admission to skilled care (or other levels of care) along with all orders for medications, treatments, diet, and any specific requirements for that admission. In today's fast-paced and competitive admission environment, this often falls to the nurse accepting the resident over the telephone. As such, more than one person must be examining admissions documentation to ensure that nothing is missed and everything necessary is present upon admission. It is not uncommon to get less-than-complete information from the source of the admission. Staying in front of this concern is paramount to success.

Consider having an admissions application that can be filled out and submitted on your website. Your survey results are online for potential applicants to review, so let them apply online after reviewing your surveyor reports. The web is a major source of referral to facilities. It is crucial to ensure that you have an internet and social media presence today. A web search is a prevalent way for facilities to direct market and build community awareness.

Make It Easy for the "Customer"

- Greet the customer
- Listen to the customer
- Identify the customer's needs
- Ask for the customer's business

"In your opinion, do you believe we can serve your loved one?" Every "lost" admission can be a substantial monetary loss to the facility. Admission to a nursing facility is a major life transition for both the new resident and that resident's significant others. A caring staff will always make sure someone—the administrator, the head nurse, the admissions director—calls the significant other after the first night with a full report on how the resident is doing. During the first 30 days of a resident admission, follow-up by staff can mean the difference between a successful admission and a resident choosing a different facility.

NAB DOMAIN 2C13: CULTURAL COMPETENCE AND DIVERSITY AWARENESS

NAB DOMAIN 1B8: CARE RECIPIENT (AND REPRESENTATIVE) SATISFACTION

As the nursing facility population continues to reflect the cultural diversity of the U.S. population, persons with language and culturally diverse beliefs and attitudes are being admitted. This diversity creates the opportunity for admissions counselors and the facility staff to recognize and accommodate the growing cultural diversity among residents. Medicare requires that facilities present all written materials in a language the resident understands and further provide care instructions and information in a language the resident understands.

Support networks, along with residents' interests and needs, will vary depending on the cultural backgrounds and experiences of the residents. This variation among resident needs provides both a challenge to be sensitive to these broadening needs and an opportunity to provide stimulating experiences for residents as they interact with each other and the community.

SOCIAL SERVICES

NAB DOMAIN 1B16: SOCIAL SERVICES PROGRAMS

Basic Elements of a Social Service Program

The qualifications for serving as a social worker are discussed in Part 6. A full-time social worker must be employed in Medicare/Medicaid-eligible facilities with 120 or more residents. Every facility must provide social services, regardless of size, which focuses on the resident's initial adjustment to the facility and their continuing accommodation to the environment. The social worker is also responsible for monitoring each resident's sociopsychological experiences and orientation in the facility.

The social worker is often most directly in contact with the resident's family or significant others. This staff member assists residents who have current or approaching financial needs that a public agency will meet. In short, the social worker functions in the nursing facility like social workers employed by the local Department of Social Services. Maintaining the quality of each resident's social well-being in a facility is a complex function.

Significantly, assisting each resident in meeting their various social, psychological, physical, environmental, family, financial, and related needs is never achievable by the social worker alone. The social worker must stimulate the various other staff members to participate in this process. A typical problem to which the administrator must be attuned is a tendency for responsive residents to receive a larger share of the social worker's time and attention. The less responsive and unresponsive have needs that also require the time of the social worker.

Despite moving toward full-time directors of admissions, the social worker is generally the first contact with prospective residents and families. Because the social worker cannot be available 24/7, it is important to have a list of persons who have been trained in the admissions process, including initial inquiries, initial interviews, facility tours, and reviewing the facility's information packet for prospective residents. It is even more important for the administrator to follow up on those processes to ensure they are working appropriately 24/7, as admissions is a 24-hour business.

Social Worker "Skills"

In addition to the required training and certification, the person's personality being considered for a social worker is important. The social worker must be a likable person who has good communication skills, can assess situations and individual residents, and is skillful at conflict resolution. In addition, social worker notes in resident records are a key aspect of recordkeeping.

Social Worker as Case Manager

Social workers are typically trained to do case management; that is, to provide one-on-one care for individuals needing their skills. In a nursing facility of 130 residents, the social work department has, in effect, 130 "cases" to manage. The social work director often needs assistants who possess similar skills and can analyze residents' needs and mobilize resources throughout the facility and community to meet resident needs.

Social Worker as Screener

When the social worker is also an admission coordinator, the social worker is responsible for assessing whether the facility can meet prospective residents' needs and whether the admission is financially feasible for the facility. A prospective resident, for example, might be receiving more therapies and expensive medications than the facility can expect to be reimbursed for adequately.

Social Worker as Information Source

Often, the social worker interviews prospective residents, provides information about the facility, and offers information about eligibility for Medicare, Medicaid, and other services. The social worker must track residents' financial status to determine when and if they might become eligible for Medicaid spend-down.

Social Worker as Advocate

The social worker's task is complex. They are directly charged with assisting a person in coping successfully with becoming a resident in a facility and successfully managing the many life adjustments required in this process. The social worker has an obligation both to the well-being of the facility and the individual resident. Often it is the social worker and the administrator who must advocate for the well-being of a resident.

The Resident Council

Most facilities assign the social worker the responsibility for forming and maintaining a functioning resident council. Resident councils can be empowering for residents who wish to participate in the management of facility life. The administration of the facility is expected to follow up and respond to resident council concerns.

Consider as the Administrator . . .

- *Should any "line authority" be given to the resident council? Or should line authority only exist with facility management?*

DISCHARGE PLANNING

NAB DOMAIN 1A11: TRANSITION OF CARE (E.G., ADMISSION, MOVE-IN, TRANSFER, DISCHARGE, AND MOVE-OUT)

Discharge planning, it is often observed, begins at admission. The assumption is made that the resident entering the facility may progress to the point where 24-hour nursing care is no longer needed and placement in a less intensive care setting becomes appropriate. This transition is especially valid for the short-term, rehab-to-home stays that are becoming more common today. The social worker is a facility leader in assisting the facility staff in determining when discharge is appropriate. Discharge can be made to the community if care goals in the facility have been met, to hospice if the illness becomes terminal, or to another institutional setting if needs have changed.

The discharge experience can be as crucial an element of the residents' feelings about their care as the actual care given while in the facility. Hospitals have learned that a successful hospital stay includes careful planning for the patient's return "home." This focus can be equally true for the nursing facility. A successful care plan includes assisting the resident in returning to the community or the next level of care.

Consider as the Administrator . . .

- *Discharge planning is increasingly done in cooperation with other agencies in the community. What steps should the administrator take to ensure that this occurs effectively?*

COMMON PITFALLS IN PRACTICE

- Admissions processes are often left to employees who are not necessarily the most qualified to complete them. Identify who these individuals are and ensure they are appropriately prepared for a quality admissions experience with your new residents.
- Many administrators lean on their social workers to do many things which are somewhat outside their circle of influence. Social workers are amazingly tasked by the regulatory requirements of their jobs today. Do not overburden your social worker with tasks that could be adequately completed by others.

2.1.13 ACTIVITIES/RECREATION

Section Concepts

- *Activities provides a very large amount of support and care to our residents, outside of the activities themselves*
- *Activities directors are tasked with meeting individual resident needs today and identifying problem areas in residents*

Consider as the Administrator . . .

- *The activities director today truly can make or break resident satisfaction. Administrator involvement with activities can also be a great help in this area. What activities might you run or take part in to make the resident experience a great one?*

NAB DOMAIN 1B1: PSYCHOSOCIAL NEEDS (E.G., SOCIAL, SPIRITUAL, COMMUNITY, CULTURAL)

NAB DOMAIN 1B2: PERSON-CENTERED CARE AND COMPREHENSIVE CARE PLANNING

NAB DOMAIN 1B8: CARE RECIPIENT (AND REPRESENTATIVE) SATISFACTION

NAB DOMAIN 1B17: THERAPEUTIC RECREATION AND ACTIVITY PROGRAMS

Nursing services primarily address the medical needs of the residents and, in that process, partially meet their social and interpersonal requirements. The task of the activities coordinator is to ensure the physical, social, and mental well-being of each resident is included in each comprehensive resident assessment and the required comprehensive plan of care. For obtunded, disoriented, or agitated patients, this assignment is indeed a challenge. The activities director and the social services worker are assigned primary responsibility for the quality of psychosocial life within a facility. It is difficult to imagine a more complicated undertaking in shaping the quality of a resident's life.

QUALIFICATIONS

The federal requirements offer several ways in which a person may become a qualified activities professional. They may be a qualified therapeutic recreation specialist or activities professional, licensed or registered by the state government, and eligible for certification as a therapeutic recreation specialist by a recognized accrediting body such as the National Certification Council for Activity Professionals. They may be a person who has 2 years of experience in a social or recreational program within the past 5 years, one of which was full-time in a patient activities program in a healthcare setting. Or they might be a qualified occupational therapist or occupational therapy assistant, or they may have completed a training course approved by the state.

The activity director is responsible for directing the development, implementation, supervision, and ongoing evaluation of the activities program. They must complete and/or direct/delegate the completion of the activities component of the comprehensive assessment and contribute to and/or direct/delegate the contribution to the comprehensive care plan goals and approaches. They must be individualized to match the skills, abilities, interests, and preferences of each resident.

The activities director must direct an activity program, which includes scheduling individual and group activities and implementing or delegating the implementation of the programs. The activities director must monitor the residents' responses and evaluate these responses to the programs to determine if the activities meet the assessed needs of the residents. Revisions to the activities plan for each resident must then be successfully planned and implemented as needed.

NAB DOMAIN 1B17: THERAPEUTIC RECREATION AND ACTIVITY PROGRAMS

The activities director must identify each resident's interests and needs. Beyond that, the facility must then involve each resident in an ongoing program of activities that appeals to their interests and enhances the resident's highest practicable level of physical, mental, and psychosocial well-being. *Activity* is any endeavor other than routine activities of daily living in which the resident participates that promotes self-esteem, pleasure, comfort, education, creativity, success, and independence. Manicures/pedicures, hair styling appointments, and makeovers can be considered part of the activities program. However, the activities must be at a dignified and age-appropriate level for the residents participating in them. For example, it would be considered a dignity concern for residents to be coloring from a children's coloring book; however, using adult-centric coloring books would be acceptable.

One to One

The facility must provide one-to-one programming for residents who will not or cannot effectively plan their own activity pursuits or those needing specialized or extended programs to enhance their overall daily routine and activity pursuit needs. More specifically, the activities program designed for each resident must be "person-appropriate." Each resident's identity must be part of the individualized activity plan with their specific needs, interests, culture, background, and the like. This one-to-one activity must be active involving staff or volunteers. It is questionable (at best) to consider listening to the radio or watching television to be an activity for a room-bound resident.

Program of Activities

The activities director must organize and lead a combination of large- and small-group, one-to-one, and self-directed activities. There must be a system that supports the development, implementation, and evaluation of the activities provided to the residents in the facility. The highest possible quality of life is the goal. Activities can be designed to reflect the resident's interests and lifestyle, be enjoyable, help the resident feel useful, and provide a sense of belonging.

Residents' Views

Residents interviewed in nursing facilities have indicated that dignity is of great importance. The foundations of dignity are feeling independent and having a positive self-image. Achieving dignity and a positive self-image includes activities that promote choice and produce or teach something, using skills from a residents' former work, religious activities, and activities that contribute to the nursing facility. Interviewed residents seldom mentioned activities just to keep busy or only facilitate socializing. They want more. The activities program is a vital and complex part of the fabric of daily life in the facility.

Variety

Residents want a variety of activities, including those that are not childish, require thinking (such as word games), are gender-specific, produce something with use, allow socializing with visitors, provide participation in community events, and are physically active.

Emerging Approaches to "Activities"

Increasingly, facilities are experimenting with providing more homelike atmospheres by creating small-cluster living areas. A primary goal is to resemble daily life at home rather than more formal activities programs. In this model, residents may be more involved in the ongoing activities in their living area, such as care-planned approaches including chores, preparing foods, meeting with other residents to choose spontaneous activities, and leading an activity. In this setting, the "activities" may be conducted by specially trained nurse's aides. Many facilities bring in volunteers from the community with special skills to provide activities as well. It is not uncommon today to see chefs coming to a facility to put on a "TV-style food show" or to have university professors come to lecture at a facility (often along with their students).

Assessment

The activities director is responsible for the activities component of the comprehensive care plan. Sufficient activities information must be gathered by the activities program director for each resident. A resourceful activities director can tap resources such as the resident assessment instrument (RAI), assessments by other disciplines (such as the brief interview for mental status, resident mood interview, and others), personal observations, the resident, and the resident family interviews. However, the activities director has their portion of the RAI, which they complete with an interview for activity preferences. The focus should be on the resident's lifelong interests, spirituality, life roles, goals, strengths, needs, and activity pursuit patterns and preferences. Some residents may be able to pursue their activities independently, without facility intervention. If so, this should be documented in the assessment and in that resident's plan of care.

Care Planning

Activities care planning involves identifying the resident's interests, preferences, and abilities and any issues, concerns, problems, or needs affecting the resident's involvement in activities. Activity goals must be based on measurable objectives and focused on desired outcomes (e.g., engagement in an activity that matches the resident's ability, maintaining attention to the activity for a specified period, expressing satisfaction with the activity verbally or nonverbally), and not simply on attendance at a certain number of activities each week.

Note: For residents with no discernable response, an "activities" plan must be provided, which may include one-to-one activities such as talking to the resident, reading to the resident about prior interests, or applying lotion while stroking the resident's hands or feet.

NAB DOMAIN 1C8: VOLUNTEER PROGRAMS

Activities program events can occur at any time and typically involve more than the activities staff. Activities can be provided by other facility staff, volunteers, visitors, residents, and family members. A coordinated effort by several departments is essential. Nursing, for example, can assist in individual activities. Residents need transportation by nursing assistants to and from planned activities. Housekeeping must set up a room for the planned activity. When activities are outside the facility, transportation personnel must cooperate. Special equipment, such as video or audio, must be set up by persons responsible for the facility's equipment. A bath/ shower or physical therapy appointment may have to be adjusted. Some medications (such as diuretics) or conditions (such as pain or incontinence) may affect a resident's participation. If not contraindicated, the timing of the administration of medications to avoid interfering with the resident's ability to participate or remain at a scheduled activity can be arranged, as can timing pain medication to take effect before an activity the resident enjoys.

Volunteers from the community are a necessity. It is not possible or desirable for the facility staff to fill all the residents' needs for contact with the outside community. Usually, the activities director coordinates a volunteer program, which supplements the caregiving functions of the staff. Volunteers must be carefully trained and supervised. Volunteers become residents' links to the community. In addition to visiting with residents, volunteers can assist in the dining room by pouring water and help with wheelchairs, among other tasks.

To protect the residents, volunteers need to fill out an application, be screened and interviewed, and undergo reference checks, followed by training. Volunteers can often be found from local religious communities and community service organizations. Local retirement communities often have a number of members who have the time and interest in volunteering. The recognition of volunteers can take the form of dinners with awards given. Posting awards on the facility hallways is an effective way of thanking volunteers.

Changing Attitudes Toward "Interventions"

A few years ago, a well-filled, busy monthly activities calendar was the standard measuring tool for judging an activities program. Interventions were more generic, such as "reality orientation" and large-group activities that included residents with differing levels of need and strength. The more "age-appropriate" activities have given way to more "person-appropriate" activities. Today's activities are based more and more on each resident's history, preferences, strengths, and needs. One resident may care for a doll or stroke a stuffed animal; another resident may prefer to reminisce about dolls or stuffed animals she once had; someone else may enjoy petting a dog but will not be interested in inanimate objects.

We are seeing a change in the types of activities and expectations surrounding them. For example, bingo is still an expectation across the board, but finding activities to cater to particular residents is key to success. Finding a way for a resident who is demented to carry out their prior work in life is desirable—with appropriate care planning. It is not uncommon to find the resident who did laundry for a living folding towels or a resident who worked in electronics working with circuit boards. Certain facilities in far West Texas have oil field equipment in them and the cockpit from a plane. This type of specialized activity allows residents to do what they did for a living and is a trend that continues to grow.

Individualizing Adaptations

NAB DOMAIN 1B2: PERSON-CENTERED CARE AND COMPREHENSIVE CARE PLANNING

The following adaptations can be considered for specific resident conditions.

For visually impaired residents: Higher lighting levels without glare; magnifying glasses, light-filtering lenses, telescopic glasses, large-print items such as playing cards, newsprint, books, audiobooks

For deaf and hard of hearing residents: Small-group activities; placement of resident near speaker; use of amplifiers or headphones; decreased background noise; written instructions, gesture, or sign language; adapted TV such as closed captioning

For residents with physical limitations: Adaptive equipment use; placement of supplies and materials to enhance visual interaction, upper extremity function (reach), and hand dexterity; lighter-weight objects for residents with muscle weakness

For residents with cognitive impairment: Task segmentation and simplification; programs using long-term memory rather than short-term memory, length of activities based on attention span

For residents with a language barrier: Translation tools and translators; publications in the resident's language

For residents with terminal illness: Life review; quality time with chosen relatives, friends, staff, and/or other residents; spiritual support, touch, massage, music. Some terminally ill residents may prefer to spend their time alone. Preferred solitude should be carefully documented as part of that resident's care plan. Hospice interventions can also be a part of their activities programming.

For residents with pain: Spiritual support, relaxation programs, music, massage, aromatherapy, pet therapy, touch

For residents who prefer to stay in their room or cannot leave their room: In-room visits by staff/other residents/volunteers with similar interests; touch and sensory activities; access to art/craft materials; access to computers, tablets, DVDs; visits from spiritual counselors

For residents with varying sleep patterns: Activities available during wake time (e.g., staff reading a newspaper, dietary making food available, nursing assistants working a puzzle, maintenance staff taking the resident on night rounds, early morning delivery of coffee or orange juice, specialized activities in the early morning or late at night)

For the recently moved-in resident: "À la carte" activities such as books, puzzles, newspapers, CDs, DVDs, video games; individual activities designed to match goals of therapy such as jigsaw puzzles

For the younger resident: Individual and group music that fit the resident's taste and era; computer and internet access

For the residents from diverse ethnic backgrounds: Special events including meals, decorations, celebrations, and music related to the residents' experiences

For Residents With Behavioral Symptoms

For the resident who is constantly walking: Provide a space and environmental cues that encourage physical exercise, decrease exit behavior, and reduce extraneous stimulation, such as seating areas spaced along a walking path or garden or a setting in which the resident can manipulate objects. Aromatherapy can please and calm these residents. Validate the resident's feelings and words, engage the resident in conversation, or provide one-on-one activities.

For the resident who engages in name-calling, hitting, kicking, yelling, biting, sexual behavior, or compulsive behavior: Provide a calm, unrushed environment, with structured, familiar activities such as folding, sorting, and matching; use one-to-one activities or small-group activities that comfort the resident, such as listening to preferred music, walking quietly with the staff, a family member, or a friend, eating a favorite snack; looking at familiar pictures; engaging in exercise and movement activities and exchanging self-stimulatory activity for a more socially appropriate activity that uses hands

For the resident who disrupts group activities with behaviors such as talking loudly and demanding attention or who has catastrophic reactions such as uncontrolled crying or anger: Offer activities in which the resident can succeed, that are broken into simple steps, that involve small groups, or are one-to-one activities such as using the computer, short and repetitive actions, and stop if the resident becomes overwhelmed; involve the resident in familiar occupation-related activities; involve in physical activities such as walking, slow exercises, or use of rocking or swinging motions

For residents who go through others' belongings: Use normalizing activities such as stacking canned food onto shelves or folding laundry; offer sorting activities such as with socks, ties, or buttons; involve them in organizing tasks such as putting supplies away; use nonentry clues such as "Do not disturb" signs or provide locks to secure other residents' belongings if requested by other residents

For residents who have withdrawn from previous activity or interests or customary routines, isolating themselves in their rooms most of the day: Provide activities just before or after mealtime where the meal is being served; provide in-room volunteer visits, music or videos of choice; encourage volunteer-type work that begins in the room but has to be completed outside the room; invite to special events with a friend; engage in activities that give the resident a sense of self-worth; invite the resident outdoors; involve them in motor exercises

For the resident who excessively seeks attention from staff or peers: Include in social programs, small-group activities, or service projects with leadership opportunities

For the resident who lacks awareness of personal safety (such as putting objects in the mouth) or engages in self-destructive behaviors or tries to harm self: Observe closely during activities, taking precautions with materials (e.g., avoiding sharp objects); involve in smaller groups or one-to-one activities that use the hands; focus attention on emotionally relaxing activities; focus attention on physical activities such as exercise

For the resident who has delusional or hallucinatory behavior that is stressful: Focus the resident on activities that decrease stress and increase awareness of actual surroundings, such as familiar activities and physical activities; offer verbal reassurance, especially in terms of keeping the resident safe; acknowledge that the resident's experience is real to them

NAB DOMAIN 1B8: CARE RECIPIENT (AND REPRESENTATIVE) SATISFACTION

Having accomplished all this, the facility must develop a method of education intended for care recipients and their support systems. Success in caregiving includes communicating the facility's care efforts to the resident and the support networks surrounding each resident. Support group meetings and educational seminars can be provided to these individuals. In addition, the facility can provide information on many topics such as the aging process, financing nursing facility care, the facility's policies, the merits of giving assistance versus learned helplessness in caregiving, volunteering possibilities, relationships with the facility caregivers, and similar topics. Such experiences allow the family and resident's social network members to meet other staff members, better understand the challenges facing the facility, and help family members and friends develop more realistic expectations of what is and what is not possible in providing care. Family forums are a good way of educating both the care recipients and their support networks about the challenges and opportunities available at the facility. Even seeing family members willing to be trained as feeding assistants and helping residents during meals is not uncommon today.

COMMON PITFALLS IN PRACTICE

- Regulations surrounding activities have changed significantly over the years. The activities programs required today need to be varied and have different activities on a daily basis.
- Activities programs in nursing facilities have been compared to activities on a cruise ship. This is not a bad comparison to at least give an idea of the quality of your activities program.
- *Do not* be the administrator who takes bingo away from the residents. This is difficult to recover from and is akin to violating a cardinal sin. Yes, it is that important.

2.1.14 HOUSEKEEPING

Section Concepts

- *Housekeeping, laundry, and maintenance are very important centers of a facility*

- *The quality of a facility is perceived based on how clean it is and the lack of smells*

Consider as the Administrator ...

- *If you were to see a housekeeper not mopping correctly, would you be well-trained enough yourself to take their mop and show them how it is done?*

NAB DOMAIN 3A7: INFECTION CONTROL AND SANITATION (E.G., LINENS, KITCHEN, HAND WASHING, HEALTHCARE-ACQUIRED INFECTIONS, HAZARDOUS MATERIALS)

NAB DOMAIN 3A4: FACILITY MANAGEMENT AND ENVIRONMENTAL SERVICES

IMPORTANCE OF "GOOD HOUSEKEEPING"

Not only do federal and state inspectors make intuitive value judgments about a facility based on its cleanliness and physical appearance, so also will most of the residents themselves and their significant others. The first impression of a facility by families visiting to seek placement for a loved one is made or broken by housekeeping the moment they walk in the door. Dirty floors and walls, empty toilet paper holders, yellowing toilets and lavatories, and offensive odors associated with them communicate a message to the residents, staff, and visitors, revealing what the facility thinks about itself. Inattention to housekeeping details leads inspectors and the public alike to wonder to what extent it carries over into resident care, sanitation in food preparations, and cleanliness of the residents themselves.

The head of housekeeping may have excellently designed job assignments for the four to eight housekeepers. The administrator can tell how effective these schedules are simply by walking around the facility. On these tours, the administrator must be able to "see" dirt and quickly identify areas that need correction or laud the housekeeping staff for doing an excellent job.

There is a surprising amount of regulation applicable to the housekeeping area. The head of housekeeping and the administrator must give attention to elements such as the required Safety Data Sheets (formerly known as Material Safety Data Sheets) for all chemicals. Typically, housekeeping schedules are set up for daily cleaning, weekly cleaning, deep cleaning, and floor cleaning schedules. In a 100-bed facility, the director of housekeeping and the director of laundry roles are often combined.

Consider as the Administrator ...

- *Have you wheeled yourself around the facility in a wheelchair? Think about this as it is a perspective that you do not necessarily have. You would be amazed at what you find from a different perspective!*

2.1.15 LAUNDRY

Section Concepts

- *Clean clothes help the facility smell better and assist in maintaining resident health*
- *Linens are an important part of daily laundry duties*

Consider as the Administrator . . .

- *If you saw your residents in clothes which did not appear to be clean, what conclusions would you expect visitors to draw when seeing the same thing?*
- *Washcloths must be reordered far more often than normal wear and tear would suggest ... what do you think might be happening to washcloths? Are there any better alternatives to washcloths? Are there reasons you may NOT want to use the alternatives?*

NAB DOMAIN 3A7: INFECTION CONTROL AND SANITATION (E.G., LINENS, KITCHEN, HAND WASHING, HEALTHCARE-ACQUIRED INFECTIONS, HAZARDOUS MATERIALS)

NAB DOMAIN 3A4: FACILITY MANAGEMENT AND ENVIRONMENTAL SERVICES

Clean linens, clean resident clothes, the availability of linens and clothes when needed, and safe and sanitary handling techniques for both soiled and clean linen are areas of responsibility of the head of laundry. Whether it is better to do laundry in-house or contract with a linen service (known as *outsourcing*, the purchasing of portions of services from outside providers) is a subject of continuing debate. Whatever the decision, there will be procedures for handling linens that the administrator can observe for conformity to regulations and facility policies.

Laundry must follow standard procedures for ensuring that microbes are effectively killed and that linen is handled using the standard precautions for preventing the spread of infections.

Having enough linens available 24/7 to all shifts, especially the weekend shift when the laundry is often closed or on reduced hours, is challenging for most facilities. Linens (sheets, towels, washcloths) tend to "walk." Washcloths, in particular, seem to disappear at alarming rates. Inspectors look for "worn" or "tattered" sheets and towels. To minimize linen problems, the facility must establish a par level (for every piece of linen in use, four others are in the system, either being washed or in storage). Replenishing the linens is best done through a regular inventory system, which triggers reordering of linens to maintain an adequate supply.

2.1.16 MAINTENANCE DEPARTMENT

Section Concepts

* *Maintenance is a full-time job, or potentially more than that*
* *Preventative maintenance is a necessity that keeps future problems from occurring*

Consider as the Administrator . . .

* *Where do you draw the line between a repair or a replacement? Which is better?*

NAB DOMAIN 3A6: PREVENTATIVE AND ROUTINE MAINTENANCE PROGRAMS (E.G., PEST CONTROL, EQUIPMENT, MECHANICAL SYSTEMS)

Distinguishing between maintenance and housekeeping responsibilities is often an issue. If a wall has a hole in it, maintenance's job is clearly to fix the hole. If that same wall is only dirty and needs washing, it is probably housekeeping's job. Each facility must designate through established policies the respective responsibilities of these two functions. The repair and upkeep of physical systems are the responsibilities of maintenance.

Typically, one full-time employee in a 100-bed facility is hired to head maintenance. When seasonal needs exceed that person's time availability, subcontracting can fill the gaps. In the summer, additional help maintaining the grounds may be needed. As ever, the facility is legally responsible for all acts of these subcontractors.

Preventive maintenance is essential. The many systems that keep the facility functioning must function 24/7 year-round. An approach of waiting for a belt to break and then planning on quick replacement is not satisfactory for a healthcare facility. A heating system breakdown on a cold night poses unique risks to a population of residents at elevated risk of hypothermia. For such reasons, the maintenance head must be on call 24/7, with the administrator and the DON as backup contacts when a maintenance emergency occurs. The maintenance person must be taught to distinguish among requests. The maintenance person is the first responder to "maintenance" emergencies, from an overflowing toilet that requires immediate action to a burned-out light bulb that can be put on the day's "to do" list. The maintenance head must understand such distinctions. However, staff should be aware of facility policy regarding their ability to use a plunger when the time is right and not call in maintenance to complete this simple task.

Preventive maintenance—anticipating when a piece of equipment will need servicing or risk ceasing to function—is a complex task requiring experienced judgment. A well-trained maintenance director can do much to anticipate troublesome, unnecessary breakdowns of equipment. The administrator can participate in the maintenance process by occasionally assuming a "maintenance mindset" and then walking through the facility touching, feeling, and judging the state of repair of all they encounter. The administrator needs to monitor all the preventive maintenance required under Life Safety Code, such as generator exercise, fire alarm testing, and water temperatures. Staying on top of this information can easily prevent citations from occurring.

SOME AREAS REQUIRING SPECIAL TEAMWORK ATTENTION FROM THE ADMINISTRATOR

NAB DOMAIN 4A3: ORGANIZATIONAL BEHAVIOR (E.G., ORGANIZATIONAL CULTURE, TEAM BUILDING, GROUP DYNAMICS)

- Patient care planning and implementation of resident care plans
- Pain management as prescribed by the physicians
- Successful billing, from recording supplies consumed to required "wording" for claims
- Housekeeping versus maintenance
- Dietary/nursing coordination in getting food to residents on a timely basis, at the right temperature, attractively presented with attention to accommodating resident preferences
- Differentiating between activities functions and the social worker function; awareness of the dangers of persons' needs falling between the cracks
- Discharge planning
- Resident advocacy to the staff and families
- Nursing/housekeeping/laundry coordination

It is a function of the administrator to ensure that everyone is doing their job and orchestrate a smooth teamwork atmosphere among their employees. Success occurs when we pay attention to details and function!

2.2 IDENTIFYING HUMAN RESOURCES FUNCTIONS

Section Concepts

- *How the personnel function evolved and what tools are available to the human resources administrator*

Consider as the Administrator . . .

- *If the facility cannot feasibly employ a full-time personnel administrator, who should be designated the human resources person among the facility staff?*

NAB DOMAIN 2C9: HUMAN RESOURCE POLICIES (E.G., DRUG-FREE WORKPLACE, DISCIPLINE, JOB CLASSIFICATION, PHOTOGRAPHY AND VIDEO, SOCIAL MEDIA USAGE, MOBILE PHONE USAGE)

NAB DOMAIN 2C: HUMAN RESOURCES

Managers in organizations have always performed certain basic human resources functions. This role often extends to all management positions within the organization, as human resource functions tend to be widespread.

HUMAN RESOURCES FUNCTIONS

Human resources functions are a range of activities that can include recordkeeping, employee recruitment and selection, training and development, compensation management, performance evaluations, and labor relations (Noe et al., 2017; Robbins & Coulter, 2018).

NAB DOMAIN 2C2: SELECTION AND HIRING PRACTICES (E.G., EEOC, INTERVIEWING, ADVERSE IMPACT, PROTECTED CLASSES, OCCUPATIONAL QUALIFICATIONS); 2C4: ORGANIZATIONAL STAFFING REQUIREMENTS AND REPORTING (E.G., PBJ); 2C12: EMPLOYEE SATISFACTION, ENGAGEMENT, AND RETENTION

A few of the functions of human resources are as follows:

- *Record keeping.* Ensuring that all necessary information is in the employee's file and that it is kept confidential. Large amounts of this information may be computerized today
- *Recruitment.* Assisting department heads in finding employees for vacant positions
- *Selection.* Assisting department heads in interviewing and assessing job applicants (Singh, 2016)
- *Training and retaining employees.* Assisting department heads in employee orientation, in-service training, and continuing education
- *Compensation management.* Assisting department heads and the payroll office in administering salary and the other benefits offered by the facility
- *Performance evaluation.* Assisting managers in conducting employee evaluations in conformity with the facility's human resources policies
- *Labor relations.* Assisting managers in creating a favorable work environment
- *Health and safety.* Drug testing, monitoring employee health status (e.g., ensuring that hepatitis B and tuberculosis immunizations are provided as required and kept current; Halter et al., 2017), worker's compensation claims

HUMAN RESOURCES MANAGEMENT AS AN OCCUPATION

Before the evolution to what we have today, human resources were the responsibility of each department manager. Usually, the department managers did initial interviewing, perhaps bringing the administrator in on the final selection. Historically, as the department supervisor's job increased in complexity, a clerical assistant took over the responsibility for specific human resources activities (such as hours worked and payroll). From this initial record-keeping activity, the responsibilities were gradually broadened until individuals began making a full-time career in what is now called human resources administration (Noe et al., 2017).

Human resources managers do not "manage" employees beyond those who work under them in the human resources department. Human resources management is a staff function; it has no line authority in the organization. All the employees in the organization are directly managed by their department supervisors, who hold line authority. It is the line managers who, in fact, are responsible for performing most of the human resources functions for the employees under them. The department heads do the actual hiring; require in-service training and development; give performance evaluations, promotions, and award raises; and discipline, suspend, and discharge their staff.

The role of the human resources manager and staff is to assist the line supervisors (e.g., the department heads in the nursing facility) to carry out human resources responsibilities according to policies set by facility ownership. Thus, human resources staff make a crucial contribution to overall employee satisfaction by ensuring that human resources policies are carried out as consistently as feasible from one department to another.

In a facility of perhaps 100 to 150 residents, no full-time human resources director is usually hired. However, some of the typical "human resources department" functions are usually given to one employee who, in effect, serves as a part-time personnel staff in the facility. This person sometimes receives the title of staff development coordinator or something similar. Alternatively, personnel record-keeping tasks may be disseminated to multiple staff members such as an assistant administrator, an administrative assistant, a staff nurse, or an employee in the business office. These employees may assist department managers with maintaining records, such as ensuring that employees are tested for tuberculosis and are offered hepatitis B vaccinations (as required by the Bloodborne Pathogens regulations).

COMMON PITFALLS IN PRACTICE
- Many new administrators assume that human resources runs itself. This is far from the truth. As with any other department, this one requires your attention, oversight, and expertise.

2.3 PLANNING EMPLOYMENT NEEDS: WRITING JOB DESCRIPTIONS

Section Concepts

- *How work is divided among the facility staff*
- *Potential problems with job descriptions*

Consider as the Administrator . . .

- *How can the work of the facility be divided so that there is no overlap?*

JOB DESCRIPTIONS

NAB DOMAIN 2C: HUMAN RESOURCES; 2C9: HUMAN RESOURCE POLICIES (E.G., DRUG-FREE WORKPLACE, DISCIPLINE, JOB CLASSIFICATION, PHOTOGRAPHY AND VIDEO, SOCIAL MEDIA USAGE, MOBILE PHONE USAGE)

Each facility needs to break down all work to be accomplished (the processor portion of the systems model) into a set of activities that one person can perform. Several definitions provided by the U.S. Department of Labor and the U.S. Office of Personnel Management (OPM) may be helpful to review at this point.

Job analysis. The process of defining a job in terms of tasks or behaviors required and specifying the qualifications of the employee to be placed in that job (Konopaske et al., 2018; Noe et al., 2017; Robbins & Coulter, 2018)

Job description. Information about the job, a statement of the job to be done, usually includes a list of duties and responsibilities in order of importance. Usually, a job description includes (a) the title, (b) the qualifications, (c) to whom the worker is primarily responsible, and (d) the duties or specific expectations (Noe et al., 2017; Robbins & Coulter, 2018; Sampson & Fried, 2021)

Job specification. A statement of the skills, education, and experience required to perform the work, usually derived from the job description (Robbins & Coulter, 2018)

Job titles (or job classifications). That which distinguishes one job from all others. Job titles may also indicate the occupational level of the job (e.g., nurse supervisor indicates a higher position [administratively, at least] than RN) or the level of authority or seniority of a job (e.g., RN levels 1, 2, and 3; Sampson & Fried, 2021)

Task. A coordinated and aggregated series of work elements used to produce an output (e.g., making beds)

Position. The responsibilities and duties performed by one individual. There are as many positions as there are employees

Job. A group of similar positions in their duties; for example, laundry, housekeeping, grounds (Robbins & Coulter, 2018; Sampson & Fried, 2021)

Job family. A group of two or more jobs with similar duties; for example, duties of the RN and the LNP (Noe et al., 2017; Robbins & Coulter, 2018)

All the work to be accomplished in operating a nursing facility must be broken down into a series of tasks. Tasks are grouped to facilitate them being performed by one individual.

Job analysis is the process of grouping a series of related tasks into a position. Each position can be described in terms of the tasks and behaviors involved and the education and training needed to perform the job successfully.

POTENTIAL PROBLEMS WITH JOB DESCRIPTIONS

The federal government examines job descriptions and specifications for possible discriminatory effects. Each requirement for a job must be necessary for the adequate performance of that job; this is "proven validity."

Example: In a situation where the area has a massive number of available job applicants, a nursing facility required 2 years of college for applicants for the nurse's aide position. This job specification is a higher educational requirement than usual. Therefore, the facility would be obligated to prove why this education level is essential to perform the job to demonstrate proven validity. The facility would also have to show that the requirement did not serve to discriminate against members of a particular group on the basis of sex or ethnic origins (Noe et al., 2017).

Once job descriptions have been written and the expected workload of the facility estimated, future employment needs can be forecasted.

COMMON PITFALLS IN PRACTICE

- A common error with a job description is that it is not detailed enough. To combat this "error," we often see the catchphrase "other duties as assigned" to cover anything that was missed.

2.4 FORECASTING FUTURE EMPLOYMENT NEEDS

Section Concepts

- *How to take a human effort inventory*

Consider as the Administrator . . .

- *Is it really possible to forecast future employment needs? Could we have ever predicted COVID-19 and how it affected the industry?*

The planning process begins with a projection of the number of residents and their expected levels of medical complexity the facility expects to serve over a period, usually during the next 1 to 5 years. This forecast can then be translated into specific personnel requirements for the future period (Noe et al., 2017; Robbins & Coulter, 2018).

TAKING A HUMAN EFFORT INVENTORY

NAB DOMAIN 2C4: ORGANIZATIONAL STAFFING REQUIREMENTS AND REPORTING (E.G., PBJ)

NAB DOMAIN 2C: HUMAN RESOURCES; 4A2: ORGANIZATIONAL CHANGE MANAGEMENT

Numerous factors must be considered in projecting the present and future availability of qualified personnel in sufficient numbers. This consideration is the process of taking a human effort inventory.

Several sources of employment information exist. The U.S. Department of Labor gathers data that are useful in estimating the future availability of needed employees (Noe et al., 2017). Many state governments also collect labor data reflecting utilization and availability in their respective state. We also see many private entities that collect data from multiple sources and quickly distill it for easy use.

Identifying Trends

It is imperative that the administrator works to continuously identify trends in the workplace. This goes for everything under the purview of the administrator, not just employment. In the following, we discuss several trends that administrators have dealt with in recent times.

Pandemic Salaries

COVID-19 presented a tremendous set of challenges for healthcare and nursing facilities in general. Much of what we did in healthcare has evolved because of the pandemic and the requirements set forth by the federal government regarding staffing and visitation (Betancourt et al., 2020). We saw a trend of nurses and other qualified staff members leaving their jobs and jump to agency jobs in other areas. The already existing shortage of personnel (specifically nurses) puts further difficulty on staffing and human resources. The absolute need for this type of personnel caused staffing agencies to offer obscene salaries during the pandemic. This situation caused friction, as agency staff were working right next to the staff who were paid three to five times *less*. This dichotomy caused many long-term employees to leave their employers to seek the higher salaries offered by travel agencies. At the time of this writing, this challenge is still a significant one in all areas of healthcare.

Pandemic Burnout

Another area of significance surrounding the COVID-19 pandemic is burnout. After the first nursing facility in Kirkland, Washington, became the first in the country to have a problem with the pandemic. We quickly began to see employees also having significant reactions to nursing facilities being referred to as a "ground zero" for this illness (Barnett & Grabowski, 2020). Not only were employees left to deal with their work life, but there was also no home–life balance. Many employees faced difficulties that included being sequestered away from their families for months without contact, experiencing salary freezes or reductions, being crippled by the fear of getting the disease themselves or passing it on to their children, and suffering from depression, emotional exhaustion, and a myriad of other conditions (Bradley & Chahar, 2020). The repercussions of the pandemic remain a significant concern today in healthcare, and providers are scrambling to assist their staff with these and many other difficulties that exist in the workplace that are entirely new to us.

Competition for Human Resources

It is practical to take an inventory of present and planned health and related facilities that are or will be competing for similarly qualified personnel. For example, if no acute care hospital exists in the geographic area but a sizable for-profit hospital is expected to be constructed within 2 years, competition may increase dramatically. Similarly, if the local hospital is one of the several local hospitals downsizing or closing their doors each year, the labor pool may suddenly increase (Hitt et al., 2017; Robbins & Coulter, 2018). Worker shortages in various functional areas within the nursing facility have increased dependence on outsourcing, including having services performed by an outside organization (such as having laundry done off-site or introducing contracted services into facilities to perform housekeeping and dietary functions; Noe et al., 2017).

Job Security

Companies no longer guarantee their employees job security. Over the past two decades, worker commitment to the employer has ceased to be a lifetime commitment. Today's employees increasingly perceive themselves as individuals who manage their careers over their lifetime, which increasingly involves several employers. This concern contributes to differences seen in employees from different generations (generation X, gen Y/millennials, gen Z/iGen). Companies are decommitting to their employees, and employees are decommitting to their companies (Noe et al., 2017; Welch & Welch, 2015). Broadly, employer loyalty often extends only to the time an employee is being paid for their time.

In-Migration or Out-Migration Patterns in the Labor Supply

Knowledge of the unemployment rate and whether the worker pool from which employees must be chosen is shrinking or enlarging is important. Statistics are usually available on the local unemployment rate. Unfortunately for the nursing facility, a low local unemployment rate can have the effect of a noticeable reduction in the quality of applicants, level of job interest, and longevity for positions such as a nurse's aide, a housekeeper, and a grounds person (Noe et al., 2017).

Wage Scale Movements in the Area

An increasing worker pool may reduce wage scales, whereas a shrinking worker pool may cause the wage scale to rise. The perceived widespread nursing shortage in recent years resulted in rapid increases in nursing salaries during those years. As the nursing shortage eased, nurses' wages began to trend slightly downward. Nursing "shortages" are increasingly cyclical. We also see certain areas with a sudden need for employees due to new businesses. These businesses often come in and offer a much larger wage than nursing facilities can compete with; thus, they experience a large outflux of employees very quickly.

Expected Impacts of Educational Institutions

Educational institutions such as local community colleges are becoming significant training sources for the human capital needed by nursing facilities. Any expected increase or decrease in training activities—for example, the addition or closing of an LPN or other program in the local community college—could dramatically affect the availability of labor, especially trained nurse's aides.

Knowledge of these trends can assist planners in taking action before an anticipated employment crisis. If a shortage is foreseen, the facility might join with other local healthcare providers in a program to attract additional health-related personnel to the area. Providers in some regions have taken this further by having all employees pulled from staffing agencies. This tactic essentially outsources all human resource functions to an outside provider, leaving the facility better able to focus on resident care.

COMMON PITFALLS IN PRACTICE

- Make no assumptions that wages or human resources issues will resolve themselves or go away. Of all the places in your facility, this one requires your attention and action.
- Know what is happening in your market. Your employees know. It is up to you to stay ahead of this knowledge to keep your employees happy and satisfied.

2.5 RECRUITING EMPLOYEES

Section Concepts

- *A way to calculate the number and types of employees that will be needed to function successfully*

Consider as the Administrator . . .

- *What is your place in recruitment? An active one? A passive one?*
- *Cultural awareness, diversity, and inclusion are important concepts in the workplace. How do you plan to integrate all these areas actively?*

NAB DOMAIN 2C2: SELECTION AND HIRING PRACTICES (E.G., EEOC, INTERVIEWING, ADVERSE IMPACT, PROTECTED CLASSES, OCCUPATIONAL QUALIFICATIONS)

NAB DOMAIN 2C5: STAFF CERTIFICATION AND LICENSURE REQUIREMENTS

NAB DOMAIN 2C13: CULTURAL COMPETENCE AND DIVERSITY AWARENESS

NAB DOMAIN 2C: HUMAN RESOURCES

NAB DOMAIN 2C4: ORGANIZATIONAL STAFFING REQUIREMENTS AND REPORTING (E.G., PBJ)

Once the forecast of the resident profile expected to be served has been translated into specific personnel requirements for the facility, these requirements become the basis for the recruitment and selection program. The forecast assists the facility in determining the number and types of employees it will need to recruit and the sources for recruitment (Noe et al., 2017).

INFLUENCE OF AFFIRMATIVE ACTION AND AMERICANS WITH DISABILITIES ACT

NAB DOMAIN 2C1: FEDERAL HUMAN RESOURCES LAWS, RULES, AND REGULATIONS (E.G., ADA, FMLA, WAGE AND HOUR, FLSA); 2C13: CULTURAL COMPETENCE AND DIVERSITY AWARENESS

Since the passage of the Civil Rights Act well over five decades ago, the process of seeking new employees has become more public. Before that time, facilities could choose employees without scrutiny by government agencies concerning possible job discrimination based on age, sex, race, marital status, religion, national origin, or handicap (Singh, 2016).

Today government agencies can review a facility for possible legal violations by examining the following: (a) the facility's list of recruitment sources for each job category, (b) recruitment advertising, and (c) statistics on the number of applicants processed by personal category (e.g., sex, age, and race), level and type of disabilities, and by job category and level. All this information is required to be collected by the facility and much more. With the advent of electronic records for employees, examining this information or printing a report is as simple as pushing a button.

The government may require a nursing facility chain or an individual facility to recruit qualified employees whose group is not proportionately represented in their present staff. For example, a facility may have no African American nurses on the staff. Suppose the government ascertains that the facility does not advertise job openings in places African Americans seek jobs, such as nursing schools, newspapers, or other sources. In that case, the government may require that the facility or chain use a governmentally defined Equal Employment Opportunity program.

Many employers are under governmental pressure to increase the number of minority members and women employed in the facility, especially at the higher levels from which these groups have traditionally been excluded. Requiring a facility to increase the proportion of minority persons is called *ratio hiring*.

Although it has not been a matter of Office of Civil Rights enforcement, disproportionately few male nurses tend to be hired, probably out of deference to the primarily female (often 75% or more) nursing facility population and the diminished availability of male nurses.

In general, it is functional to seek a diversified workforce representative of the community which the facility serves. Furthermore, seeking a diverse staff can only help the facility to be successful. When we see homogeneous teams of employees providing care, we see a decrease in the care's efficacy (Gomez & Bernet, 2019). We see localized disparities in care being provided by a staff that is not as diverse as it should be. Conversely, we see many positive correlations between the more diverse team and their results. Diverse teams of professionals have been shown to provide improved resident care, increased skill and innovation, improved risk management, better financial performance, and improvement in many other aspects of resident care (Gomez & Bernet, 2019).

The Americans with Disabilities Act (ADA) has also influenced the hiring process in several ways, as discussed in more detail in the following sections.

INFLUENCE OF THE LABOR MARKET

The *labor market* is the geographic area from which applicants are to be recruited. Recruitment for a new administrator or DON is often national in scope today, using the internet, job searches, and social media to find the right candidate. The new administrator may be willing to move across the country or to a different part of the state where they reside. When staffing for jobs requiring little skill, the scope of the labor market will tend to be a relatively small geographic area surrounding the facility. The new janitor or nurse's aide is unlikely to be willing or economically able to move across the country to accept a position at the facility. This expectation is much different for the administrator, and the newly licensed administrator should be ready to go where the job takes them, especially in their first position after licensure.

If there is a surplus of labor at recruiting time, the facility may be flooded with applications. However, when we have a shortage of qualified staff, as nursing currently reflects, it takes considerable initiative and creativity to fill positions.

Internet Applications

Online applications are an expectation of today's job seekers. Many facilities have their own websites with employment application capabilities. No matter how potential employees are applying, the process needs to be easy and seamless. Potential employees simply close the window of complicated application processes.

Impacts of Transportation

The ease with which employees can commute to the facility directly impacts the geographic area from which the facility can recruit. The absence of an efficient public transportation system, especially for evening and night workers, will oblige the facility to hire only persons who have access to automobiles or can walk to work.

Nursing facilities in the central city face unique problems in finding suitable employees. Population migration to the suburbs traditionally leaves fewer qualified persons living in the city center, where suburbanites are little inclined to commute. Some larger institutions have arranged special transportation to and from work for suburban employees to attract competent staff. Quite a few facilities have transportation vans and recruit employees from out of town. Employee transportation is an area where creativity can be very beneficial to finding solutions.

RECRUITMENT SOURCES

Recruitment sources both within and outside the facility should be considered. Present employees may be an excellent source.

Present Employees

The current employees of the facility can be a primary source for filling vacancies. Hiring from within to promote present employees is a policy decision with multiple advantages (Noe et al., 2017).

Career Ladders

Career ladders are paths along which the employee can hope to progress. They constitute a major source of employee incentive and satisfaction. Persons entering the facility are encouraged to stay if there is a reasonable expectation that, when openings occur, there will be advancement possibilities from within the organization. This practice stimulates employees to develop skills that will be necessary to qualify for promotion (Noe et al., 2017). An excellent example of such career ladders can be seen in hospitals where these ladders are built into different certifications they might hold, such as Magnet status or Pathway to Excellence certification (McClay & Mileski, 2018).

Job Posting and Job Bidding — On the Bulletin Board or the Internet

A job that becomes available is posted on appropriate bulletin boards, and employees are encouraged to bid or apply. Through this device, employees become more aware of the actual requirements of positions and the selection processes for filling vacancies. Such information can be placed on the facility's website. The advancement of present employees has the obvious advantage of recognizing and rewarding successful workers. It also benefits the facility by placing a person who already understands the organization and is loyal to its policies.

However, hiring from within may inhibit introducing new ideas and fresh approaches into the facility. There are times when the management may purposely seek to bring in an outsider who will be expected to reorganize or reengineer a department or work area. We see this being done more often today when employers attempt to acquire a much more diverse workforce.

Outside Sources

Unless reducing staff size is a goal, every vacancy presents the option to promote from within or hire from outside.

Promotion from within might trigger a series of promotions. Suppose the nursing supervisor is promoted to the DON. In that case, the charge nurse may be moved up to nursing supervisor, and the senior RN to charge nurse, thus creating an opportunity for several moves up in seniority or level and eventually opening a beginning RN position from an outside source (Noe et al., 2017).

Referrals

Employees, residents, and their significant others are good sources of referrals. Satisfied employees, residents, and family circles constitute a valuable asset for the recruiting effort (Noe et al., 2017). It is not uncommon to see family members wanting to come to work at the place where their loved one resides. Many family members can be trained as nurse's aides or seek employment in other facility areas.

Employee referrals can be especially beneficial. When a staff member's recommendation is accepted, they are receiving special recognition from the facility. In addition, the employee will have a vested interest in assisting the recruit to adjust to the environment and be productive. However, the facility must be careful to avoid referrals that lead to nepotism (favoring one's family members) or the formation of closely knit groups or cliques composed of persons who have close outside ties and tend to exclude others. Employee, resident, and family referrals are, in essence, word-of-mouth recommendations that reflect the facility's reputation.

Advertisements

Advertisement in appropriate media, such as newspapers, professional and trade journals, and the internet, are the most common methods for contacting prospective applicants. Many facilities post jobs with different online job boards (e.g., Indeed, Simply Hired, Career Builder, Monster). Other facilities recruit directly through social media sources successfully (e.g., LinkedIn, Facebook, Twitter). It is not uncommon for jobs to be advertised, shared, retweeted, and pushed around the internet to thousands of potential applicants today. Visibility is key to getting jobs filled with qualified applicants.

Public Employment Agencies

State governments operate local public employment agencies using federal payroll tax rebates from the U.S. Department of Labor. Public employment agencies can provide lists of unemployed individuals and currently drawing unemployment insurance benefits (Noe et al., 2017). Many state unemployment agencies maintain online job boards that allow employers to post jobs for free. Many of these agencies have local offices that need to know the facility's administrator. They can help with recruitment and job training for new nurses, aides, cooks, and many other positions.

Private Employment Agencies

Agencies in the private sector offer specialized services, more closely matching the needs of the potential employer and employee. Fees are charged.

Most often, the employee pays the agency. However, the employer sometimes shares in the fee and occasionally pays it directly to the agency. The facility may also sign a contract with a private employment agency over some time. If this is the chosen solution, the contract should be carefully reviewed to avoid unwanted or unintended commitments, including a fee to the agency for all new employees, whether found by the agency or the employer.

Search Firms

Search firms generally focus their efforts on middle- and upper-level management positions. Clients for search firms usually are employers who agree to pay the search firm for finding a suitable candidate. The search firm operates in a more far-flung geographic area than is typically possible for the employer (although the internet is changing even this), and it can offer a nationwide inventory. These firms can save employers time and energy by providing extensive screening before any candidate is recommended.

Professional and Industry Organizations

Many professional and industry groups, such as healthcare facilities' associations and nurses' associations, may maintain rosters of their members seeking employment, which they publish in their journals and post at meetings. Much interviewing, both formal and informal, occurs at association meetings for job openings. The American College of Health Care Administrators (ACHCA) offers its members access to employment openings through their website for nursing facility administrators. Company websites may list job openings. Many jobs are also found at continuing education offerings that administrators and nurses require. Quite a few corporate executives go to such meetings with the sole purpose of returning with a list of potential recruits for their company.

Educational Institutions

Accredited schools are an increasingly important source for nursing facility personnel. Community colleges and technical institutes train students to be RNs, LPNs, nurse's aides, and many other trade-related professions (Noe et al., 2017). The savvy administrator should have a friendly relationship with those at their local colleges and institutes and find ways to get to know those students before they graduate. Nursing facilities often act as clinical sites for these students as well. Whether the administrator goes to the students (lunch or welcome meetings) or the students come to the administrator (clinicals), there is an opportunity to get to know students first and recruit them before anyone else in the job market.

Unsolicited Applications

Some unsolicited employment inquiries will arrive at the facility by mail or in person. Although the proportion of such suitable applicants may not meet job specifications, there are important reasons to pay careful attention to them. It is good public relations practice to extend courteous treatment to applicants who approach the facility on their initiative and deal with them openly about the likelihood of employment with the organization and requirements to become suitable candidates.

Some administrators report a tendency for long-term care and hospital employees to seek a job change every few years. They may be entirely competent people who periodically look for a new work situation while remaining within their field. Such individuals may submit unsolicited applications simply to let a facility know of their availability. It is also essential to consider what jobs these employees are applying for and if their pay is equitable with other local facilities. Generally, facilities have relatively similar pay scales. However, when one facility pays 15 to 25 cents more per hour, that can mean the difference between paying an electric bill or having birthday parties for their children or not for certain employees at lower pay rates. It seems a simple expectation that many employees will put out applications hoping for a better offer than they currently have.

COMMON PITFALLS IN PRACTICE

- The more innovative you can be in hiring employees, the more successful you can be.
- Interviews happen when someone walks in the door, not at your convenience. Many wonderful employees leave and never come back, as your competition hired them. Take a few minutes, make the connection, and complete the hire!

CASE STUDY

The New Human Resources Director Takes Hold

Ralph has been asked by the administrator to assume the role of human resources director.

Shortly after he began, the DON asked Ralph to seek out a new third-shift supervisor and two nurse's aides as soon as possible. Ralph was given copies of their job descriptions.

Ralph had recently worked for 2 years at the nearby community hospital as a nursing assistant. He knew three dissatisfied RNs who would likely jump at the opportunity to be night supervisors. He also knew half a dozen nurse's aides who liked him and were tired of working with acutely ill patients.

The next day Ralph went over to the hospital, where he told two of the nurses and three of the aides about The Laurels job openings. He left notes on the lockers of five others.

Ralph was right. Two of the nurses he contacted and four of the aides filled out applications at The Laurels within 3 days. This direct contact saved Ralph from paying to advertise or even having to post the position openings.

Ralph reviewed the six applications. Both of the nurse applicants had had 2 years of hospital gerontological nursing in their background. Ralph added "2 years gerontological nursing experience required" to the RN night supervisor job description and returned it to the personnel policy manual.

All four of the nurse's aide applicants had completed high school and attended the local technical institute for 1 year. Ralph added "high school diploma and 1 year of a technical institute or equivalent training required" on the facility's nurse's aide job description.

The DON looked over the six applications and told Ralph to ask both nurses and two of the aides to see her for a job interview.

Ralph set the interviews for the first of the following week.

- *Evaluate Ralph's performance as the new human resources employee.*
- *Were Ralph's actions at the hospital acceptable?*
- *Were Ralph's changes to the job descriptions a good idea, or will they disqualify many otherwise qualified applicants?*

2.6 HIRING STAFF

Section Concepts

- *Hiring has many often-conflicting dos and dont's of which the facility administration must be aware*

Consider as the Administrator . . .

- *With so many restrictions on interviews and the hiring process, how can the facility hire competent employees?*

NAB DOMAIN 2C1: FEDERAL HUMAN RESOURCES LAWS, RULES, AND REGULATIONS (E.G., ADA, FMLA, WAGE AND HOUR, FLSA); 2C2: SELECTION AND HIRING PRACTICES (E.G., EEOC, INTERVIEWING, ADVERSE IMPACT, PROTECTED CLASSES, OCCUPATIONAL QUALIFICATIONS)

NAB DOMAIN 2C7: EMPLOYEE TRAINING AND ORIENTATION

NAB DOMAIN 2C: HUMAN RESOURCES

Recruitment is the process of locating prospective staff. *Personnel selection* is the process of deciding which applicants best fit the job requirements for which they are being considered. Often, however, this prospective staff member is evaluated not only for one of several positions the organization has open at that moment but simultaneously for anticipated slots expected soon as well. Nurses with extensive acute care experience, for example, will be interviewed and kept in mind by a facility moving toward offering subacute care. Any RN is often considered for DON potential upon an interview.

Through experience, employers have learned that when individuals are carefully selected for clearly defined positions, the result may be a faster adjustment to the position, greater job satisfaction, and a minimum number of inappropriately hired applicants versus job needs in the organization.

MEASURING THE IMPACTS OF LEGISLATION

Employers are directing greater attention to the job selection process. Often, intense scrutiny is given to employers by the government enforcers of the Civil Rights Act, the Equal Employment Act, and, more recently, the ADA.

The Civil Rights Act prohibits discrimination in employment practices based on race, color, religion, sex, or national origin. This Act uses the U.S. Equal Employment Opportunity Commission (EEOC), which was created by the Wagner Act, to implement the provisions of the Civil Rights Act. A later amendment, known as the Tower Amendment to Title 7, permitted the use of ability tests in employee selection procedures. Subsequently, the courts and the EEOC have made numerous rulings that determine the construction and use of ability tests (Library of Congress, 2021).

The Equal Employment Act is an amendment to Title 7 of the Civil Rights Act. It is intended to cover all employers of 15 or more persons and numerous other groups, such as educational institutions. Enforcement machinery was authorized and subsequently set up. Today human resources policy is shaped by these acts and the court decisions and regulations instituted by authorized governmental agencies. They affect such employment practices as retirement rules and considerations during pregnancy.

Several years ago, federal agencies jointly published a far-reaching document titled *Uniform Guidelines on Employee Selection Procedures* (2017), establishing the standards by which federal agencies determine the acceptability of validation procedures used for written tests and other selections.

The guidelines require the employer to demonstrate that the selection procedures used are valid in predicting or measuring employee performance in a specific job. They define discrimination as adverse impact:

> The use of any selection procedure which has an adverse impact on the hiring, promotion, or other employment or membership opportunities of members of any race, sex, or ethnic group will be considered to be discriminatory and inconsistent with these guidelines, unless [the] procedure has been validated in accordance with these guidelines. (Uniform Guidelines on Employee Selection Procedures, §1607.3)

Adverse impact is defined as occurring whenever the selection rate for any racial, ethnic, or sex group is less than 80% of the group's rate with the highest selection rate.

If 200 of 1,000 White applicants are selected (a selection rate of 20%), at least 16% of the minority applicants must be selected. Several court rulings, such as *Griggs v. Duke Power Company*, have already clearly established the principle that any human resources tests and activities must avoid having any discriminatory effect, whether intended or unintended (Noe et al., 2017).

The *Uniform Guidelines* have, in effect, become a handbook for decision-making in human resources matters. The human resources selection process must now be reported to state and federal compliance agencies, usually on EEOC forms that require accurate data on the actual hiring results of the nursing facility. What used to be the exclusive concern of the facility administrator and human resources officer can now be carried into the courtroom (Noe et al., 2017).

NAB DOMAIN 2C1: FEDERAL HUMAN RESOURCES LAWS, RULES, AND REGULATIONS (E.G., ADA, FMLA, WAGE AND HOUR, FLSA); 2C2: SELECTION AND HIRING PRACTICES (E.G., EEOC, INTERVIEWING, ADVERSE IMPACT, PROTECTED CLASSES, OCCUPATIONAL QUALIFICATIONS)

The facility assumes responsibility for informing employees of pertinent laws surrounding their employment. Informing employees is done through a series of posters which the U.S. Department of Labor requires to be posted to provide employees notice of these laws. The list of postings required is ever-growing. Included in this list required for nursing facilities (not necessarily comprehensive) are the following:

- Fair Labor Standards Act (wage and hours)
- Immigration and Nationality Act (applies to aliens authorized to work in the United States)
- Occupational Safety and Health Act (OSHA—workplace safety and health)
- Worker's Compensation
- Employee Retirement Income Security Act (ERISA—pensions)
- Uniformed Services Employment and Reemployment Rights Act (USERRA—rights to reemployment for those called to military service)
- Employee Polygraph Protection Act (EPPA)
- Garnishment of wages
- Family and Medical Leave Act
- Vietnam Era Veterans' Readjustment Assistance Act (VEVRAA)
- Whistleblower Protections

MATCHING THE FACILITY'S HUMAN RESOURCES NEEDS AND APPLICANTS

Taking on the right person for a position is a complex task. The employer understandably wants to find out as much about the applicant as possible to determine their likelihood of success in a position (Robbins & Coulter, 2018).

Methods of Obtaining Information

There are several methods for learning about applicants. Most organizations use written application forms, interviews, and background checks. The search for a new administrator or DON may involve appointing a committee, lengthy exploration, extensive interviewing, obtaining departmental employee input, and the final selection. Filling a vacancy for a nurse's aide is much less complicated. In both cases, however, all the information solicited must be demonstrably job-related or predictive of success in that position (Noe et al., 2017). Many employers also make it a practice today to assess candidates via their social media sites and postings. The social media presence of a potential employee needs to be assessed as that presence will become directly reflective of the facility.

Reliability and Validity of Information

Information that is valid and reliable is necessary for making an informed decision about an applicant's skills, knowledge, aptitudes, level of motivation, and likely fit with the organization (Noe et al., 2017; Robbins & Coulter, 2018).

The *reliability* of the tests, interviews, and other tools used in selecting among applicants refers to the consistency with which the same results are obtained over some time and when used by different testers (*interrater reliability*).

In measuring applicants' abilities, reliability means that an applicant will achieve the same or nearly the same score or results when taking the test at different times, for example, a week or two apart. If a test were to give differing results from week to week, it would be unreliable, just as a set of scales used to weigh produce in a store must reliably give the same weight week after week every time produce of equal weight is placed on it. Reliability also requires that different applicants with the same skills score the same on the test. If word-processing skills are being measured, applicants with the same skill level must score the same on the test.

A test or selection procedure provides validity when it measures what it is intended to measure and does so well. In essence, *validity* measures how effectively an instrument does its job (Noe et al., 2017; Robbins & Coulter, 2018).

TWO TYPES OF VALIDITY

Personnel experts have relied on at least two types of validity for several years: content validity and construct validity. Governmental agencies use content and construct validity in judging the results of a facility's hiring program (Noe et al., 2017).

Content Validity

Content validity is the degree to which a test, interview procedure, or any other selection tool measures the skills, knowledge, or performance requirements needed to fill the position for which the applicant applies. As more and more facilities begin to offer medically complex care, a nursing position may require the ability to administer drugs intravenously (IVs). A test establishing that the applicant can perform IVs skillfully has content validity.

Construct Validity

Construct validity is the extent to which a selection tool measures a trait or behavior perceived as necessary to function in a job. Intelligence is an abstract construct established by putting together answers to a series of questions that yield a measure of the theoretical construct (Cole & Kelley, 2020).

The following is an example of construct validity: A nursing facility administrator's requirement of a "friendly facial expression" toward residents is an example of a construct (trait) that the administrator believes is needed for the position.

To validate a friendly facial expression as a job requirement, the administrator would have to identify the work behaviors required for the position, identify the required constructs (e.g., smiling), and then show by empirical evidence that this selection requirement is genuinely related to the construct.

It is of fundamental importance for a nursing facility to require that all staff treat residents in a cheerful or friendly manner, although this directive may be challenging to achieve. In a Fort Worth, Texas, case, a federal judge ruled that American Airlines had the right to discharge an otherwise good flight attendant because he did not smile enough. The flight attendant had sued the company, contending that he was a good employee and met all requirements of the job except for the smile. The federal judge upheld American's policy of requiring a friendly facial expression as "essential in the competitive airline industry."

APPLICATION FORMS—PREEMPLOYMENT QUESTIONS

Employers must avoid questions that might be construed as violating the Civil Rights Act, Title 7, or the ADA. Before hiring a person, questions regarding age, sex, race, national origin, education, religion, arrest and conviction records, marital status, credit rating (Title 7), or disabilities (ADA and Title 7) should be avoided. The interviewer must review any unsolicited requests for reasonable accommodation under this Act. If the applicant is a minor, that is, younger than 18 years, federal and state child labor laws may specify work hours, type of work, machinery to be operated, and supervision requirements. Recently, about 1,500 complaints based on religious discrimination were filed annually (Noe et al., 2017).

Table 2.2 lists some handy suggestions for questions that are unacceptable (and some that are acceptable) during job interviews.

TABLE 2.2 Unacceptable and Acceptable Interview Questions

Illegal interview queries	Questionable interview queries
Age or genetic information	Height/weight
Birthplace	Financial information
Country of origin	Unemployment status
Citizenship	Background check information
Disabilities	Medical questions or examinations
Gender or sex	
Sexual orientation	
Marital status	
Family status	
Are you pregnant? (even when visibly pregnant)	
Race, color, or ethnicity	
Religion (any query is forbidden)	
Previous workplace injuries	
What can you ask?	
Are you legally allowed to work in the United States?	
Can you read, write, and speak in English?	
Can you show proof of citizenship?	
Can you perform all the duties in the job description?	
How will you perform the functions of the job?	

HANDICAP-RELATED QUESTIONS

The EEOC has issued many types of guidance over the years intending to clarify what questions employers may ask that might be related to handicap as viewed under the ADA. This guidance has made it clear that an employer may ask an applicant about the nature of any need the applicant may have for adjustment to a handicap only after making a job offer. It is only at this point that the employer may consider what a reasonable accommodation might be. Before offering a job, it is unlawful to ask questions such as "Do you need a reasonable accommodation to perform the essential functions of the job? If so, what kind?"

To clarify what preemployment interview questions are permissible and which are not, Table 2.3 integrates information from the EEOC; it is not meant to be a comprehensive list. Employment-related questions are an ever-changing area. It is best to stay as current as possible on the most recent changes to any laws or regulations surrounding employment law. Many companies have legal counsel as part of their regular business to keep up with such concerns.

TABLE 2.3 Preemployment Interview Questions With Equal Employment Opportunity Commission Guidance

Lawful	Unlawful
Do you drink alcohol?	How much alcohol do you drink per week?
How well can you handle stress?	Do you ever get ill from stress?
Are you currently illegally using drugs?	Have you ever been treated for drug problems?
Do you regularly eat three meals per day?	Do you need to eat a number of small snacks at regular intervals throughout the day in order to maintain your energy level?
How did you break your leg?	How did you come to use a wheelchair?
Do you have a cold?	Do you have AIDS?

INTERVIEWING APPLICANTS

Interviews are used extensively in evaluating job applicants. Each organization will develop its style and identify its varying information needs as it conducts interviews (Noe et al., 2017). Many administrators develop their individual styles for interviews.

Preliminary Interviews

One approach is to use a short preliminary applicant questionnaire and a brief conversation based on the questionnaire. This technique serves to screen out unsuitable candidates, using a minimum of time and organizational resources.

Telephone/Video Interviewing/Screening

Before setting up interviews with candidates, the interviewer can elicit a good bit of information, such as the following:

- Present employment
- Why are they looking for a position; what kind of next position is being sought
- Candidate's salary requirements
- Why candidate left previous positions, past salaries
- Persons supervised, if a manager, and their job functions
- Give candidate information about the facility
- Set up an interview if, after the preceding explorations, mutual interest exists

Interviewing Methods

Interviewing methods vary but can generally be classified into three types according to the degree of structure used: the nondirective, the in-depth, and the patterned interview.

In the *nondirective interview*, the interrogator refrains from influencing the applicant's remarks, allowing maximum freedom to ask questions and give information. The interviewer's task is to pay special attention to attitudes, values, or feelings that the candidate may exhibit.

This approach maximizes the amount of information the applicant may reveal and is often called an open-ended interview technique. The interviewer asks only broad general questions, such as "Tell me about how you did and how you liked your last job," or "What is it about working in a long-term care facility that attracts you?" or "Where do you want to be in your career in the next 5 years?" There is no prescribed set of questions.

An *in-depth interview*, sometimes called a directed interview, provides more structure in the form of specific question areas to be covered. Examples of questions appropriate to the in-depth interview include:

- What do you consider your most important skills for this job?
- Tell me about your last job.
- Under what type of supervision techniques do you function best?
- What did you like most about your last job?
- What are your feelings toward older people?
- What do you like most, dislike most about older persons?

The *patterned interview* allows the least amount of freedom to both the interviewer and the applicant. All questions are sequential and highly detailed. Generally, a summary sheet must be filled out by the interviewer interpreting the results of the encounter. The patterned interview allows a similar interview for each candidate for the job, allowing for easier comparison.

In every case, make every effort to make the interviewee comfortable and be on time for the interview.

Some Approaches

- Avoid forming strong impressions during the early minutes of the interview.
- Allow the candidate to do most of the talking.
- Do not clue the candidate into precise goals early in the interview.
- Ask specific questions about past job behavior.
- Probe for all the information needed.
- Take notes but not on the application form.
- Use second and third interviews when appropriate.

Interviews in the Days Post-COVID-19

COVID-19 has changed every possible aspect of business. Today, many employers are not allowing in-person interviews at all. Technology has allowed us to forego in-person meetings, and many employers are taking advantage of this. We see many interviews conducted via online platforms such as Zoom or Microsoft Teams. Many applicants complete the entire interview process outlined earlier virtually and are only brought in for meaningful observation if they are a final candidate for a position. Otherwise, applicants rarely set foot in the facility. Another example of innovation by nursing facility administrators!

General Areas for Questions

Provided here are some generalized sample questions for use during interviews. There is no "right" question to ask during an interview. The overall purpose of the interview is to help assess if a candidate can do the job well and see if they will fit into the corporate culture and if they are willing to perform the duties necessary to be successful. You are interviewing them as much as they are interviewing you.

Professional Maturity

- What has been the most challenging assignment you have ever had, and how did you handle it?
- What would you do if (name an adverse situation that an employee in that job might encounter)?
- What actions have you taken if you disagreed with a supervisor's decision?
- What is the impact or role of your department on your current facility's objectives?

Skill Level

- What are your current job responsibilities?
- What results were achieved in terms of successes and achievements?
- What do you feel you can learn from this position?
- What are your greatest strengths? What areas need improvement?
- What was the most significant contribution you made to your current position?
- How would your references rate your technical competence?
- The ability to solve problems is critical to this position. Please provide an example of how this ability has been important to your success.
- What significant trends do you see in your profession?

Character

- What do you consider the most essential aspect of a job?
- Where do you see yourself in 2 years? 5 years? 10 years?
- What have you liked best about your present (recent) supervisor(s)? Liked least?
- Why should we hire you?
- How successful do you think you have been so far in your career?
- How long would it take you to make a meaningful contribution to this facility?

Accumulate a Reference List

Increasingly, facilities "raid" each other. One might say, "I have two jobs in this category. Do you know another person?" Then also hire the people referenced—excellent workers generally do not walk in the front door! It is a widespread procedure for sister facilities in the same corporation to "share" employees in this fashion.

Research Findings on the Use of Interviews

A good deal of research has been conducted on the reliability and validity of interviews as a tool for judging job applicants:

- Structured interviews are more reliable than unstructured interviews.
- When there is more information about a job, interrater reliability is increased; several interviewers are more likely to come to the same decision.
- Interviews can explain why a person would not be a good employee but not why they would be a good one.
- Factual written data seem to be more important than physical appearance.
- Interviews are often the best way to evaluate interpersonal skills and level of applicant motivation.
- Allowing the applicant time to talk provides a larger behavior sample. In addition, one can learn more from listening than by talking.
- An interviewer's race affects the behavior of the person being interviewed.

Responding to the Market... Apply This Afternoon, Be Interviewed This Afternoon

Although the processes mentioned earlier may serve well when there is a large applicant pool for jobs in the facility, the reality is that nurses, nurse's aides, and similar facility employees often change jobs. The applicant may have taken the afternoon off to find a new job. Making such applicants feel welcome and offering an interview at the point of application may increase a facility's ability to have the first choice in obtaining needed new hires. Prioritizing interviews can mean stopping tasks of the administrator and department heads to perform an interview when an employee walks in. Missing this opportunity may be a permanent loss of that potential employee. Healthcare employees are in high demand and need to be treated as such.

BACKGROUND INVESTIGATION

If the interviewer decides that the candidate is of interest to the organization, background information can be sought.

It is advisable to obtain from applicants a signed request for references. Increasingly, former employers are reluctant to put any recommendations into writing for fear of lawsuits. Many will only provide information about the date of hire, position(s) held, and date of separation.

Background Checks

Background checks are increasingly important. Despite most employers' adoption of a neutral policy on employment—for example, revealing only a name, job, title, and dates of employment—it is important to persevere. They recommend a screening process consisting of (a) background checks: trustworthiness, honesty, gaps in employment, required licenses, relevant background, for example, for a driver; (b) drug tests (the ADA does not protect drug users); and (c) criminal background checks (which may be mandatory). Here the so-called business-necessity rule applies. Employers must consider all job-related circumstances around a conviction to determine if the person would be a safe employee in the facility.

Some allowable considerations are (a) time of conviction, (b) nature of conviction, (c) number of convictions, (d) facts of each case, (e) job relatedness, (f) length of time between conviction and application, and (g) efforts at rehabilitation. Generally, any person convicted of substance abuse becomes a high risk for the facility. Reference requests should be obtained on at least two jobs, preferably the most recent or for the past 3 years (whichever is longer). For applicants with no work experience, school, volunteer, or personal references can be used. For nurse's aide applicants, two basic checks must be made:

- The state registry to verify current certification and whether the applicant has met training and competency requirements
- The substance abuse registry in each state the facility has a reason to believe the applicant has worked as a nurse's aide to determine whether any record of resident abuse or neglect or misappropriation of a resident's property has occurred
- Sometimes criminal background checks must be made

The Privacy Act (Public Law 93–579) gave federal staff the right to examine their human resources records, including letters of reference, unless they waived this right when they requested the letter. Although not mandated by federal law, the Privacy Act seems to have led to employers' tendency to permit staff to review and change their human resources files.

Negligent hiring lawsuits can be minimized by gathering as much pertinent information as possible about applicants. Discrimination charges can be minimized by focusing on job-related criteria.

It is important to note that many states have precise guidelines surrounding criminal histories and how they play into being hired (or not). Be sure to ascertain the requirements in the facility's state to prevent hiring individuals who are otherwise barred from employment in nursing facilities. Murder, Medicare/Medicaid fraud, manslaughter, theft, abuse, neglect, and misappropriation are just a few of the more common convictions that stop an applicant from becoming an employee.

Credit Reports

Under the federal Fair Credit Reporting Act (Public Law 91–508), the employer must advise applicants if credit reports will be requested. If the candidate is rejected because of a poor credit report, they must be so informed and given the name and address of the reporting credit agency.

Physical Examination

All facility staff must have periodic health examinations to ensure freedom from communicable disease. The practical impact of this stipulation is to seek a pre-employment physical examination to ensure new staff meets this criterion. There is debate as to whether requiring a physical before offering a job is permitted or whether one must offer the job and then require a physical before the employee begins work. In essence, all applicants must be informed that a condition of employment will be the preplacement health exam following the conditional job offer.

There are several practical reasons for a physical examination. It establishes the physical capability of the applicant to meet the job requirements (a delicate proceeding given the tenor of the ADA). It provides a baseline against which to assess their later periodic physical examinations. The employment-related physical examination is especially valuable in determining claims of work-associated disabilities under workers' compensation laws. The laboratory analyses that are part of the exam can detect illicit drugs in the applicant and may detect communicable diseases to which the residents should not be exposed (Noe et al., 2017).

Suppose the physician determines that the new employee cannot perform the job's essential functions due to a disability under the definition of the ADA. In that case, the facility must follow policy on reasonable accommodations for individuals with disabilities. If, instead, the physician determines that the employee cannot perform the job's essential functions, but their inability does not meet the definitions of the ADA, the employee is notified that they are not qualified for the position.

Usually, the health file is not considered part of the human resources file due to its confidential nature; only authorized persons may have access to the employee's health record on a "need to know" basis.

CASE STUDY

The Interviews

The first RN applicant, a Black female, sat uncomfortably in her chair opposite the DON, who believed her patients preferred White female mid-career nurses. The DON read over the application, and then they had the following conversation.

"I see you've lived here a long time. Were you born here?"
"Yes, ma'am."
"What areas of town have you lived in?"
The applicant recited all four addresses in various parts of the town where she has lived.

(continued)

"Were your parents born here, too?"

"No, ma'am."

"Where did they come from?"

The applicant proudly tells the DON that her parents migrated here from Puerto Rico.

The DON observes that many folks in the community have come from there.

"A lot of you folk are Seventh Day Adventists. Do you have any objections to working on Saturdays, so people have some full weekends off?"

The applicant responds that she will work on the weekends if needed.

"Honey, I noticed you were using a cane when you came walking kinda slow up the front walk. Can you get on without that cane?"

"I have to use it at least a couple of hours a day."

"What have you got that makes you have to use a cane?"

The applicant indicates that is because of a permanent back injury from two jobs ago.

"Do you ever get muscle spasms that keep you from doing your work properly?"

The applicant indicates that she might need some consideration in her work pattern and schedule.

"Drugs can make a condition like that a lot worse than it needs to be. Have you ever had to be treated for drugs?"

"No, ma'am."

"We've had a lot of problems with nurses and aides drinking lately. How much of a problem is that to you?"

The applicant assures the DON that she does not drink excessively.

"How about callouts? Does your back injury make you miss much work?"

The applicant assures the DON that she gets to work every day as scheduled.

"We like for our employees to be active in the community. Which organizations are you a member of?"

The applicant recites all the organizations she has participated in within the community.

"Is your RN license up to date?"

The applicant assures the DON that her license is up to date. She states that it was renewed just a month ago.

The DON seemed satisfied with the applicant's license.

The second applicant interview for the evening supervisor was relatively brief. The DON did not feel that her patients or residents would want a man coming into their rooms at night.

The DON felt pressed for time. It was almost noon. She asked Ralph (from human resources) if he would interview the aides. Ralph did so. He sat and chatted with both of them together for half an hour, letting them do most of the talking.

A couple of days later, Ralph reviewed the four applicants with the DON. The DON told him to hire the Black female RN and the two aides he interviewed if he liked them.

(continued)

- *How do these interviews fit with the EEOC and ADA interviewing requirements?*
- *What problem areas do you see with the interviews?*
- *Are group interviews a good idea? A bad idea?*
- *How many "illegal" questions were there here?*

Consider as the Administrator . . .

- *Some grocery stores hire persons with minor handicaps as a public relations strategy. Is that a strong decision for a nursing facility? At what point does such a strategy backfire?*

THE DECISION TO HIRE

Who should decide which applicant to hire? Not the human resources staff. Generally, the final decision to hire is given to the head of the department in which the recruit will work. The facility administrator can define their role in the final decision-making or leave it entirely up to the department head.

Two Approaches to the Hiring Decision

The hiring decision itself is complex. Two basic approaches have been identified in the literature: clinical and statistical.

In a clinical approach, the decision-maker reviews all available information about the match of the applicant and the job and then decides.

In the statistical approach, the decision-maker identifies the most valid predictors and then weights them according to complicated formulas. This method has been shown superior to the clinical approach. However, few facilities routinely have enough staff time available to make this approach practical. A compromise is for the decision-maker to rate each applicant for a position on several dimensions, such as test score results, education, experience, apparent interest level, and the like, assigning numerical scores on each dimension to each candidate. The results can provide a systematic set of comparison data for reaching the final decision.

Achieving Construct Validity for Hiring Nursing Facility Staff

Heart Behind the Numbers

It is not enough to establish that an applicant has the technical skills needed for a job. Staff must realize that caring for frail, older adult nursing facility patients is often less dependent on the staff's technical knowledge than on their compassion for others. Knowing the technique for gait training for a disabled person is useless if the staff member cannot encourage the person to leave the chair. As the nursing facility population becomes more medically complex, *both* caring and technical skills become increasingly important. Sensitivity, compassion, and caring have construct and technical competence and will increasingly have validity as hiring criteria in nursing facilities.

It is not just the administrator or the DON who needs passion; all staff in the facility need to be passionate in carrying out their tasks. A sales vice president of a large U.S. camera firm explained who makes the best salespeople—translated here for the nursing facility. Drawing a vertical line down his flip chart, he had on one side basic skills and competencies: knowing the tasks to be performed, being well informed about what competing facilities were doing, having a good employment record, and experience in long-term care. These are all the usual requirements.

Passion Index

On the right side of the chart, he wrote "Fire in the heart," commenting that if he had to choose, he would choose someone with fire than one well trained and well recommended. He felt that staff who have fire demonstrate increased motivation, will work harder, go the extra mile, and are more resourceful at meeting resident or facility needs. Nurses and nursing assistants who have the drive and enthusiasm for caring for the resident can be taught technical skills they lack. Applicants who lack fire in their hearts or passion for their work are not so easily taught.

Counting Grades

How much do grades count? Do the highest grade point averages in nursing school or the nursing assistant test point consistently to the best candidates? Consider the following findings. More than half of the Fortune 500 companies' chief executive officers had a B or C average in college. Two thirds of U.S. senators come from the bottom half of their class. Three fourths of U.S. presidents were in the lower half of their school classes. More than half of millionaire entrepreneurs did not finish college.

OFFERING THE JOB

Once the successful candidate is chosen, they should be informed. Information such as proposed salary, job title and level, starting date, and other relevant information should be communicated. Typically, a specific period during which the offer may be considered is stated. In every case, the candidate needs to be informed about starting date, pay rate, where and when to report, and their supervisor's name.

The offer letter can be an excellent time to include the human resources handbook. The handbook (discussed later in detail) describes facility policy on matters the prospective employee should be aware of as part of their evaluation of the proposed position. Setting a 3-day time limit for the newly hired staff member to complete all paperwork is appropriate. In fact, many facilities simply integrate the paperwork into their new hire orientation proceedings.

Unsuccessful applicants should be informed by letter, email, or per policy as soon as the job is filled.

Overall, 14% of all employed U.S. civilians work in the health field (Laughlin et al., 2021). Nursing facilities hire nearly as many healthcare workers as all physicians' offices and clinics. Table 2.4 shows a distribution of selected healthcare workers and where they work in the field. It is important to understand such numbers as they allow the administrator to have a better idea of where to look for their newest employees.

TABLE 2.4 Persons Employed and Percent Distribution in Selected Healthcare Sites, United States, 2019

	Millions	Percentage Distribution
Total healthcare workers	22.26	100
Nursing care facilities	1.76	7.93
Residential care facilities without nursing	1.16	5.22
Home healthcare services	1.48	6.66
Hospitals	7.05	31.69
Offices and clinics of physicians	1.99	8.95

Source: Adapted from Laughlin, L., Anderson, A., Martinez, A., & Gayfield, A. (2021). *Who are our health care workers?* U.S. Census Bureau. https://www.census.gov/library/stories/2021/04/who-are-our-health-care-workers.html

COMMON PITFALLS IN PRACTICE

- Good interviews are an art form. Get some extensive experience in this area before you attempt to interview potential employees alone. Sit in on plenty of interviews. Have someone sit in the ones you do and critique you.
- Be certain to understand forbidden areas for questioning. This changes quickly and often. Stay on top of your field.
- Just because a question during an interview is not illegal, that does not necessarily make it appropriate to ask. Use good judgment when interviewing.
- The interview is just as much about you wanting to hire the employee as it is about them interviewing you and wanting to work with you. The interview is a two-way street. Always remember this!
- It is important to hire the best candidate for the job. There are so few available employees today that some facilities offer jobs to qualified candidates simply because "they have a pulse." Whereas you need employees to care for residents, this is a problematic way to hire new employees. A better hiring practice is to hire only those who are passionate about the job and the population they will be working with.

2.7 TRAINING STAFF

Section Concepts

- *To understand the importance of the first day on the job*
- *To understand how to develop and maintain an employee handbook*

Consider as the Administrator . . .

- *Is the employee handbook an actual contract with the employee?*

NAB DOMAIN 2C1: FEDERAL HUMAN RESOURCES LAWS, RULES, AND REGULATIONS (E.G., ADA, FMLA, WAGE AND HOUR, FLSA); 2C2: SELECTION AND HIRING PRACTICES (E.G., EEOC, INTERVIEWING, ADVERSE IMPACT, PROTECTED CLASSES, OCCUPATIONAL QUALIFICATIONS); 2C3: COMPENSATION AND BENEFITS PROGRAMS (E.G., TIME OFF, HEALTHCARE INSURANCE, EMPLOYEE PAY AND PAYROLL); 2C6: PROFESSIONAL DEVELOPMENT (E.G., MAINTENANCE OF CREDENTIALS, CONTINUING EDUCATION); 2C7: EMPLOYEE TRAINING AND ORIENTATION; 2C9: HUMAN RESOURCE POLICIES (E.G., DRUG-FREE WORKPLACE, DISCIPLINE, JOB CLASSIFICATION, PHOTOGRAPHY AND VIDEO, SOCIAL MEDIA USAGE, MOBILE PHONE USAGE); 2C10: EMPLOYEE RECORD-KEEPING REQUIREMENTS; 2C13: CULTURAL COMPETENCE AND DIVERSITY AWARENESS

NAB DOMAIN 4A4: LEADERSHIP PRINCIPLES (E.G., COMMUNICATIONS, STYLES, MENTORING, COACHING, PERSONAL PROFESSIONAL DEVELOPMENT)

NAB DOMAIN 2C: HUMAN RESOURCES

ORIENTATION

First Day on the Job

Orientation is the foundation for employment. An "unoriented" employee is a severe liability.

The first day on the job will potentially leave a lasting impression (Noe et al., 2017; Sampson & Fried, 2021). It is an opportunity for the facility. The new employee traditionally brings an initial reservoir of goodwill toward the facility. Enthusiasm and anxiety characterize the first day. A sensitively managed orientation program can help the new employee reduce anxiety and build positive images of the new work environment.

Typical first-day activities can include the following:

- Official welcome to the new employee
- Completion of all new hire paperwork
- Introduction to as many of the staff as is appropriate
- Tour of the facility, including the location of lockers for safekeeping of personal effects, staff lounges, restrooms, parking arrangements
- Instructions on use of any time clock
- Safety rules, such as infection control and emergency procedures, especially those concerning fire and staff assignments in case of fire
- Explanation of residents' rights

- Discussion of appropriate policies and procedures—to include information on preventing abuse and neglect
- Mandatory education requirements, such as OSHA Bloodborne Pathogen training
- Discussion of contents of the human resources handbook

There is only one "first day on the job" for each new employee. Whether the orientation is for the DON or a nurse's aide, each staff member is equally essential for the organization's success. If the place is organized to take notice of the new employee and attempts to meet their needs on the first day, this latest member of the staff will be more likely to assist the facility in meeting its needs during the following months and years.

Facilities of 300 beds are as capable of a personalized orientation program as those with only 80. In practice, by having a designated human resources process, the larger organization may have a functional advantage over the smaller, where orientation may be left to chance and good intentions without assigned responsibility for this introduction.

Using a Checklist

Precisely because orientation is both a critical and complex task, the use of a checklist is valuable. Those charged with familiarizing the new staff member with the organization are less likely to overlook any element of the employee's new responsibilities as they review each item on the list. One researcher suggests that using a checklist may help reduce employee turnover by assisting each new employee to gain an initial realistic and more transparent set of expectations about the new positions. Turnover is always expensive (Robbins & Coulter, 2018; Sampson & Fried, 2021). Estimates vary from $1,000 to more than $25,000, depending on position and length of training needed, before an employee efficiently performs their job.

Others consider it advisable that both providers and receivers of the orientation be required to sign each activity on the checklist. This double-check system maximizes the probability that the orientation will be completed. When this document is placed in the employee's human resources file, the signed orientation form becomes a legal basis for establishing that the information was received. A single staff member can be responsible for the orientation and its documentation from the introduction to the signed checklist.

THE HUMAN RESOURCES POLICY HANDBOOK

The human resources policy handbook, often called the employee's handbook or the staff manual, is a compilation of the facility policies related to work conditions. Whereas a job description relates to only one job, the general human resources policies cover all staff.

Each facility will have its own handbook. Chains generally have sets of policies that apply to all their staff, allowing local facilities to add their policies within the broader policy guidelines and any requirements specific to state or local government regulations.

The main elements most often included in such a handbook are a statement of general policies, details of benefits, and general information relevant to the conditions of employment. The human resources handbook can be considered the rules or terms under which staff is hired and carry out their work.

A. Introduction and welcome to the facility
B. History and background of the facility; mission, vision, values statements; handbook disclaimer
C. General employment policies
    1. Equal opportunity employment (conforming to the Civil Rights Act) or sexual harassment policy, age discrimination policies
    2. Classification of staff into full-time and part-time by number of hours worked per week and working hours of the facility
    3. Confidentiality of information about residents and facility matters (HIPAA compliance)
    4. Resident's rights statement
    5. Employee's records—confidentiality, employee access policy, usual contents: (a) application for employment; (b) preemployment checks, letters, records of phone calls; (c) credit checks; (d) performance evaluations, promotions; (e) federal and state withholding certificates; (f) correspondence; (g) disciplinary actions; (h) grievances; (i) attendance; (j) signatures for receipt of human resources policy manual, orientation activities, and in-service attendance records; (k) health-related materials such as annual physical results, hepatitis B vaccination records (bloodborne pathogens requirements), annual tuberculosis tests results, and records of injuries or other medically related matters; and (l) license or certificate verification; and (m) other relevant materials (Singh, 2016)
    6. Reporting policies—required call-in times prior to shift if unable to come to work
    7. Discipline system—if a progressive system with a listing of each rule and a statement of disciplinary action; the number and method (oral or written) warnings before dismissal. For example, failure to follow a dress code may allow an oral warning and one or more written warnings before dismissal. In contrast, physical abuse of a resident could bring immediate suspension or investigation and, if appropriate after investigation, dismissal
    8. Uniforms or appearance
    9. General conduct expected, for example, respect, vulgarity, courtesy, attendance and punctuality, working quietly, absenteeism, visitors to staff, and outside work
    10. Gifts and tipping (not permitted from residents or their families or significant others or sponsors)
    11. Eating, drinking, smoking, and kitchen traffic rules
    12. Use of alcohol and illegal drugs
    13. Parking, mail, rest breaks, meal breaks, lost and found, phone calls to staff (a never-ending concern), smoking and use of tobacco policy (many facilities

have banned smoking by employees entirely), employment of relations, and search of staff (package and purse inspection)

14. Destruction of nursing facility property
15. Suggestion box, permitted uses of bulletin boards, solicitation or distribution of literature rules
16. Probationary period, use of anniversary or other dates for human resources reviews, and seniority policies
17. Health requirements and physical examinations
18. Employee debts and garnishment of wages
19. Performance ratings, promotion policies, and interdepartmental transfer policies, and job posting
20. Wages and salaries, timecards/timeclock/punching, pay plan, date procedures for determining payroll calculations, payrolls, deductions, overtime policy, and severance pay
21. Grievance procedures
22. Hospitalization and first-aid treatment
23. Facility position on unions
24. Resignation notice and procedures and exit interview
25. On-the-job injuries policies
26. Inservice education requirements
27. Reimbursement for specified expenses (e.g., travel, meals, memberships)
28. Confidentiality of company affairs or nondisclosure of information
29. Family and medical leaves, and worker's compensation insurance
30. Fire and disaster or evacuation plans
31. Incident reports

D. Benefits
1. Holidays
2. Vacations, leave-accumulation policies
3. Leaves of absence: sick leave, funeral leave, military leave, maternity leave, jury duty, and extended leave
4. Health benefits and dental benefits
5. Tax-deferred savings plans (e.g., 401(k) or 403(b))
6. Stock purchase plan (if any), known as employee stock option plans
7. Retirement benefits
8. Insurance: life insurance, unemployment compensation, occupational disease insurance, workers' compensation insurance, disability insurance (Noe et al., 2017), long-term care insurance, and others
9. Shift differential (if paid)
10. Other benefits, such as childcare benefits or meals at work
11. Group rates: chains and groups of facilities can negotiate reduced rates on a variety of items such as accident insurance, life insurance, liability policies, and the like

In recent years, employee handbooks have been a subject of concern to management. Some courts have held the handbooks to be an enforceable contract between the employer and the employee. Entering disclaimers in the handbook has not prevented staff from successfully suing in court. Should an employee file for an unemployment claim at some point in the future, the administrator is held to the letter of their employee handbook in most circumstances.

COMMON PITFALLS IN PRACTICE
- Lousy orientations yield lousy employees. Take an active part in your orientations. Show that the administrator is more than just a figurehead in the front office.
- The orientation sets the tone for the entire employment of an employee. If the orientation is lacking detail, you can expect the same from your employees when they hit the floor. Your orientation sets that example and expectation. Ensure your orientation is high-quality and motivational.

TRAINING

NAB DOMAIN 2C6: PROFESSIONAL DEVELOPMENT (E.G., MAINTENANCE OF CREDENTIALS, CONTINUING EDUCATION); 2C7: EMPLOYEE TRAINING AND ORIENTATION; 2C8: PERFORMANCE EVALUATION

NAB DOMAIN 4A3: ORGANIZATIONAL BEHAVIOR (E.G., ORGANIZATIONAL CULTURE, TEAM BUILDING, GROUP DYNAMICS)

As we have noted, *directing* is ensuring that each work role is successfully communicated to the employee. Directing is the process of (a) communicating to the staff what is to be done and then (b) assisting them in performing their role successfully.

The administrator's role is to ensure that each team member receives needed professional development throughout the worker's career at the facility. Some team members, such as nurses and nurse's aides, typically are subject to continuing education requirements. Others, such as the maintenance supervisor, may have no external education requirements. However, a program of sending this staff member to educational seminars and training opportunities may pay off handsomely in improved facility functioning.

Purpose

The purpose of the orientation program is to provide an initial introduction to the new employee. The purpose of training is to communicate the organization's needs to the staff and assist them in meeting those needs. Training is a continuous process, formally beginning the first day on the job and extending for the employee's association with the facility. Each employee will have an individual learning curve (Noe et al., 2017).

Steps in Establishing Training Needs

Staff members responsible for establishing the nursing facility's training program commonly analyze three elements in planning for this course: (a) the organization,

(b) the tasks, and (c) the person carrying out the work (Noe et al., 2017; Robbins & Coulter, 2018).

Organizational analysis examines the facility's goals, resources, and internal and external environments to determine where training efforts should be focused. Many in-service topics are mandated for the various departments each year. These can form the initial framework for training needs (Noe et al., 2017).

Task analysis involves a review of job descriptions and activities essential for performing each job. The emphasis of training programs can then be placed on specific tasks that are inadequately carried out or simply in need of reinforcement because of their importance to the facility, such as fire drills and disaster preparedness. Additionally, whenever a facility begins accepting more medically complex residents, training for new techniques for the nursing staff is often in order.

A person or employee *skill analysis* can be made to arrive at the skills, knowledge, and attitudes required in each position. Person analysis means interpreting each position in terms of the personal attributes or behaviors necessary for performing the job acceptably.

Once the goal of a training program has been determined, the following steps can be taken: (a) formulate instructional objectives, (b) develop instructional experiences to achieve these objectives, (c) establish performance criteria to be met, and (d) obtain evaluations of the training effort.

On-the-job training is conducted by a staff member assigned to assist a new or continuing employee in acquiring the abilities needed in a position in the facility. Ideally, on-the-job training permits the trainee to be an additional or extra worker for the first few days, allowing observation and a progressive involvement in performing the tasks and behaviors required (Noe et al., 2017).

In-service training refers to employee education offered throughout the work career of the employee. Generally, in-service education consists of small seminars for groups of staff. Various educational techniques are used, including flip charts, films, lectures, videos, role-playing, case discussions, and the like. Many facilities today also utilize online courses to meet in-service needs, so they can be done when the employee has spare moments throughout their day. In many busy facilities, three or more in-service training programs occur every week.

The nursing facility is a training site for numerous educational programs. Most facilities participate as training sites for nursing schools, physical therapy programs, pharmacy programs, and similar allied health training programs in nearby colleges and training programs (Noe et al., 2017).

EVALUATING TRAINING

Evaluation of training efforts can be complex. Although tests can indeed be devised to measure memorization, the nursing facility seeks to assess something more complex: changes in employee behavior. To quantify behavioral changes, state learning objectives as behavioral objectives and provide some way to measure the attainment of these objectives.

Behavioral objectives can be measured by observing whether staff carrying out their duties exhibit the behaviors sought as the objective of the training. Usually, the goal is for the employee to acquire a skill or change an attitude (Noe et al., 2017). Using performance-centered behavioral objectives can assist evaluation.

Performance-centered objectives in nurse's aide training might be (a) demonstrate proper procedures for turning a resident who is suffering from decubitus ulcers (pressure injuries) and (b) consistently greet any patients encountered in the hallways using a pleasant tone of voice.

Both of these are performance-centered objectives. The aide-in-training can physically demonstrate proper techniques for turning a resident who has a pressure injury. Furthermore, the person's demeanor toward residents encountered in the hallways can be monitored by the trainer or staff members (Noe et al., 2017).

Diversity Training

NAB DOMAIN 2C7: EMPLOYEE TRAINING AND ORIENTATION; 2C13: CULTURAL COMPETENCE AND DIVERSITY AWARENESS

The composition of the nursing facility staff reflects the changing demographic landscape. Diversity training is designed to change employee attitudes about diversity and develop skills needed to work in teams with employees of, for example, differing values, gender, ethnic, racial, and religious backgrounds, and sexual preferences. Employees can gain an appreciation and acceptance of cultural differences among themselves (Cole & Kelley, 2020; Noe et al., 2017; Robbins & Coulter, 2018). Diversity training itself is generally designed to help in facilitating intergroup interactions, reduce prejudice or preconceived notions, and bring awareness to areas of discrimination. Awareness of these areas helps all employees work better together as a cohesive group. Employees come from different backgrounds, cultures, and beliefs. Allowing for an environment as the administrator that embraces this makes for a much better workplace for everyone involved.

COMMON PITFALLS IN PRACTICE
- *Ongoing* training is an integral part of your success as an administrator. Training of some sort should be happening all the time in the facility.
- Big rooms of employees listening to training hear about the first 30 seconds of what you are communicating. Individualized training or training in small groups on the hall is much more effective.

2.8 RETAINING EMPLOYEES

Section Concepts

- *You will learn what the facility needs from the employee and what the employee needs from the facility*
- *You will learn strategies to meet both facility and the employee needs*
- *You will learn ways to keep valued employees*

Consider as the Administrator . . .

- *What motivates employees? Where does money fit into the equation, if at all?*

NAB DOMAIN 2C12: EMPLOYEE SATISFACTION, ENGAGEMENT, AND RETENTION

NAB DOMAIN 1B3: CARE RECIPIENT BILL OF RIGHTS AND RESPONSIBILITIES; 1B8: CARE RECIPIENT (AND REPRESENTATIVE) SATISFACTION; 4A3: ORGANIZATIONAL BEHAVIOR (E.G., ORGANIZATIONAL CULTURE, TEAM BUILDING, GROUP DYNAMICS)

NAB DOMAIN 2C: HUMAN RESOURCES

2.8.1 WHAT THE FACILITY NEEDS FROM THE EMPLOYEE

A facility needs employees who have a passion for their job and will consistently make decisions according to its policies. This adherence is possible to the extent that each staff member can be characterized as having the following:

- A high degree of interest in the job—a willingness to make every effort
- A genuine dedication to the well-being of residents' quality of care and quality of life—passion for the work
- A strong positive self-image permitting employees to see beyond their own needs and instead be concerned with the needs of residents and their significant others
- Skills, both technical and interpersonal, in communication and human relationships
- The capacity and willingness to make decisions following the best interest of the facility, every act contributing toward providing the highest quality of life for the residents, their significant others, the facility staff, and the community
- The ability to be self-starting, reliable, creative, and able to exercise appropriate positive leadership—a fire in the heart
- Career commitment to the facility

The preceding parameters are the description of an ideal employee. Few staff members will be able to embody all these qualities fully. However, these characteristics can be constantly encouraged and developed among the employees, the quality of life enjoyed by the residents and staff should be high.

Tracking the Employee

Employers need to ensure that employees are giving the quality of care sought by the management. Some companies use ID badges that include infrared sensors, an accelerometer, a microphone sensor, and a wireless communication device. These technologies allow management to know who talks to whom, how often, where, and how acceptably. Beyond auditory information, small video cameras are available to track actual resident caregiving. Patient privacy matters are paramount, but treating residents with respect and providing effective professional care are essential (Topol, 2015). Such devices can monitor for possible resident abuse and such matters as adequate handwashing and the successful use of facility resident care protocols.

2.8.2 WHAT EMPLOYEES NEED FROM THE FACILITY

What employees require of the facility can be divided into five areas: (a) social approval; (b) self-esteem; (c) security; (d) use of power, accomplishment, service, and exercise of leadership; and, perhaps most important, (e) to work for an organization with a vision that allows the employee to participate in a more significant meaning, giving each a sense of purpose and pride in accomplishment.

The degree to which any individual might seek employment satisfaction will vary, both among the entire staff and within the same member, as their situation changes over time.

SOCIAL APPROVAL

Most people rely on a network of approving and satisfying social interrelationships. Whether or not they express it openly, many of them enjoy engagement in activities sanctioned by significant others—persons to whom an individual looks for favorable regard of behavior patterns, ideas, and values. Family, members of the community, or one's social group are typical examples of *significant others*.

When an employee feels the work community or significant others are disapproving, negative feelings about the job begin and possibly create a feeling that being a "good" employee is worth the effort.

SELF-ESTEEM

NAB DOMAIN 2C11: EMPLOYEE GRIEVANCE, CONFLICT, AND DISPUTE RESOLUTION; 4A3: ORGANIZATIONAL BEHAVIOR (E.G., ORGANIZATIONAL CULTURE, TEAM BUILDING, GROUP DYNAMICS)

Adequate self-esteem is essential in order to function. Individuals need a positive self-image, that is, to feel good about themselves, what they are doing, and the world about them. Each person requires status. Most people want to be part of an organization with a sense of purpose to dedicate their energies with pride.

ECONOMIC SECURITY

In this case, we define *security* as the financial benefits provided by the facility. An employee may remain insecure without sufficient income for maintenance, health insurance for eventualities, vacations for refreshment, and funds to meet future retirement expenses.

HYGIENE FACTORS

Hygiene factors are those such as salary, company policies, and working conditions. In theory, when hygiene factors are adequate, they do not bring about appreciable levels of employee satisfaction. Hygiene factors, then, are the minimum work conditions (Cole & Kelley, 2020; Noe et al., 2017).

ADDITIONAL INTRINSIC NEEDS

Some employees expect even more of the work situation. Their intrinsic needs arise out of the essential nature of their personality.

Wielding power and having authority in certain situations are intrinsic needs. Intrinsic needs are also met from the satisfaction of completing tasks, achievements, and holding a leadership position. Giving service can be a fulfilling behavior.

PARTICIPATION IN A VISION

Employees want to work for a corporation that stimulates their dreams and aspirations and touches their hearts. They enjoy collaborating with highly motivated people who are accomplishing work that matters, that has purpose and meaning—something beyond just striving to be the largest or the best-known or the highest-income company. The staff needs the administrator to take a personal interest in them—to be recognized as an essential team member. The administrator should strive to know the staff on a first-name basis. Getting to know employees, their children, and other little bits of personal information about them improves perceptions. When the administrator inquires specifically how that ballet recital or piano concert went for their employees' children, this truly drives home that employees are cared about as individuals.

2.8.3 STRATEGIES AVAILABLE TO THE FACILITY TO MEET BOTH ITS OWN AND THE EMPLOYEES' NEEDS

Section Concepts

- *Ways to retain employees often surround meeting their needs*
- *Retention involves understanding your employees and where they are coming from*
- *Maslow's hierarchy affords a way of understanding employee needs*
- *The role that leadership takes in employee satisfaction is a large one*

Consider as the Administrator . . .

- *How important is your buy-in to meeting employee needs?*
- *How well should you know your employees?*

Retaining high-performing employees over an extended time is economically desirable for the facility. The financial costs of training each new staff member can be high, especially if the employee participates extensively in in-service training programs offered by the facility and takes advantage of any additional on-the-job training to improve skills.

In the nursing facility setting, employee continuity is critical for the residents, providing an overriding element of stability and continuity in their lives. Employees in nursing facilities often form personal relationships with the residents. They may be regarded as significant friends or even family by residents who have lost their own family and many cherished others.

A motivated, contented staff, capable of contributing significantly to the quality of resident life, consists of employees who are enjoying a high level of job satisfaction and are thus enabled to provide a high level of resident care.

An administrator in a large California chain facility states it is successful because it primarily concentrates its energy on the staff. Only highly motivated, happy staff, this chain facility believes, give loving care to residents. Their zest, enthusiasm, and evident concern about their staff members enable staff to treat residents and other employees in the same manner.

A FACILITY PHILOSOPHY OF HUMAN RESOURCE MANAGEMENT

NAB DOMAIN 2C: HUMAN RESOURCES; 2C11: EMPLOYEE GRIEVANCE, CONFLICT, AND DISPUTE RESOLUTION; 2C12 EMPLOYEE SATISFACTION, ENGAGEMENT, AND RETENTION; 2C13: CULTURAL COMPETENCE AND DIVERSITY AWARENESS; 4A3: ORGANIZATIONAL BEHAVIOR (E.G., ORGANIZATIONAL CULTURE, TEAM BUILDING, GROUP DYNAMICS); 4A4: LEADERSHIP PRINCIPLES (E.G., COMMUNICATION, STYLES, MENTORING, COACHING, PERSONAL PROFESSIONAL DEVELOPMENT)

What motivates employees? Each day the administrators of more than 17,000 U.S. nursing facilities make decisions based on their assumptions about what motivates their staff. These conclusions reflect the administrator's beliefs about human resource management and may be consciously or unconsciously held. We will explore one general theory about employee motivation.

Theory X and Theory Y

Douglas M. McGregor, a management theorist, published a book expounding what he called Theory X and Theory Y. McGregor wrote that the behavior of administrators is strongly influenced by their beliefs (Cole & Kelley, 2020). McGregor postulated that most managers adhere to Theory X and believe employees naturally dislike work, preferring to receive extensive direction from superiors, avoid taking responsibilities in the organization, possess low ambition, and are motivated by job security over any other factor (Robbins & Coulter, 2018). This approach requires that managers use fear or punishment to motivate employees, all of whom must be closely watched to ensure work is accomplished.

McGregor insisted that Theory X is not valid and that managers should instead be guided by Theory Y. Theory Y (Robbins & Coulter, 2018) is based on the following assumptions:

1. Using energy to work is as natural as using energy to play or rest. The administrator can control working conditions and create work as a source of satisfaction, voluntarily performed, rather than as a source of punishment to be avoided.
2. If individuals are committed to the organization's goals, they will exercise self-direction and self-control without the threat of punishment or external behavior controls.
3. Rewards for achieving organizational objectives bring employee commitment; employees can achieve personal self-satisfaction in achieving organizational goals.
4. The average employee, when properly motivated, will accept and seek responsibility.
5. Most employees can exercise imagination, ingenuity, and creativity in assisting the organization in achieving its goals.
6. Most jobs underutilize the capabilities of employees.

McGregor's theory caused considerable discussion in management circles. One researcher doubted McGregor's theory and so surveyed 259 managers in 93 companies. He found that managers did not wholly accept either Theory X or Theory Y. In their opinion, the reality is more complicated than either theory. Not surprisingly, a few years later, this led to Theory Z.

Theory Z

Several writers proposed that, on balance, Theory Y is correct, but what motivates employees changes over time and is dependent on changing societal values. They argued that administrators must constantly come up with new strategies for motivating employees. In their view, a straightforward productivity–reward system is overly simplistic. The appropriate focus appears to be a satisfactory quality of life, both for the individual and group.

Consider as the Administrator . . .

- Which theory (X or Y or Z) or what blend among these theories most reflects your view of what motivates employees?

PERSONALITY TESTS

Some facilities utilize a variety of tests to evaluate applicants and employees. The most widely known is the Myers–Briggs Type Indicator personality test (Noe et al., 2017; Robbins & Coulter, 2018). As many as 2 million people take this test each year in the United States (Noe et al., 2017). The test consists of 100 questions asking respondents how they feel or act in a variety of situations. The test places respondents into categories of introverted or extroverted, sensing or intuitive, thinking or feeling, and perceiving or judging. These characterizations are then used to place a person in one of 16 personality types. Someone whose test results show that they are extroverted–intuitive–thinking–perceiving is classified as a conceptualizer. Myers–Briggs and other tests are sometimes used to classify persons into left-brain and right-brain categories, the theory being that left-brained people are systematic, thorough, balanced, and ask detailed questions about each situation. In contrast, right-brained individuals are more intuitive, quick, and less complex in their approach to decision-making.

MEETING THE EMPLOYEE'S NEED FOR SOCIAL APPROVAL

Individuals need to be part of an enterprise that is regarded by significant others as successful. Hence, approval of the nursing facility by significant others is vital to nursing facility employees.

In the community, the word-of-mouth reputation of the facility is fundamental. The opinions expressed by people or groups regarded as experts influence the nursing facility's staff, current, and future customers. These experts may include those at the local hospital, home health agency, hospice, the local physicians, the case managers at the local health maintenance organizations, independent practitioner organizations, professional provider organizations, workers' compensation, and similar groups. TV reports about their workplace shape employees' feelings. Online star ratings can make a significant difference, whether from the CMS, Google, or Yelp.

To cite an example, in one large city, a nursing facility operated by the county was attacked in the news media for 4 years and threatened with decertification for Medicare and Medicaid by federal and state officials because its sanitation and resident care were regarded as significantly substandard. During those 4 years, it was difficult to hire staff. Nurses, janitors, physical therapists, nurse's aides, and maintenance people who worked there were harangued by friends, neighbors, and workers in other healthcare facilities. Why were they willing to work under such conditions? Eventually, after a succession of three administrators over those 4 years, an improving level of care became apparent.

Employees do care about the reputation of their organization.

MEETING THE EMPLOYEE'S NEED FOR SELF-ESTEEM

Why does one nurse's aide strive harder than another? Why does one RN look for additional responsibilities while another seeks to avoid taking any? Why do wage incentives stimulate some individuals and not others? Why does a career advancement track within the facility stimulate some employees to strive to climb the ladder while others ignore the opportunities offered?

What motivates employees varies not only for the individual employee but also over time for the same employee. Motivation is a difficult concept to define. It has been described as the factor that energizes employees directing or channeling their behavior and sustaining it (Robbins & Coulter, 2018; Sampson & Fried, 2021).

An individual's needs, desires, and expectations change. When one need or desire is achieved at a satisfactory level, the salience or strength of others is modified. For a nurse who has just been licensed to practice, acceptance by other nurses may be a priority until this recognition is achieved. At that point, other needs, such as maximizing income, may take precedence.

Understanding Motives

The complexity of motives has been described by researchers who attempted to apply motivational psychology to the work situation (Robbins & Coulter, 2018). They point out the following:

1. Identifying motives is complex. Some employees will work hard to obtain more money, but why? An intensely felt need for additional money may create an increased drive at work to obtain more money, create economic security, or obtain a financial goal. Once accomplished, the willingness to work harder may be replaced by time off from work as a primary motivation.
2. Motives are always mixed. Individuals experience a wide range of motives that strengthen and weaken as their circumstances change, and some needs are met while others are frustrated.
3. The same incentive—for example, increased health insurance benefits—may generate different responses. Individuals also differ in the ease with which their needs are satisfied.
4. Some motives may recede when satisfied (as with hunger or thirst). Others, such as a desire for increased status or more salary, may become intensified when, for example, more status or more income is achieved.

It is beneficial to understand that each employee has their own set of priorities. Everyone has differing priorities; however, ever-changing employee circumstances make it difficult for the administrator to identify at a given point. Keeping this dynamic in mind will help the administrator to understand employee motivation with more ease and hopefully assist in finding ways to help each employee.

Giving employees increased roles in the decision-making processes of the facility is known as *job enrichment*. An example is assigning a nurse supervisor and aides complete responsibility for the care of a set of residents, rather than special responsibilities such as separate nurses doing medications, others doing a range of motion exercises, and the like (Cole & Kelley, 2020; Robbins & Coulter, 2018). *Job depth* refers to the extent to which an employee has the power to influence decisions. When the DON consults the aides on a floor about whether they are prepared to receive a proposed admission, these aides have increased job depth (Robbins & Coulter, 2018).

Maslow's hierarchy of needs concept is perhaps the most often cited human needs model in the literature (Figure 2.2). Maslow theorizes that needs become salient—powerfully motivating—at each successively higher level, mainly after the needs at each lower level are satisfactorily met. Until the individual meets survival and basic security (lower-level) needs, these will dominate motivation and attention (Cole & Kelley, 2020; Sampson & Fried, 2021).

Once lower-level needs are met to a satisfactory degree, the individual's motivation can become more dominated by social, self-esteem, and self-actuating needs (levels 3, 4, and 5). Maslow's model is widely used. In our view, it seems to be a functional and helpful explanation of some of the more basic dynamics of employee motivations.

Although the lower-level needs may decrease in strength when achieved, the higher-level needs, especially self-actualization, continue to grow stronger as they are

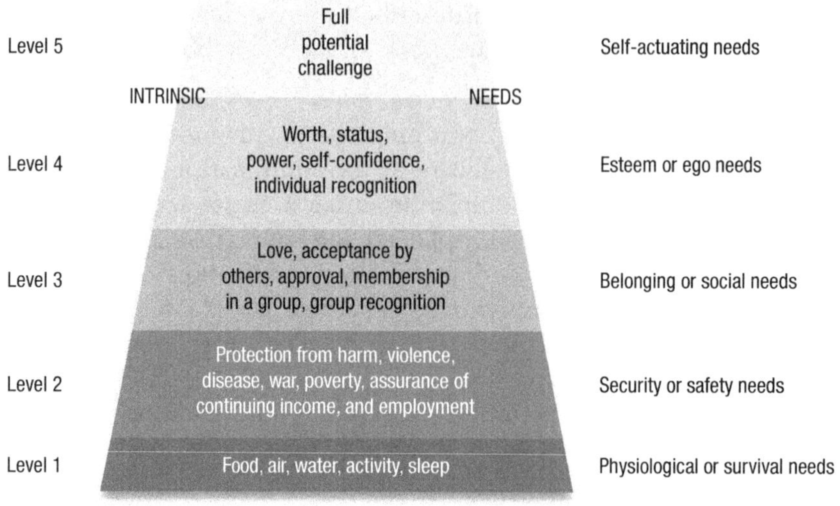

FIGURE 2.2 Maslow's hierarchy of needs concept.

being met. Examples of these needs or motivations are cited earlier as "additional intrinsic needs," such as being in authority, wielding power, accomplishing goals, and exercising leadership.

Consider as the Administrator . . .

- *Is Maslow's hierarchy of needs concept evident in a facility, or is this too abstract to help analyze employee behaviors? Or is it very apparent to see that many of your employees are focused on the first two levels of the hierarchy? What can you do to help them attain higher levels in the workplace?*

A word of caution: Each individual has a unique, ever-changing pattern of needs. In our view, what motivates an individual depends on a combination of life experiences and, as scientists are increasingly suggesting, on each individual's genetic and chemical makeup.

Childhood experiences such as economic deprivation may cause an employee to be anxious about financial security, no matter how much income is earned. The social and economic class with which an employee identifies affects their perceptions of their "needs." Being raised as a male or a female can influence the needs individuals will manifest on the job.

Personality Types: A and B

Attempts have been made to identify basic personality types. Investigators who focused on the causes of heart disease described two personality types. Type A is characterized as hard-driving, achievement-oriented people who strive to succeed to the highest level whatever the area of activity, whether in sports, job titles, or on-the-job productivity (Konopaske et al., 2018). Type A individuals, especially those chronically angry, appear to be at increased risk of heart disease (Robbins & Coulter, 2018).

Type B personalities are characterized as having only moderate achievement needs, less competitive, and more satisfied with moderation, whether in sports, titles, or on-the-job productivity.

Type A employees come to the facility with a high internalized motivation level. They are overachievers in comparison with Type B employees. Why? Much has yet to be learned about motivation, genetic influences, and chemical balances within individuals.

An Exercise to Try

Supervisors' ideas about what motivates the staff and employees' ideas often differ significantly. The following is a list of concepts the reader can ask a set of supervisors and employees in their facility considering the most important aspects of their jobs.

Ask participants to rank the following on a scale of 1 to 10, where 1 = *most important*, 10 = *least important*:

- To be treated fairly
- Consistency from management
- Job security
- Interesting work
- Full appreciation for work done
- Good wages
- Good working conditions
- Feeling "in" on things
- Promotion and growth within the facility company
- Sympathetic understanding of personal problems
- Tactful discipline
- Management loyalty to workers

In the following sections, we discuss nine areas available to an employer seeking to retain staff through meeting needs for approval:

- Leadership by vision
- Training programs
- Career paths
- Performance feedback and goal setting
- Recognition
- Power
- Respect for creative potential
- Teams
- Appointing "ninjas of joy"

Leadership by Vision

Most facilities have set goals. Meetings exhorting employees to meet those goals, such as making the month's budget or keeping census up, are, in the end, limitations. Goals limit unless goals are part of and remain part of a vision. Organizations such as nursing facilities need a vision to fire up the employees, engage their spirits, and set long-term directions for their efforts. Each department manager needs a vision of what their department can achieve to provide meaning to each employee's efforts. Visions or dreams are goals with wings. The ideal of visions and dreams supply enthusiasm, vigor, and direction for the facility's efforts. Goals are short-term targets to be achieved, such as ensuring that all the paperwork for admissions is completed promptly and all the doctor's telephoned orders are signed within the time permitted. Employees want to feel that they are doing more than contributing to the profit ratio. They want to be part of a movement, a compelling vision, something that grasps their imagination. Employees want to be part of a facility with a vision, a dream about the quality of life of each resident and staff member. Keep this in mind when working to motivate team members.

Training Programs

Training programs increase employee skills and simultaneously communicate to employees that management values those skills.

The programs themselves serve numerous functions. They demonstrate management's interest in the staff and provide an additional arena for exchange among employees and an increased opportunity for feedback to the administration about the degree of skills and understanding of facility goals among employees. As these dynamics occur, the level of employee satisfaction can improve. With the new skills or insights, the employee experiences an increased feeling in tune with the organization's performance expectations.

Career Paths

Offering a career path means providing upward mobility within the organization. Creating career mobility in a freestanding nursing facility is more challenging than within a chain that owns and operates 400 facilities.

Making career paths available within the facility communicates to the employee that the organization wants to meet their desires to succeed and progress in job level and income. For the nurse's aide, a career path might include facility support through released time or tuition assistance. This support for education makes enrollment at a local college or technical institute to become an LPN or an RN more feasible.

The charge nurse might receive support to participate in a program to become a geriatric NP. The kitchen worker might be assisted in attending classes that lead to qualifying as a dietetic service supervisor.

The labor market can be an influencing factor. Depleting the worker pool is a concern for a freestanding facility in a rural area with a limited number of persons in the potential pool of nurse's aides or kitchen workers. It may be challenging to justify career assistance, leading to an undesirable depletion of these essential workers.

Remember, providing career paths that create upward mobility increases worker satisfaction and improves employee retention rates. Not all aides will aspire to become licensed nurses because they are not all similarly motivated. However, the availability of a career program can improve workers' attitudes. Those who choose not to participate are satisfied with knowing the option is available to choose if they wish. In general, the presence of options has value for employees.

Performance Feedback and Goal Setting

Employees receive informal feedback on their job performance daily. Formal reaction and the formal process of goal setting for an individual employee occur under more structured circumstances. This structured feedback is known as the performance evaluation and customarily includes establishing goals for the employee to achieve until the subsequent scheduled performance evaluation (Noe et al., 2017; Robbins & Coulter, 2018).

To Err Is to Learn

The facility administrators' attitude toward errors and failures is critical to success—failure should be evaluated. Failure itself is not a crime. The problem is not learning from failure. It is not whether the medication nurse will make mistakes. It is what they do after making them that determines how good that nurse is.

Mistakes Are Inevitable

Mistakes are both inevitable and an opportunity to learn. If managers demonstrate a no-blame culture, the employees will respond more openly about their mistakes. Employee mistake cover-up requires significant energy and usually leads to more lies to shore up the initial one. The "mistake concealer" is a problem for the facility. The employee who comes into the department manager's office and says, "I screwed up," is an employee with whom there is good communication, creating an opportunity for the individual and facility to learn. Management needs a positive attitude toward mistakes. Employees prefer to work in an open, honest atmosphere where management helps them learn from their mistakes (Cole & Kelley, 2020).

Recognition

Employees want to be thanked. Most employees seek recognition for their work. Much of their behavior can be interpreted through *expectancy theory*, pioneered by Victor Broom several years ago (Cole & Kelley, 2020; Noe et al., 2017; Robbins & Coulter, 2018). Expectancy theory holds that the motivation to perform (make an effort at work) is a mathematical function of individuals' expectations about future outcomes multiplied by the employee's value on these outcomes (Konopaske et al., 2018). *Expectancy* is a belief that a particular action will have a particular outcome.

The charge nurse who believes that working long hours and asserting themselves will lead to quick promotion to nurse supervisor is an example of expectancy. It serves as a guideline for the charge nurse in seeking promotion to nurse supervisor. The charge nurse expects the behavior to be rewarded. Recognizing employees' expectancies can help a supervisor understand how they are motivated.

If the charge nurse's long-worked hours and assertiveness lead to promotion, the expectation is reinforced. According to reinforcement theory (Cole & Kelley, 2020), behaviors depend on a reward. When rewards follow performance, performance improves. Conversely, when rewards do not follow performance, performance deteriorates. If the charge nurse had not been promoted, performance might have deteriorated (Noe et al., 2017).

In *reinforcement theory*, the outcome reinforces the employee's response either positively, leading to repeating the response, or negatively, reducing its use. Influencing employee behavior through reinforcement is called *operant conditioning*, literally influencing working behavior by conditioning the employee's response through rewarding (or punishing) the behavior (Noe et al., 2017).

When employees perform in the desired manner and are given praise and recognition for that behavior, the manager is engaging in what may be called *behavior modification*. Behavior modification involves using operant conditioning, usually through rewards, praise, and positive recognition, when an employee performs as desired by the facility.

The following is a possible pattern for modifying employee behavior to conform to facility goals:

- Maintain a consistent work environment
- Consciously identify the desired behaviors of employees
- Decide on the rewards to be used
- Clearly communicate to the employees both the desired behaviors and the rewards
- Reward desired behaviors immediately
- Scale rewards to the behavioral achievement attained, that is, vary the rewards and minimize the use of punishments

Power–Control

Nursing facility administration needs to define policies to govern their decision-making. However, this has both positive and negative aspects. The positive aspect is that the staff is given guidance and an appropriate framework to make decisions for the organization.

The negative aspect is that deciding beforehand, through policymaking, can substantially deprive the employee of a feeling of personal involvement in decision-making for the organization.

Feelings of Powerlessness

Christopher Argyris is a behavioral scientist who has observed a tendency for organizations to overlook a desire that he believes most employees have to function in a mature, adult manner. In the literature, this is referred to as the *immaturity–maturity theory*, which holds that most organizational designs treat employees as immature, thus frustrating their need to function as responsible adults.

Argyris believes that the typical organization tends to ignore individual potentials for competence, for taking responsibility, for constructive intentions, and productivity. He maintains that staff members are treated as immature in the typical lower-level job of the nurse's aide, the laundry worker, or the housekeeper. This attitude alienates and frustrates these workers, leading to the justification of rejecting responsible behavior and tempting them to defy the organization by allowing the quality of their work to deteriorate.

He sees the same problems among managers working within organizational structures that create hostile environments for trust, candor, and risk taking (Chies, 2021). This culture encourages conformity and defensiveness, which engender products of detailed substantiation for unimportant problems and invalid information for critical issues. Low-quality information leads to ineffective problem-solving, poor decisions, and weak commitment to solutions.

Argyris points to the lack of a coherent set of policies to cover all decision-making in the facility: leaving the employee only a minor role in significant decision-making. This structure leads to a high level of employee frustration.

Common reactions to frustration can be selecting a substitute goal that is attainable or engaging in maladaptive behavior. An employee barred from making meaningful decisions may cease trying and concentrate on a leadership role in an outside voluntary organization. Alternatively, the employee relieves their frustration through aggressive or abusive behavior toward other employees or the residents.

Combating Powerlessness: Employees as "Owners"

People do not want to care for things they do not have a vested interest in caring for, such as washing a rental car before returning it. A solution to this problem is to attempt to make everybody an "owner." Giving all employees a sense of ownership in the facility means treating each employee as a team member. Allowing employees to control aspects of their work and encourage their contribution to a goal in line with the facility goal provides them ownership of their work.

Ownership implies that all employees exercise some actual portion of control in the facility. Of course, each employee does exercise some fraction of control over the workplace. It is up to the individual staff member to decide whether to give care pleasantly or in an "I don't care" or "you don't deserve my respect" manner when alone with the resident.

"Businesspersons"

If the organization treats every employee as a "businessperson," the employees will respond in kind and fully engage in the dual goal of giving quality care and earning an adequate income. Such an employee is committed to making the facility a success. A feeling of control over outcomes accompanies the sense of ownership that may be accomplished by job enlargement, increasing the number of tasks an employee performs to find increased satisfaction through involvement in a process from start to finish. Consider two examples: one from the experimental laboratory and the other from the field (Cole & Kelley, 2018; Noe et al., 2017).

An industrial psychologist gave the subjects in a study some challenging puzzles and some tedious proofreading. Although they were attempting to accomplish these tasks, the psychologist played a loud tape recording of one person speaking Spanish, two speaking Armenian, and a copy machine in use.

Half of the subjects were given a button to push to stop the noise. The other half had no control over the noise. Those with buttons to push solved five times as many puzzles and had one-fourth fewer errors in proofreading, although never once did any subject with buttons to push ever push the button! Those who perceived control over their situation outperformed those who felt they had little or no control. In numerous repetitions, the same results were obtained.

The same results were achieved in the field: Workers who were given buttons to push achieved superior results for the company. The Ford Motor Company plant in Edison, New Jersey, gave every worker on the assembly line a button to push that shut down the assembly line. The Ford workers shut down the assembly line

30 times the first day and an average of 10 times a day after that. After the first day, the shutdown lasted an average of 10 seconds—just time to make this or that slight adjustment, turn a bolt, or the like.

What happened at the plant? Production remained steady. Three other factors changed significantly. The number of defects dropped from 17 per car to fewer than one. The number of cars requiring additional work after coming off the line dropped by 97%. A backlog of union grievances plummeted. Why? Because the line workers felt they had some meaningful control in their jobs, they had a sense of ownership in the plant. Employees who have a sense of ownership in the facility will try to do what is best. With this perception, the nurse's aide can meet their social needs such as self-esteem, self-acceptance, and status.

How can nurse's aides be given ownership in the facility? One DON accomplished it by consulting the aides before admitting a patient to their area. When the aides told the DON that the care load was too great at one particular juncture, the DON refused the proposed admission.

These aides had a sense of control over their work situation. They worked harder than previously and exercised their control judiciously to ensure the quality of resident care was not compromised by over-admitting. These nurse's aides had a button to push. They never pushed it without a good reason.

Nurse's Aide "Ownership"

Why should nurse's aides be involved in running the facility? The Ford Motor Company has a practice of soliciting input from all hourly workers. The assembly-line workers are asked to comment on the manufacturability of parts and are members of advanced design teams. Hourly workers offered 1,155 suggestions for changes in design or production for three small trucks. More than 700 of these suggestions were adopted. Techniques involving nurse's aides in the organizational decision-making can provide personal fulfillment and growth, leading to higher staff retention.

The nursing facility administrator is commonly conceived to have at least three immediate constituencies: the staff, the residents, and the residents' significant others. It has been established that one of the administrator's particular tasks is to create and enforce as many as possible opportunities for residents to feel in control of their lives. However, it is also the administrator's responsibility to create and enforce as many opportunities as possible for staff to feel in control of their work. Not an easy task for either group (Halter et al., 2017). The forces on institutionalization appear to move toward removing control from the residents naturally. Similarly, the forces of regulations and the accompanying need for conformity in the workplace naturally move toward removing control over work from the staff members. In a study of staff self-perceived influence on decision-making (498 staff in 51 nursing homes), nurse assistant involvement in shift reports, frequency of unit staff meetings, and administrators' decision-making autonomy from the governing board were found associated with increased levels of nurse's aide involvement in decision-making (Kruzich, 1995).

One administrator gives nurse's aides 50 cents an hour for each employee they get and *keep* at the facility. When the administrator asked an aide how she was doing, she replied, "My company's fine." She had six employees in her "company" and was earning $3.00 more per hour now. Creative incentives are endless.

Respect for the Creative Potential of Each Employee—Maintaining Passion

The "business" of every nursing facility is providing resident care. Here are two ways to create and sustain superior patient care: first, by taking exceptional care of residents by providing superior services and quality of care and, second, by constantly innovating.

These goals do not require genius or mystical strategic moves. Excellence in patient care comes from a bedrock of listening, trust, and respect for each person's dignity and creative potential.

Achieving excellence in resident care depends on the administrator enabling the housekeepers, kitchen staff, laundry workers, maintenance persons, accountant, secretary, and the nursing staff to "buy" into the facility.

Stow the Fire Hoses

Most individuals and organizations tend to resist change. There is a tendency to "fire hose" employee suggestions or ideas for new ways to accomplish the facility's goals. Common responses to new suggestions include "it's not within the budget," "it'll never work," "we've already tried that," "yeah, but things are fine the way they are," and "we don't do it that way around here."

Conventional wisdom holds that everything happens in cycles. The belief is that things will cycle back to normal, back to the good old days. Such criticizing of new ideas leads to sticking with the tried-and-true approach. The new reality is that change should be followed by a period of adaptation and then more change. One of the most common causes of change is regulations, and very few, if any, regulations have ever been eliminated.

Membership on a Team

We have mentioned the team concept several times and will return to it in the discussion of resident care planning.

Industries have repeatedly discovered that small groups produce higher quality and more personalized service and innovations than larger entities. American companies, such as General Motors, Hewlett-Packard, and Emerson Electric, now typically limit the size of the plant they will build to between 200 and 500 employees. The Japanese organize their largest industrial plants into small teams of 10 to 40 workers. Ask each worker, "What do you need to do a better job?"

NAB DOMAIN 2C11: EMPLOYEE GRIEVANCE, CONFLICT, AND DISPUTE RESOLUTION; 2C12: EMPLOYEE SATISFACTION, ENGAGEMENT, AND RETENTION; 4A3: ORGANIZATIONAL BEHAVIOR (E.G., ORGANIZATIONAL CULTURE, TEAM BUILDING, GROUP DYNAMICS); 4A4: LEADERSHIP PRINCIPLES (E.G., COMMUNICATION, STYLES, MENTORING, COACHING, PERSONAL PROFESSIONAL DEVELOPMENT)

The nursing facility consists of numerous teams. Effective caregiving is accomplished by the teams in the facility working together. One way to label teams is by job description:

- Department and functional area heads
- Nurses and nurse's aides
- Dietary
- Housekeeping and laundry
- Medical and allied health staff, such as the physicians, physical therapists, occupational therapists
- Social services and activities
- Business office staff
- Admissions
- Maintenance
- Medical and patient records

There are other ways of describing "teams" within a functioning facility. However, described, each team must smoothly mesh their daily activities to form a single team of caregivers. The administrator's job is to ensure teams cooperatively accomplish the facility's excellence in caregiving.

Conflicts inevitably arise between the teams and among members of each team. Sometimes conflict is due to personality clashes and arguments about the proper division of work among the teams. Who cleans up the spill in the nursing hallway: the person finding the spill, the maintenance staff, or the nursing staff? Is it the activity leader's job to find six additional chairs for the unexpectedly large number of residents who showed up, or is it the maintenance department's responsibility to bring the extra chairs? It is necessary to remember and remind the staff that *healthcare is a team sport in these situations.*

Skill in resolving conflicts among teams and individuals is necessary for the administrator and each department–functional area heads. The facility needs a known and enforced process for identifying and resolving conflicts among teams and individual staff members. Conflicts can arise among residents, family and visitors, delivery persons, or any other area of human interaction within the facility. Constant training and staff skill building in conflict resolution are necessities for smooth facility caregiving.

A Natural Head Start

The nursing facility enjoys a natural advantage over most companies. Federal regulations have demanded a small-team approach. Those who drew up the federal requirements already knew what industry is beginning to realize: Employees perform better when they are part of a team (Noe et al., 2017).

Team membership is a valuable tool in efforts to retain employees because it helps meet the employee's need for social involvement, communication with other employees, and meaningful personal involvement in the real work of the facility.

As a matter of practical reality, the work of a nursing facility cannot be accomplished without the departments functioning as a single team. Achieving and maintaining this necessary teamwork is one of the nursing facility's constant challenges (Welch & Welch, 2015).

Trying Easy

Increasingly intense regulatory efforts and continuous squeezing of the funds can lead to a "faster and better" mentality. For example, focusing on speed to make medication rounds quickly, finish all the paperwork, cut costs, get the resident ready for that meal, and get the trays out fast.

The pressures from low reimbursement levels to give more service with fewer employees can reduce quality and service. Creativity and innovation are losers to speed. High turnover rates among directors of nursing and nursing assistants are testimony to this.

Turnover

Turnover rates are as high as 100% in some facilities. Recent studies show up to an even more alarming 124% (Gandhi et al., 2021). The nurse administrator position typically requires 110% or greater effort from persons without adequate prior training. Conventional wisdom tells us to move at 110% to get the necessary work done. The administrator can assist employees to give a passionate 90% rather than pressuring for 110% efforts. A passionate 90% is more effective than a panicked 110% effort. From an "easy" passionate 90%, the employee gets job satisfaction; from the "harder" 110% effort, the employee gets job dissatisfaction. Patients who hear the proverbial "we're working short today" know that there will be lower quality and care that shift (Noe et al., 2017; Robbins & Coulter, 2018).

Ninjas of Joy

Work ought to be fun. Several West Coast Silicon Valley firms have led the way toward the idea that work should be fun. The dress may be informal, life is laid back, and having fun is valued. One early Western philosopher, Aristotle, observed that pleasure in the job puts perfection in the work. If it is possible to hire people who love their work activities—nurses who love nursing, nursing assistants who love taking care of older people, maintenance persons who love to tinker and repair and maintain—the facility will be a pleasant place to spend one's hours.

There are many different philosophies available for use to assist in making the workplace a fun, yet professional atmosphere. One of note is the FISH! Philosophy. The FISH! Philosophy surrounds four principles that workplaces put into action in a variety of ways through input from employees to create a dynamic environment that helps take the focus away from work as work and leans it more toward work as fun (Lundin et al., 2000). The authors have witnessed this at work in many facilities from implementations as simple as signage to remind employees of the principles to as extravagant as the walls of a facility being painted to look like the inside of an aquarium, underwater ocean views, and the bottom of a lake. This is truly a fun way to get employees on the right track!

Interpersonal Relationships, Dispute Resolution, and Group Dynamics

NAB DOMAIN 4A3: ORGANIZATIONAL BEHAVIOR (E.G., ORGANIZATIONAL CULTURE, TEAM BUILDING, GROUP DYNAMICS)

Inevitably, disputes will arise among staff, between staff and residents, among contractors, and among family members. The administrator must be aware of tensions within the facility and seek to smooth out ripples among groups. Furthermore, they must perform the role of arbitrator, conciliator, and mediator, which requires skills developed through personal experiences or formal classes.

The Importance of Having Fun

It is perhaps more important to have fun in a nursing facility than in most work settings. As one writer observed, coal miners used to take birds into the shafts as early warnings of danger. Laughter and good humor are the canaries of the work shift: When the laughter dies, it is an early warning that life is slipping from the facility. Ben and Jerry's, the ice cream manufacturer, appointed "joy gangs," whose responsibilities are to put more joy into their workplace. These gangs establish activities and events that encourage the employees to loosen up and have fun with each other. Not necessarily an easy task in the nursing facility environment, but one which could be used to make an amazing difference in the workplace.

Burnout and turnover are high among nursing facility staff. Work should have elements of fun each day if employees and residents are to experience quality living. Laughter extends life for both employees and residents.

MEETING THE EMPLOYEE'S NEED FOR ECONOMIC SECURITY

For this discussion of activities available to employers seeking to retain staff, we use the term *security* to mean the finance-related benefit package provided for the employees. Employee behaviors are often rewarded through incentive plans (rewards that motivate employees) designed to achieve facility goals.

A Simplified Model

One way to view what employees need from the facility is as follows:

"What"	Knowledge of what the organization needs
"How"	Skills to do what the organization needs
"Will"	The desire to do what the organization needs
"Equipment"	The tools to get the job done to professional standards
"Time"	Enough staff to permit the desired behaviors

COMMON PITFALLS IN PRACTICE

- Retention of employees is your job #1. If you ever believe that you are doing a good job in this area, increase your efforts by at least 50%. It is *not* your perception of your actions but your employees' perceptions of what you are doing that matter.
- Many new administrators believe their job is a 9–5 one. This is far from the truth. You have a whole separate facility operating at night that needs your attention.
- If you are treating your day employees to pizza, you better be doing the same for your night staff as well. Night staff will tell you that they are neglected by the administration, and for the better part, they are correct. This seems to come to a head during nurses' week when there are all kinds of stuff during the day shifts but nothing at night. *Never* forget your night shift!!!
- If you see an employee who seems to be worried or preoccupied—they are. Stop your day and find out what is happening with them. You can often help. This might simply be that they need to talk to someone, they are having a problem you can assist them with, or they simply are overwhelmed with work, which is amazingly common in our COVID-19 world.

2.9 EVALUATING EMPLOYEES

Section Concepts

- *How to evaluate employees*
- *There are many approaches to employee evaluations*

Consider as the Administrator . . .

- *Are employee evaluations all that important? Or are there better ways to impart this information to your employees?*
- *Should employees have a real-time knowledge of their performance in the workplace and your feelings on it?*

NAB DOMAIN 2C8: PERFORMANCE EVALUATION

NAB DOMAIN 2C9: HUMAN RESOURCES POLICIES (E.G., DRUG-FREE WORKPLACE, DISCIPLINE, JOB CLASSIFICATION, PHOTOGRAPHY AND VIDEO, SOCIAL MEDIA USAGE, MOBILE PHONE USAGE)

JOB PERFORMANCE EVALUATION: A LINE MANAGER FUNCTION

Job performance evaluation is a task assigned only to line managers. Such a responsibility distinguishes staff from line management functions: Staff, having no line authority, should not be assigned line responsibility for human resources matters—hiring, evaluating, promoting, reprimanding, suspending, or discharging employees—because to do so violates the concept of each employee reporting to but one manager (Konopaske et al., 2018).

PURPOSE OF JOB PERFORMANCE EVALUATION

W. Edwards Deming's (1986) third deadly sin is

> Evaluation by performance, merit rating, or annual review of performance. These, Deming asserted, destroy teamwork and nurture rivalry. Performance ratings build fear, leave people despondent, bitter, beaten, and encourage management mobility.

Acknowledging this, what does a department manager do? How can the facility judge the performance of its employees? Deming, and others, would argue that being a productive team member affords the facility managers adequate evaluation and control over an employee's performance. Perhaps so.

There may be problems with doing away with annual or other reviews of employee performance. The frequent change of staff, including department managers, in the average nursing facility, means that the organization's "memory" can be short. For an employee seeking to "build a career" at a facility, if there are no records, their progress over an extended period is more subject to the impressions of department managers who may pass through (Noe et al., 2017).

As a practical matter, all employees are judged internally and by coworkers throughout the day. The organization needs some method of creating a record regarding employee performance. This record serves to reward the excellent employee, identify employees requiring action plans, and provide sufficient documentation if dismissal is required (Cole & Kelley, 2020).

A job performance evaluation intends to focus the employee's energies on the performance level expected of them. These evaluations serve as personnel performance quality monitoring for department heads. A well-performed performance evaluation nurtures the behaviors needed for the facility's success and rewards those performing good work (Noe et al., 2017; Sampson & Fried, 2021).

The EEOC and, more recently, the ADA have done much to stimulate employers to keep accurate evaluation records of employees' work. Court hearings and unemployment proceedings require carefully documenting worker performance.

Performance Evaluation: Three Basic Objectives

Three primary objectives of performance evaluations are (a) to give employees feedback about their work performance, (b) to provide a basis (plan) for directing future employee efforts toward organizational goals, and (c) to provide a basis on which managers will decide on promotions, compensation, and future job assignments (Noe et al., 2017; Robbins & Coulter, 2018; Sampson & Fried, 2021).

The performance evaluation can force communication that might not otherwise occur concerning the manager's feelings about the employee's work. Setting up a performance evaluation system may formalize the department manager's impressions of the employee's daily work. Most industries use performance evaluation. A Bureau of National Affairs study revealed that among the industries studied, 84% had regular procedures for evaluating office personnel and 58% for evaluating line workers. The majority of evaluations were given on an annual basis.

Those lacking any written system for long-term performance evaluation exposed the individual more nearly to the "whim" of the manager who heads the employee's department.

OUTLINE OF THE PERFORMANCE EVALUATION PROCESS

First, the manager defines the functions, tasks, demands, and expectations of the job and translates them into performance criteria (Noe et al., 2017; Robbins & Coulter, 2018). Implementing evaluations requires forms and procedures to be developed, including standardized methods of rating employees to be used by supervisors in conducting evaluations.

Approximately 2 weeks before an evaluation, the manager completes the form and sends a copy to the employee with the meeting time and place. This timing gives the employee time to prepare for the meeting.

At the evaluation, the manager reviews the completed form and may modify sections if appropriate. Performance goals for the next period are reviewed and modified to create an agreement between the employee and manager.

At the end of the session, both the employee and manager sign the evaluation. Provision is made for any addendum the employee may wish to write or for the employee to indicate disagreement with the findings. In the event of such a difference of opinion, appeal procedures are generally available.

Even so, the performance evaluation process is not without its faults.

THE PERFORMANCE EVALUATION PROCESS: PROBLEMS ENCOUNTERED

Whatever the importance to the facility, and however rational the evaluation process may seem, resistance to its effective utilization often arises, making the program difficult to implement.

Often evaluations are given when the employee hopes for an annual raise, focusing primary attention on past performance rather than future performance goals. The managers are generally not rewarded for the time they take to give thorough evaluations. Most managers are uncomfortable with face-to-face judgmental roles. Employees are often sensitive to adverse evaluations, leading managers to avoid conflict. Employees desire that the appraising manager meet at least three criteria. The appraiser should have had adequate opportunity to observe the employee's work. Employees want the appraiser to understand the employee's job thoroughly and have clearly stated standards to judge the employee's efforts. The manager ought to judge the work from an informed viewpoint. Nurse's aides, for example, want someone trained as a nurse, who presumably understands the nature of their job, to write their evaluation.

Performance evaluations sometimes fail. One major nursing facility corporation has identified as contributing causes: (a) a lack of previously agreed-on objectives, (b) poor skills of the manager, (c) a lack of a defined evaluation process, and (d) managerial behavior that does not contribute to the self-esteem/self-image of the employee. Employees, the corporation points out, do not typically outperform their self-image. High performance can be anticipated if their self-image is high, and the converse if their self-esteem is low. Performance evaluation, they point out, should not be the first time people hear about things. A significant goal is to be a coach, not a critic. A point to remember: Evaluate performance, not the person. One can be candid and specific about performance without attacking the person. Employee evaluation happens daily in the nursing facility.

METHODS OF RATING EMPLOYEES

Rating Scales

Rating scales consistently list several characteristics, traits, or requirements of the employee's position on a line or scale. The evaluator checks off the degree to which the employee is believed to meet a trait or requirement. For example, scales recording degree of initiative and work quality might appear as follows:

Initiative
Lacks initiative—Meets requirements—Highly resourceful

Work quality
Needs to improve—Meets standards—Exceeds standards

Global Ratings

Often the manager will be asked to provide a global rating for the employee. This rating is typically regarded as a summary score based on the components of the evaluation. Generally, each employer establishes a numeric or alphabetic scale for the facility.

For example, 1 might represent the highest and 5 the lowest rating. Inevitably, the scale comes to resemble the grading system everyone has known in elementary and secondary school: Whatever the symbols used, the person comes to understand that they are an A, B, C, or D performer—or an F, in which case a termination notice might be pending. However much or little the manager may write or discuss with the employee, the employee's concern is, "Am I a '1' performer, and if not, why not?" This focus reflects the employee knowledge that the "1" performers get priority access to whatever rewards the system offers as promotions, bonuses, salary increases, or high status. Overall, the Likert scale (correctly pronounced LICK-ert, according to Dr. Rensis Likert) is a relatively easy way to provide a measure like these and have employees gain a quick and easy understanding of their standing.

Errors Made by Managers Using Rating Scales

Rating scales, too, have their problems. At least three types of errors occur:

The leniency error. To avoid conflict, some supervisors give consistently high ratings. The lenient supervisor's ratings are difficult to accurately compare with those of a stricter and more demanding supervisor.

The error of central tendency. Other supervisors consistently give only average scores to employees regardless of whether their performance is poor or outstanding. Everybody is average, even if they are not.

The halo effect. The halo effect occurs when a supervisor who values one particular type of job behavior (e.g., punctuality) permits the presence or absence of this one trait to affect several or most other trait ratings. A habitually late employee might be excellent in resident care but be rated low in most categories because the supervisor is irritated by the persistent tardiness (Robbins & Coulter, 2018).

Rating by Essay

The use of essays or paragraphs describing employee progress is less frequent than rating scales. It is challenging to compare employees when the essay method permits supervisors to write whatever evaluative comments occur. A total rating by essay is viewed as a timewaster, as supervisors have many employees to evaluate, and this method competes with their ability to do other tasks. Instead, using a rating scale with a brief essay at the end provides value to the evaluation.

Possible Outcomes From Evaluations

Evaluations are primarily intended to give feedback to the employee about performance to date and projected activities. Some of the possible results can be transfer, promotion, or demotion or, in the case of reductions in force, the basis for discharge.

Transfer. A transfer is the placement of an employee to another position that is approximately equivalent to the present position. A nurse, for example, may find that working on the medically complex hall is beyond their current level of technical skills and ask for a lateral transfer to a lighter care hall.

Promotion. A promotion is employee placement at a higher level within the company structure. There are at least two recognized bases for promotions: merit and seniority. Seniority is concerned with the length of service and tends to be automatic. The merit system relies on performance evaluations of supervisors. Under the seniority system, a nurse who serves the required number of months or years is automatically promoted to the next level. Under the merit system, a nurse may or may not be promoted, depending on supervisor evaluation.

Demotion. Demotion is the change of assignment of an employee to a lower level in the organization, usually with less pay, fewer responsibilities, and reduced status. Demotions are often accomplished by the use of transfers (Noe et al., 2017).

A formerly more productive employee may be transferred to another position, with pay and status remaining intact. Another alternative to demotion is transferring to a position with little responsibility or power.

Layoff. Layoffs are generally temporary dismissals and are potentially demoralizing to the remaining employees and those laid off. Ambiguous layoff policies increase anxiety among the remaining employees. However, such policies also tie the hands of management, who might, for example, seek to retain a recent but especially valued employee. Employees carefully scrutinize layoffs for fairness and equability in their implementation.

Discharge. When companies downsize, some basis for deciding who is dismissed is exercised. Discharging those employees with the lowest evaluation ratings first is a frequently used approach.

NAB DOMAIN 4A4: LEADERSHIP PRINCIPLES (E.G., COMMUNICATION, STYLES, MENTORING, COACHING, PERSONAL PROFESSIONAL DEVELOPMENT)

COP VERSUS COACH

Deming advises against performance evaluation reviews because it places the manager as a policer rather than a coach. The performance evaluation usually focuses on "areas for improvement," the negative side of the employee's work. The focus is on what the employee is not doing right rather than on strengths. The department manager is the employee's coach. The coach's job is to bring out the best in the individual. When managers cite employees' weaknesses in the performance evaluation, the employee feels more busted than trusted. It is the employee's strengths, not weaknesses, that will carry the employee through to success. One can get by improving on weaknesses; one can become great by building on strengths.

Something to consider here is that this "area for improvement" type situation is wrought from our current regulatory environment to a large degree. Quality assurance and performance improvement programs (as mandated) could not be effective if there were no areas for improvement.

Evaluation Dos and Don'ts Learned by One Corporation

A major national nursing facility chain suggests the following valuable ideas about evaluations:

- Evaluation information should be given only to those who have a definite reason and legal rights.
- Evaluations should be conducted in private.
- It is unfair to an employee not to be frank with them in an evaluation interview and discuss areas of needed improvement.
- The evaluation form should accurately reflect the employee's performance.
- Effective evaluation interviews that produce results take time.
- Evaluations should be made only on those things that are relevant to the job.
- A supervisor will find it difficult to follow up on an "I'll try harder!" solution from the employee. Solutions need to be specific and measurable.
- If policy permits, the employee has a moral and ethical right to see their evaluation form.
- Overrating all employees is a mistake in the long run and not fair to them.
- Recent events, both positive and negative, can unduly bias a performance evaluation interview.

COMMON PITFALLS IN PRACTICE

- Evaluating employees adequately is not an easy job or one to be taken lightly. Gain experience in this area from someone who does a great job of it. Work through an evaluation (whatever your method) to gain an understanding. Get others' opinions of your evaluation before you go live with it. Your opinion might often be in opposition to others in a facility, which should make you question why.

- It is difficult to not hurt feelings when you are providing constructive feed-back on performance. Consider the sandwich approach. Tell the employee one thing they do great, sandwich the bad in the middle, and then follow with other redeeming qualities. This way, the employee is not only hear-ing bad from you. This is an excellent strategy for *any* feedback that is negative.

2.10 PAYING EMPLOYEES

Section Concepts

- *Theories of compensation that have been offered*
- *What the wage policies are*
- *Information on deciding how much to pay*

Consider as the Administrator . . .

- *How can employee compensation be best used to help the facility achieve the employee performance the facility desires?*

NAB DOMAIN 2C1: FEDERAL HUMAN RESOURCES LAWS, RULES, AND REGULATIONS (E.G., ADA, FMLA, WAGE AND HOUR, FLSA); 2C3: COMPENSATION AND BENEFITS PROGRAMS (E.G., TIME OFF, HEALTHCARE INSURANCE, EMPLOYEE PAY AND PAYROLL)

NAB DOMAIN 2C9: HUMAN RESOURCE POLICIES (E.G., DRUG-FREE WORKPLACE, DISCIPLINE, JOB CLASSIFICATION, PHOTOGRAPHY AND VIDEO, SOCIAL MEDIA USAGE, MOBILE PHONE USAGE)

The nursing facility is labor intensive—any healthcare environment is. In most facili-ties, wages and benefits make up more than half of the operating costs. One can esti-mate that about 65% of nursing facility expenditures are personnel costs. Estimates are that benefits made up 39% of employee compensation (Singh, 2016). Employee compensation nationally constitutes 55% of all industries and 62% of nursing indus-try costs (Noe et al., 2018). Careful management of wages and benefits is one of the significant sources of cost control available to the nursing facility administrator.

MONEY IS LIQUID VALUE

Benefits

Economic theory holds that employees prefer a dollar in cash over a dollar's worth of any specific commodity because the cash can be used to purchase the commodity or something else; that is, cash is less restrictive. Nevertheless, benefits as a per-centage of wages and salaries approximate 31.3% (U.S. Bureau of Labor Statistics, 2021). Government programs requiring certain benefits, such as Social Security ben-efits, have partly caused this shift. Favorable tax treatment of specific benefits, such as tax-deferred 401(k) plan contributions, have also contributed to this trend (Noe et al., 2018).

The wages paid to the employees typically determine their standard of living. Wages also affect their status in both the facility and the community. Wages are perceived as a statement by the facility about the relative worth of the skills of each employee.

The most liquid benefit a facility can give to its employees is the paycheck. Health insurance, sick leave, and the like have value. However, the benefit most highly valued by the employee is the dollar value of the paycheck, which provides maximum control over the product of their work effort.

For the typical nursing facility employee, the wage rate is salient. Even a difference of a few cents per hour can spell satisfaction or dissatisfaction with wages for an individual making comparisons with a similarly qualified coworker.

THEORIES OF COMPENSATION

Compensation is generally considered the reward given to employees in exchange for their work effort. How willing an employee may be to work hard and assist the facility toward its goals can depend on how justly the employee feels their wages and benefits fit their work effort (Noe et al., 2018).

Equity Theory

According to equity theory, employees seek an exchange in which their wages and benefits are equal to their work effort, especially when compared to wages and benefits paid to similarly situated coworkers (Cole & Kelley, 2020; Robbins & Coulter, 2018). If the individual feels equitably paid, less tension may exist. If, however, they suspect that others with similar skills and investment of effort receive more, a tension exists that most employees will seek to resolve.

Typical worker responses to perceived inequities are asking for a pay raise, reducing their effort, filing a grievance, or seeking employment elsewhere. Alternatively, the employee may encourage those perceived as similarly situated but benefiting more not to work so hard.

Wage Policies

Developing and administering compensation policies are critical administrative duties. Policies should cover areas such as the following (Noe et al., 2017; Robbins & Coulter, 2018; Sampson & Fried, 2021):

- The rate of pay, set below, at, or above the prevailing community practice
- The discretion supervisors can exercise in differentiating an individual's pay from the set scale
- The amount of spread between pay rates for employees with seniority and pay rates for new employees
- Periods between raises and the weight given to seniority and merit in determining a new pay rate

Hourly Wages or Salaries?

Most facilities distinguish between hourly employees (wage earners) and persons paid stated salaries periodically. Wage earners or hourly employees generally are required to punch in and out on a time clock and are paid only for hours worked as verified on the timecard. Salaried workers, in contrast, are paid a set wage regardless of the hours worked, which may or may not be required to be recorded on a time clock. Usually, department managers in the nursing facility are paid a set salary. However, some department managers—for example, the head of dietary who encounters numerous occasions for long days—may negotiate to work hourly.

HOW MUCH TO PAY: THE WAGE MIX

Determining wage rates and benefits is a complex task affected by several factors called the *wage mix* (Noe et al., 2017):

- The labor market
- Prevailing wage rates
- Cost-of-living increases
- Ability to pay
- Collective bargaining
- Individual bargaining
- Value of the job

The Labor Market

Once governmental requirements for minimum wage rates are met, and sometimes the influence of unions also considered, supply and demand dramatically affect the wage rate. During the early decades of the last century, physicians restricted their numbers to lower than the demand; this resulted in favorable influences on their incomes. Similarly, the nurse shortage of the early 1990s resulted in dramatic increases in the wages earned by nurses. In many cases, the DON's salary increased beyond that of the administrator. Administrators then demanded that their wages be increased to maintain a higher compensation than the DON (Singh, 2016).

Prevailing Wage Rates

According to a government study, more than half of the businesses surveyed indicated that the prevailing wage scale in their communities for comparable jobs was the most influential factor in determining wages paid (Noe et al., 2017).

In general, the local hospital's wage rate sets the prevailing wage rate against which the other healthcare providers set their pay scales. This pattern is especially true in states with lower Medicare and Medicaid reimbursement rates.

Many organizations take wage surveys for the community or region. A single facility may conduct a survey, or agreements with other facilities may create sharing of wage information. In most communities, nursing facilities share wage information with each other and other health providers.

Cost-of-Living Increases

During periods of inflation, a cost-of-living adjustment may be made in wage rates. The purpose of cost-of-living increases is to assist workers in maintaining their purchasing power. These increases, often embodied in escalator clauses of labor contracts, provide for wage adjustments based on some index, usually the Consumer Price Index (CPI). The CPI is a government-defined measure of the cost of living compared to a base point, usually a few years earlier, designated as 100. A change in the cost of living is then expressed as a percentage of the base figure of 100.

Collective Bargaining

Where employees are unionized, nursing facilities are subject to union influences, regardless of wage rates paid. Unionization in healthcare is a growing trend nationwide. This trend has increased because of COVID-19 and will most likely continue to do so.

Individual Bargaining

Individuals with especially desirable skills may be able to negotiate a higher wage than others in similar positions. When a highly qualified maintenance director or DON is sought, the facility may bargain with such a person and offer them a premium wage.

Key Job Comparisons

In the nursing facility, the wages paid to the nurses tend to become the benchmark against which the earnings of other staff members are compared and established (Noe et al., 2017).

Wage Classes and Rates

To approach equity and allow flexibility for supervisors evaluating employees, wage classes or grades and wage rates are customarily established. All jobs within that class are paid at the same rate or within the same rate range. A *rate range* is a variation permitted within a class or grade (Noe et al., 2017). For example, all nurse's aides start at $10 per hour, with a 25-cent premium for each year of experience they have.

Merit Pay

The use of merit pay is a complex matter. Usually, a merit increase grid is developed for each merit pay position. The size and frequency of pay increases are tied to (a) the individual's performance rating and (b) the position of that individual's pay in the merit increase grid. Merit pay often increases individual competition among staff, thus reducing the willingness to perform as a team. A fair and accurate performance system satisfactory to most employees is challenging to develop and administer, thus leading to increased levels of employee dissatisfaction and perhaps turnover (Noe et al., 2017). Group incentives are helpful but also have limitations since they may pit groups against each other. This response is undesirable in the intimate atmosphere of the nursing facility setting where all departments (groups) must cooperate (work as a team) if quality care is to be delivered (Noe et al., 2017).

COMMON PITFALLS IN PRACTICE

- Despite what you might be told in research, understand that cash is king. That 10-cent raise for a minimum wage employee equates to $208. That is a utility bill, a Christmas present, a prescription, or school uniforms.
- Always be aware of the rate of pay in your community. Make adjustments, if necessary, with the help of your corporation.
- Be on the lookout for the "Buc-ees effect." Buc-ees is a chain of travel centers, well known for their clean bathrooms, hundreds of gas pumps, and high salaries. Many employers are coming into markets paying double what you can pay. That means employees will be leaving your company and going where they get paid more. Do not take it personally. Take what is happening in your community into account when you are forecasting the future of your facility.

2.11 DISCIPLINING EMPLOYEES

Section Concepts

- *Common disciplinary problems the facility faces*
- *Several approaches to disciplining employees*

Consider as the Administrator . . .

- *Discipline is always a messy affair. Employees are always watching how other employees are being treated and demand at least equal treatment. This is despite whether that employee's contribution is equivalent or not.*

NAB DOMAIN 2C9: HUMAN RESOURCE POLICIES (E.G., DRUG-FREE WORKPLACE, DISCIPLINE, JOB CLASSIFICATION, PHOTOGRAPHY AND VIDEO, SOCIAL MEDIA USAGE, MOBILE PHONE USAGE)

The following are some of the more common staff disciplinary problems faced by nursing facilities:

- Excessive or unexcused absences or tardiness
- "No call, no show"
- Leaving the facility or work area without permission
- Violation of rules about smoking, intoxication, narcotics, gambling, fighting, and firearms
- Failure to follow safety procedures, especially the Bloodborne Pathogens Act requirements

- Failure to accept direction
- Failure to report accidents
- Failure to take resident safety and welfare into account
- Verbal, physical, or other abuse of residents—or failure to report it
- Theft, punching another employee's timecard, and falsifying records
- Insubordinate behavior or abusive language
- Failure to report their condition of illness
- Solicitation or acceptance of gratuities from residents, families, or significant others
- Immoral, indecent, or disorderly conduct
- Refusal of required employee testing (COVID-19)

NEED FOR RULES AND THEIR CONSEQUENCES

Each facility should carefully state and consistently enforce policies regarding disciplinary actions (easier said than done!). The employees must be made fully aware, before any infraction occurs, of both the facility's rules and the disciplinary action that will be its consequence. Although policies and rules may have been formulated, these policy statements remain confusing unless they are continually reinforced by positive (motivating) and negative (disciplining) actions. Unless the facility can document that it had a "just cause" for firing an employee, there is a significant chance that the employee will collect unemployment benefits (Singh, 2016). Unemployment hearings are one of the most important reasons to keep impeccable documentation surrounding employee performance, discipline, and education.

Grievance Procedures

 NAB DOMAIN 2C11: EMPLOYEE GRIEVANCE, CONFLICT, AND DISPUTE RESOLUTION

Grievance procedures are an important safety valve for policies regarding disciplinary actions. Employees need to know that there are equitable procedures through which their reactions and views can be expressed when they feel they have received unfair treatment (Cole & Kelley, 2020).

Progressive Discipline

For most offenses, progressive discipline—beginning with verbal warnings, followed by written warnings for any subsequent violations—makes the most sense. Progressive discipline may prevent the repetition of an offending behavior after only a verbal warning, thus bringing about an early solution to the problem.

Dismissed employees have the right to present their case to their state unemployment commission, and many do. The employer must keep a well-documented record of having made every reasonable effort to persuade the employee to conform to facility policy before dismissal. The administration must demonstrate that disciplinary actions were based on rational judgments about the offending behavior, not on personal vindictiveness or excessive emotional reactions of supervisors to employee behavior. Employee expectations should be clearly outlined in the employee handbook, and that handbook should be acknowledged (in writing) by the employee upon employment and yearly after that.

Each facility needs to define policies governing suspension and discharge procedures clearly. Typically, several managers, including the administrator, participate in a decision to suspend or discharge an employee.

One major nursing facility chain recommends that the following be assured:

- That the requirement reasonably relates to the facility's operation and that the requirement has been properly communicated
- That management has investigated the matter fairly, objectively, and in a timely manner
- That requirements and penalties are and have been administered fairly and objectively, without any form of discrimination
- That the situation is dealt with, and a penalty determined in a manner consistent with past practice for similar situations
- That the penalty is appropriate to the seriousness of the infraction
- That misconduct (e.g., patient abuse, theft, and substance abuse) is reported to the appropriate agency for investigation according to state or federal regulations
- That where discharge is the penalty, employees have warning or knowledge of the probable consequences of their actions

It is furthermore important to ensure that you are following your own policies and procedures as outlined in your employee handbook. You will be held to this standard by state unemployment agencies, the EEOC, and any other entity questioning your hiring/firing practices.

Discharging Employees

Terminating employees, especially executives, can be eased by helping that person find alternative employment. This method is called *disemployment, outplacement*, or *dehiring* (Noe et al., 2017; Robbins & Coulter, 2018). Outplacement counseling or transferring problems are when managers themselves may assist the employee in finding another position or hire an employment firm to do so (Noe et al., 2017).

Employee Records

NAB DOMAIN 2C10: EMPLOYEE RECORD-KEEPING REQUIREMENTS

Careful and complete employee records are a necessity. Each employee's complete work history must be documented. In any situation requiring the facility to produce documentation, such as a worker's compensation claim, complete and accurate documentation in well-maintained employee records is the key to the smooth functioning of the facility. Good records are vital in any disciplinary or dismissal activities. In addition, eligibility for vacation, leaves, and most benefits the facility offers depends on complete and up-to-date employee records.

NAB DOMAIN 1A3: DISEASE MANAGEMENT (E.G., ACUTE VS. CHRONIC CONDITIONS); 2B8: INTERNAL INVESTIGATION PROTOCOLS AND TECHNIQUES (E.G., INCIDENTS, ADVERSE EVENTS); 2B9: MANDATORY REPORTING REQUIREMENTS (E.G., INCIDENTS, ADVERSE EVENTS, ABUSE, NEGLECT, FINANCIAL EXPLOITATION, FRAUD)

Certain events at a nursing facility must be reported to authorities.

Most states have requirements that abuse, neglect, superficial–substantial injuries of unknown source, and misappropriated property be reported to the state regulatory entity and, in some cases, local authorities, typically within 24 hours (or immediately in some cases). Some states have hotlines or websites into which a report must be made in that same time frame. The administrator must be notified immediately (24/7) of all allegations, and all allegations must be investigated.

The CMS requires that the facility do the following:

- Report all alleged violations of resident rights and all substantiated incidents to the state agency and all other agencies as required and take all necessary corrective actions depending on the investigation results.
- Report to the state nurse's aide registry or licensing authorities any knowledge it has of any actions by a court of law, which would indicate that an employee is unfit for service.
- Analyze the occurrences to determine what changes are needed to policies and procedures, if any, to prevent further occurrences.

Most states have lists of diseases that must be reported within 24 hours to the state health department. These lists typically include, at a minimum, the following:

- AIDS/HIV
- Influenza
- Hepatitis A, hepatitis B
- Measles (rubeola)
- Meningococcal disease
- Rubella
- Syphilis
- Tuberculosis
- Whooping cough
- Listeriosis
- Foodborne disease
- Campylobacter
- Anthrax
- Botulism
- Overdose of a controlled substance
- Coronavirus
- And many more

As a general rule, it is better to overreport than underreport occurrences at the facility relating to resident care and infections. Reporting protects the facility, the resident, the employees, and the public.

COMMON PITFALLS IN PRACTICE

- "Protect thyself." You never should be alone in your office or other space with a single employee.
- Have an "open door policy." This is two-fold. First, people can come and see you to discuss things. Second, your door is always open. Do not allow anyone to close your door for you. The door remains open. This way the potential for you to be accused of something untoward is lessened.
- A clear way to proceed in treating your employees involves you treating each employee *firmly*, *fairly*, and *consistently*. When you treat everyone the same, you have a defensible stance. Just ensure that you are on the right side of the law in your actions!
- Discipline is *ugly*. This is why discipline is a team sport. You *never* discipline alone. You always have a member of management in the room with you. It is not unheard of for employees being terminated to make outlandish claims against their boss, to threaten you personally, or to call the state within nanoseconds of being escorted from a facility. Always be prepared!

CASE DISCUSSIONS

The New Human Resources Director Takes Hold

This case illustrates the things human resources directors should avoid. Ralph failed to communicate and work with the DON. Ralph failed to follow the advertising requirements of equal opportunity rules. It is unethical for Ralph to "raid" the local hospital. It is also bad business. Usually, facilities are dependent on the local hospital's goodwill for resident referrals to the facility. In failing to post the openings, Ralph not only ignored hiring rules, but he also likely angered the facility employees who wanted to apply for these openings whenever they occurred. So much for upward mobility in Ralph's facility! It was inappropriate for Ralph to alter job descriptions to fit the qualifications of applicants. It violates hiring rules, and he had no authority to make such changes.

Is it sexual discrimination for the DON to have only the female applicants interviewed? Ralph's mistakes go further.

The Interviews

Just about every question the DON asked was unlawful. The only legal question asked was, "Is your RN license up to date?" However, the DON failed to verify the RN's license. The DON could and should have looked it up online before the interview.

The DON should not have asked:

- *Where were you born?* = unpermitted attempt to identify the national origin
- *Where have you lived in town?* = unpermitted attempt to identify socioeconomic origins

(*continued*)

- *Were your parents born here?* = unpermitted inquiry about national origin or genetic makeup
- *A lot of you folk are Seventh Day Adventists* = unpermitted attempt to identify religion
- *Do you have objections to working on Saturdays?* = unpermitted attempt to identify religion
- *I noticed you were walking slowly up the walk* = unpermitted inquiry that would reveal a handicap
- *What have you got that makes you have to use a cane?* = unpermitted attempt to reveal a handicap
- *Do you ever get muscle spasms?* = unpermitted attempt to identify possible handicap; must be a job requirement that no muscle spasms ever occur to ask this
- *Have you ever been treated for drugs?* = unpermitted attempt to identify past drug behaviors
- *How much of a problem is drinking?* = unpermitted attempt to identify general behavior that may be unrelated to the job description
- *Does your back injury make you miss much work?* = unpermitted phrasing
- *Which organizations are you a member of?* = unpermitted broad request to learn all organizational affiliations

It is a poor interviewing technique for the DON to read over an application while the applicant waits. Probably it is true that the DON's residents "would not want a man coming into their rooms at night," but not hiring male applicants for that reason leaves the facility open to a sexual discrimination suit.

Given Ralph's lack of qualifications, it was inappropriate for the DON to ask Ralph to interview the two aide applicants. Indeed, it was not appropriate for Ralph to interview both aides together. Altogether, all interviews except for the question about the license being up to date violated EEOC and ADA interviewing requirements.

WHAT WOULD YOU DO?

You are the administrator of Smooth Leaves Rehab. You have received many complaints about the food from residents and were recently the victim of F804 (food and drink that is palatable, attractive, and at a safe and appetizing temperature) during a survey.

You put a plan of correction into place which you found to be completely acceptable, as did the state. You did in-kitchen monitoring of the meals and temperatures, and even tasted the food yourself before any of it left the kitchen. Despite your best efforts, residents still complained that the food was cold, unappetizing, and tasteless.

(continued)

As a result of this, you became annoyed one day and decided to take matters further into your own hands. You found the "main complainer" resident surrounding this issue, and you asked if you might join them and their table for lunch. You waited for the meal trays to be delivered and when that resident's meal was brought, you asked if you might steal it from them and have another meal delivered immediately. They agreed. Both you and the resident ate the meal together and critiqued it. The resident complained that the food was cold, and you pulled out your infrared thermometer and checked the temperature and found it to be within appropriate limits. You then explained food temperatures to the resident and compared them to the regulations which do not allow for food which is "too hot" or "too cold" as it can cause issues or even burns to residents. You need to provide safe food for everyone. You then discussed the taste of the food, and you found out that the resident likes very spicy food. You discussed with them how you cannot serve spicy food and that food needs to be relatively bland to meet the needs of each resident. You found out that this resident liked hot sauce on everything, and you got a bottle for them on their table. After this, the resident was quite happy with the meals and your complaints decreased.

1. What would you do from here?
2. Will you continue having meals with your residents as you did with this resident? Is this a good idea or a bad one?
3. Was your fix of checking all the food in the kitchen before it was served a good one?
4. What other things could you do to make residents more satisfied at meal service?

REFERENCES

Algase, D. L., Moore, D. H., Vandeweerd, C., & Gavin-Dreschnack, D. J. (2007). Mapping the maze of terms and definitions in dementia-related wandering. *Aging & Mental Health, 11*(6), 686–698. https://doi.org/10.1080/13607860701366434

Alzheimer's Association. (2021). *Wandering*. https://www.alz.org/help-support/caregiving/stages-behaviors/wandering

Barnett, M. L., & Grabowski, D. C. (2020, March). Nursing homes are ground zero for COVID-19 pandemic. *JAMA Health Forum, 1*(3), e200369. https://doi.org/10.1001/jamahealthforum.2020.0369

Bast, R. C., Croce, C. M., Hait, W. N., Ki Hong, W., Kufe, D. W., Piccart-Gebhart, M., Pollock, R. E., Weichselbaum, R. R., Wang, H., & Holland, J. F. (2017). *Holland-Frei Cancer Medicine* (9th ed.). Wiley.

Betancourt, J. A., Rosenberg, M. A., Zevallos, A., Brown, J. R., & Mileski, M. (2020, December). The impact of COVID-19 on telemedicine utilization across multiple service lines in the United States. *Healthcare, 8*(4), 380. https://doi.org/10.3390/healthcare8040380

Bradley, M., & Chahar, P. (2020). Burnout of healthcare providers during COVID-19. *Cleveland Clinic Journal of Medicine, 5*(9), 10. https://doi.org/10.3949/ccjm.87a.ccc051

Centers for Medicare & Medicaid Services. (2013). Certification and Survey Provider Enhanced Reporting (CASPER) database. 58.

Chies, S. (2021). *Pratt's long-term care: Managing across the continuum* (5th ed.). Jones & Bartlett.

Cohen, L. W., Zimmerman, S., Reed, D., Brown, P., Bowers, B. J., Nolet, K., Hudak, S., & Horn, S. (2016). The Green House model of nursing home care in design and implementation. *Health Services Research, 51*(Suppl. 1), 352–377. https://doi.org/10.1111/1475-6773.12418

Cole, G. A., & Kelley, P. (2020). *Management theory and practice* (9th ed.). Cengage Learning.

Deming, W. E. (1986). *Out of the crisis*. Massachusetts Institute of Technology, Center for Advanced Engineering Study.

Gandhi, A., Yu, H., & Grabowski, D.C. (2021). High nursing staff turnover in nursing homes offers important quality information: Study examines high turnover of nursing staff at U.S. nursing homes. *Health Affairs, 40*(3), 384–391. https://doi.org/10.1377/hlthaff.2020.00957

Gomez, L. E., & Bernet, P. (2019). Diversity improves performance and outcomes. *Journal of the National Medical Association, 111*(4), 383–392. https://doi.org/10.1016/j.jnma.2019.01.006

Halter, J. B., Ouslander, J. G., Studenski, S., High, K. P., Asthana, S., Supiano, M. A., & Ritchie, C. (2017). *Hazzard's geriatric medicine and gerontology* (7th ed.). McGraw Hill.

Harrington, C. H., Carillo, H., Garfield, R., Musumeci, M., Squires, E., & Kaiser, Family Foundation. (2018). *Nursing facilities, staffing, residents, and facility deficiencies, 2009 through 2016*. Henry J. Kaiser Family Foundation.

Hitt, M. A., Ireland, R. D., & Hoskisson, R. E. (2017). *Strategic management: Concepts and cases: Competitiveness and globalization* (12th ed.). Cengage Learning.

Johnson, J. K., & Sollecito, W. A. (2020). *McLaughlin and Kaluzny's continuous quality improvement in health care* (5th ed.). Jones & Bartlett.

Kane, R. L., Ouslander, J. G., Resnick, B., & Malone, M. (2018). *Essentials of clinical geriatrics* (8th ed.). McGraw Hill.

Konopaske, R., Ivancevich, J. M., & Matteson, M. T. (2018). *Organizational behavior and management* (11th ed.). McGraw Hill.

Kruzich, J. M. (1995). Empowering organizational contexts: Patterns and predictors of perceived decision-making influence among staff in nursing homes. *The Gerontologist, 35*(2), 207–216. https://doi.org/10.1093/geront/35.2.207

Laughlin, L. Anderson., A, Martinez., A, & Gayfield, A. (2021). Who are our health care workers? *United States Census Bureau*. https://www.census.gov/library/stories/2021/04/who-are-our-health-care-workers.html

Library of Congress. (2021). *The Civil Rights Act of 1964: A long struggle for freedom—Legal timeline*. https://www.loc.gov/exhibits/civil-rights-act/legal-events-timeline.html

Lundin, S.C., Paul, H., & Christensen, J. (2000). *FISH: A way to boost morale and improve results*. Hyperion.

McClay, R., & Mileski, M. (2018). The benefits of status—Is working at a magnet or pathway to excellence hospital for you? *Nursing Made Incredibly Easy Journal, 16*(4), 26–29. https://doi.org/10.1097/01.NME.0000534115.91012.37

Michel, J. P., Beattie, B. L., Martin, F.C., & Walston, J. (2017). *Oxford textbook of geriatric medicine* (3rd ed.). Oxford University Press.

Mileski, M., Pannu, U., Payne, B., Sterling, E., & McClay, R. (2020, June). The impact of nurse practitioners on hospitalizations and discharges from long-term nursing facilities: A systematic review. *Healthcare, 8*(2), 114. https://doi.org/10.3390/healthcare8020114

Mileski, M., Topinka, J. B., Lee, K., Brooks, M., McNeil, C., & Jackson, J. (2017). An investigation of quality improvement initiatives in decreasing the rate of avoidable 30-day, skilled nursing facility-to-hospital readmissions: A systematic review. *Clinical Interventions in Aging, 12*, 213–222. https://doi.org/10.2147/CIA.S123362

National Institute for Elopement Prevention and Resolution. (2021). *NIEPR definition for elopement*. http://www.hospitalelopement.com/index.html

Noe, R. A., Hollenbeck, J., Gerhart, B., & Wright, P. (2017). *Human resource management: Gaining a competitive advantage* (10th ed.). McGraw Hill.

Robbins, S. P., & Coulter, M. (2018). *Management* (14th ed.). Pearson.

Sampson, C. J., & Fried, B. J. (2021). *Human resources in healthcare: Managing for success* (5th ed.). Health Administration Press.

Singh, D. A. (2016). *Effective management of long-term care facilities* (3rd ed.). Jones & Bartlett.

Spath, P. L., & Kelly, D. L. (2017). *Applying quality management in healthcare: A systems approach* (4th ed.). Health Administration Press.

Statista. (2021). *Number of active physicians in the U.S. in 2020, by specialty area.* https://www.statista.com/statistics/209424/us-number-of-active-physicians-by-specialty-area/

Thomas, W. H. (1996). *Life worth living: How someone you love can still enjoy life in a nursing home: The Eden alternative in action.* Vanderwyk & Burnham.

Topol, E. (2015). *The patient will see you now: The future of medicine is in your hands.* Basic Books.

Uniform Guidelines on Employee Selection Procedures, 29 C.F.R. § 1607. (2017).

U.S. Bureau of Labor Statistics. (2021). *Employer costs of employee compensation summary.* https://www.bls.gov/news.release/ecec.nr0.htm

U.S. Department of Labor Statistics. (2021). *Occupational employment and wages, May 2020—29-1141, registered nurses.* https://www.bls.gov/oes/current/oes291141.htm

U.S. Department of Labor Statistics. (2021). *Occupational employment and wages, May 2020—29-2061, licensed practical and licensed vocational nurses.* https://www.bls.gov/oes/current/oes292061.htm

U.S. Equal Opportunity Employment Commission. (2000). *Enforcement guidance on disability-related inquiries and medical examinations of employees under the A.D.A.* https://www.eeoc.gov/laws/guidance/enforcement-guidance-disability-related-inquiries-and-medical-examinations-employees

Welch, J., & Welch, S. (2015). *The real-life M.B.A.* Harper Collins.

PART 3

Learning to Manage the Organization's Finances

What You Will Learn in Part 3

- *How the administrator fits into the financial aspect of nursing facility operation*
- *The need for strategic business planning*

Consider as the Administrator . . .

- *Just how much actual financial control does the administrator wield?*

3.1 THE ADMINISTRATOR'S ROLE AS FINANCIAL MANAGER

Section Concepts

- *Knowing who controls which parts of the finances in the facility is imperative to success*
- *Business planning requires money*
- *Budgeting allows a clear understanding of expected financial performance*

Consider as the Administrator . . .

- *Can you prosper with an incorrect (inflated or deflated) budget?*

NAB DOMAIN 2A5: REVENUE AND REIMBURSEMENT (E.G., PDPM, PDGM, ACOs, HMOs, MEDICAID, PRIVATE PAYORS); 2A7: INTEGRATION OF CLINICAL AND FINANCIAL SYSTEMS (E.G., EMR/EHR, MDS); 2A8: INTERNAL FINANCIAL MANAGEMENT CONTROLS (E.G., SEGREGATION OF DUTIES, ACCESS)

NAB DOMAIN 2A9: SUPPLY-CHAIN MANAGEMENT (E.G., INVENTORY CONTROL)

NAB DOMAIN 2A2: FINANCIAL ANALYSIS (E.G., RATIOS, PROFITABILITY, DEBT, REVENUE MIX, DEPRECIATION, OPERATING MARGIN, CASH FLOW)

An administrator's duties encompass nearly every aspect of managing the facility, from assisting in professional medical staff recruiting to ensuring the efficient operation of the laundry department. Not surprisingly, the administrator is also responsible for the income and expenses of the facility. The administrator is the one person held accountable for the entire financial operation of the facility.

SELECTING AND EVALUATING FINANCIAL PERSONNEL

Although we explore individual functions in more detail later, let us say here that the *bookkeeper* primarily records the daily cash transactions of the facility, keeping track of all money going out or coming in. The *accountant* uses the information compiled by the bookkeeper to generate reports on the facility's financial standing. The bookkeepers and accountants record the financial transactions. However, the administrator is the chief financial officer of the *facility*. Not the bookkeepers, the accountants, or even the chief financial officer of the corporation can claim this title. On a local level, the administrator is the final word on finance.

The administrator must ensure that the business office process runs smoothly—that the bookkeeper is qualified for the job and has access to the information needed for recording all the facility's financial transactions (Zelman et al., 2020). Thus, the administrator must have some knowledge of bookkeeping to discern whether this critical task is being carried out as it should be.

The administrator may also have to select an accountant, possibly an employee or a consultant. If the administrator manages one nursing home within a chain, the accountant will probably be a corporate office employee. Therefore, the administrator should have some understanding of accounting to assess the accountant's performance and interact with them on an equitable level.

Increasingly, the administrator must understand and monitor how effectively the Minimum Data Set (MDS) is being completed, ensuring that the facility receives the highest reasonable and accurate Patient Driven Payment Model (PDPM) case-mix group (CMG) reimbursement for each resident served. Small changes in this area can mean considerable changes to case mix and reimbursement. Minor inaccuracies in this area can lead to leaving millions of dollars on the table each year.

The administrator must be able to interpret the financial reports developed by the accountant and the corporate office. The administrator's primary role as financial manager is to use the financial information to make informed decisions about the facility. The administrator needs to know how these reports are prepared, especially the Medicare/Medicaid reimbursement requests. It is also important to understand how to read these reports to correct any inaccuracies within them. All too often, things get coded incorrectly, and the administrator needs to be the one to fix this.

"CORPORATE" PURPOSES; FACILITY OWNERSHIP PATTERNS

Corporate offices often use individual facilities for various purposes, such as balancing the corporation's cash flow and tax affairs through the network of facilities instead of actual individual facility performance. One facility may be represented with a high debt load, while a similarly situated facility may demonstrate a low debt load. The administrator must grasp the nuances of these matters to compare their figures after debt service and taxes with those of a sister facility carried at a different debt load. They may vary, yet the level of success of staff performance may be comparable.

Nursing facility ownership patterns have been somewhat stable for several years. From 2009 to 2016, the percent of for-profit facilities was about 69%, nonprofits about 23.5%, with government-owned facilities at 6.9% (Harrington et al., 2018). Over time we have seen an increase in the number of for-profit facilities, despite an overall lower quality of care provided in them.

STRATEGIC BUSINESS PLANNING

NAB DOMAIN 2A1: BUDGETING AND FORECASTING; 2A2: FINANCIAL ANALYSIS (E.G., RATIOS, PROFITABILITY, DEBT, REVENUE MIX, DEPRECIATION, OPERATING MARGIN, CASH FLOW); 2A3: REVENUE CYCLE MANAGEMENT (E.G., BILLING, ACCOUNTS RECEIVABLE, ACCOUNTS PAYABLE, COLLECTIONS)

NAB DOMAIN 4B2: STRATEGIC BUSINESS PLANNING (E.G., NEW LINES OF SERVICE, SUCCESSION MANAGEMENT, STAFFING PIPELINE)

The following are steps the administrator takes in strategic business planning for the facility.

Maintaining Enough Income

In addition to bookkeeping and accounting, we also take a close look at costs. There are many different types of expenses. We explore how viewing costs in different ways can provide the administrator with information not included in the financial reports prepared by the accountants.

As the facility's ultimate financial manager, the administrator must ensure the availability of funds for conducting business: to purchase supplies and pay salaries and to meet the regular payments on any borrowed funds. Without these purchases and payments, the facility cannot operate. When money is not available to meet expenses, the facility cannot continue to operate for very long and may be obliged to close its doors.

Facility income is derived from the data entered into the MDS and sent periodically to the federal government. Suppose the MDS is not accurately filled out. In that case, the facility may lose significant income by underreporting the amount of care given to each resident, as measured by PDPM case-mix groups. The more efficient utilization of the clinically relevant factors under PDPM, the higher the PDPM reimbursement for each resident. Conversely, it is equally important not to overstate the care given, as overbilling is also a significant concern with legal repercussions.

The Centers for Medicare & Medicaid Services (CMS) carefully monitors the level of care deemed appropriate for each resident each day. Suppose a resident is found to have been left at a higher CMG level for a week longer than the CMS deems appropriate during an annual survey. In that case, the facility may be required to reimburse Medicare for the excess dollars received.

Setting Rates

How does the administrator (or corporation) guarantee that the facility will receive sufficient funds? The administrator needs to know how to set rates for the services offered and produce the number of residents who will require these services. Appropriate rates for resident care services must reflect their true full costs, so the administrator must measure these costs. Therefore, monitoring CMGs and overall case mix in the facility is a crucial part of the day for the administrator.

Consider as the Administrator . . .

- *Would you prefer to set rates at, just below, or just above the market? Why?*
- *How much control do you have as the administrator when setting rates?*

Planning and Budgeting

Financial management is essential to planning and budgeting. To make a financial plan or a budget, the administrator must predict both the costs of running the facility and the money it can expect to earn in the coming year(s). Knowledge of the facility's past financial performance and insight into the reason for earlier budget shortfalls or successes are essential for preparing a realistic and valuable budget. The administrator who is not familiar with all the departments' costs and earnings cannot expect to guide the organization on a reliable path in the future. To a certain degree, the administrator must also predict (or forecast) the future based on what they know about coming changes, trends, business opportunities, or regulatory changes.

RESPONSIBILITY TO OTHERS

NAB DOMAIN 2A5: REVENUE AND REIMBURSEMENT (E.G., PDPM, PDGM, ACOs, HMOs, MEDICAID, PRIVATE PAYORS); 2A7: INTEGRATION OF CLINICAL AND FINANCIAL SYSTEMS (E.G., EMR/EHR, MDS)

Finally, as director, the administrator is responsible for the effective operation of the nursing facility—to its residents and their significant others, to the employees, to the owner(s) or stockholders, and the facility's governing body. When signs of ineffective financial management become apparent, the administrator is held accountable to each party.

Because nearly every decision made will have financial implications, an understanding of financial management is incumbent on the administrator, the person ultimately responsible for the facility's performance, even in chain-operated homes. If finances are poorly or improperly handled, the administrator is likely to be judged ineffectual by owners/operators despite any positive relationships with the staff or capabilities in other aspects of administration.

Maximizing cash flow into the facility is part of the administrator's financial goal, including ensuring maximum reimbursement from payers such as Medicare, Medicaid, and private insurance companies. Section GG (functional abilities and goals) of the MDS measures the safety and quality of performance of the activities of daily living (ADLs). This section heavily impacts a resident's PDPM CMG categorization. ADL assistance is typically provided by nursing assistants, one of the lower-cost employees. The care given must be documented by each resource used (the more care required, the higher the reimbursement). For example, if a resident may need one person to help them transfer from bed to toilet on the day shift but require two persons to assist in the evening, this resident may be classified as a two-person assist for transfer for reimbursement purposes (Chies, 2021; Singh, 2016). One must know the coding rules to maximize income. Additionally, staff focuses on what the administrator communicates frequently. If the administrator's focus is on reimbursement and the optimization of PDPM CMG levels, then so will the focus be of those responsible for appropriate documentation and billing.

NAB DOMAIN 2A5: REVENUE AND REIMBURSEMENT (E.G., PDPM, PDGM, ACOs, HMOs, MEDICAID, PRIVATE PAYORS); 2B3: ETHICAL CONDUCT AND STANDARDS OF PRACTICE

If the MDS coordinator does not accurately assess the resident, the facility may lose thousands of dollars annually. If, however, the MDS coordinator or administrator claims heavier care levels (hence more reimbursement dollars) than permitted, the facility may be fined and required to pay back "extra" monies received. "Upcoding" is a severe violation and a fraudulent practice. It is vital to avoid fraudulent claims by accurately assessing and billing. Assessment is a complex, ever-changing process with many nuances because Medicare contracts with several intermediaries (usually large health insurance companies) to manage Medicare reimbursements. These intermediaries' interpretations vary over time and between assessors. For these reasons, financial accountants have established what is known as the generally accepted accounting principles (GAAPs).

COMMON PITFALLS IN PRACTICE

- New administrators often attempt to exert too much influence in this area from a general standpoint. Be sure to include your corporate entity before you change anything involving finances in the facility.

3.2 GENERALLY ACCEPTED ACCOUNTING PRINCIPLES

Section Concepts

- *Accounting principles to which the administrator must adhere*

Consider as the Administrator . . .

- *To what extent are the GAAPs circumvented in the real world?*
- *How quickly could a lack of ethics in this area cause issues for you?*

NAB DOMAIN 3B1: FEDERAL HEALTHCARE LAWS, RULES, AND REGULATIONS

NAB DOMAIN 2A2: FINANCIAL ANALYSIS (E.G., RATIOS, PROFITABILITY, DEBT, REVENUE MIX, DEPRECIATION, OPERATING MARGIN, CASH FLOW); 2A3: REVENUE CYCLE MANAGEMENT (E.G., BILLING, ACCOUNTS RECEIVABLE, ACCOUNTS PAYABLE, COLLECTIONS)

NAB DOMAIN 2A4: FINANCIAL STATEMENTS (E.G., INCOME/ REVENUE STATEMENT, BALANCE SHEET, STATEMENT OF CASH FLOWS, COST REPORTING)

The accounting system defines how financial records must be kept, and the GAAPs are used by nearly every type of organization, including nursing facilities. Financial records refer primarily to the "books" and financial statements of the facility. Books are a set of records that list, in a prescribed manner, each monetary transaction (all money earned or spent) of the facility.

Maintaining the books constitutes bookkeeping. The books are used to prepare the financial statement. The financial statements are simply a summary of all the transactions recorded in the books, and they reflect the soundness of the organization's financial status.

The books and financial statements are prepared according to a series of rules known as the GAAPs. These are consistent standards of accounting that allow the financial records to be understood by the various parties who have an interest in the financial position of the facility and permit financial statements of different homes or other organizations to be more easily compared (Singh, 2016). A discussion of selected GAAPs follows.

An entity is a fundamental concept of accounting, under which the nursing facility is regarded as a whole, entirely separate from the affairs of the owners, managers, or other employees. This designation means that if a party, such as an owner, withdraws or adds to the facility's funds, this transfer must be recorded in the books to reflect the effect on the facility's finances.

CONSISTENCY CONCEPT

Another basic rule of accounting is the consistency concept. This concept requires that the accounting reports for a facility be prepared in the same way from year to year to compare the reports between two or more different periods accurately. The consistency concept does not require that the organization prepare reports in a manner that is not suitable to the needs of management but suggests that the method of reporting should be carefully selected and used consistently with strictly limited changes. Financial statements that are prepared in a different format every year will make comparisons difficult.

CONCEPT OF FULL DISCLOSURE

Related to consistency is the concept of full disclosure, which means that all financial information—all money spent, earned, invested, or owed by the facility—must be shown in the financial records to represent its financial standing accurately. The concept of full disclosure has significant legal implications, as failure to disclose all financial information may affect the amount of taxes a facility owes or the level of reimbursement it should receive from Medicare, Medicaid, and other third-party payers (Chies, 2021).

TIME PERIOD CONCEPT

Also known as the accounting period, the time period is the interval covered by the financial reports, usually 1 year. The accounting period should be consistent from one year to the next; the fiscal year (the 12 months designated for financial record-keeping) should begin on the same date every year. For example, a time period may be January 1 through December 31 or September 1 through August 31. Some companies use different dates to meet their needs better, but 1 year is usually a stable number. Accounting records are frequently prepared more frequently, usually monthly, to provide management with current information. These shorter time periods should also remain consistent. Typically, monthly financial reports are prepared and distributed to the management, while quarterly (every 3 months) and annual reports are prepared and distributed to managers and owners.

OBJECTIVE EVIDENCE CONCEPT

The objective evidence concept requires accounting records to be prepared with documented records that the facility keeps. A documented record should accompany every transaction, meaning that there should be specific objective evidence of the transaction such as receipts for paid bills, bills (or invoices) for money owed by the facility, bank statements indicating interest earned periodically, or receipts for cash received by the facility each day or designated period. These are called the *source documents* of the transactions. Objective evidence, either paper or electronic, is necessary so that estimates need not be used.

Instead of estimating the cost of supplies purchased during a month, for instance, all invoices are filed in an orderly fashion and used as objective source documents in determining the cost of supplies for the month. Estimates should be used as infrequently as possible, as they introduce an element of error and inconsistency in the accounting reports. When estimates are necessary, the process used to arrive at the estimated figure should be noted in the financial statement.

Typically, the administrator of a local facility relies on corporate to ensure that financial management policies, procedures, and practices comply with applicable federal and state rules and regulations. Even so, the administrator should assure themselves that the financial practices of the facility conform to the law. There may be local taxes or procedures with which the facility must comply, such as a local sales tax on meals if the facility charges employees or family members or taxes collected by the beauticians who serve residents in the facility.

Consider as the Administrator . . .

- *It is commonly accepted that financial reports are tailored to market expectations and the actual financials of a company. How, then, can one evaluate a company's financial position?*
- *How important is it from an ethical standpoint to have "correct" financials? Is it acceptable to make tiny changes to make the company look better from a financial standpoint?*

3.3 TWO APPROACHES TO ACCOUNTING: CASH ACCOUNTING AND ACCRUAL ACCOUNTING

Section Concepts

- *That the facility must function on accrual accounting rather than cash accounting*

Consider as the Administrator . . .

- *A few facilities function using the cash accounting approach. Under what circumstances would this be feasible?*

> **NAB DOMAIN 2A4: FINANCIAL STATEMENTS (E.G., INCOME/ REVENUE STATEMENT, BALANCE SHEET, STATEMENT OF CASH FLOWS, COST REPORTING); 2A5: REVENUE AND REIMBURSEMENT (E.G., PDPM, PDGM, ACOs, HMOs, MEDICAID, PRIVATE PAYORS)**

There are two systems of accounting: cash and accrual (Berger, 2014). The difference is primarily the time period in which expenses and revenues are recorded in the books. *Revenues*, the money coming into the facility, can be recorded for the period when the funds from resident care are earned or when the facility receives the payment.

Expenses, defined in more depth later, are the money spent by the facility and can also be recorded in two ways. In accounting terminology, money paid out is called an *expenditure* and can be recorded when payment is made for items purchased. Or the item can be recorded as an expense when the facility uses it.

The time of recording is the difference between the two accounting systems and results in two very different ways of preparing the financial records. The type of accounting used must be consistent.

CASH ACCOUNTING APPROACH

> **NAB DOMAIN 2A3: REVENUE CYCLE MANAGEMENT (E.G., BILLING, ACCOUNTS RECEIVABLE, ACCOUNTS PAYABLE, COLLECTIONS)**

In cash accounting, expenses are recorded when the cash is disbursed, and revenues are recorded when the facility receives the money. Thus, the cash system of accounting simply records expenditures and receipts (the actual flow of cash out of and into the facility) as they occur. Organizations using the cash system of accounting do not include "noncash expenses" such as depreciation because depreciation (the cost of wear and tear on equipment) is a cost of providing services to residents that does not involve a cash expenditure.

Cash accounting also does not recognize prepaid expenses, such as insurance paid up for months or years ahead. A premium for a 3-year insurance policy is recorded as an insurance expense in the month it was paid and would be listed only as an insurance expenditure for that month. The fact that it was a prepaid expense and would last over several accounting periods is not acknowledged. Also, money owed to the facility for services already provided would not be recorded as accounts receivable but would be counted as revenue only after the facility received payment. The chief advantage of cash accounting is simplicity; it is like one's checking account.

Cash accounting, however, has several disadvantages. One is that expenses and revenues for a single time period are not attributed to that same period. For example, medical supplies might be paid for in August but used up over 4 months. For instance, supplies purchased in August, but lasting over 4 months, would have only expenses recorded for August. The cost of providing medical services in September, October, and November would not include the cost of those medical supplies. Thus, the total cost (TC) and revenues, and therefore the actual profit or loss for those months, could not be accurately measured. Therefore, an adequate measure of financial performance from month to month becomes nearly impossible.

The cash accounting system does not recognize the real cost of depreciation of the facility's building, plant, major equipment, or other capital items. It also does not recognize money owed to creditors by the facility (known as accounts payable, a deferred expense) or money owed to the facility for services provided (accounts receivable, a deferred revenue).

Finally, because the only means of recording expenses and revenues is when cash changes hands, the accounting records are subject to mismanagement by those involved in the accounting process. For these reasons, the cash system is infrequently used. Perhaps 99% of all nursing facilities use the accrual accounting approach.

ACCRUAL ACCOUNTING APPROACH

Under the accrual system of accounting, revenues are recorded when they are earned and expenses when they are incurred, regardless of the time the cash transactions take place. The previous definition of expense can now be more precisely stated as a cost used up or "expensed."

Using accrual accounting, the cost of supplies purchased in August is expensed over the months the supplies are used. So the accounting records for each month would show a medical supplies expense equal to the cost of the supplies used in that month.

Complexity is the main disadvantage of the accrual basis of accounting, but it has numerous advantages. Most important, it allows the facility to measure the revenues earned after paid expenses or losses incurred by matching each period's revenues and expenses. It also includes depreciation, accounts receivable, and prepaid expenses in the accounting records, providing a more accurate picture of the facility's actual financial position. The accrual method is less subject to tampering, as several forms of objective evidence usually back expenses and revenues. The following discussion of accounting and recordkeeping is based on accrual accounting.

COMMON PITFALLS IN PRACTICE
- New administrators often like to make changes. However, make changes in places where you can do so. Financials and accounting approaches are often set in stone. This is one area in which you should work with what you have!

3.4 THE TWO MAIN STEPS IN THE ACCOUNTING PROCESS: RECORDING TRANSACTIONS AND PREPARING FINANCIAL STATEMENTS

Section Concepts
- How to interpret financial statements

Consider as the Administrator . . .
- To what extent can financial statements accurately reflect what is occurring in the facility?

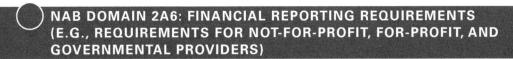

NAB DOMAIN 2A6: FINANCIAL REPORTING REQUIREMENTS (E.G., REQUIREMENTS FOR NOT-FOR-PROFIT, FOR-PROFIT, AND GOVERNMENTAL PROVIDERS)

NAB DOMAIN 2A4: FINANCIAL STATEMENTS (E.G., INCOME/ REVENUE STATEMENT, BALANCE SHEET, STATEMENT OF CASH FLOWS, COST REPORTING)

RECORDING TRANSACTIONS IN JOURNALS AND THE GENERAL LEDGER

The accounting process involves two main steps: keeping the books and preparing the financial statement. *Bookkeeping* is a system of recording all revenues and expenses and matching those revenues to expenses during the same time period. This process is necessary for *financial statement* preparation, which summarizes the nursing facility's economic well-being within a time period.

The accounting process is fairly universal and will be described in chronological order, from the chart of accounts to the preparation of the financial statements.

CHART OF ACCOUNTS

The chart of accounts is simply a list of every account in the facility. The accounts are organized into six main groups:

- *Assets.* Things owned by the facility
- *Liabilities.* Items owed by the facility, or its obligations
- *Capital.* Money invested in the facility, also known as the facility's net worth
- *Revenues.* Earnings from operations or other sources
- *Expenses.* Costs of salaries, supplies, and other items consumed, usually through the provision of services
- *Fund account.* Any funds that have been established for restricted or unrestricted uses

As can be seen from the sample Chart of Accounts in Table 3.1, the first digit indicates the categories into which the account falls; the second digit usually is a subcategory. For example, RN salaries are an expense (Category 5) in the nursing department and have an account number 5201.

Note that the salary expense account number for every other department ends with a 1 also. This system of classifying accounts is helpful. It identifies every account of the facility and thus is a means of control; expenses, for example, are automatically applied to a specific source so that unexpected or unauthorized expenses cannot accumulate unnoticed. The numbered system also saves time by recording a number rather than a long title on many documents. It is especially convenient for a computerized bookkeeping system as it allows for sorting.

TABLE 3.1 Chart of Accounts, The Laurels

Assets		Liabilities	
Current Assets		*Current Liabilities*	
1101	Cash—petty	2102	Accounts payable—supplies
1103	Cash—payroll account	2104	Notes payable—short term
1106	Cash—operating fund	2107	Mortgage payable—short term
1112	Investments—money market fund	2109	Debts payable—current
1114	Investments—C of D	2111	Emp. benefits payable
1117	Investments—depreciation fund	2113	Emp. health insurance payable
1122	Accounts receivable—Medicare	2115	Salaries payable
1123	Accounts receivable—Medicaid	2201	Taxes
1124	Accounts receivable—private	2204	Taxes payable—state
1126	Accounts receivable—other	2205	Taxes payable—municipal
1131	Interest receivable	2207	Taxes payable—federal
1163	Unexpired liability insurance	2221	Interest payable
Noncurrent Assets		*Noncurrent Liabilities*	
1302	Land	2303	Notes payable—long term
1305	Land improvements	2313	Mortgage payable—long term
1402	Building—main	2323	Bonds payable
1414	Building—Welsh Hall	2401	Pensions payable
1426	Building—garage/storage		
1430	Building improvements	*Capital*	
1502	Furniture—main	3001	Owner's equity
1504	Furniture—Welsh Hall	3101	Net income (Loss)
1512	Equipment—main		
1514	Equipment—Welsh Hall	*Improvements Revenue*	
1516	Equipment—office		
1518	Equipment—kitchen	*Nursing Care*	
1519	Equipment—laundry	4001	Medicare
1521	Equipment—transportation	4003	Medicaid
1524	Equipment—land maintenance	4005	Private
Contra Assets, Accum. Depr.		*Ancillary*	
1602	Accum. depr.—main bldg.	4212	Physical therapy
1604	Accum. depr.—Welsh Hall	4214	Occupational therapy
1606	Accum. depr.—garage/storage	4216	Social services
1630	Accum. depr.—bldg. improvements	4218	Speech therapy—contract
1642	Accum. depr.—furn., main		
1644	Accum. depr.—furn., Welsh	*Uncompensated Care*	
1651	Accum. depr.—equip., main	4311	Contract. discount—Medicare
1654	Accum. depr.—equip., Welsh	4313	Contract. discount—Medicaid
1666	Accum. depr.—office equip.	4315	Contract. discount—Other
1668	Accum. depr.—kitchen	4332	Donated care
1669	Accum. depr.—laundry	4341	Bad debts
1671	Accum. depr.—transportation	4351	Patient refunds
1674	Accum. depr.—land maintenance		
1680	Accum. depr.—bldg.		

(continued)

TABLE 3.1 Chart of Accounts, The Laurels (*continued*)

Expenses		

Administration

5001	Salaries—administration
5002	Salaries—clerical
5003	Consultation fees
5006	Health insurance
5011	Payroll tax
5013	Taxes—income
5015	Taxes—property
5022	Insurance—liability
5026	Pension fund
5032	Supplies
5034	Telephone
5035	Travel
5037	Postage
5039	Licenses and dues
5042	Repairs
5411	Payroll tax
5432	Supplies
5442	Repairs
5461	Contract services

Housekeeping

5501	Salaries
5506	Health insurance
5511	Payroll tax
5532	Supplies
5542	Repairs

Rehabilitation

Physical Therapy

5601	Salaries
5606	Health insurance
5611	Payroll tax

Plant Operation

5101	Salaries
5106	Health insurance
5111	Payroll tax
5122	Utility—electricity
5124	Utility—gas
5126	Utility—water
5128	Utility—sewage
5132	Supplies
5142	Repairs

Nursing

5201	Salaries—registered nurses
5202	Salaries—licensed practical
5203	Salaries—aides
5206	Health insurance
5211	Payroll tax
5222	Pharmacy

5224	Laboratory
5232	Supplies
5237	Uniform
5242	Repairs

Dietary

5301	Salary—dietitian
5302	Salary—food service
5306	Health insurance
5311	Payroll tax
5332	Supplies
5342	Repairs

Laundry

5401	Salaries
5406	Health insurance
5632	Supplies
5642	Repairs

Occupational Therapy:

5661	Salaries
5666	Health insurance
5671	Payroll tax
5682	Supplies
5692	Repairs

Social Services

5701	Salaries
5706	Health insurance
5711	Payroll tax
5732	Supplies
5742	Repairs

Activity

5801	Salaries—beautician
5802	Salaries—crafts
5806	Health insurance
5811	Payroll tax
5832	Supplies—beauty
5833	Supplies—crafts
5835	Transportation
5837	Special events
5842	Repairs

Capital Expenses

5904	Interest—mortgage
5907	Interest—long-term debt
5914	Debt service—mortgage
5917	Debt service—long-term debt
5934	Depreciation—plant
5936	Depreciation—equipment

THE JOURNALS

NAB DOMAIN 2A3: REVENUE CYCLE MANAGEMENT (E.G., BILLING, ACCOUNTS RECEIVABLE, ACCOUNTS PAYABLE, COLLECTIONS); 2A4: FINANCIAL STATEMENTS (E.G., INCOME/REVENUE STATEMENT, BALANCE SHEET, STATEMENT OF CASH FLOWS, COST REPORTING)

Any transaction that takes place will affect an account. The journals are the first place that transactions are recorded; they are the books of original entry. Each facility will have its own system of journals, but generally, there are six journals:

- *Cash Receipts Journal.* Records all cash received for services provided, for example, sales by refreshment machines
- *Billings Journal.* Lists all bills sent for services rendered
- *Accounts Payable Journal (Purchase Journal).* Records all purchases made that will be paid within the next few months
- *Cash Disbursements Journal.* Records all payments made for services and supplies used for resident care and facility operations
- *Payroll Journal.* Summarizes all payroll checks distributed during the pay period
- *General Journal.* A record of nonrepetitive entries

The journals are characterized by another concept of accounting: double-entry bookkeeping. For each transaction, two entries are made in the appropriate journal, a debit and a credit.

A *debit* in accounting simply means the left side of the journal account; *credit* refers to the right side. When all debits and credits are totaled at the end of each month, they should be equal. Thus, for every debit entered, one or more credits are entered that equal the debit, and vice versa. Table 3.2 indicates which transactions are recorded as debits and which as credits.

Journal entries are set in the shape of a "T" and thus are often called T-accounts. Data from the journal entries and objective evidence are the source documents.

The following is an example of the *Billings Journal* process. When a bill is sent to a resident or to that person's payer, the bill represents revenues earned by the facility that it expects to receive. This account receivable is an asset because it is cash to which the facility is entitled. Thus, a bill to Ms. Jones for $1,000 would be recorded in the debit column as an increase in assets. On the credit side, $1,000 would be recorded as an increase in revenue. This journal entry is illustrated in Figure 3.1. The source document for this entry would be a copy of the invoice sent to Ms. Jones.

Billings to all service recipients for the month entered in the journal in this manner should demonstrate the sum of debits equal to the sum of credits each month.

TABLE 3.2 Transactions Recorded as Debits and Credits

Debit	Credit
(+) Increase in assets	(−) Decrease in assets
(+) Decrease in liability	(−) Increase in liability
(−) Decrease in capital	(+) Increase in capital
(−) Decrease in revenues	(+) Increase in revenues
(−) Increase in expenses	(+) Decrease in expenses

			Debits	Credits
3/02	Acc't Receivable - Jones, F.		1 0 0 0 00	
3/02	Revenue			1 0 0 0 00
3/02	Acc't Receivable - Ross, M.L.		2 0 0 00	
3/02	Revenue			2 0 0 00

FIGURE 3.1   The Laurels Billings Journal.

Notice that the Billings Journal is used only for billing a service; the service recipient's payment of the bill will be recorded in the *Cash Receipts Journal*. The complete transaction would be recorded as follows:

Billings Journal

Debit	Credit
3/2	Acc/Rec $1,000.00 (accounts receivable)
3/2	Revenue $1,000.00

Cash Receipts Journal

Debit	Credit
4/22	Cash $1,000.00 (accounts receivable)
4/22	Acc/Rec $1,000.00

The credit in the Cash Receipts Journal would not be due to an increase in revenue but to a decrease in accounts receivable. Under the accrual accounting system, revenue is recognized when the services are provided rather than when the cash is received.

General Journal

The *General Journal* records transactions that do not adequately fit into any of the other journals. Note that the first five journals all record cash transactions; the General Journal is used to make adjustments in the books to conform to the accrual system of accounting.

As with medical supplies, the supplies purchased in August will be only partially consumed in that month. However, the *Cash Disbursements Journal* would record the cash expenditure for the supplies purchased in August. Under the accrual method of accounting, only the costs of supplies used in August would be included in the August financial reports. To compare the TC of providing services with the revenues earned in the same period, an entry must be made to the General Ledger. This adjusting entry allows adjustment of the medical supplies expenditure in the Cash Disbursements Journal to the cost of medical supplies used up in August.

An expenditure of $300 for medical supplies is made in August. The inventory records compiled at the end of August revealed that $75 remained in inventory. The adjusting entry in the General Journal would be as follows:

Debit	Credit
8/29	Medical Supplies $225.00 (an increase in expenses)
8/29	Inventory $225.00 (decrease in expenses)
8/29	Inventory $75.00 (increase in asset)
8/29	Medical Supplies $75.00 (decrease in expenses)

In addition to adjustments for inventory, entries for depreciation and prepaid expenses are also recorded in the General Journal to reflect the cost of using the plant or equipment over the time period and the amount of prepaid expenses used up.

The General Journal can also be used to correct errors made in the other journals. The General Journal accounts are usually repeated from month to month and should be standardized to the extent possible. Standardization prevents the omission of unapparent but genuine costs.

General Ledger

At the end of each month, after all adjusting entries have been made in the journal accounts, the financial information in all journals is *posted* (written or entered in) to the General Ledger.

The *General Ledger* can be thought of as a summary of all debits and credits contained in the journals for the time period. It usually has a page for each account in the Chart of Accounts.

The purpose of the ledger is two-fold. First, it keeps a continuous balance of the amount in any account for each month. It also enables a "trial balance" to be done. Before preparing the financial statements, the total of all debit columns in all journals must equal the total amount from all the credit columns. By accumulating all journal entries in one book, the ledger, debits, and credits can be easily added up and compared. When total debits equal total credits, the books are said to "balance." Thus, a trial balance has been calculated. If total debits do not equal total credits, there is an error in one or more journal entries.

Under the double-entry concept of accounting, each debit recorded in a journal must be matched by a credit of an equal amount. The trial balance, therefore, indicates whether an error has been made in recording transactions.

With so many accounts, there is ample opportunity for error. Thus, accuracy in preparing the journal and ledger entries will save a great deal of time searching for possible mistakes. The relationship between the journals and General Ledger is shown in Figures 3.2 and 3.3.

The General Ledger should be arranged in the order in which the accounts will appear in the financial statements. Once the trial balance and gain/loss statements are prepared, the ledger is closed. This process is discussed in the following description of the financial statements.

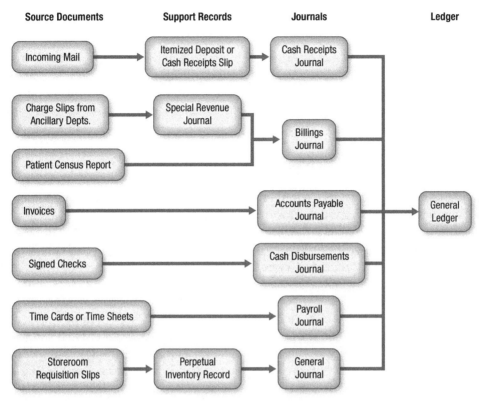

FIGURE 3.2 Source documents, support records, journal, and ledger.

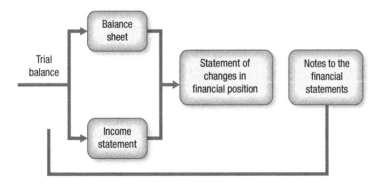

FIGURE 3.3 The financial statement.

PREPARING THE FINANCIAL STATEMENTS: THE INCOME STATEMENT AND THE BALANCE SHEET

The financial statements are the summary of all transactions made during a particular period and their effect on the facility's finances. The GAAPs require that the financial statements include four reports (Cole & Kelley, 2020; Singh, 2016; Zelman et al., 2020):

1. Income statement or profit/loss statement
2. Balance sheet or statement of financial position

3. Statement of changes in financial position
4. Notes to the financial statements

The income statement and balance sheet are prepared directly from the General Ledger (Figure 3.3) and subsequently described (Brigham & Houston, 2019). The statement of changes in financial position and the notes to the financial statements are prepared from the income statement and balance sheet, and they are discussed in less detail.

Profit and Loss: The Income Statement

The income statement shows whether revenues were sufficient to cover expenses and whether the facility made or lost money during the period.

In accounting, *income* does not refer to the funds coming into the facility but to revenues minus expenses or the profit or loss experienced by the facility (or income compared to expenses in not-for-profit operations). Although net income indicates that the facility made money or had some revenues above expenses, a net loss indicates that the facility lost money in the period covered by the income statement. A net loss, or any negative figure on the financial statements, is usually shown in parentheses.

Revenues are listed first on the income statement (Table 3.3), usually starting with the largest source of revenues. From the General Ledger, all the revenues earned from providing room and board and other services are calculated as routine services, separated by the level of care or type of service.

TABLE 3.3 The Laurels Income Statement

Revenues	July 'X1	Year to Date	Vertical Analysis Percentages (YTD)
Operating revenues			
Nursing	357,603	2,207,814	
Total nursing	357,603	2,207,814	
Ancillary			
Physical therapy	9,974	61,839	
Occupational therapy	9,890	59,340	
Social services	2,866	16,909	
Total ancillary	22,730	138,088	
Gross operating revenues	380,333	2,345,902	
Less deductions	45,640	281,508	
Net operating revenue	334,693	2,064,394	
Nonoperating revenue			
Miscellaneous			
Meals	430	2,494	
Concession	1,358	8,691	
Beauty shop	790	4,819	
Total miscellaneous	2,578	16,004	
Interest	2,640	15,312	
Total nonoperating revenue	5,218	31,316	
Total revenues	339,911	2,095,710	

(*continued*)

TABLE 3.3 The Laurels Income Statement (*continued*)

Revenues	July 'X1	Year to Date	Vertical Analysis Percentages (YTD)	
Expenses				
Operating expenses				
Salaries				
Nursing	135,192	833,151	68%	
Dietary	15,582	93,492	8%	
Administration	9,551	54,441	4%	
Laundry	3,409	20,454	2%	
Housekeeping	13,435	81,282	7%	
Maintenance	5,287	32,145	3%	
Physical therapy	9,652	60,808	5%	
Occupational therapy	3,450	20,735	2%	
Social services	2,146	13,305	1%	
Total salaries	197,705	1,209,812	100%	59.0%
Supplies	31,393	189,928		9.2%
Activity	2,065	12,390		0.6%
Capital equipment	200	1,600		0.1%
Utilities	8,764	52,584		2.6%
Telephone	163	1,043		0.1%
Insurance	4,000	24,018		1.2%
Taxes (real estate)	3,313	19,878		1.0%
Capital costs				
Interest	27,816	166,896	30%	8.1%
Mortgage payment	24,029	144,174	26%	7.0%
Depreciation	39,627	237,762	43%	11.5%
Total capital costs	91,472	548,832	100%	
Total expenses	339,078	2,060,085		100%
Net income (loss)	833	35,625		
Income tax (@ 45%)	375	16,031		
Profit after tax	458	19,594		

YTD, year to date.

NAB DOMAIN 2A4: FINANCIAL STATEMENTS (E.G., INCOME/ REVENUE STATEMENT, BALANCE SHEET, STATEMENT OF CASH FLOWS, COST REPORTING); 2A6: FINANCIAL REPORTING REQUIREMENTS (E.G., REQUIREMENTS FOR NOT-FOR-PROFIT, FOR-PROFIT, AND GOVERNMENTAL PROVIDERS); 4B4: BUSINESS DEVELOPMENT (E.G., SALES, MARKETING, PARTNERSHIPS, ACOs, CONTRACTS AND AGREEMENTS, NEGOTIATIONS)

Except for for-profit facilities paying taxes and the not-for-profit facility not paying income taxes, there are no actual differences in the accounting and financial processes between these two types of providers. Not having to pay taxes gives not-for-profit facilities a slight competitive edge. Both types of facilities must produce more income than expenses after all sources of paying expenses are applied. Both types of facilities report income or losses on operations. The for-profit usually refers to excess revenue over expenses as profit; the not-for-profit refers to income variously, such as "excess of income over expenses."

At the end of the day, whether an entity is for-profit or not-for-profit, their business model is the same—they both must make money. Businesses that do not make enough money to cover expenses close quickly. In many areas, we see nursing facilities in the top five employers in a town (if not in the top two). An unprofitable business closure can be devastating to the community, the employees, and the residents who will need to be relocated to other communities. Making money is part of what businesses do!

When all revenues earned from providing services, or operating revenues, from the General Ledger have been computed, any deductions from income are subtracted from the gross operating revenues. Deductions from operating revenues might include money owed to the facility that cannot be collected (known as bad debts or charity care), or they might be due to contractual discounts.

In the process of setting rates at which they will reimburse the facility for care, Medicare, Medicaid, and other third-party payers sometimes pay the nursing facility somewhat less than the facility's total charges. This discount from the regular price of providing care is known as a contractual discount. This discounted rate is the price at which the facility has agreed to provide care when it admits the insured resident. Contractual discounts are therefore deducted from operating revenues instead of included as an expense. Today, most hospitals are forced by competition to offer contractual discounts to large groups such as health maintenance organizations (HMOs) and managed care entities. Nursing facilities are similarly affected by competition and the desire to admit residents from such large third-party payers.

This competition can also work in reverse. The nursing facility can negotiate discount rates from providers, thus paying less than the face amount of bills received by the facility. It may be possible, for example, for the facility to get physicians to permit the facility to pay physicians what Medicare would pay the physician, not the dollar amount the physician's office bills.

Total deductions are subtracted from the gross operating revenue to get the new operating revenue. Net operating revenues for The Laurels for July are $334,693. Nonoperating revenues, income from sources other than direct resident care, are listed subsequently. In July, The Laurels earned $900 in interest from funds invested in a local bank and $4,318 from a certificate of deposit. Miscellaneous sources of revenue are also included directly from the appropriate page in the General Ledger. Miscellaneous revenues for The Laurels are from guests' meals, the beauty shop, or concession income.

Expenses are listed next, starting with the largest item, which is usually salaries. All salaries are listed by department. The salary expense generally includes any employee benefits and payroll taxes paid by the facility.

Supplies, separated by department in the ledger according to the Chart of Accounts, are combined into one expense item in The Laurels' income statement. A capital expense of $200 was incurred in July by the purchase of equipment.

Capital equipment is assets that will be used by the facility to provide services for more than 1 year and will not be sold in the course of operations. In addition to equipment, capital items also include such assets as the building, beds, and furniture. If we were to look at the General Ledger under the Chart of Accounts number for capital equipment expenses, we would discover that the $200 was used to purchase office equipment for The Laurels.

Farther down on the income statement, there is an expense called capital costs. A *capital cost* is an expense related to the use of capital items. At some earlier time, The Laurels had borrowed money for new dining and lounge furniture and money to purchase the building, both at an annual interest rate of 14%. For the month of July, the total interest expense was $27,816. Interest expenses, then, are one cost of using capital.

A mortgage payment expense of $24,029 for July is a second source of capital costs. Another cost of using capital is depreciation. The cost of wear and tear on The Laurels' depreciable assets was estimated to be $39,627 for 1 month (see Section 3.7: The Concept of Depreciation for estimation of this expense).

The total expenses are subtracted from total revenues (TRs) to give the net income (profit or loss). This amount is the net income before taxes. Subtracting percentage for income tax shows that The Laurels' profit after taxes is $458. Although depreciation is a real cost of providing services, it does not represent an actual cash outflow, and depreciation may be added to the after-tax profit to give the actual cash standing of the facility.

The income statement, then, shows the operating performance of the facility for a period. It is usually prepared both on a monthly and an annual basis.

Closing the Books

Because revenues and expenses are measured for finite periods of time, these accounts must be brought to a sum of zero to be recorded over again for a new period. Bringing the expense and revenue accounts to zero defines "closing the books" (Zelman et al., 2020).

To close the General Ledger:

1. For all revenue and expense accounts with a credit balance, add a debit equal to the credit to bring the account to zero.
2. For all revenue and expense accounts with a debit balance, add a credit equal to the debit to bring the account to zero.

According to double-entry accounting, compensation must be made for these new debits and credits in some other account.

1. Add up all the newly added debits.
2. Add up all the newly added credits.
3. Subtract the debits from the credits.
4. Enter the difference in the retained earning account, as follows:
   a. If the difference is a profit, enter it as a credit.
   b. If the difference is a loss, enter it as a debit.

Thus, all revenue and expense accounts have been brought to zero, and the books are balanced and ready for a new period.

Statement of Financial Condition: The Balance Sheet

Unlike the income statement, which summarizes operating performance over a period of time, the balance sheet records the financial position of the nursing facility at one point in time. The income statement shows the ending balance of the revenue and expense accounts, while the balance sheet summarizes the facility's assets, liabilities, and capital accounts. This document is called a balance sheet because the asset accounts must balance with the liability and capital accounts. This relationship can be expressed as an equation, called the accounting equation:

$$\text{Assets} = \text{Liabilities} + \text{Capital}$$

The balance sheet for The Laurels for the year is shown in Table 3.4. Assets are listed on the left in order of liquidity.

A current asset is the possessions of the facility that will be or theoretically can be turned into cash within 12 months. Prepaid insurance is considered an asset because

TABLE 3.4 The Laurels Balance Sheet

	July 31, 'X1	July 31, 'X0
Assets		
Current assets		
Cash	60,700	2,834
Accounts receivable (less bad debts of $9,032)	53,517	61,397
Securities	225,275	10,500
Inventory	62,006	54,880
Prepaid insurance	2,400	3,600
Total current assets	403,898	133,211
Noncurrent assets		
Equipment	1,983,000	1,981,200
Plant	5,767,004	5,767,004
Less accumulated depreciation	2,772,192	2,362,300
Plant and equipment	4,977,812	5,385,904
Property	2,650,000	2,650,000
Total fixed assets	7,627,812	8,035,904
Total assets	8,031,710	8,169,115
Liabilities		
Current liabilities		
Accounts payable	2,852	24,606
Notes payable	33,625	355,271
Benefits payable	24,843	630,388
Current portion of long-term debt:		
Mortgage	230,680	192,233
Long-term debt	75,000	75,000
Total current liabilities	367,000	1,277,498
Noncurrent liabilities		
Mortgage payable	3,460,202	3,690,883
Debts payable	675,000	750,000
Total noncurrent liabilities	4,135,202	4,440,883
Total liabilities	4,502,202	5,718,381
Net worth		
Retained earnings		
Year to date	35,625	27,507
Total	370,956	335,331
Owner's equity	3,122,927	2,087,897
Total net worth	3,529,508	2,450,735
Total liabilities and capital	8,031,710	8,169,115

the coverage is something owned by the facility. The income statement records the proportion of the prepaid insurance used in the month of July ($4,003), and the balance sheet shows the amount of insurance that remains.

Noncurrent assets will not be liquidated within the year; they usually include plant (the building), property, and equipment. These assets may be called fixed assets and recorded by cost at the time of purchase rather than their current market value.

The *historic cost* concept is another basic tenet of accounting and relates to the ongoing concern concept: Because capital assets are held rather than liquidated, their current market value is of little relevance. However, the value of these assets to the facility must include annual depreciation on plant and equipment. Accumulated depreciation is subtracted from the historic cost of the depreciable assets. Although land usually appreciates in value over time, it does not do so simply through the facility operations, so it is recorded at historic cost, with no value depreciation.

Therefore, *depreciation* is an expense associated with asset use and is included both as an expense on the income statement and a contra asset (literally, "against an asset") on the balance sheet. Note that employees are not included as an asset because assets are owned by the facility, and organizations do not own employees.

Liabilities are the obligations of the facility. Current liabilities are obligations that must be met within 12 months, such as bills from suppliers (foodstuffs, medical or office supplies) and short-term bank loans.

On this particular date, The Laurels owes its suppliers $2,852. If this debt were paid tomorrow and a balance sheet made up for that day, The Laurels would have no accounts payable on its balance sheet. *Notes payable* refers to loans that are repaid within 12 months. The Laurels owes $33,625 to a local bank for interest on its borrowed funds and has a portion of long-term debt due within the year. The noncurrent liabilities sections show which debts these are. The Laurels has payments due on its debt for new furniture and a portion of its mortgage payment.

Capital accounts, or new worth, are recorded below the liabilities. This section is also called owners' equity, shareholders' equity, fund balance, or retained earnings, depending on the origin of the funds that make up this section. It includes funds that the owners have put into the facility, whether one person, a partnership (two or more unincorporated owners), a corporation, or a charitable organization. Net worth also usually includes retained earnings or the net income that has been put back into the facility over the years.

If the facility incurs a net loss, this amount is subtracted from the net worth. The Laurels net worth includes the retained earnings of the year to date and the retained earnings from its earlier years of operation. It also shows that the owners have invested $3,122,927 in the facility over the years. If this amount were from stockholders, it would be called shareholders' equity; if from a charitable organization, it would be a fund balance.

The most important thing to remember about the net worth is that it is not a cash pool. The funds recorded as net worth are monies that have been put into the facility at some time; it is merely a record of these funds, not cash available for operations or investment.

To summarize, the balance sheet shows the facility's financial position for only one point in time. Its relationship with the income statement is the retained earnings, which usually include the net income in the net worth.

Thus, the previous basic accounting equation is expanded to

$$\text{Assets} = (\text{Liabilities} + \text{Owner's equity}) + (\text{Revenues} - \text{Expenses})$$

Statement of Changes in Financial Position

Also called the statement of changes, this financial report shows the significant transactions over the period covered by two balance sheets, demonstrating how working capital was used during that period. *Working capital* refers to the current assets and current liabilities from the balance sheet. The amount of working capital available is

$$\text{Current assets} - \text{Current liabilities}$$

The statement of changes shows the transactions that caused the amount of working capital to change over a period. Therefore, it is a handy document for those interested in knowing how the facility acquires and uses its funds (Zelman et al., 2020).

The sources of funds are revenue excess over operations expenses, interest income, and contributions to the facility (or owners' equity). Noncash items, such as depreciation or money designated for repayment of debts, are added as a source of funds because the facility still has cash (a current asset).

The uses of funds would include nonoperating expenses such as repayment of a portion of a debt or additions to property. The uses of funds are subtracted from the sources of funds giving the change in working capital over the period. This difference should equal the change in working capital calculated from the balance sheets at the beginning and end of the period covered.

Notes to Financial Statements

The notes to financial statements are included to explain the accountant's interpretation or calculation of figures or variation in the books due to a change in their organization, which may not be readily understood by those reviewing the financial statements. The financial statements are not considered complete without each of these notes.

Staff Functions in the Accounting Process

The number of staff persons in the business office and their degree of specialization will vary with the facility's size, complexity, and ownership. In general, however, those responsible for the accounting functions will be the bookkeeper, the accountant or comptroller, and the administrator.

The bookkeeper maintains the journals and ledger and performs the trial balance. An accountant or comptroller may also check the trial balance, but their primary task is preparing the financial statement.

For all practical purposes, it is legally mandatory that a nursing facility have its books officially audited, that is, audited by a person who is a certified public accountant (CPA). It is almost impossible to do business without having the facility's books audited by a CPA, who, in effect, serves as the public's representative.

Administrators of a chain-owned facility will generally send the data from the books to a regional or corporate office, where the financial statements and a variety of other schedules will be compiled and returned.

COMMON PITFALLS IN PRACTICE

- Many new administrators do not give enough attention to the financials. It is important for you to comb through these documents. Find errors, find things not classified to the right accounts, and make corrections where necessary. Your goal is to have the cleanest financials possible that tell the best financial picture of your facility.
- Keep in mind that financials will be used against you in practice. Your supervisor will inquire as to why you spent so much in this account, not enough in that account, or none in some other account. You will need to have justifications for each of these accounts—which is why you need to ensure your financials are a clean and accurate portrayal of what happened in your facility for the month.

3.5 PUTTING FINANCIAL STATEMENTS TO WORK: WORKING CAPITAL, RATIO ANALYSIS, AND VERTICAL ANALYSIS

Section Concepts

- *How to use working capital, ratio analysis, and vertical analyses to understand functions of the facility cash flow*

Consider as the Administrator . . .

- *Is it possible to fully and accurately allocate all costs in the facility?*

NAB DOMAIN 2A6: FINANCIAL REPORTING REQUIREMENTS (E.G., REQUIREMENTS FOR NOT-FOR-PROFIT, FOR-PROFIT, AND GOVERNMENTAL PROVIDERS)

NAB DOMAIN 2A8: INTERNAL FINANCIAL MANAGEMENT CONTROLS (E.G., SEGREGATION OF DUTIES, ACCESS)

NAB DOMAIN 2A2: FINANCIAL ANALYSIS (E.G., RATIOS, PROFITABILITY, DEBT, REVENUE MIX, DEPRECIATION, OPERATING MARGIN, CASH FLOW)

NAB DOMAIN 2A4: FINANCIAL STATEMENTS (E.G., INCOME/REVENUE STATEMENT, BALANCE SHEET, STATEMENT OF CASH FLOWS, COST REPORTING)

The net income is an essential and readily identifiable item of interest on the financial statements. What other information can be gleaned from these reports? There are several the administrator can use. Three tools are discussed subsequently.

WORKING CAPITAL

Current assets minus current liabilities equals the working capital available, which can also be considered the funds available to the facility year (Brigham & Houston, 2019).

Suppose the administrator of The Laurels facility wants to learn if enough funds are available to purchase $60,000 worth of capital equipment for the nursing department. Where can this information be found?

The net income for the month of July—and the entire year—has been reinvested in the facility, as indicated by the net worth section of the balance sheet; these funds may or may not still be available. Although the net worth shows the funds that have been invested in the facility, it is not a pool of cash. Recall that net worth is a record of funds that have been invested in the facility over time and that most of the funds shown here are therefore not available for spending or investing.

The administrator might also check the cash accounts of The Laurels to determine available cash for purchasing the items. But this is not suitable either because the balance sheet demonstrates that The Laurels owes $367,000 to various creditors, and the available cash may be needed to meet these obligations.

To get an idea of the funds available to purchase the needed equipment, the administrator must look at the amount of working capital available. Current assets remaining after current liabilities have been subtracted yield the amount of money that the administrator has at their discretion.

The administrator finds that there is only $36,898 in working capital available to purchase equipment for the nursing department meaning the facility probably should not purchase new equipment at this time. Because current assets include relatively nonliquid accounts, such as inventory and prepaid insurance, the working capital may be calculated by excluding these accounts from the total current assets. The administrator will have to consider needs versus wants and determine if equipment for the nursing department is currently a necessity or a preference. It would be prudent to evaluate this closely because a need, such as an HVAC repair, roof repairs, or pesky plumbing problems, might arise at any time.

Consider as the Administrator . . .

- *How important is working capital to a company's well-being?*
- *Are there ways to have capital without simply having cash?*

RATIO ANALYSIS

Another common approach to analyzing financial statements is to perform ratio analysis. Financial managers generally express the information in financial statements as a series of ratios (Zelman et al., 2020). An infinite number of ratios may be derived from financial statements, but the discussion here is confined to several of the more common measures of financial performance.

Usefulness of Ratios

Ratios provide helpful information. Financial ratios are no more than fractions using the numbers in the financial statement and are therefore relatively simple to calculate quickly and easily.

Ratio analysis allows the administrator to identify trends in many measures of financial performance of the facility by comparing the same ratio for several periods. Ratio analysis of the financial statements can also be used to compare the financial performance of several facilities. It is one of the most valuable tools the administrator has.

It has already been mentioned that the amount of working capital available is calculated by subtracting current liabilities from current assets. A positive amount of working capital indicates that the facility can meet its current obligations with its existing assets.

If all resident revenues were collected before or immediately after they were earned, the facility would not need excess working capital. But because third-party payers, such as Medicare and Medicaid, pay nursing facilities for services sometimes well after services were rendered, the facility must maintain a certain level of working capital to meet expenses during the "lag time" before the payments are received. (If part of a chain or a group of facilities, the same problem is faced by the corporate managers who have the same gaps between services rendered and payments received but on a more extensive scale.) Even nursing facilities that have a predominantly private-pay resident population must plan for collections of resident bills to extend over a period of weeks to months. How much working capital should the facility maintain to cover its lag time? One way to get an idea of an appropriate amount is to perform a current or acid-test ratio.

Current Ratio

$$\text{Current ratio} = \text{Current assets} / \text{Current liabilities}$$

The Laurels has:

$$\$403,898 / \$367,000 = 1.1$$

A current ratio greater than one shows that The Laurels can meet its current obligations with a working capital surplus. Does this mean that a current ratio of 2.5 is even better? Not necessarily, a high current ratio may show that the facility has too much money tied up in current assets and that it may make better use of some of these funds by investing them in an interest-bearing bank account or its equivalent (Zelman et al., 2020).

Interpreting Ratios

Interpretation of an appropriate current ratio exemplifies a point of caution with the use of any ratio. A ratio itself reveals very little about the facility's performance and should be compared either over time or with the rest of the industry. A current ratio of 1.1 may be acceptable if the past ratios for The Laurels have been as follows:

Year 1	Year 2	Year 3	Year 4
0.80	0.85	0.90	1.00

A ratio of 1.1 could also indicate a decline in working capital if past ratios have been much higher than 1.1. Industry comparisons are also meaningful. If the average current ratio for the nursing facility industry, preferably in the same region, is 1.0, then

The Laurels may be managing its working capital well. If the industry average is 0.9, then The Laurels might rethink the level of funds it is keeping available. Thus, the interpretation of all ratios is relative to both past performance and industry averages. The Laurels' administrator will determine the appropriate current ratio and adjust working capital to maintain that ratio.

The Quick Ratio

Another commonly used ratio is the quick ratio. This ratio is like the current ratio but is a more rigorous and representative measure of current assets, such as only cash and accounts receivable. Sometimes marketable securities are used to cover current liabilities.

$$\text{Quick ratio} = (\text{Cash} + \text{Acc. Rec.} + \text{Mkt'ble Sec})/\text{Current liabilities}$$
$$(\$60,700 + \$53,519 + \$25,275)/\$139,494 = 0.4$$

The quick ratio reveals that The Laurels is not quite able to cover its current obligations with its most available assets but is quite close to the industry average (Zelman et al., 2020).

Average Collection Period Ratio

The average collection period ratio is another helpful ratio, showing the average lag time of accounts receivable. While nursing facility administrators have little direct influence in expediting third-party fund collections (such as Medicare and Medicaid), timely collection of resident privately paid monies decreases working capital needs (Brigham & Houston, 2019), making the average collection period ratio very important information.

$$\text{Average Collection Period} = 365 \times \text{Accounts received}/\text{Net operating revenues}$$
$$= 365 \times \$53,517/\$334,693$$
$$= 58 \text{ days}$$

Because most insurers can reimburse the nursing facility up to 3 to 5 months after billing, an average collection period of 58 days may be appropriate for a facility with most public-paid residents. The length of time between billing Medicaid and receiving payment varies radically among the states. Some pay immediately; some states delay payment for months to manage their cash flow.

Average Payment Period Ratio

NAB DOMAIN 2A2: FINANCIAL ANALYSIS (E.G., RATIOS, PROFITABILITY, DEBT, REVENUE MIX, DEPRECIATION, OPERATING MARGIN, CASH FLOW); 2A3: REVENUE CYCLE MANAGEMENT (E.G., BILLING, ACCOUNTS RECEIVABLE, ACCOUNTS PAYABLE, COLLECTIONS)

A related ratio is the accounts payable average payment period, which shows the average number of days used to pay creditors. Too many days in the payable period may develop into a poor credit relationship with suppliers. At the same time, too few days may indicate that funds should be invested for a longer time before creditors are paid (Brigham & Houston, 2019).

Average payment period = 365 × Accounts payable/Supplies expense
$$= 365 \times \$2,852/\$31,393$$
$$= 33 \text{ days}$$

Days Cash on Hand

Because payment for bills is generally sought by the 30th day at the latest, The Laurels seems to be performing well in its efforts to make timely payments to suppliers. If the average payment period was much shorter, The Laurels might consider waiting for 30 days to pay some of its creditors and investing these funds in an interest-earning account. If a discount is offered for payment within 10 days or some short, specified period, early settlement of accounts payable might be more cost-effective. Supplier payment time frames may be negotiable, inflexible, or have fast turnaround times. Those working in a chain may find corporate employees unable to turn around invoices in the timeframe required by suppliers, thus making part of your job an active search for suppliers with kinder payment terms for the facility.

The opportunity cost (loss of fund use options) must be considered for accounts payable and receivable considerations. In times of low interest rates, the opportunity cost is less than in times of high interest rates, when using money is more costly.

The facility must calculate expected cash outflow for each period and ensure enough cash is available to pay bills appropriately.

Net Operating Margin Ratio

NAB DOMAIN 2A2: FINANCIAL ANALYSIS (E.G., RATIOS, PROFITABILITY, DEBT, REVENUE MIX, DEPRECIATION, OPERATING MARGIN, CASH FLOW)

The net operating margin is the proportion of revenues earned to the expenses used to earn those revenues. A low operating margin may indicate that rates for services should be raised or expenses reduced.

Expense Analysis

NAB DOMAIN 2A2: FINANCIAL ANALYSIS (E.G., RATIOS, PROFITABILITY, DEBT, REVENUE MIX, DEPRECIATION, OPERATING MARGIN, CASH FLOW)

The Laurels' negative operating margin shows that operating revenues do not cover operating expenses. The administrator should consider increasing charges for services, if the market will allow it, or reducing operating costs to increase the facility's operating margin. Reducing operating costs is, more often than not, the only remedy to this concern. Another approach to this ratio is operating income as a percentage of revenues. This ratio is best compared with industry averages for an indication of performance.

Debt-to-Equity Ratio

The debt-to-equity ratio measures the facility's long-run liquidity or ability to meet its long-term debts. A "small" proportion of debt to equity indicates that the facility could incur more long-term debt if the need were indicated. A high debt-to-equity ratio (compared to the industry) probably shows that the facility may have more debt than may be advisable, all other things being equal. This ratio is of particular interest to would-be creditors.

$$\text{Debt/equity} = \text{Long-term debt/Total equity}$$
$$= \$4,135,202/\$3,534,360$$
$$= 1.17$$

These are some of the more commonly used ratios. There are, of course, many other parameters of financial performance that will be of interest to the administrator.

Other formulas of value to the nursing home administrator:

$$\text{Average length of stay} = \frac{\text{Total patient days in the year}}{\text{Number of admissions in the year}}$$

$$\text{Percent of occupancy} = \frac{\text{Average daily census}}{\text{Number of beds}}$$

$$\text{FTE (full-time equivalent)} = \frac{\text{Total number of hours worked or budgeted}}{40 \text{ (an FTE is a position that only works 5 days/week)}}$$

FTEs × 1.4 = Number of line staff positions if you want to know how many nursing assistant positions, for example, you can have 7 days/week

$$\text{Costs per patient day} = \frac{\text{Costs in month}}{\text{Total patient days in month}}$$

$$\text{Hours per patient day} = \frac{\text{Number of hours worked}}{\text{Number of patients}}$$

$$\text{Turnover rate in percent} = \frac{\text{Number of employees terminated} \times 100}{\text{Number of total FTEs}}$$

These ratios can be evaluated by time or department.

VERTICAL ANALYSIS

A third method of analyzing the financial statements is to perform a vertical analysis. A vertical analysis converts each item on the income statement, balance sheet, or another financial report to a percentage of some total item on the same document.

A vertical analysis of The Laurels' income statement, using the year-to-date values, is shown in Table 3.5. Like the ratios presented earlier, these ratios are advantageous when compared over time or with other facilities. For example, an unusually high ratio of supplies to total expenses in July may indicate that supplies are being wasted or pilfered, provided there has not been a change in the type of services that would warrant a greater use of supplies. In contrast, although July's percentage may be higher than any other month, if supplies as a proportion of total expenses are consistently higher in July, the administrator knows that this is a pattern that may or may not be a matter or cause of concern.

TABLE 3.5 The Laurels Income Statement: Vertical Analysis

Revenues	July 'X1	Year to Date	Vertical Analyses	
Operating revenues				
Nursing				
Skilled				
Intermediate				
Total nursing	357,603	2,207,814	100%	94%
Ancillary				
Physical therapy	9,974	61,839	45%	
Occupational therapy	9,890	59,340	43%	
Social services	2,866	16,909	12%	
Total ancillary	22,730	138,088	100%	6%
Gross operating revenues	380,333	2,345,902		100%
Less deductions	45,640	281,508	12%	
Net operating revenue	334,693	2,064,394		88%
Nonoperating revenue				
Miscellaneous				
Meals	430	2,494	16%	
Concession	1,358	8,691	54%	
Beauty shop	790	4,819	30%	
Total miscellaneous	2,578	16,004	100%	51%
Interest	2,640	15,312		49%
Total nonoperating revenue	5,218	31,316		100%
Total revenues	339,911	2,095,710		
Expenses				
Operating expenses				
Salaries				
Nursing	135,192	833,151	68%	
Dietary	15,582	93,492	8%	
Administration	9,551	54,441	4%	
Laundry	3,409	20,454	2%	
Housekeeping	13,435	81,282	7%	
Maintenance	5,287	32,145	3%	
Physical therapy	9,652	60,808	5%	
Occupational therapy	3,450	20,735	2%	
Social services	2,146	13,305	1%	
Total salaries	197,705	1,209,812	100%	59.0%
Supplies	31,393	189,928		9.2%
Activity	2,065	12,390		0.6%
Capital equipment	200	1,600		0.1%
Utilities	8,764	52,584		2.6%
Telephone	163	1,043		0.1%
Insurance	4,000	24,018		1.2%
Taxes (real estate)	3,313	19,878		1.0%
Capital costs				
Interest	27,816	166,896	30%	8.1%
Mortgage payment	24,029	144,174	26%	7.0%

(*continued*)

TABLE 3.5 The Laurels Income Statement: Vertical Analysis (*continued*)

Revenues	July 'X1	Year to Date	Vertical Analyses	
Depreciation	39,627	237,762	43%	11.5%
Total capital costs	91,472	548,832	100%	
Total expenses	339,078	2,060,085		100%
Net income (loss)	833	35,625		
Income tax (@ 45%)	375	16,031		
Profit after tax	458	19,594		

The administrator can accumulate valuable information from the financial statements by performing both ratio and vertical analyses. By comparing these ratios over time and with other facilities, trends and patterns in the facility's operation can be identified, perhaps one of the most critical functions of financial statement analysis. Being aware of such patterns enables the administrator to pinpoint problem areas in the facility and make more knowledgeable financial decisions.

COMMON PITFALLS IN PRACTICE

- There are many ways to pull information from your financials and put it to work for you. Many of the ratios provided here can help you more easily understand your financials. There are many more and different types of ratios and formulas out there to help you along!

3.6 ADDITIONAL ACCOUNTING PROCEDURES THAT HELP THE ADMINISTRATOR MAINTAIN CONTROL OVER THE FACILITY

Section Concepts

- *How to use financial information to better control the facility by carefully managing:*
  - *Accounts receivable*
  - *Patient census reports*
  - *Third-party payers*
  - *Medicare cost reconciliation statements*
  - *Account write-offs*
  - *Cash handling*
  - *Planned bill paying*
  - *Inventory control*
  - *Payroll management techniques*

Consider as the Administrator . . .

- *Can the administrator rely on the business office to successfully manage these aspects of financial management, or does the administrator need independent skills in this area?*

NAB DOMAN 2A2: FINANCIAL ANALYSIS (E.G., RATIOS, PROFITABILITY, DEBT, REVENUE MIX, DEPRECIATION, OPERATING MARGIN, CASH FLOW); 2A3: REVENUE CYCLE MANAGEMENT (E.G., BILLING, ACCOUNTS RECEIVABLE, ACCOUNTS PAYABLE, COLLECTIONS)

NAB DOMAIN 2A4: FINANCIAL STATEMENTS (E.G., INCOME/ REVENUE STATEMENT, BALANCE SHEET, STATEMENT OF CASH FLOWS, COST REPORTING)

Although accounting processes are similar in every institution, the procedures for managing finances will vary from facility to facility, and so will the best control methods. In financial management, *control* refers to the development and maintenance of systematic ways to identify problems when they occur to permit the administrator to intervene appropriately. To maintain control, the administrator and the staff usually develop policies for all office procedures. Identifying possible financial problems as soon as they arise enables the staff to deal effectively with them through recognized policies.

There are several tools available to assist the administrator in controlling financial operations. Procedures should be arranged so that no single person has complete responsibility for any area of the facility's finances. Establishing a system of checks and balances allows part of one person's task to be completed or reviewed by another. Furthermore, each employee can be required to take vacation time so that no one has uninterrupted control of specific office tasks. It is essential to have procedures in place that minimize employee temptation. Even the best procedures set up by the most sophisticated corporations have not prevented the occasional embezzlement of facility funds. One such example is the HealthSouth scandal several years ago, and even outside healthcare in corporations such as Enron. Eternal vigilance is necessary for money matters. Speaking up when something does not seem correct is also an essential skill, regardless of the consequences.

ACCOUNTS RECEIVABLE: BILLING FOR SERVICES RENDERED BY THE FACILITY

The facility cannot receive money for services rendered until the resident has been billed for them. Delays in billing create an opportunity cost: the loss of use or availability of funds when cash owed to the facility is not yet in its possession.

Financial Review of Potential Residents

Some states require that admissions be on a first-come, first-served basis for any potential resident for whom the facility can provide appropriate care. Other states allow the facility to make admissions decisions based, in part, on financial considerations.

At the time of admission, the payment source should be established. If the client is not paying with their own funds, a written agreement to pay must be obtained from the person who controls the resident's funds. In addition, present and potential

Medicare and Medicaid needs should be determined. These agencies will typically pay for care only after an authorization number has been established for a recipient. A significant number of persons who enter the facility as Medicare or private-pay persons quickly spend down their savings. The social worker must anticipate which persons will become Medicaid eligible and begin the application process several months before actual eligibility for a steady payment stream for care rendered to be achieved. The paperwork and requirements for this in many states are nearly insurmountable and take much time, facility resources, and family or responsible party input.

Just as the facility must remove temptations from its employees to embezzle facility funds, so also must the facility constantly seek to minimize temptations for residents' money managers to withhold monies legitimately due to the facility. Experience has taught that Social Security and similar checks that have been pledged to pay for the resident's care are best sent directly to the facility rather than to a family member who may feel more pressing financial needs than payment of the facility charges. Social Security checks coming to the facility are called a "representative payee" arrangement, which many facilities use. It is also a remedy that facilities can levy when a family or responsible party "forgets" or chooses not to pay the facility. Facilities can appeal to the Social Security Administration to become the representative payee due to fraudulent activities by those responsible for paying the resident portion of care.

Resident Intake

When the resident's payment source has been confirmed at admission, proper intake must be made up for each person, listing the name, room number, source of payment, and daily (or routine) service charges. The charges and the billing and collections procedures must be explained to each resident and/or sponsor. Billing is most often done through an electronic record system that may be separate from the facility's electronic medical records system.

Preparation of Invoices

In every case, each service not bundled into the daily rate must have charge slips created periodically by each service center. Because these charges are distinct from routine room-related services, a Special Revenues Journal(s) may be used to record them. What these charges might be is often dependent on the payer source. However, we could see charges for medical supplies, briefs, laundry service, therapy charges, and a myriad of other potential services.

Routine Charges

Once the ancillary charges for the billing period have been determined, they are added to the resident's routine charges. The routine charge is for "room and board" services, which usually include basic nursing care, room, and meals. Facilities package their charges based on several considerations. Some offer a broad continuum of services from which residents may choose.

Daily Census Form

$$\text{Average daily census (ADC)} = \frac{\text{Total patient days}}{\text{Days in the month}}$$

The routine charge may be determined on a daily, weekly, or monthly basis and is calculated with the aid of the Daily Census Form. This charge summarizes the facility's occupancy that lists, for each day, admissions, discharges, and transfers by the level of care if the facility offers more than one. The Daily Census Form is usually prepared by the nursing unit (often called the "midnight census") and is submitted to the business office (Singh, 2016). This midnight census form is a crucial document for billing purposes in the facility.

Patient Census Report

The bookkeeper draws up a Patient Census Report (usually for the month) by compiling the information from the patient census forms (Figure 3.4).

The Patient Census Report is used to calculate the total routine charge for each resident or service recipient (e.g., outpatient physical therapy charges). Routine and ancillary services are finally calculated for each resident and service recipient and entered on each resident(s) or service recipient's Accounts Receivable Ledger card (Accounts Receivable, Invoice Supplement; Figure 3.5) and in the Billings Journal (Singh, 2016).

NAB DOMAIN 4B4: BUSINESS DEVELOPMENT (E.G., SALES, MARKETING, PARTNERSHIPS, ACOs, CONTRACTS AND AGREEMENTS, NEGOTIATIONS)

NAB DOMAIN 2A4: FINANCIAL STATEMENTS (E.G., INCOME/ REVENUE STATEMENT, BALANCE SHEET, STATEMENT OF CASH FLOWS, COST REPORTING)

The Billings Journal should be divided by payer type (private pay, Medicare, Medicaid, Department of Veterans Affairs [VA], hospital reserve bed contract, HMO, preferred/professional provider organization [PPO], independent practitioner organization [IPO], worker's compensation fund, or similar third-party payer). These divisions facilitate billing payers. In addition to building new long-term care facilities of its own, the VA subcontracts for short-term care with private nursing facilities. The number of nursing facility stays being paid for by the VA increased in recent years. There are approximately 133 State Veterans Homes nationally, accounting for nearly 24,000 beds. This number continues to grow on an annual basis. The billing process and services covered vary with each payer. Each bill should itemize any ancillary charges (when permitted by the payer) to expedite the processing of invoices by third-party payers. In most cases these days, billing requires electronic submission, which typically results in more timely payments and fewer errors in billing.

THE LAURELS

MONTH/YEAR

06/x1

ROOM AND BED	ROOM RATE	PATIENT NAME LAST	INITIAL	PATIENT NO.	1	2	3	4	5	6	7	8	9	10	11	12	13	14	15	16	17	18	19	20	21	22	23	24	25	26	27	28	29	30	31
117	70	Jones			x	x	x	x	x	x	x	x	x	x	x	x	x	x	x	x	x	x	x	x	x	x	x	x	x	x	x	x	x	x	
118	70	Rose			x	x		x	x	x	x	x	x	x	x	x	x	x	x	x	x	x	x	x												

DAY OF MONTH

TOTALS

	Private	Agency	Medicaid	Medicare	Other	Billings
	240.00		2100.00			2340.00
	100.00		1400.00			1500.00

TOTALS

FIGURE 3.4 Patient census report.

ACCOUNTS RECEIVABLE
INVOICE SUPPLEMENT

ADDITIONAL CURRENT ENTRIES – COMPLETE SECTIONS A AND B

ADJUSTMENTS TO PRIOR MONTHS – COMPLETE SECTIONS A AND C

SECTION A

FACILITY NO.	FACILITY NAME: THE LAURELS				
PATIENT NUMBER	INVOICE NUMBER 3012-756-01	YR/MO X1/06	NUMBER /	INVOICE DATE 6/29/X1	PATIENT NAME Rose, M. L.

SECTION B

AREA
C = CERTIFIED
R = RESIDENTIAL

LEVEL
UNCLASSIFIED SKILLED
7 = RESIDENTIAL
8 = HOLD/DOD

STATUS CODES
1 = PRIVATE
2 = AGENCY
3 = MEDICARE
4 = VETERAN
5 = OTHER

PAYMENTS

TRAN CODE	DATE MO/DAY	OPEN ITEM	DESCRIPTION	PRIVATE	AGENCY	MEDICARE	VETERAN	OTHER
	/							
	/							
	/							
	/							
			TOTAL					

ACCOMMODA.

TRAN CODE	DATE MO/DAY	ROOM-BED	MO DAYS	RATE	AREA	LEVEL	PRIVATE	AGENCY	MEDICARE	VETERAN	OTHER
	6/29	118	30	70.00	S	8	275.00		2100.00		
	/										
	/										
	/										
						TOTAL	275.00		2100.00		

STATUS	NON-COLLECT

ANCILL

TRAN CODE	DESCRIPTION			PRIVATE	AGENCY	MEDICARE	VETERAN	OTHER
	PHYSICAL THERAPY					240.00		
			TOTAL			240.00		

STATUS	NON-COLLECT

FIGURE 3.4 Patient census report (*continued*).

EXPLANATION OF ADJUSTMENTS	TRAN CODE	TRAN CODE	OPEN ITEM	NO. OF DAYS	RATE	AREA	LEVEL	PRIVATE	AGENCY	MEDICARE	VETERAN	OTHER	STATUS	NON-COLLECT
	65													
	65													
	65													
	65													
	65													
A	65													
D	65													
J U S T	65													
M E N T S	65													
	65													
	65													
	65													
	65													
	65													
	65													
	65										TOTAL			

SECTION C

FIGURE 3.5 Ledger card.

Billing Medicare, Medicaid, Other Third Parties, and Private Payers

Billing is an increasingly complex process because of the increasing variety of payment agreements nursing facilities often negotiate with third parties. Medicaid patients' care costs are customarily billed and paid for monthly, usually with one composite bill for all Medicaid residents submitted to the state or its designated payer. Many facilities bill weekly for their Medicaid residents to enhance cash flow. Medicare bills, in contrast, are typically submitted for each resident and sent to a fiscal intermediary. Medicare (and Medicaid) payers sometimes pay promptly and occasionally send for many clarifications on bills, the purpose of which is to delay the final payment to the facility to ease cash flow problems experienced by the third-party payers. It is a complicated game in some states.

> **NAB DOMAIN 2A5: REVENUE AND REIMBURSEMENT (E.G., PDPM, PDGM, ACOs, HMOs, MEDICAID, PRIVATE PAYORS); 2A7: INTEGRATION OF CLINICAL AND FINANCIAL SYSTEMS (E.G., EMR/EHR, MDS); 4B4: BUSINESS DEVELOPMENT (E.G., SALES, MARKETING, PARTNERSHIPS, ACOs, CONTRACTS AND AGREEMENTS, NEGOTIATIONS)**

More and more third-party payers are negotiating contracts with nursing facilities that also vary in the method of payment. Often a third-party payer (e.g., an HMO) will negotiate a separate payment schedule for each member it sends to a nursing facility. Other third-party payers may negotiate a flat rate for all members they refer to a particular nursing facility, regardless of acuity level. For some residents, the monthly fee negotiated by the third-party payer will be all-inclusive; others will be on an itemized service use basis. In these circumstances, both the facility administration and the third-party payer administration are jockeying for a position that covers their actual costs, whatever the payment arrangement. Intense pressures on third-party payers to hold down costs are being passed on to the nursing facility. This situation is an area the administrator must focus on because it can quickly devolve into an untenable position when you have a full census but not enough money to cover your costs. Case mix is a daily focus in the facility.

Electronic Health Records Systems

The Health Information Technology for Economic and Clinical Health (HITECH) Act, a part of the American Recovery and Reinvestment Act of 2009 (ARRA), has focused on nursing facilities having electronic health records (EHRs). This Act, coupled with the rollout of *International Classification of Diseases, Tenth Revision* (ICD-10), coding has truly changed the face of how nursing facilities operate resident records, billing, and even quality improvement initiatives. Despite the ARRA dating to 2009, many facilities today cannot afford the EHR conversion. These facilities have bought into electronic systems for specific things, which they must have and are often required by law. Despite all the incentives that were part of the HITECH Act and the ARRA, the stimulus package did not include nursing facilities in the benefits offered to hospitals and providers.

Despite the lack of financial support, some facilities have fully integrated clinical and billing electronic systems. These are often useful to the administrator for a quick review for "flags" of concerning situations (such as facility-acquired pressure injuries or falls). Other information readily available includes billing requirements, resident prescription plans, drug allergies, and provider visits. EHRs have become a fantastic timesaver for billing and all the different moving parts of patient care.

Accounting for Deductions From Revenue

Besides contractual discounts, charity care and bad debts are also sources of deductions from revenue (Berger, 2014). Charity care is provided to a resident when the service is not reimbursable and cannot be paid privately. Bad debts, in contrast, are resident accounts that are past due but are still subject to collection (Singh, 2016).

Contractual discounts are often the largest source of deductions from revenue in nursing facilities. Because most deductions cannot be confirmed until payment has been received, they are accounted for in the Billings Journal when known rather than estimated. The payment from public insurers will be accompanied by a Medical Assistance Remittance and Status Report (or similar name). This report lists the resident's name and claim number, the service dates, the description of services rendered, the total amount billed to the program, and the allowed and nonallowed charges, with an explanation code stating why the service was not reimbursed. The T account for deductions from revenue would be as follows:

Billings Journal

Debit	Credit
2/27	Contractual discount $450.00
2/27	Accounts receivable $450.00

Submitting and Resubmitting Claims

NAB DOMAIN 2A2: FINANCIAL ANALYSIS (E.G., RATIOS, PROFITABILITY, DEBT, REVENUE MIX, DEPRECIATION, OPERATING MARGIN, CASH FLOW); 2A5: REVENUE AND REIMBURSEMENT (E.G., PDPM, PDGM, ACOs, HMOs, MEDICAID, PRIVATE PAYORS)

The amount of the deduction is also included on the resident's Accounts Receivable Ledger Card. If the deduction is invalid, the fiscal intermediary should be contacted for an explanation of the deduction. The claim can then be resubmitted accompanied by the information needed to justify the request for payment. Medicare intermediaries are constantly issuing bulletins defining and redefining what covered charges include and exclude. Understanding Medicare billing, especially Medicare Part B billing, is a complex yet essential task. In an era of razor-thin net operating margins, appropriate billing can significantly impact a facility. So can inappropriate billing.

Medicare has many rules, one of which is that facility bills will be paid as expeditiously as possible so long as the amount of "inappropriately" billed services does not exceed 5% of all the facility's Medicare billings. What Medicare deems appropriate and inappropriate is a moving target requiring constant business office attention. Once this 5% threshold has been violated, each subsequent bill from that facility is scrutinized, and payment is slowed. Some facilities have found weekly interdisciplinary "Medicare Meetings" with nursing (usually the director of nursing and other relevant nurses), the business office manager, the director of rehabilitative therapies, the admissions/social worker director, and the administrator helpful. At these meetings, each Medicare resident is reviewed for the appropriateness of Medicare-specific care being given and an assessment made of future days of appropriate Medicare coverage anticipated during the 100-day limit for each spell of illness experienced by this person. This type of Medicare meeting ensures that all pieces of the puzzle are the same, all staff is on the same page, and everyone is doing what the care plan states for the resident. If a discrepancy in suggested and documented care does not match during a Medicare audit, all billing may be nullified. An example of this could be if therapy suggested two-person transfers and a certified nursing assistant was documenting one-person transfers. One instance is all that it takes to make billing inappropriate in the eyes of Medicare.

Medicare Plan D

Medicare Plan D benefits facility cash flow since some drugs previously covered out of the preset Medicare rate being paid to the facility are now covered, for the first time, under Medicare Plan D.

Medicare Cost Reconciliation Settlement

When Medicare pays a facility for providing care to patients/residents, the reimbursement amount is based on the cost of that care. However, instead of calculating the actual cost of providing care for each Medicare beneficiary in each facility, Medicare makes an estimate of how much the care for residents in each facility should have cost and then pays the facility periodically based on that estimate. Suppose this estimated amount of reimbursement received during the year is less (or more) than the cost of providing the care. In that case, Medicare will make up the difference at the end of the year by paying the facility a Medicare Cost Reconciliation settlement or requiring that any overpayment be returned. Any funds due from Medicare are recorded in the Cash Receipts Journal as follows:

Cash Receipts Journal

Debit	Credit
11/23	Due from Medicare $375.00
11/23	Contractual discount $375.00

Sometimes services that are not allowable by the insurer (e.g., occupational therapy or some types of dental care) will be provided to patients who cannot pay for them. These services are considered charity care and are "written off" as essentially nonbillable. A specific account should exist in the Chart of Accounts for this type of care, separate from other kinds of uncollectible costs. Each facility needs policies to govern the circumstances and extent of charity care that will be provided.

COLLECTING MONEY OWED TO THE FACILITY

An appropriate collections policy will depend on the facility's previous experience with its payers. For bills delinquent by 1 month, a letter may be sent as a reminder. After an appropriate interval, a telephone call to the payer (logged into a written record) may be made. The collections policy must indicate if and under what circumstances a collections agency or other procedure will be used. Ultimately, a lack of payment can potentially lead to forced discharge from a facility. It is important to know these laws and follow them to the letter when a financial discharge is being instituted.

Account Write-Off Recommendation

Problem collections are most effectively handled with an attitude of diplomacy and firmness. An effort should be made to accommodate the payer if there is a valid reason for delinquent payment. Suppose a resident's accounts are eventually determined to be uncollectible. In that case, some type of account write-off recommendation form (Figure 3.6) is filled out, with one copy retained in the resident's file and another going to the accountant for recording the total of uncollectible accounts.

Like hospitals and other healthcare providers, nursing facilities are victims of the cost-shifting phenomenon in the United States. Public relations and other considerations make discharging residents for uncollectible bills exceedingly tricky when the resident does not have another place to go. However, we still find ourselves left in this situation occasionally.

HANDLING CASH

Cash is easily mismanaged. It is easily concealed. The typical facility will keep only a small amount of cash on the premises, often not more than $500, as most transactions will take place through business office accounts.

Cash-Handling Procedures

All cash must be handled by at least two employees, both of whom are bonded. One person should be responsible for receiving the cash (e.g., opening the mail or taking a check in person). This person should not be the same one who is responsible for making bank deposits. Checks should be stamped "For Deposit Only" in the facility's name immediately on receipt and a daily remittance list prepared for all cash received. This employee should retain one copy of this list, and another should go to the person making the bank deposits. Many facilities today do not accept any cash or checks. They are willing to assist the resident or family with an electronic check, so funds go directly from their account to the facility's accounts with no one touching the money in between.

Facility _____ # _____ Date _____

Patient Name _____ # _____ P__ A__ M__ VA__ Other __ Balance $_____

Admission Date _____ Discharge Date _____ Expired: Yes ☐   No ☐

Readmission Date _____ Discharge Date _____

Readmission Date _____ Discharge Date _____

Name and address of responsible party _____

_____

Home Phone _____ Business Phone _____

Date and amount of last payment _____

Brief history of account: _____

_____

_____

_____

Should account be assigned to a collection agency?   Yes ☐   No ☐

  Facility opinion by _____ Date _____

  *Regional concurrence by _____ Date _____

**Corporate concurrence by _____ Date _____

If Medicare—include all intermediary correspondence.

Is coinsurance involved?   Yes ☐   No ☐   If yes, please provide dates and amounts: _____

_____

_____

_____

_____ /_____
Administrator   Date

_____ /_____
Regional Controller   Date

_____ /_____
District Director/Director of Operations   Date

*For all accounts over $250.00
**For all accounts over $500.00.

FIGURE 3.6 Recommendations for a write-off of an uncollectible account.
A, Medicare Part A; P, Private; M, Medicaid; VA, Veterans VA.

Cash receipt slips should then be prepared, with one copy going to the payer and another to the accountant or the accountant's file. The bookkeeper should record the cash received in the Cash Receipts Journal and on the patient's sheet in the Patient Accounts Receivable Ledger (Figure 3.7).

Cash should be deposited in the bank daily to prevent it from being mislaid and to allow the maximum amount of interest to be earned on the funds. At the end of each month, entries in the Cash Receipts Journal are posted into the General Ledger, and these figures are checked against the cash receipts entries in the Patient Accounts Receivable Ledger.

PATIENT'S NAME LAST NAME INITIAL	C A S H	MISCEL- LANEOUS	PRIVATE	AGENCY	MEDICARE	VETERAN	OTHER	POSTED TO INVOICE NO.
			FACILITY NO. _____			PAGE ____ or ____		
			DATE OF DEPOSIT 09/12/20X1			FACILITY NAME THE LAURELS		
Jones, F.A.					2375 00			3012- 756-01
TOTALS FOR EACH COLUMN	Ⓐ							
ACCOUNT		1211	1212	1213	1210	1217		

MISCELLANEOUS RECEIPTS SUMMARY				REDEPOSITED ITEMS RECEIVED FROM	AMOUNT
ITEM	ACCOUNT	AMOUNT			
EMPLOYEES MEALS - FOOD SALES	4820				
VENDING MACHINE INCOME	4860				
TOTAL A MUST EQUAL TOTAL B		Ⓑ			

TOTAL OF
THIS DEPOSIT $ _____
ACCOUNT 1130

FIGURE 3.7 Accounts receivable record.

COMMON PITFALLS IN PRACTICE

- Knowing the business office manager's job as well as your own job is truly crucial to your success in collections. You may find yourself tasked with helping clean up old collectibles or filling in for a vacationing employee. This is one area you cannot be weak in.

ACCOUNTS PAYABLE: THE FACILITY'S BILLS

NAB DOMAIN 2A3: REVENUE CYCLE MANAGEMENT (E.G., BILLING, ACCOUNTS RECEIVABLE, ACCOUNTS PAYABLE, COLLECTIONS)

Accounts payable are monies owed to creditors for purchases made by the facility. A nursing facility's creditors usually furnish foodstuffs, linens, medical supplies, pharmaceuticals, laboratory tests, and office, housekeeping, and maintenance supplies, for example. A file should be set up for each regular vendor or supplier and a Miscellaneous Vendor file for all unusual or incidental purchases.

When a purchase order is made out and sent to the supplier, a copy of the purchase order should be placed in the appropriate file. All supplies, except for foodstuffs, should be delivered to a storeroom when the order is received. A receiving slip will accompany every shipment. The employee receiving the goods should check the slip against the items received and against the purchase order at the time of receipt. This process ensures all purchased items were delivered and that no extra supplies were received beyond the ordered items. Any back-ordered items on the receiving slip should be noted. The approved receiving slip is then placed with the purchase order in the vendor file.

Invoices from creditors are usually sent to the facility at the beginning of each month. The receiving slip and purchase order should be checked against the invoice to confirm that unit pricing is the same as when the shipment was ordered and that all supplies charged in the bill were received.

The administrator should approve all invoices according to most owner policies, but practically speaking, the administrator designates appropriate individuals to share in this task. These invoices are then recorded in the Accounts Payable Journal by department. For example, medical supplies and pharmaceuticals may be attributed to nursing, foodstuffs to dietary, linens to housekeeping. Invoices are then placed in an invoice file.

At the end of the month, the accounts in the Payables Journal are added up. This sum should equal the total of all invoices in the invoice file. Bills are usually payable within 30 days. Creditors should be paid on the latest possible date unless a discount is offered for early payment. This procedure does not mean that accounts payable should be chronically delinquent while available funds remain in the bank, but rather that the facility earns maximum interest and remains solvent by waiting until the invoice is due rather than paying it immediately. It is vital to maintain a good credit relationship with suppliers, often middle persons or distributors, who are dependent on reasonably prompt invoice payment for their business operations.

At the beginning of the month, paying all invoices in the file should cover all bills due that month. Two designated employees should sign checks, and all payments should be recorded in the Cash Disbursements Journal when checks are written. Invoices should be marked "Paid" and placed in the vendor file, along with the receipt-of-payment statement when it is received. These source documents are retained until the end of the year for the accountant's records.

COMMON PITFALLS IN PRACTICE

- Simply assuming that your bills are getting processed and paid is a mistake. Accounts payable is just as important to your financial performance as accounts receivable. All too often, bills end up "missing" from a month or they are misplaced. You need to know the money going out of your facility. You should be very involved in supply chain management and authorizing orders—this way you *know* you are on budget each month.

INVENTORY: CONTROLLING SUPPLIES AND EQUIPMENT

NAB DOMAIN 2A9: SUPPLY-CHAIN MANAGEMENT (E.G., INVENTORY CONTROL)

A system of inventory control is needed to measure the amount and type of supplies used by each department. Under accrual-method accounting, all expenses incurred should be matched with the revenues earned in a period (Brigham & Houston, 2019). Consistent records of the cost of supplies consumed enable price and as-used comparisons to be made over time between departments or services. These records are also valuable in the budgeting process (Singh, 2016).

A system of inventory control discourages waste and pilferage of supplies and provides a means of keeping supplies at optimal levels. On the one hand, overstock, especially time-dated supplies, has an opportunity cost: the cost of monies unnecessarily tied up in inventory and a possible cost of obsolescence. Excess inventory also increases the opportunity for pilferage. On the other hand, frequent shortages of needed supplies can impinge on the quality of care and result in frustration among staff or require that costly rush orders be used to meet supply needs. In the 1970s, Toyota began to utilize a management approach to this continuing problem called "just in time" (JIT). JIT allows for a facility to purchase just what they need "in time" to use it. This purchasing method has been advantageous for many facilities due to limited storage for medical supplies, food, and other consumables. However, JIT assumes that there will be no disruptions in the supply chain. Outside influences on the supply chain, such as hurricanes, snowstorms, and other occurrences which can grind suppliers to a halt, and contingency plans must be in place for those situations.

Ideally, the focal point of inventory control is a locked central storeroom (Figure 3.8). Supplies should be delivered to a locked central storeroom with limited employee access as soon as they are received. The access is usually one employee each shift, although supply access must be balanced between availability when needed and avoiding unwarranted use. Smaller facilities may find a central storeroom impractical. In these cases, decentralized storerooms can become the responsibility of personnel in the individual department.

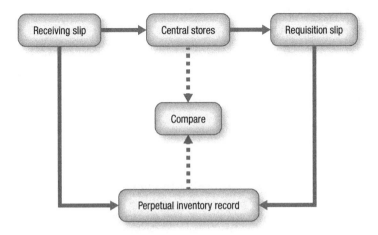

FIGURE 3.8 Perpetual inventory record.

Perpetual Inventory

A perpetual inventory system is recommended to maintain a precise inventory count on hand; that is, an accurate count of supplies used and those remaining in the storeroom. At the beginning of each fiscal year, and probably more often, all stored inventory should be physically confirmed. This confirmed count is the Beginning Inventory for the period.

Additions to inventory are noted from the receiving slips included in each shipment of supplies. The Beginning Inventory and the Inventory Received by the storerooms make up the Total Available Inventory. When supplies are removed from a storeroom, the department must fill out a requisition slip identifying the supplies and issue date. Supplies issued by storerooms should indicate the supplies utilized to provide services but will not account for those supplies remaining in each department or sub-location that have not yet been used.

For this reason, department heads should be encouraged to keep initial levels of supplies in their departments. Requisition slips should be initialed by a department head or other designated person. Requisition slips provide a check on the unjustified removal of supplies from the storeroom(s) and are the objective measure of the supplies consumed during a particular period.

The receiving and requisition slips are the source documents for keeping the perpetual inventory record (Table 3.6). At the end of each year or other period, the inventory in the storerooms should be counted and compared with the ending inventory from the perpetual inventory record. If physical storeroom counts and the inventory records do not match, then causes may include pilferage, requisition slip misuse, or inaccuracies in the recordkeeping system.

The business office should maintain a list of all inventory items used by the facility, the number of items in one unit, and the current price per unit. This log acts as a reference for determining the cost of the inventory used by each department and for establishing the total volume of supplies remaining in the storeroom(s).

TABLE 3.6 The Laurels Perpetual Inventory Record

Item #400: Syringes, Disposable	# of Units	Cost/Unit ($)	Cost ($)
July			
Beginning inventory	4	7.00	28.00
Goods received	5	7.00	35.00
Total goods available	9	7.00	63.00
Ending inventory	3	7.00	21.00
Goods used	6	7.00	42.00
August			
Beginning inventory	3	7.00	21.00
Goods received	6	7.00	42.00
Total goods available	9	7.00	63.00
Ending inventory	4	7.00	28.00
Goods used	5	7.00	35.00

LAST IN, FIRST OUT/FIRST IN, FIRST OUT

To account for the effects of inflation or deflation on the inventory value, the GAAPs recognize two methods of inventory costing: last in, first out (LIFO) and first in, first out (FIFO). The LIFO method assumes that inventory added last to stores is used first, thus making (in the case of inflation) the value of the goods remaining in inventory lower than that of the goods used to provide services. The FIFO method assumes the opposite: the older and less expensive supplies (in the case of deflation) are used for services, and the higher-priced goods remain in inventory longer. The difference in the effect of these two methods is shown in Table 3.7. Either approach of inventory cost may be adopted, but the one selected should be used consistently and should be mentioned in the notes to financial statements.

TABLE 3.7 The Laurels Inventory

Item #400: Syringes, Disposable	# of Units	Cost/ Unit ($)	Total Cost ($)	# of Units	Cost/ Unit ($)	Total Cost ($)
August						
Beginning inventory	3	7.00	$21.00			
Goods received	6	7.00	$42.00			
Total goods available	9	7.00	$63.00			
Ending inventory	4	7.00	$28.00			
Goods used	5	7.00	$35.00			
September		Last in, first out			First in, first out	
Beginning inventory	4	7.00	28.00	4	7.00	28.00
Goods received	5	8.00	40.00	5	8.00	40.00
Total goods available	9	4 @7.00	68.00	9	4 @7.00	68.00
		5 @8.00		OR	5 @8.00	
Ending inventory	5	4 @7.00	36.00	5	8.00	40.00
		1 @8.00				
Goods used	4	8.00	32.00	4	7.00	28.00

COMMON PITFALLS IN PRACTICE
- Waste is a huge area of concern in a nursing facility. Knowing the flow of what is coming in, what is getting used, and how much is being appropriately utilized is very important. It is not unheard of to find closets filled with unused supplies because they just kept coming each month due to a standing order with the supplier. This can prove to be a very large area of loss for the facility monthly.

PAYROLL

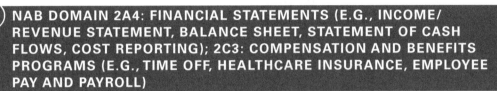

NAB DOMAIN 2A4: FINANCIAL STATEMENTS (E.G., INCOME/ REVENUE STATEMENT, BALANCE SHEET, STATEMENT OF CASH FLOWS, COST REPORTING); 2C3: COMPENSATION AND BENEFITS PROGRAMS (E.G., TIME OFF, HEALTHCARE INSURANCE, EMPLOYEE PAY AND PAYROLL)

Payroll is another source of cash outflow. It is the largest expense in the nursing facility, accounting for more than 50% of TCs in most cases. It also makes up about 85% of the facility's controllable costs.

A *controllable cost* is one over which the administrator has influence. Because it is the primary expense of the facility, accurate accounting records are essential.

PAYROLL JOURNAL

The Payroll Journal lists all paychecks disbursed in the period by department. At the end of the pay period, the hours worked are entered in the Payroll Journal, as derived from the timecards or sheets and the salaried employee staffing plan. Overtime hours are compensated at a higher rate and are listed in a column separate from the regular rate. Gross pay is calculated by multiplying hours worked by the hourly rate:

(Pay rate × Regular hours) + (Overtime rate × Overtime hours) = Gross pay

Payroll Deductions

Payroll deductions must be subtracted from gross pay to arrive at the employee's net pay. Deductions include federal, state, and sometimes municipal taxes, as well as various other possible deductions.

Federal, state, and local tax is a set percentage based on the employee's income and supplied by the corresponding government agencies. The Federal Insurance Contribution Act (FICA) deduction is the employee's contribution to the Social Security fund.

A certain proportion of the employee's paycheck is withheld, matched by the employer, and remitted quarterly to the Internal Revenue Service (IRS), which collects taxes for the federal government. Because this payroll tax is part of the cost of providing services, it must be attributed to the period in which the employee was earning the wages. The cumulative payroll tax is entered in the Payables Journal as a credit to the taxes payable and a debit to cash each month.

Other deductions from the employee's pay may include meals and uniform expenses. If the employee health plan requires an employee contribution, this would also be noted in the Payroll Journal as a deduction. Deductions for each employee are calculated and subtracted from gross pay to give the net pay. A separate column should exist for bonuses or other adjustments to net pay. At the end of each month, salary totals for each department are posted to the General Ledger. A page from a typical Payroll Journal is shown in Figure 3.9.

The employees who divide their time between two or more departments should be listed in the department where most hours are spent, with a portion of their earnings and taxes allocated to the second department. Some reimbursement programs, such as Medicare, may require recordkeeping for daily employee hours spent attributable to each Medicare resident. This area has become a significant focus with the relatively new focus of CMS Payroll Based Journaling (PBJ).

Payroll Based Journaling

One of many provisions in the Affordable Care Act requires facilities to electronically submit direct care staffing information based on payroll and other data. This provision is called *Payroll Based Journaling* (PBJ). This information is usually collected by multiple department heads to help ensure that the data are available and correct. This information is part of the Nursing Home Five-Star Quality Rating System, a CMS method to communicate differences among nursing facilities to the consumer. PBJ itself has ever-changing nuances and software. Thoroughly discussing it is outside the scope of this textbook. However, it is essential that the administrator keep abreast of the body of knowledge surrounding this.

Separate Payroll Bank Account

The facility should maintain a separate bank account solely for payroll. The person preparing the payroll does not write their own paycheck. All paychecks should have two signatures or be approved by the administrator before being disbursed. The paycheck number and the date of issue are recorded in the Payroll Journal to identify misplaced checks or stop payment on checks that are not cashed within a reasonable period. Checks are best distributed to each employee in person.

Payroll preparation and maintenance are primarily a function of bookkeeping, although larger facilities may have a separate department devoted to this task. Most facilities and corporations today have outsourced payroll functions to an independent company. This company maintains the payroll itself, writes checks, disburses monies, makes quarterly tax payments, and entirely streamlines the process. However, there is still a need for a payroll person at the individual facility to ensure that hours are correctly submitted to the payroll company.

COMMON PITFALLS IN PRACTICE
- Payroll has always been—and continues to be—an important function in the facility. The bottom line is your employees need to be paid. This requires on-time, every-time payroll. Employees do not tend to be sympathetic when their paychecks are not at the facility or in their bank accounts when they should be.
- Furthermore, payroll is linked to your Five-Star rating today by PBJ. When payroll is inaccurate, so is your rating. This must be kept correct and streamlined.

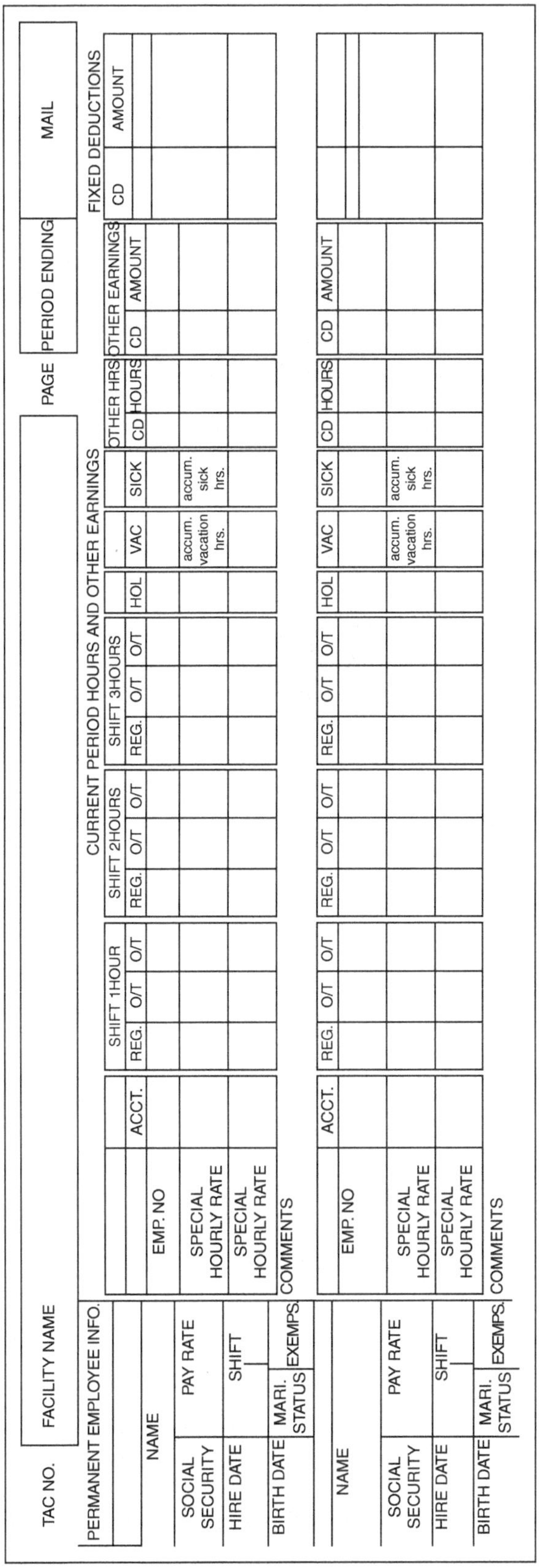

FIGURE 3.9 Page from a Payroll Journal.

PROTECTING THE RESIDENTS' FUNDS

Legal Responsibilities

NAB DOMAIN 2A10: RESIDENT TRUST ACCOUNTS FOR PERSONAL FUNDS

Residents frequently ask nursing facilities to safeguard the residents' assets. Agreeing to take responsibility for these assets must be confirmed through a legal contract signed by both the facility and the resident or their sponsor. This contract establishes a trust relationship between the resident and the facility, and sound procedures for managing these assets must be adhered to so that the relationship is not violated. Administrators vary in what they will protect for residents. Some may keep jewelry and similar items in safekeeping. In general, experience suggests that cash be the primary or only resident asset the facility will take responsibility to safeguard. Valuables other than cash are best managed by a resident's legal representative.

Separate Accounting

As a check on resident cash, a separate book should be kept recording the information, as shown in Figure 3.10. A copy of a receipt signed by the patient/resident or sponsor is kept in an envelope accompanying this book. There must be clear information showing not only deposits but also disbursements to residents. Residents, or their responsible party, must directly approve these disbursements. Inappropriate money dispersal can (and will) result in the facility reimbursing resident funds to this account. There are federal regulations surrounding this; however, there are also nuances each state expects. Be sure to understand these nuances and get to know your resident trust fund auditors.

Page _____ of _____

Facility   THE LAURELS _____ # _____ Month ending _06/30/X1_

Patient Name	Beginning Balance	Deposits	Disbursements	Ending Balance
Jones, F.A.	$210.00	$90.00	$25.00	$275.00

FIGURE 3.10 Patient/resident trust funds trial balance.

Use of Interest-Bearing Accounts

Resident funds deposited with the facility are to be managed under federal requirement F567/§483.10(f)(10)(i)-(ii). Additionally, residents are entitled to a full accounting of their funds entrusted to the facility, which cannot be commingled with facility funds, and quarterly statements of the account must be provided (CMS, 2017).

Footnote

Matters such as inventory and payroll should not occupy too much of the administrator's time. However, it is important that the staff properly manage these details. Experience shows that when the administrator understands the fine points of financing and occasionally reviews these matters knowledgeably with the team, they also tend to pay attention to details. The result is that the administrator is thus freed to deal with broader policy, while procedures such as payroll and managing resident accounts function smoothly.

3.7 THE CONCEPT OF DEPRECIATION

Section Concepts

- *The concept of depreciation—how to use it in managing facility finances*

Consider as the Administrator . . .

- *Should depreciation be funded?*
- *How important is depreciation to your financials? Monthly? Yearly?*

NAB DOMAIN 2A2: FINANCIAL ANALYSIS (E.G., RATIOS, PROFITABILITY, DEBT, REVENUE MIX, DEPRECIATION, OPERATING MARGIN, CASH FLOW)

Depreciation has been mentioned to some extent already. Capital assets are those used to provide services during more than one time period; in the course of operations, they lose value due to use, wear and tear, or obsolescence.

The accrual system of accounting spreads the asset's cost over the time it is used to address the loss of value to capital assets. This spread is essential because the TC of purchasing the asset should not be attributed only to the purchase month when in actuality it is an expense that provides services for several years to come.

IDENTIFYING DEPRECIABLE ASSETS

Assets that can be capitalized or depreciated differ from other facility assets because they are used in operations for more than one time period and will not be converted into cash within the year. Many facilities set a minimum value for depreciable assets, usually somewhere about $500. A calculator, for example, may be used in the business office for many years. However, its acquisition cost may be so low that the depreciation expense over its useful life would be negligible. The asset must be tangible and owned by the facility. Thus, leased equipment cannot normally be depreciated. Some leases in which the lessor agrees not to take depreciation can under some circumstances be depreciated.

All new assets meeting these criteria are considered depreciable assets. Any alterations of the current fixed asset that affect its value or useful life, such as renovation, are depreciable expenses. Repairing damages or regular maintenance of the asset cannot be considered part of the depreciable expense. Many of these expenses are large ones—think a $500,000 chiller on the roof, $50,000 worth of new resident beds, or $250,000 worth of foundation repairs.

DETERMINING DEPRECIATION EXPENSE

There are several methods of calculating depreciation expenses. However, all methods are based on the asset's historical cost, its useful life (sometimes preset by tax or other regulations), and its salvage value, if any.

Historical Cost

The historical cost of the asset includes acquiring the asset that is depreciated over several periods. In addition to the purchase price, the cost of taxes, shipping and delivery, installation, and so forth can be included, along with any other one-time costs associated with acquiring the asset.

Useful Life

The asset's useful life is the number of years the item can be expected to be used by the facility. This amount must be an estimation. However, the IRS has useful life estimates for most assets that are mandated in reporting taxes or, in most instances, in calculating depreciation reports for Medicare, Medicaid, and some other third-party payers.

Salvage Value

A capital asset may have some value at the end of its useful life. A van, which generally has an IRS-determined useful life of 5 years, might be such an asset.

STRAIGHT-LINE DEPRECIATION

There are several methods for figuring the depreciation expense once the historical cost, useful life, and salvage value are determined. Straight-line depreciation is a depreciation method in which the historical cost of an asset is spread evenly over its useful life. The depreciation expense would be the same in every period in which the asset functions.

Historical cost / Useful life = Annual depreciation expense

If The Laurels purchases new physical therapy equipment worth $20,000 with an estimated useful life of 5 years, the annual depreciation expense for the equipment would be:

$$\$20,000 / 5 = \$4,000 \text{ per year depreciation}$$

After the first year, the value of the physical therapy equipment on the books would be:

$$\$20,000 - \$4,000 = \$16,000$$

Hence, the $16,000 is called the *book value* of this asset.
Straight-line depreciation has the advantage of simplicity.

ACCELERATED DEPRECIATION

This method attributes most of the depreciation expense to the first years of the asset's life, thus enabling the facility to write it off more quickly, thereby gaining a tax advantage through earlier tax recognition of the investment. Among the several types of accelerated depreciation are the sum-of-the-years digits and double-declining balance.

PURPOSES OF DEPRECIATION

We have already mentioned that depreciation must be calculated to adhere to the accrual system of accounting. To ignore the cost of depreciation is to underestimate the expense of providing services and overestimate the value of the facility's assets. For this reason, depreciation is included on the income statement as an operating expense and subtracted from the historical cost of fixed assets on the balance sheet to reflect its impact on the financial position of the home.

Asset Replacement

Probably the most important reason for recognizing depreciation is asset replacement. Because an asset will eventually have to be replaced, it should be expensed over its useful life to accumulate the funds needed for its replacement. Typically, an asset purchased 10 years from now will be more expensive than the original; however, that is not always the case. Some assets remain about the same for replacement, while the replacement cost for others may decrease. Computers, for example, have become less expensive but provide the same computing capacities because of advances in technology and producer competition.

Few facilities actually "fund" depreciation, that is, put cash in an interest-bearing account reserved for replacing equipment. Such a fund would appear in the balance sheet's capital or new worth section as "Funded Depreciation." However, it is essential to note that many facilities include a "Capital Expenditure" line in their budgets should an expensive piece of equipment fail, allowing the facility to take no financial loss on the purchase. The facility still must pay for the purchase. Even so, the money was already coming out monthly as a budgeted item and will not necessarily negatively affect the facility's annual budget.

ENTERING DEPRECIATION INTO THE ACCOUNTING RECORDS

A portion of the depreciation expense may easily be attributed to each period by dividing the annual depreciation expense by the number of accounting periods in the year. Because depreciation is entered in the General Journal at the end of each month, The Laurels' new physical therapy equipment depreciation expense after the first month of purchase, under straight-line depreciation, would be as follows:

General Journal

	Debit	Credit
1/29 Depreciation expense	$333.33	
1/29 Reserve for depreciation		$333.33

Categorization of Fixed Assets

The chart of accounts should have an account for each type of fixed asset owned by the facility. These assets can be categorized generally as:

- Land and improvements
- Buildings
- Fixed equipment
- Major movable equipment
- Minor movable equipment
- More specific categories that are more useful to the facility

In addition, depreciation schedules should be maintained for each category of assets (Table 3.8), and each type of depreciation, if accelerated and straight-line, are both used.

TABLE 3.8 The Laurels Depreciation Schedule

Item	Cost ($)	Date Purchased	Life	Method Depreciated	Year	Depreciation, per Year	
						Annual ($)	cumulative ($)
Plant: main	5,767,004.00	6/20X0	30	Strt. line	X0	192,233.47	192,233.47
Hall Welsh					X1	192,233.47	384,466.94
Hall &					X2	192,233.47	576,700.41
Garage							
					X3	192,233.47	768,933.88
					Etc.		
Kitchen	398,600.00	6/20X0	15	Strt. line	X0	26,573.33	26,573.33
equipment					X1	26,573.33	53,146.66
					X2	26,573.33	79,719,99
					X3	26,573.33	106,293.32
					Etc.		

If two differing schedules are used to depreciate the same assets—one for reimbursement and one for other purposes—there will be a difference in depreciation expense for each asset every year. Because the total amount of depreciation taken for each asset should be the same (total depreciation will equal the historical cost less salvage value), this difference between the two depreciation expenses is a timing difference. Depreciation is a charge that must be deferred to another period or an accrued revenue if the depreciation is recognized in a later accounting period.

COMMON PITFALLS IN PRACTICE

- Depreciation is often an expense on your financials that you have no control over. This is often handled by corporate bookkeeping departments. However, it is important to understand your company's policy on depreciation (often a dollar amount spent) and to identify if the expense has been realized in your financials. Depreciation often accompanies a huge expenditure, and you would be hard-pressed to come back (financially speaking) after you spent $500,000 on new HVAC chiller systems for your facility if it hit your financials in 1 month.

3.8 USING "COSTS" IN MANAGERIAL DECISIONS

Section Concepts

- *How to "cost find"*
- *Formulas that reveal what is happening in the facility*

Consider as the Administrator . . .

- *Is there any way to manage "fixed" costs?*

NAB DOMAIN 2A2: FINANCIAL ANALYSIS (E.G., RATIOS, PROFITABILITY, DEBT, REVENUE MIX, DEPRECIATION, OPERATING MARGIN, CASH FLOW); 2A3: REVENUE CYCLE MANAGEMENT (E.G., BILLING, ACCOUNTS RECEIVABLE, ACCOUNTS PAYABLE, COLLECTIONS)

EFFICIENCY

Efficiency may be defined as input over output, or the amount of input used for a specific output level. As a component of input, costs are generally easier to control than revenues or other output measures. Revenues are subject to limitation by competition from providers of similar services and government regulation through insurance and medical assistance programs. An administrator's knowledge of costs and the ability to control and reduce them permit liquidity of limited funds, making them available for other uses. This skill is essential to the successful operations of a facility.

3.8.1 TYPES OF COSTS: VARIABLE, FIXED, AND SEMI-VARIABLE

VARIABLE COSTS

All costs can be regarded as variable, fixed, or semi-variable. Variable costs are those that fluctuate directly and proportionately with changes in volume. If the volume is increased or decreased by a certain percentage, variable costs will rise or fall, respectively, by the same percentage. The cost of disposable medical supplies in the nursing department will vary directly with the number of similar types and level of care of patients served. The cost of food in dietary or postage for resident billing will also vary with resident volume.

FIXED COSTS

Fixed costs, on the other hand, do not relate to changes in volume. The cost of the director of nursing's salary will not change with fluctuations in the number of residents. The director's salary can vary, but any change will result from an administrative decision rather than in response to patient volume because federal regulations require a full-time director of nursing. If volume varies enough, the volume will affect many "fixed" costs. For example, a substantial increase in resident volume may require a new administrative position in the nursing department to accommodate the additional patient load. Fixed costs, then, are said to be fixed only over a relevant range of volume.

SEMI-VARIABLE COSTS

Semi-variable costs vary disproportionately with volume and do not fit neatly into a variable or fixed category. A semi-variable cost might be total nurse's aides' salaries, which depend more on resident volume and resident level of care needs.

Utility costs are often based on usage ranges rather than actual usage and may also be considered semi-variable costs. It is helpful to think of semi-variable costs as having a much narrower relevant range than fixed costs. Semi-variable costs are often broken down into fixed and variable components for use in calculations. For simplicity, we limit our discussion here to fixed and variable costs.

TOTAL VARIABLE COSTS

Although total variable costs (TVC) change with volume, variable costs per unit do not. If disposable syringes are $1 each, the cost per syringe per patient will be $1, whether 100 or 150 patients receive injections using those syringes. Total fixed costs (TFC), however, do vary per unit with changes in volume. If the director of nursing's salary is $85,000 (exclusive of benefits) and they oversee the care of 100 residents, the director's salary cost would be $850 per resident. If that same director of nursing oversees 150 residents, the cost drops to $567 per resident. Familiarity with the costs of the facility maximizes the administrator's ability to control its finances.

The behavior of variable and fixed costs is summarized in Table 3.9. As can be seen, fixed costs decrease with an increase in volume. Because the nursing facility generally has a high proportion of fixed costs, maintaining a high volume of service is of paramount concern to administrators.

TABLE 3.9 Behavior of Fixed and Variable Costs

	Director of Nursing		Disposable Medical Supplies	
Patients	TFC	FC/Unit	TVC	VC/Unit
100	$44,000.00	440	100	$1.00
125	$44,000.00	352	125	$1.00
150	$44,000.00	293	150	$1.00
	No change	Change	Change	No change

FC, fixed costs; TFC, total fixed costs; TVC, total variable costs; VC, variable costs.

A closer study of the concept of fixed and variable costs reveals how to use it in decision-making. Because all costs can be considered fixed or variable (even semivariable costs),

$$\text{Total fixed costs} + \text{Total variable costs} = \text{Total costs}$$

Because TVCs are a function of the variable cost per unit and the number of units, the previous equation can be expanded to

$$\text{Total fixed costs} + (\text{Variable cost per unit} \times \text{Volume units}) = \text{Total costs}$$

$$\text{Total fixed costs} + \left(\frac{\text{Variable costs}}{\text{units}} \times \text{Volume units}\right) = \text{Total costs}$$

$$\text{Breakeven volume in units} = \frac{\text{Fixed cost}}{\text{Rate} - \text{variable cost}}$$

Thus, if three of these values are known, the remaining value can be calculated.

The administrator of The Laurels wants to find the average variable cost of medical supplies used per resident during the month. The General Ledger shows that the TCs of the nursing department for 1 month is $12,000. The administrator has determined that fixed cost accounts in that department amount to $9,000 and that medical supplies are its only variable cost. The patient census report for the month shows that there have been 3,000 resident days or an average of 100 residents over 30 days. To calculate the variable cost per patient in the nursing department:

$$\frac{(\text{Total costs} - \text{Total fixed costs})}{\text{Volume units}} = \frac{\text{Variable costs}}{\text{Units}}$$

$$(\$12,000 - \$9,000)/100 \text{ residents} = \$30 \text{ per resident}$$

Thus, the variable cost of providing nursing services in this particular month was $30 per resident.

VOLUME OF SERVICE UNITS

These equations can be used to determine the volume of service units required to break even. Because TCs equal TRs at the breakeven point, TRs can be substituted for TCs in the preceding equations to give the costs or volume needed to break even (Zelman et al., 2020).

If the TC of the physical therapy department is $6,500 per month, and the TFCs are $5,200, and the variable cost per patient visit to physical therapy is $8, how many patient visits are needed per month to break even in this department?

$$\text{Total costs} = \text{Total revenue}$$
$$= \$6{,}500 = \$5{,}200 + (\$8 \times \text{Volume unit})$$
$$\text{Volume units} = (\$6{,}500 - \$5{,}200)/\$8$$
$$\text{Volume units} = 162.5 \text{ visits per month}$$

We have assumed that the physical therapists are employees of the facility and that their salaries comprise a significant portion of the department's fixed costs. If physical therapy is provided on a contractual basis, the therapists' wages will become a variable cost if they were paid for each visit.

COMMON PITFALLS IN PRACTICE

- There is much more that goes into "cost" as presented here. Not only do you need the understanding of this information, but you also need to be able to put it into context. Your financials get hit every month for certain "fixed" items, but the costs become variable for other costs. This variability has become amazingly problematic today as costs for an item or service can vary from one day to the next.

3.8.2 ADDITIONAL TYPES OF COSTS: INDIRECT COSTS AND DIRECT COSTS

Section Concepts

- *Understanding cost centers allows you to better "see" where the money is being spent in the facility*

Consider as the Administrator . . .

- *The idea of knowing how you spend your money must be a daily part of your job. What happens if this knowledge gets away from you?*

Costs may also be categorized as direct and indirect. To discuss them effectively, however, we must first define *revenue* and *cost centers*.

REVENUE CENTERS

NAB DOMAIN 2A3: REVENUE CYCLE MANAGEMENT (E.G., BILLING, ACCOUNTS RECEIVABLE, ACCOUNTS PAYABLE, COLLECTIONS)

NAB DOMAIN 2A2: FINANCIAL ANALYSIS (E.G., RATIOS, PROFITABILITY, DEBT, REVENUE MIX, DEPRECIATION, OPERATING MARGIN, CASH FLOW)

Revenue centers are units of the facility, usually departments, that typically generate revenue through resident care. Revenue centers in the nursing facility will generally be nursing, possibly physical therapy, occupational therapy, pharmacy, laboratory, and medical support. It may also be any other department or center earning revenue, such as a cafeteria that serves many guest meals or a profitable daycare program. If pharmaceuticals or medical supplies are included in routine care and are not separately charged, they would not be revenue centers. Any area that can be charged directly to the resident could be considered a revenue center. However, it is important to point out that many things are included in the per diem received from Medicare, Medicaid, managed care, or other sources. When costs are included in that per diem, they cannot be charged as separate items.

As facilities add service areas such as assisted living wings, home healthcare, and hospice care, these become additional revenue centers. Interest may also be considered a revenue center if the facility earns significant interest revenue from investments.

COST CENTERS

Cost centers are units of the facility identified with certain costs. Revenue centers are almost always cost centers because the revenue-earning departments also have costs directly associated with them. Interest as a revenue center has little or no costs associated with it. All other departments, such as administration, maintenance, housekeeping, and usually dietary and laundry, are cost centers. Depreciation, interest, insurance, telephone, utility, and transportation expenses may also be considered cost centers. These are all identifiable costs of the facility. The concept of cost centers will become more apparent as we proceed.

DIRECT COSTS

Direct costs are those directly attributable to a revenue center or incurred for direct resident care. In the nursing facility, direct costs are often called *resident care costs.* Direct costs of the nursing department would include all nursing salaries, payroll taxes, benefits, medical supplies, expenses associated with capital equipment used only in the department, and any other costs associated directly with this department.

INDIRECT COSTS

Indirect costs cannot be directly associated with a revenue-producing center yet support the functions of the resident care centers (or other care centers, such as an adult daycare center). Indirect costs of the nursing department include administration, payroll, utility, housekeeping, maintenance, dietary, laundry, plant depreciation, tax, and interest expenses that keep these departments running. For this reason, indirect costs are also known as *support service costs.*

Support Service Costs

Indirect costs must be allocated to each revenue-producing cost center to be included in the charge for services for that revenue center and reflect the TC of providing that service. Support costs must be systematically spread over all revenue-producing departments to find the TCs of the department. This process is known as *cost finding*, as it yields the TCs of the resident care centers (and other centers such as adult daycare).

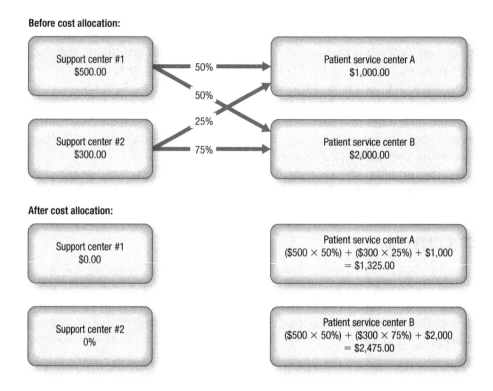

FIGURE 3.11 Cost allocation between two support and revenue centers.

The concept of cost finding is illustrated schematically in Figure 3.11. The TCs of both the support and service (or revenue-earning) centers are shown. To find the TC of providing resident services A and B, some portion of the support center cost must be allocated to each revenue center. Support Center No. 1 divides its support equally between Service Centers A and B, so 50% of Support Center No. 1's costs are attributed to each Resident Service Center.

Support Center No. 2 provides more services to Patient Center B, which is reflected in the proportion of Support Center No. 2's costs allocated to Service Center B. When the costs of both support centers are apportioned, the TC of providing services A and B are known.

VALUES OF COST FINDING

Cost finding yields a representative picture of the entire expense of providing each service. This information is used in deciding whether a particular service should be discontinued or supported. For example, unless all direct and indirect costs of providing a service, such as adult daycare, are calculated, it is difficult to determine the cost-effectiveness of offering such a service. Cost allocation is a subjective process in that there is an almost infinite number of ways to perform cost allocation properly. At one point, numerous facilities offered adult daycare. However, when programs were evaluated for the actual costs of earning the daily charges, most programs were determined cost-ineffective.

ALLOCATING INDIRECT COSTS

There are several methods for allocating indirect costs, among them the step-down and reciprocal methods. Providers reimbursed on a cost basis must usually use the step-down method unless another method is approved. We discuss the step-down method in detail and briefly explain the reciprocal method at the end of this section.

The step-down method derives its name from the shape of the completed worksheet. It involves systematically allocating all cost centers over all other cost centers that use the "services" of the allocated cost-center expenses. Support costs are spread over revenue centers and other support cost centers (Zelman et al., 2020).

Once a support cost is divided among the other cost centers, no more costs can be allocated to that department. Therefore, the order in which support costs are allocated affects the final cost of the revenue centers. As a rule, cost centers used by most of the other cost centers are allocated first.

The basis of allocation also affects the outcome of the cost-finding process. In allocating housekeeping costs to the departments that use housekeeping services, the basis for allocation might be the number of employees in the department, the square footage of the departments, or some other criteria. Likewise, administrative costs might be allocated based on the number of employees, total salary of employees, volume of services provided, or TRs earned in each department. These alternatives are examples only; clearly, the basis for allocation varies.

Third-party reimbursement will indicate the basis for allocation to be used for residents for whom that third-party reimburses. The facility's method should remain consistent to enable the comparison of the resulting costs in different periods.

The Step-Down Process

Cost allocation is best illustrated through a step-by-step example of the step-down process. The example provided in Table 3.10 is necessarily simplified; cost allocations for most healthcare organizations are usually performed electronically because of the volume and complexities involved in larger, more departmentalized, or multiprogram facilities.

Other Methods of Cost Finding

Two other approaches to cost finding are the reciprocal and cost-apportionment methods. The reciprocal is like the step-down method except that it recognizes reciprocal services provided between cost centers, such as administration and maintenance. Because of the calculations involved and the extent of these services in most organizations, reciprocal allocation is performed electronically.

RATE SETTING

One of the primary uses of the cost-finding process is to develop a basis for setting rates for the services provided by the revenue centers. Once the costs of the revenue centers are known, the average cost per unit of service can be calculated by dividing the TC of the revenue center by the expected service volume.

TABLE 3.10 The Laurels Step-Down Worksheets: Preliminary Worksheet

Cost Centers	Capital (sq. ft.)	Plant (sq. ft.)	Admin.ᵃ (FTE)ᵃ	Main.ᵃ (sq. ft.)	Laundry (lbs. dry)	Housekeep (sq. ft.)	Dietary (meals)	Soc. Serv. (visits)	P.T. (visits)	O.T. (visits)	NURSING	TOTAL
Support and revenue centers												
Administration	3.0%	3.0%										
Maintenanceᵇ	1.5%	1.5%	0.5%									
Laundry	9.0%	9.0%	3.0%	9.4%								
Housekeeping	8.0%	8.0%	7.4%	8.4%	5.0%							
Dietary	10.0%	10.0%	7.3%	10.5%	15.0%	12.8%						
Social services	0.5%	0.5%	0.1%	0.5%		0.6%						
Physical therapy	7.0%	7.0%	2.5%	7.3%	2.5%	8.9%						
Occupational therapy	2.0%	2.0%	0.4%	2.1%	2.5%	2.6%						
Nursing	59.0%	59.0%	78.8%	61.7%	75.0%	75.2%						
TOTAL	100.0%	100.0%	100.0%	99.8%	100.0%	100.0%	100.0%	100.0%	100.0%	100.0%	100.0%	100.0%

ᵃFTE = Full-time equivalent employees.
ᵇTotal maintenance costs include all utility costs.

First, determine the unit of service. In the physical therapy department, a unit of service is usually calculated as a 15-minute segment for which charges are made.

The average unit-of-service cost offers a basis for rate setting because rates should approximate the cost of providing the service. But other factors, such as demand for services, competitive rates, expected inflation rates, contractual discounts, and frequency of uncollectibles, must be considered in achieving realistic rates.

COMMON PITFALLS IN PRACTICE

- Where you allocate costs often becomes amazingly important when you are reviewing your financials. Putting costs in the wrong area can skew your performance (either positively or negatively).

3.9 BUDGETS AND BUDGETING

Section Concepts

- *There are several ways to prepare budgets*
- *The five steps in the budgeting process*

Consider as the Administrator . . .

- *What is the best way to "use" a budget in the day-to-day management of the facility?*
- *Should your department heads clearly understand what their budget is and how much money they have to spend yearly/monthly/daily? Should you share financial performance data with them?*

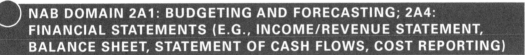

NAB DOMAIN 2A1: BUDGETING AND FORECASTING; 2A4: FINANCIAL STATEMENTS (E.G., INCOME/REVENUE STATEMENT, BALANCE SHEET, STATEMENT OF CASH FLOWS, COST REPORTING)

CONSIDERATIONS IN BUDGETING

The budgeting process in the nursing facility is a period of planning. The physical budget is more than a record of anticipated expenses for the next fiscal year. It represents a careful examination of internal and external changes that management believes will affect the facility's operation and the strategy to deal with these changes for some time to come. Thus, the budget reflects the administrator's short- and long-term goals for the facility. Most organizations also have a 3- to 5-year budget plan to guide long-range planning (Zelman et al., 2020). Keep in mind that this process is imperfect and is based not only on history but also on forecasting the future of what we believe will happen within our facility, within the industry, and with all pertinent regulations. This process will expect you to know what is happening in the industry and politically, as politics often significantly impact our industry.

A budget is a dynamic tool used throughout the year, rather than a static document that is filed away to remain only in the memory of the budget participants. Budgets change as conditions change. It provides a meaningful comparison between actual and projected expenditures and revenues. Administrators are most successful when working with some part of the budget daily, whether for determining the level of staffing for the facility or the number of briefs to be purchased or verifying the dietary manager's order. Budget is everywhere!

Most facility administrators use the budget in a monthly review with department managers on how the year unfolds and what changes should be undertaken.

3.9.1 TWO METHODS OF BUDGET PREPARATION

Consider as the Administrator . . .

- *How do you get the best budget for your facility?*
- *Should your budget be a mystery to your department heads, or should they be actively involved in the process of budgeting?*

Budgeting is done in many ways, and each facility or multi-facility operation will develop its particular style. In general, two methods of budget preparation are used: the top-down and the participatory method (Berger, 2014). In the more common multi-facility chains, much of this budgeting comes down from corporate for your review long before it goes into effect. It is imperative that you are a part of this process, as it will gauge your success for the following year.

TOP-DOWN APPROACH TO BUDGETING

With the top-down approach, the administrator (or corporate) alone prepares the annual budget, with little or no guidance from department heads. This method is most suitable for smaller facilities with few departments, where the administrator is familiar with all the costs of the facility. Top-down is also often the approach used by chains, in which case the local administrator is given a "suggested" budget with the corporation's goals already built into it. The top-down method is quick but has the disadvantages of possibly stifling innovation or imposing an unpopular or unrealistic budget on department heads or chain facility administrators (Berger, 2014).

THE PARTICIPATORY APPROACH

The participatory method of budgeting requires input from staff members on several levels of the organization. The administrator provides guidelines for preparing departmental budgets completed by the department heads and other key personnel. The administrator then reviews these budgets, adjusts as necessary, and combines them into one organizational budget.

Participatory budgeting is usually appropriate for larger facilities. Although it is time-consuming, it furnishes an opportunity for communication between the administrator and department heads and results in input to the budget from those who are most knowledgeable about the daily operation of the individual departments.

This section uses participatory budgeting to describe the budgeting process. The top-down approach uses the same progression but fewer steps than participatory budgeting.

Participatory budgeting augments the role each participant plays in the operations of the facility. Department heads and others become more aware of the costs of their areas, resources available to the facility, and needs of the other departments. Budgeting also recognizes the roles of participating staff. Although the budget process is often time-consuming and frustrating, the team is rewarded by knowing that their experience and ideas are valued.

Finally, the budget communicates information about the facility to external parties, such as the board of directors or stockholders, third-party payers, planning agencies, accreditation teams, rate review commissions, and unions. The administrator must often be able to justify proposed expenses and revenues to these external parties.

COMMON PITFALLS IN PRACTICE

- It is important to understand your corporate expectations in this area. Some corporations find the sharing of specific financial information acceptable with department heads. Others patently forbid the sharing of financial data. Be sure to not overstep your authority in this area.

3.9.2 FIVE STEPS IN THE BUDGETING PROCESS

Consider as the Administrator . . .

- *Is it possible to skip any of these steps and still have an adequate budget?*
- *Does a good budget involve your grasp of the manager's tasks of planning, organizing, forecasting, evaluation, innovation, and others?*

NAB DOMAIN 2A1: BUDGETING AND FORECASTING; 2A7: INTEGRATION OF CLINICAL AND FINANCIAL SYSTEMS (E.G., EMR/EHR, MDS)

There are other ways to prepare the budget, whether by the administrator alone or with the input of key personnel. The optimal method will depend on, among other considerations, the size of the facility, whether it is freestanding or a unit in a small or large chain, and the administrator's time constraints.

In designing the budgeting process, the administrator first decides what information is desired and how detailed it must be and then maps out the logistics of the activity. The administrator determines who the participants will be. In the case of top-down budgeting, the administrator and perhaps other administrative personnel, such as the bookkeeper, comptroller, or business manager, will be involved. Participatory budgeting usually includes the administrator, the accountant or the comptroller, the bookkeeper, the human resources director, department heads, and assistants. The budget development timetable must be defined. At least 2 to 5 months before the beginning of the next fiscal year should be allowed for the entire process.

STEP 1: ASSESSING THE ENVIRONMENT

The initial step in the budgeting process is an assessment of the external and internal environments. The budget cannot be prepared in a vacuum. The political, economic, and social environments outside the nursing facility walls are not static. Although the administrator does not have control over these aspects of the external environment, ignorance of the trends affecting the nursing facility industry, and failure to anticipate their effects on the facility's operations, leave the administrator less able to deal effectively with changes. Such trends may occur as one or more of the following:

- Increased or decreased competition
- New types of competition (e.g., local hospital opening long-term care beds, increasing capacity to treat at home by local home healthcare agencies, or the emergence of additional hospice care agencies)
- Altered reimbursement policies
- Amended licensing laws
- Revised regulations
- Swings in the economy
- Inflation, deflation, or stagnation
- Changes in prevailing wage rates
- Reduction or enlargement of the potential service population
- Changes in availability of key personnel
- Changes in disease patterns among residents
- Changing system pressures from hospital discharge patterns due to penalties for readmissions
- Changing third-party payer situation, with new patterns emerging of providing and paying for care
- Increasing acuity level among the resident population
- Changes of president of the United States, state governors, or other high-ranking political officials
- Others

Fluctuations in the external environment may significantly affect the plans and operations of the facility.

STEP 2: PROGRAMMING

After the external environments and their anticipated effects on the facility have been evaluated, objectives for the coming year are determined. This process is sometimes known as *programming*, as it develops a program for the facility to follow. Through this "programming," the administrator can alter internal operations over which they have control to respond to the external (and internal) influences on the facility.

How might an administrator use programming to cope with external events? In periods of rising inflation, the cost of living goes up, resulting in a demand for higher wages. Suppose the administrator is aware of this trend. In that case, an objective might be to index the salaries, that is, raise them by a certain percentage to approximate the increased costs of living by a specific time during the following year. An increase in salary expense can then be included in the budget, thereby preventing a situation in which funds are not set aside for this purpose. Such oversight could result in recruiting problems, high staff turnover, or a strain on operating funds when a salary increase is finally provided.

A new competitive facility nearby could warrant a contingency fund set aside in the following year's budget to raise salaries to meet the new competitor's salary scale, if necessary. Similarly, funds for facility capital improvements could be earmarked to remain competitive. It is much easier to budget for upcoming changes than to justify their expenses later.

Other considerations for programming are changes in (a) service volume, (b) services offered, (c) payer mix, (d) human resources needs, and (e) capital needs. The cumulative effect of expected external and internal events should determine the facility's objectives for the next year(s), forming the basis of assumptions made in the budgeting process.

The completed budgeting process should result in four types of budgets: the operating budget, the cash budget, the capital budget, and the pro forma financial statements.

STEP 3: DEVELOPING THE OPERATING BUDGET

The operating budget has two parts: the expense and revenue budgets (Zelman et al., 2020).

The Expense Budget

The expense budget, the type with which we are most familiar, lists the anticipated expenses of the facility for the coming year and is primarily prepared by the department heads. The budget timetable should indicate when the final departmental expense budgets are due.

The heads of all service units should indicate the expected resident service volume, while support departments (such as dietary) should estimate the number of meals that will be served. Budgeting offers an opportunity for communication among departments. After all, dietary must know expected resident volume to calculate the number of meals to be served and types of diets likely to be prescribed.

Additionally, department heads should review staff positions and note any recommended changes in the staffing pattern. In larger facilities, recommendations for salary changes may be the responsibility of the human resources director. Wages may be based on competitive salaries in the community or union agreements if applicable.

Department heads should also check equipment in their departments for repair or replacement needs. This assessment would include estimates of repair or replacement costs, supported by professional estimates, manufacturer price sheets, and the like. If equipment needs are extensive, it may be worthwhile for department heads to develop a plant and equipment budget for their departments, facilitating the preparation of the capital budget.

The cost of supplies and other expenses is often a significant portion of departmental expenses. Any change in the volume of supplies needed and the cost per unit should be noted on the budget. Catchall or miscellaneous categories should be kept to a minimum, as there can be little control over unidentified costs.

Anticipated expenses should be broken down by months or another customary accounting period used in the facility. Monthly expense budgets also facilitate the preparation of the cash budget year (Brigham & Houston, 2019).

Determining Expenses

In determining expenses, several strategies can be used. One tactic is to increase all the current year's expenses by a certain percentage. Although this method is quick, it defeats the purpose of budgeting and the effort involved in environmental assessment and programming. Some expenses change, and others do not. Never do we see all expenses increase by the same percentage across the board. Administrators would be much better served to research specific changes and to make them across individual budget lines.

It is more productive for the department head to identify monthly and yearly trends in costs and utilization to help reduce expenses. For example, occupancy of the nursing unit might be consistently below average during the winter holidays but regularly above average in late January and February. Identifying such trends is helpful in budgeting for monthly costs on volume levels. It is also often helpful to identify the source of variances in the current year's budget and allow for them to prepare the new budget.

A checklist can ensure that all expense items in departments are included in setting up the expense budget. A good source for this checklist is the chart of accounts, which should list all expense accounts by department.

All budget participants ought to know how and by whom the final budget levels are decided. Finally, the organizational expense budget is separated by months, and the individual department budgets are retained to compare actual with budgeted performance in each department throughout the year.

The Revenue Budget

NAB DOMAIN 2A1: BUDGETING AND FORECASTING; 2A3: REVENUE CYCLE MANAGEMENT (E.G., BILLING, ACCOUNTS RECEIVABLE, ACCOUNTS PAYABLE, COLLECTIONS)

The second section of the operating budget is the revenue budget, which projects the monthly income for the next fiscal year. Not every department will need to prepare a revenue budget, as fewer departments determine revenues than expenses. Additionally, nonoperating revenues are generally under the control of the administrator. Service revenues are based on the prices charged for services, which are determined by administrative decisions. Hence, the revenue budget is usually prepared at the administrative level.

Operating Revenue Estimates

To estimate operating revenues, all revenue centers are listed, with the number of residents appearing by type of payer. Total resident service revenues are calculated by multiplying the expected service volume in each revenue center by the charge per unit of service. As mentioned in the previous section on the Values of Cost

Finding, rates for services may be determined in several ways. For publicly insured persons, the allowable rate per unit of service may be somewhat less than charges, and their reimbursable rate should be used to project revenues.

For private-pay residents, charges can be based on the cost plus profit for providing the service, using the results of the cost-finding process and breakeven analysis. Rates may also be based on competitive charges for similar services in the community or on the price that the market will bear (Zelman et al., 2020).

Nonoperating Revenues

Nonoperating revenues, such as interest income, borrowed funds, and charitable donations, depend on any number of factors but are usually predictable monthly. These revenues are added to the monthly operating revenues to arrive at the total expected revenues.

TRs can then be compared with total budgeted expenses. If revenues seem inadequate to meet expenses, the administrator can check the validity of the predicted service volumes. If service levels seem reasonable, the administrator can seek to increase patient service volume, reduce budget expenses, or raise rates.

Using the Operating Budget: Variance Analysis

As a managerial tool, the operating budget is used throughout the fiscal year to measure performance by a *variance analysis* technique, which compares actual versus budgeted monetary and volume values at the end of each month.

Actual expenses that deviate significantly from the budgeted amounts can be investigated to identify the source of the variance. Such variances may be anything from an inadvertent miscalculation of costs or patient volume to serious mismanagement by a particular department. Typical sources of overage are items such as an unanticipated increase of employees or labor pool being used or unauthorized overtime. After identifying the source of variances, the budget can be adjusted accordingly, or the cause can be stopped. Budget variance analysis provides the administrator with an important means of control over the finances of the facility.

STEP 4: THE CASH BUDGET

The next step in the budgeting process is the preparation of the cash budget. As its name implies, it is prepared on the cash basis of accounting, although it is based on the revenues and expenses from the operating budget. Note that the operating budget is designed on the accrual basis of accounting: Projected revenues are based on the income earned in the period, not on the amount of cash received for services during the month (Berger, 2014; Zelman et al., 2020).

The cash budget estimates the cash inflows and outflows for the next 12 months, enabling the administrator to identify months with possible cash shortages and overages. This information can be used to defer non-urgent expenditures to a month with high cash inflows or retain overages in 1 month to cover anticipated cash shortages in the next. A cash budget helps anticipate effects of such events as three pay periods occurring in one month or anticipated large Medicare payments at known intervals. Facilities having corporate ownership may have little need for a cash budget since the corporate funds can cover any temporary shortages in cash flow needs of the facility. Some administrators rely on the cash budget for daily operations and sometimes prepare weekly or even daily cash budgets a month in advance.

Determining Cash Inflows and Outflows

Determining cash inflows and outflows must precede developing the cash budget. Projecting cash flow can be somewhat complicated because the facility has less control over cash inflows, especially those received from third-party payers. First, all the payer sources must be identified. These will usually be private payers, Medicare, Medicaid, insurance companies, managed care, the VA, and all other known or anticipated sources of income for services expected to be rendered. The lag time between the billing of services and receipt of payment is determined. Most private payers pay so within 30 days of billing, but time lags for Medicare, Medicaid, or insurance may vary considerably. Even so, expected monthly revenue percentages from each payer can be anticipated.

When cash inflows from resident services are known, monthly cash receipts from nonoperating sources are computed to give total cash receipts for each month.

Cash outflows are somewhat easier to estimate, as most cash disbursements, such as salaries and supplies, are made at prespecified intervals. Monthly cash disbursements can be determined using the expense budget and the facility's experience with suppliers and creditors. Such as a triennial payment for insurance that is consistently due in a specific month.

As with the operating budget, the cash budget is updated as conditions or needs change throughout the year, whatever the reason. The cash budget can be a useful planning tool.

STEP 5: THE CAPITAL BUDGET

The capital budget summarizes all anticipated capital (items with a life of more than 12 months) expenditures in the budget year (Brigham & Houston, 2017). Although many capital purchases and projects may be needed, all might not be readily affordable in the course of a single year. The capital budget expresses capital project decisions regarding timeline and financing. Suppose a competitor is to open a large all-new facility nearby. In that case, a contingency capital item might be funding to renovate a portion of the facility to compete should census drop precipitously. We often see such funds made available to fund niche markets outside what the new facility will be offering, such as capital toward the renovation of one wing into a secured unit.

Pro Forma Financial Statements

The budget process concludes with the development of the pro forma financial statements. The pro forma statements are the preliminary financial statements based on budgeted amounts. The pro forma income statement, for instance, is derived from the operating budget and shows the net income (or loss) expected under the budgeted expenses and revenues (Zelman et al., 2020).

The budgeting process can be costly in terms of time for the administrator and all other budget participants. However, it involves a thorough investigation of the facility's finances through such tools as cost finding, breakeven analysis, rate setting, programming, and cash flow analysis. Through these processes, budgeting familiarizes the administrator with the costs of running the facility and maximizes their ability to manage successfully.

COMMON PITFALLS IN PRACTICE

- The budgeting process is highly convoluted and involves many moving pieces. Find a skilled administrator to be your mentor. Have them assist you in your efforts to understand all the different parts of a budget, reasons why you spend money, reasons why you do not, and other areas you will navigate.
- Some corporations leave the budget entirely up to you. Some corporations provide you a "canned" budget and expect your input (as such, be ready to discuss all areas of the budget intelligently). Other corporations simply hand you a budget and say good luck. Understand which is your corporate model. Also understand that you can be successful with any of these models.

3.10 FINANCE: THE BROADER CONTEXT

Section Concepts

- The sources of law and the court systems
- Several legal terms
- How to do risk management for a nursing facility
- Business and financial concepts and terms
- Insurance terms
- Terms associated with wills and estates
- Ways in which financial and clinical systems are becoming integrated

Consider as the Administrator . . .

- Malpractice insurance premiums have skyrocketed. Many individual facilities and chains now self-insure or have minimal levels of insurance. Is the decision to self-insure a reasonable economic decision? Is having absolute minimum levels of insurance required by law a wise operational decision?

NAB DOMAIN 2A7: INTEGRATION OF CLINICAL AND FINANCIAL SYSTEMS (E.G., EMR/EHR, MDS)

We now turn to examine the broader business and economic context within which the nursing facility manages its affairs.

Technology has created the expectation of integrating clinical and financial systems of reimbursement. Financial reimbursement is tied directly to the clinical (healthcare) given by the facility. Focusing on the case mix and the levels of care surrounding the documentation to justify the care being given to each resident is paramount to success. Moreover, a further focus on preventing hospitalizations, rehospitalizations, and adverse events from occurring must be a part of daily business. This same integration will be used by the facility to improve services and monitor quality and quality assurance.

3.10.1 SOURCES OF LAW

NAB DOMAIN 3B1: FEDERAL HEALTHCARE LAWS, RULES, AND REGULATIONS; 3B3: CERTIFICATION AND LICENSURE REQUIREMENTS FOR THE ORGANIZATION

The daily business of the nursing facility is conducted within the context of the United States legal system.

Constitution. The Constitution is the written agreement establishing the fundamental law of the United States of America, setting forth the conditions, mutual obligations, and rights of the federal and state governments, and laying out basic principles of government. The Bill of Rights guarantees specific individual rights.

Statutes. Statutes are the laws under which we live. In the United States, they are the Acts passed by the federal and state legislatures. Lesser governmental bodies, such as county commissions, adopt ordinances and administrative agencies function through regulations.

Common law. Common law is the accumulation of opinion handed down by judges. It is an outgrowth of court decisions over hundreds of years. Our common law originated in England, where judges followed unwritten principles of "common sense" in addition to statutory laws. Common law principles change over time with the changing values and needs of society.

Regulations. To implement statutes (laws) passed by legislative bodies, the executive branch of government (the president and the various federal agencies they oversee) writes regulations through these administrative agencies. These regulations are the official interpretations of the intent of each statute. As a consequence, regulations become, in effect, part of the law. One may challenge a regulation on the grounds that the "official interpretation" is unconstitutional or inconsistent with the legislative intent of the statute that the regulation implements. This approach is the basis for the Informal Dispute Resolution (IDR) process that nursing facilities may exercise for citations with which they disagree.

The federal requirements for nursing facilities are an example of regulations written by the federal government's executive branch and include details of how the legislation will be interpreted and implemented. CMS employees wrote the federal requirements for nursing facilities. The federal requirements published in the *Federal Register* have the effect of law when federal inspectors visit a nursing facility and issue deficiencies based on both the written regulations and a set of "interpretive guidelines." The Omnibus Budget Reconciliation Act (OBRA) regulations (also called the Nursing Home Reform Amendments) is an example of these guidelines. Although not law or regulation per se, these interpretive guidelines are very real "guidelines" used by federal certification inspectors to record deficiencies and levy fines.

These requirements (not the interpretive guidelines) and other federal administrative agency regulations are published in the *Code of Federal Regulations* (often referred to as CFR).

The president of the United States has the prerogative of issuing executive orders under various statutes. Executive orders also have the effect of law. President Johnson's Executive Order 11246 requiring all federal contractors to use affirmative action guidelines designed to hire and promote women and minorities within their organizations is an example of this.

Code. A code is a compilation of statutes and regulations. The statutes and the implementing administrative regulations are systematically collected and placed into codes of law. The United States Code (USC) is an example.

Consider as the Administrator . . .

- *At what point in any process do regulations become "unreasonable"? Do we see unrealistic regulations surrounding the operation of nursing facilities?*

3.10.2 THE COURT SYSTEMS

Federal courts. The United States Constitution authorized the creation of the Supreme Court and any other courts Congress chooses to establish. Currently, entry into the federal court system is at federal district courts (general courts of original jurisdiction). *Jurisdiction* is the power to hear and decide a case.

Situated between these and the federal Supreme Court are 12 courts of appeal, which together cover the 50 states and hear cases in the event a party is dissatisfied with the judgment of the federal district court based on what the dissatisfied party views as an error.

The federal government also operates other courts, such as the Court of Claims, the Court of Customs and Patent Appeals, the Tax Court, and federal bankruptcy courts.

State courts. The court systems vary from state to state. The lowest level of the state system is the magistrate court, which deals with misdemeanor cases, traffic violations, and small claims (about $1,000 or less). Above the magistrate courts are the state circuit courts, or district courts, where more serious cases are tried.

Circuit or district courts have original jurisdiction over both civil and criminal cases. Most states have state courts of appeal, which generally do not have original jurisdiction and therefore limit themselves to appeals from lower courts. Finally, each state has a state supreme court, the court of final appeal in all matters except those involving a federal issue appealable to the U.S. Supreme Court.

3.10.3 LEGAL TERMINOLOGY

Inevitably, the administrator of every nursing facility will, at some point, be required to understand how legal matters are handled. The following definitions are helpful vocabulary enabling the administrator to function in the legal world.

Accuse. To directly charge a person with committing an offense that is recognized as being against the law. The accused person becomes the defendant and must answer the complaint or accusation through the legal process.

Acquit. To set a person or corporation free of accusation(s). Acquittal is a decision (verdict) of not guilty and is rendered by either a jury or a judge (in nonjury trials). Under the principle of double jeopardy, a person or corporation cannot be tried again for the same accusation after a verdict of not guilty.

Actionable. Conduct giving rise to a cause for legal action. For example, actionable negligence occurs only when a person unreasonably fails to perform a legal duty and that failure results in damage or injury to another person. If there is no resulting damage, there may not be actionable negligence even though the person made a mistake.

Adjudication. Decision or disposition of a case by announcing a judgment or decision by the court or other body.

Admission. The acknowledgment of certain facts by a party in a civil or criminal case. Admission does not necessarily constitute a confession of guilt. For example, the defendant may admit that they were driving the automobile but deny running the red light. The term *confession* is generally restricted to an acknowledgment of guilt.

Affidavit. A written statement given under oath before an officer having the authority to administer oaths. A notary public is such a public officer and is authorized to signify by their signature that they witnessed the execution (signing) of certain documents, such as affidavits, deeds, and wills.

Aggrieved party. One whose legal rights have been invaded or who has suffered a loss or injury. "Aggrieved party" is frequently used in connection with proceedings by administrative agencies. For example, an aggrieved party could be a person contesting the revocation of their professional license in an administrative proceeding.

Amicus curiae. Directly translated from Latin: a friend (*amicus*) of the court (*curiae*). An *amicus curiae* brief is a written document providing the court with information that might escape attention. A long-term care ombudsperson might, for example, appear in a court case on behalf of a resident. The "friend of the court" has no absolute right to appear in the proceeding and must obtain the court's permission before intervening.

Appeal. The request by a party to a lawsuit for a higher court to review a lower court's decision when they believe the lower court committed an error.

Appearance. The coming into court of a person upon being summoned to do so. Appearance without receiving a summons is a voluntary appearance. Appearance in court after papers have been served is an involuntary appearance.

Arbitrator. An impartial person chosen by the parties to an argument to decide the issue between them. Arbitration is used to avoid unnecessary and costly court actions.

Arraignment. An early step in a criminal proceeding at which the defendant is formally charged with an offense.

Assault. *See* Tort.

Battery. *See* Tort.

Burden of proof, or burden of persuasion. The obligation of the person bringing an action to prove facts in a dispute. In criminal cases, the state must prove its case beyond a reasonable doubt. In civil cases, the burden of proof is met by a "preponderance" of the evidence, that is, at least 51%.

Civil law. Pertains to a crime—any act the government has deemed injurious to the public and actionable in a criminal proceeding. The criminal acts may be felonies (serious crimes such as murder, arson, rape, armed robbery) or misdemeanors (less serious crimes such as minor traffic violations). A criminal violation may result in either a jail sentence, a fine, or both.

To picture the interaction of civil and criminal law, assume that an employee intentionally runs over a resident in the facility parking lot. The employee may be sued by the resident for money damages in a civil action and may also be brought to trial on criminal charges by the district attorney for the same act. (The nursing facility will probably be sued civilly by the resident, particularly if the employee has very little money.)

Consent, informed. Consent given after complete information regarding the matter has been provided to the person consenting. In the nursing facility context, patients must understand the nature and risks of specific treatments before the facility can claim exemption from responsibility for resulting complications.

A diabetic resident may, for example, volunteer to participate in an experimental diet program. Unless the resident fully understands the risks involved, the facility may be held liable for subsequent complications. The facility should require the resident to sign an adequately prepared consent form.

Consent to one treatment or procedure is not necessarily consenting to another treatment or procedure, even if such treatment or procedure is beneficial. If a patient resident consented to a tonsillectomy, but the surgeon also removed the appendix, the surgeon may have committed a battery.

Counterclaim. A counterdemand by a defendant against a plaintiff (accuser), not merely responding to the accuser but asserting an independent cause of action against the accuser. For example, suppose the patient in the knitting needle illustration (see Torts) sued the orderly for damages for assault or battery. In that case, the orderly might counterclaim with a demand for damages for assault or battery.

Damages. Money awarded by a court (or jury) to a person whom the action of another has wronged. The terms used to describe the various types of damages available differ from state to state and depend on the kind of case. Generally, actual damages, consequential damages, and incidental damages are designed to compensate the person wronged.

Nominal damages are an award of a small sum of money in recognition of the invasion of some legal right of the plaintiff, which results in no actual injury or pecuniary loss to the plaintiff. Punitive damages are designed to punish the defendant for bad conduct and deter the defendant from such behavior in the future. Punitive damages are also sometimes called exemplary damages. Double and treble damages are a type of punitive damages sometimes provided for by particular statutes.

Defamation. An injurious communication about the reputation or good name of the victim to a third person. An oral defamation is a slander. Written defamation is libel.

Libel is a written publication that exposes someone to public scorn, hatred, contempt, or ridicule, especially if related to an individual's profession or livelihood.

Slander, because it is spoken, is more difficult to establish. The action for slander has been restricted by courts due to free speech rights and to avoid overloading the courts with trivial cases. Only if slanderous statements lead to actual damages (e.g., loss of employment) can they be actionable unless the words imply crime, unchastity, or relate to a person's profession or business.

In the cases of both libel and slander, there must be communication to a third party; for example, showing a third party written words or speaking slanderous words in the presence of a third party.

Defendant. In criminal cases, the accused. In civil cases, the one who is sued must "defend" against a claim of wrongdoing brought by another.

Deposition. A statement given under oath is reduced to writing and authenticated by a notary public. A deposition allows the attorneys for both sides to find out what the person deposed (deponent) knows about the relevant event.

Directed verdict. A verdict given by a jury at the direction of a judge. If, for example, a plaintiff fails to make a reasonable case or a defendant fails to make a necessary defense, the judge may direct the jury to render a specified verdict.

Discovery. Pretrial devices used by the parties' lawyers to gather information or knowledge about the case. Discovery devices include depositions, interrogatories to parties, and requests for documents and articles. The purpose of discovery is to facilitate pretrial settlements and reduce surprises at trials so that cases may be decided on their merit (rather than by ambush).

False imprisonment. *See* Tort.

Fraud. Intentional deception that results in injury to another.

Indictment. A formal, written accusation by a public prosecutor submitted to a grand jury and charging a crime. The grand jury is a body authorized to investigate crimes and accuse (i.e., indict) persons within its jurisdiction when it decides that a trial ought to be undertaken.

Injunction. A judicial direction to a party to do or to refrain from doing some act. Injunctions guard against future acts but do not remedy past acts. When the court issues an injunction, the party to whom it is issued is said to be "enjoined."

Litigants. The parties to a lawsuit; that is, the plaintiff and the defendant.

Malice. The intentional doing of a wrongful act, without just cause or excuse, with the intent to inflict injury. Under some circumstances, the law will imply evil intent. Therefore, malice (in law) does not necessarily mean personal hate or ill will. The law will imply malice in an act done with reckless disregard for another's safety, even though the actor did not dislike the injured party. For example, the law may impute malice to the act of one who shoots a rifle into a crowd of strangers.

Motion. An application to the court asking for an action favorable to one's side.

Negligence. The failure to exercise the degree of care a reasonable person would exercise under the same circumstances, resulting in injury to another. Negligent conduct falls below the standard established by society (a jury) for the protection of others from an unreasonable risk of harm. Negligence may arise from either an overt act or from a failure to act.

The term *negligence* is used in several different ways:

- **Comparative negligence.** In some states, one can recover damages even though they were negligent themselves. For example, a resident slips and injures themself partly due to the unreasonably slippery floors in the facility and partly because the resident had chosen very slippery shoes. The facility is negligent because it failed to warn the resident that the floors were unusually slippery. But the resident was also negligent because they wore shoes that had slippery soles. In states with comparative negligence, the jury determines how much of the patient's injury should be blamed on the facility's negligence and how much the resident is to blame. The jury then apportions the damages (money) accordingly.

- **Contributory negligence.** Contributory negligence is like comparative negligence in that the victim is partly responsible for their injury. However, in states where the doctrine of contributory negligence applies, all recovery by the victim is barred. Contributory negligence is a favorite of defendants because they can win the case by convincing the jury that the victim was just the slightest bit to blame for their injury. For example, a resident family suing the facility for damages surrounding the death of their father. The father was diagnosed with emphysema and chronic obstructive pulmonary disease (COPD). The father refused to stop smoking two packs of cigarettes a day. The father's behavior clearly contributed to his demise, despite his knowing the adverse health effects of smoking.
- **Negligence per se.** Conduct treated as negligence without proof. It is usually necessary to show a failure to exercise a reasonable degree of care. Negligence per se is found where the act complained of violates a safety statute. Negligence per se also includes acts that are so clearly harmful to others that it is plain to any reasonable person that negligence must have occurred.
- **Criminal negligence.** Recklessness or carelessness resulting in injury or death is punishable as a crime. Criminal negligence implies reckless disregard for or indifference to the safety or rights of others.

Product liability. The liability of manufacturers and sellers for products they place on the market that cause harm to a person because of defects.

Prosecutor. A public official, either elected or appointed, who conducts cases on behalf of the government against persons accused of crimes.

Res ipsa loquitur. A Latin phrase that translates as "the thing speaks for itself." The defendant's negligence is inferred from the mere fact that the event happened and that the instrumentality causing the injury was under the defendant's exclusive control. *Res ipsa loquitur* could apply to an otherwise unexplained gas furnace explosion in a nursing facility.

Res judicata. Latin for "a thing decided." Once a court of competent jurisdiction has decided a matter, that decision continues to bind those parties in any future litigation on the same issue.

Retainer. A fee paid to an attorney in advance for services on a case. In exchange, the attorney must refuse employment by the client's adversary in the case.

Risk, assumption of. The principle that a person may not recover compensation for an injury they received when they voluntarily exposed themselves to a known danger.

Search warrant. A written order from a judge permitting certain law enforcement officers to conduct a search for and seize specified things or persons. Warrants are issued on sworn testimony or affidavits supporting probable cause. Law enforcement officers may not search or seize items or persons not within the scope of the search warrant.

Stare decisis. A Latin phrase meaning "to stand by that which was decided earlier." The doctrine of *stare decisis* means that once a court has laid down a principle of law as applicable to a specific set of facts, it will adhere to that principle in all future cases in which the facts are substantially the same. *Stare decisis* gives the law a measure of predictability. However, a court will reverse itself occasionally where considerations of public policy demand it. For example, nonprofit healthcare institutions were once immune from lawsuits. Public policy has required that such immunity no longer apply.

Subpoena. A written order issued by a court requiring the appearance of a person in court. A person failing to appear may be held in contempt of court.

Subpoena duces tecum. A written court order for a person to bring to a judicial proceeding particular objects or documents in their possession. The court may, for example, require a nursing facility administrator to bring resident records to a court proceeding.

Summons. A written instrument notifying a defendant that a lawsuit has commenced against them. Failure to appear may result in a default judgment, wherein the defendant has a judgment entered against them for failure to appear.

Tort. A wrong. From Latin meaning "twisted." A tort exists when (a) a legal duty is owed by a defendant to a plaintiff, (b) that duty is breached, and (c) the plaintiff is harmed as a direct result of the breach of duty.

For example, the duty to provide care to residents is imposed on the nursing facility by virtue of holding itself out as a healthcare provider. If the facility breaches its care-providing duty to a resident, and there is direct resident harm, a tort has occurred. The general term *tort* includes several specific types of bad or wrongful conduct. Assault, battery, false imprisonment, and negligence are among the types of conduct labeled by the law as torts.

An *assault* is an attempt to inflict bodily harm on another person that creates well-founded fear of imminent peril. An assault does not require actual touching. An assault can be the basis for a civil action (not a criminal practice) and/or a criminal action (violation of criminal laws). In the civil action for assault, the person assaulted brings the action seeking to be awarded money. In the criminal action for assault, the district attorney brings assault charges for the purpose of punishment.

The tort of assault is closely linked to, and often confused with, the tort of battery. *Battery* is the unlawful touching or application of force to another human being without their consent. There must be an intent to touch, actual touching, and a lack of consent for a battery to occur. If the touching is knowingly consented to, it is not a battery.

Assault has been defined as a "failed battery" because an assault must cause apprehension of immediate harmful contact without actual contact. For example, if the doctor ordered pills, and the nurse approaches the resident with a 4-inch long needle, causing resident apprehension to immediate contact, it is an assault. If the nurse uses the needle (a touch), it becomes a battery (unless the resident has consented).

To illustrate the differences between assault and battery, consider the following. A female resident's breast is bumped by an orderly during transport. If it is purely accidental, no battery has occurred. If the orderly intended to bump into the resident's breast, it might be a battery. The angry patient retaliates by throwing a knitting needle at the orderly. If the knitting needle misses, but the orderly is apprehensive about immediate harmful contact, the resident has committed an assault. If the knitting needle hits the orderly, it is a battery (even if the orderly was not apprehensive of the contact). The orderly then throws a towel at the resident. If it hits the resident, it is a battery. If it misses the resident, but the resident apprehends immediate harmful contact, it is an assault.

False imprisonment is another tort occasionally related to assault and battery; it is the confining of another human being within fixed boundaries against their will. Numerous circumstances within the nursing facility can give rise to claims of false imprisonment. If a competent resident refuses bed (side) rails, but the nurse raises the bed (side) rails despite protest, false imprisonment has occurred.

If a physician leaves orders to restrain a competent resident in a wheelchair, but that resident refuses, tying the resident in the wheelchair will constitute false imprisonment. (Tying the resident in the wheelchair may also be a battery.) Another typical example of false imprisonment occurs when the competent resident demands to be released from the facility but is not allowed to leave.

Tortfeasor. The person who commits a tort.

Warrant, arrest. A written order for the arrest of a person from a judge having authority in that jurisdiction.

Witness. A person who gives sworn testimony in a court proceeding.

COMMON PITFALLS IN PRACTICE

- Don't think you need to understand all this legal jargon? You would be very wrong. We work in a very litigious field. It is not a matter of "if" you get sued, it is a matter of "when." Be prepared for the day that lawsuits present themselves, unemployment claims are filed, Equal Employment Opportunity Commission claims are levied, or a myriad of other entrances for you into the legal arena.

3.10.4 RISKS ASSUMED BY THE OPERATION OF A LONG-TERM CARE FACILITY

Section Concepts

- *How much control over risks being assumed in day-to-day facility operation does the administrator have?*
- *The act of obtaining a license to operate and operating a long-term care facility brings a set of risks to the facility. Some of these are defined subsequently.*

Consider as the Administrator . . .

- *The administrator assumes liability for what happens in their facility 24/7. Is it possible to maintain presence in the facility for all 24 hours of a day?*

NAB DOMAIN 2B2: WORKERS' COMPENSATION; 2B11: HEALTHCARE RECORD REQUIREMENTS (E.G., CONFIDENTIALITY, DISCLOSURE, SAFEGUARDING, HIPAA, HITECH)

NAB DOMAIN 2B: RISK MANAGEMENT

NAB DOMAIN 2B7: SCOPE OF PRACTICE AND LEGAL LIABILITY

NAB DOMAIN 1B1: PSYCHOSOCIAL NEEDS (E.G., SOCIAL, SPIRITUAL, COMMUNITY, CULTURAL)

EMPLOYER'S LIABILITY ACTS

Various states have statutes that set forth limits of employer liability to employees for their injuries. Generally, the employer is held responsible only for injuries to employees occurring in their work. Workers' compensation acts and the Federal Employer's Liability Act are examples. Employer liability acts usually pay for physician and hospital costs. These statutes negated the earlier claims by employers that the employee knew the hazards of a job and accepted them when agreeing to work for the facility.

Often these statutes also hold the employer responsible for negligent acts of fellow employees within the zone of employment. The *zone of employment* is the physical area within which employers are liable (legally responsible) under workers' compensation acts. This zone usually includes the parking areas, entryways, and other areas under the employer's control.

STRICT LIABILITY

An employer held strictly liable is subject to liability without fault; that is, without the employee having to show employer fault.

VICARIOUS OR IMPUTED LIABILITY (RESPONDEAT SUPERIOR)

The employer is held responsible for the acts of employees within the scope of their employment. For example, if a nurse's aide carelessly drops a resident from a wheelchair, causing injuries to the resident, the employer is typically held liable for the injuries. *Respondeat superior* is a Latin term meaning "let the master answer for the acts of their servants," or "let the employer answer for the acts of their employees."

SCOPE OF EMPLOYMENT

Scope of employment is the range of employee activities the employer is legally responsible for according to the courts. It includes any acts performed in the process of carrying out one's duties. Ascertaining the scope of employment is essential when determining the employer's liability for the actions of its employees.

When hurrying to aid another resident, a nurse's aide knocks down and injures a resident on crutches. The aide is likely to be found as acting as a servant by the scope of employment. The result is that the employer is liable for the accident. An employee may be considered acting within the scope of employment even if they are doing their job contrary to the employer's instructions.

In early 2015, a Tarrant County, Texas, jury returned a $16.7 million negligence verdict against a nursing facility when the afternoon supervisors, against facility policy, sent an obviously drunken nurse's aide home. The jury concluded the facility was liable because they knew the employee had a drinking problem, knew she was drunk, and allowed her to drive instead of taking her home or seeing that she had a ride. The facility had ensured the same employee a ride 3 months prior when this exact situation had occurred. The failure of an afternoon supervisor to not follow facility policy resulted in the $16.7 million verdict, which included $5 million in punitive damages against the facility.

BORROWED SERVANT

A borrowed servant is a person under the temporary employment of another person. In a nursing facility, a nurse employed by the local community college as a nursing instructor but temporarily working under the direction of the nursing facility's director of nurses might be found to be a borrowed servant. The nursing facility might be found liable for the wrongful acts of the "borrowed" nurse based on the concept of respondeat superior.

INDEPENDENT CONTRACTOR

NAB DOMAIN 2B13: CONTRACTED SERVICES (E.G., ROLES, RESPONSIBILITES, OVERSIGHT, BACKGROUND CHECKS)

An independent contractor agrees with another person to perform a particular job and remains in control of the job's means and methods. Because an independent contractor is not an employee, the doctrine of *respondeat superior* has no application to the independent contractor. Therefore, the nursing facility would not ordinarily be liable for the negligence of an independent contractor.

Determining whether a person is acting as an employee, with the facility liable for the employee's negligence, or as an independent contractor, without this liability, depends on several factors:

- The extent to which the facility controls the details of the work
- Whether the person is engaged in a distinct occupation or profession
- Whether the work is usually done under the direction of the employer or by a specialist without supervision
- The skill required
- The portion of time the person is employed
- Who supplies the equipment used
- Whether the work is part of the regular business of the facility

- Whether the facility and worker believe they have formed an employer/employee relationship
- Whether or not the person is in business

Depending on the circumstances, physical therapists under contract to the nursing facility and private duty nurses may (or may not) be found to be independent contractors. Because facilities would naturally prefer to have a few of their employees be viewed as independent contractors to reduce liability, courts give great weight to the label the facility places on the worker. Facility liability is more likely to be ascribed if a resident's injury is sustained during treatment by a physical therapist under contract than one caused by an outside painting contractor employee.

MANAGING RISKS

How Much Risk?

How much risk is faced in an average 100-bed nursing facility over a year? If each nursing facility resident will have at least 20 contacts with staff members each day, more than 2,000 staff/resident contacts occur daily in this typical nursing facility. Over the course of a month, 60,000 contacts occur within that facility. Annually that number is nearly three quarters of a million staff/resident contacts. Based on the almost 17,000 nursing facilities certified by Medicare/Medicaid, approximately 12 billion contacts occur each year. Each of these 12 billion annual contacts potentially incurs risks to the facility. Consider the following.

Care Decisions of a Nurse's Aide

An Alabama jury awarded $2.5 million in punitive damages to the family of an 86-year-old nursing facility resident who strangled to death while restrained in a Posey vest. Not realizing that Posey vests are color-coded, the nurse's aide chose a vest to match the resident's gown rather than based on body size. She then placed the vest backward on the resident, causing the resident to choke to death. The J. T. Posey Company, a codefendant, was found not guilty of negligence because it had warned the nursing home that the vests' V neck should be placed in front. Nurse's aides give the preponderance of hands-on care in nursing facilities.

RN and Allied Health Professional Performance

In a Pennsylvania nursing facility, a night-shift RN, annoyed by the "disturbing" noise produced by a resident's respirator, turned the respirator off while she and a respiratory therapist cleared a 65-year-old man's breathing passages. Then, without turning the respirator back on, they left the room. Twenty minutes later, an alarm on the respirator sounded in the resident's room. The RN returned to the room and found the patient dead in what the coroner called a "therapeutic misadventure."

Staff Performance Under Stress

At a 150-plus-bed nursing facility in a southern state, nine persons died, 141 people were hospitalized, and 98 received significant injuries and treatment for smoke inhalation from a fire started by smoking materials at the foot of a resident's bed.

State and local officials said the nursing facility had undergone recent inspections and was in compliance with state fire codes. An administrator for the group of facilities said the nursing facility was entirely up to code, was well equipped to deal with fires, prohibited smoking in bedrooms, and had fire alarms, smoke and heat detectors, and fire-resistant doors. Fire and effective or ineffective staff responses can occur at any time. Situations such as this one are why many facilities have outright banned smoking.

Uncontrolled Resident Behavior

In a Texas facility, a male resident murdered his three roommates with the arm of a wheelchair and then went back to bed as if nothing had happened. The event was spurred on by sounds the other residents were making during their sleep.

Uncontrolled Director of Nurses Behavior

A jury awarded $15 million to the estate of a resident whose family claimed that the resident was given Darvocet (a mild painkiller) under the instructions of the director of nurses in place of morphine (a more powerful painkiller) for a period of 1 month. The jury debated for less than 2 hours. Facility owners could show that the resident's physician had written prescriptions for both morphine and Darvocet to be administered as judged medically needed. The jury, nevertheless, found for the plaintiff's family.

This case illustrates the growing importance of pain management as part of a facility's risk management program. Older nurses were taught a minimalist approach to pain management. Today, more aggressive pain management is an expectation and is an important area to monitor as surveyors very highly cite pain management.

NAB DOMAIN 2A7: INTEGRATION OF CLINICAL AND FINANCIAL SYSTEMS (E.G., EMR/EHR, MDS); 2A8: INTERNAL FINANCIAL MANAGEMENT CONTROLS (E.G., SEGREGATION OF DUTIES, ACCESS)

NAB DOMAIN 2B4: COMPLIANCE PROGRAMS; 2B5: RISK MANAGEMENT PROCESS AND PROGRAMS

NAB DOMAIN 2B7: SCOPE OF PRACTICE AND LEGAL LIABILITY

What Is a Risk?

A *risk* can be defined as any event or process that can lead to actions that result, directly or indirectly, in economic losses or damage to the facility or its reputation (Figure 3.12).

Each of the events demonstrates risks to be managed. Several definitions of risk management appear in the literature: A program that attempts to provide positive avoidance of negative results; liability control; loss prevention; prediction of resident injury; avoidance of exposure to predicted and other risks; and minimization of malpractice claims helps to reduce loss.

HAZARDS IN THE NURSING FACILITY ENVIRONMENT

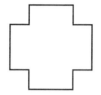

Accident hazards

- Slips, trips, and falls on wet floors
- Burns and scalds from hot sterilizing equipment
- Injuries to legs and toes by falling heavy objects; for example, food containers and medical instruments
- Acute poisoning due to inhalation or ingestion of disinfectants or sterilizing compounds or their vapors
- Acute back pain, resulting from awkward body position or when performing over-strenuous movements when handling heavy residents
- Musculoskeletal damage as a result of lifting incapacitated residents
- Acute poisoning due to accidental release of a chemical

Biological hazards

- Hazard of contracting a communicable disease from the residents
- Exposure to pathogenic microorganisms in body fluids of residents, especially for blood-borne diseases (AIDS, hepatitis, etc.)

Ergonomic, psychosocial, and organizational factors

- Fatigue and low-back pain due to the lifting or other handling of heavy residents and to prolonged working while standing or walking
- Stress, strained family relations, and burnout due to shift and night work, over-time work, and contact with sick residents, in particular terminal cases and their relatives
- Physical violence and verbal abuse, in particular from residents with mental impairments

FIGURE 3.12 Accident hazards in the environment of the nursing facility.

Essentially, risk management identifies and solves problems before they get out of hand, thus preventing damages or legal actions. As discussed earlier in the text, much of the administrator's daily work surrounds risk management, quality assurance, and improvement. EHR use has made this task much more manageable than previously, as many EHR software suites include risk management. This information often is shown in a dashboard at the computer or notification on a smartphone allowing immediate intervention. Today's technology allows increased timely intervention, and it will be amazing to see how technological applications continue to evolve.

Facilities must ensure that the environment is as free of accident hazards as possible to prevent unexpected and unintended injury. Figure 3.12 illustrates the extensive and common exposures that nursing facilities and workers face, ranging from slips and falls to physical violence and verbal abuse from the increasing proportion of patients who have mental impairments. Many facilities each year receive deficiencies for accident hazards in their environment.

EXTERNAL REPORTING REQUIREMENTS: CORPORATE RESPONSIBILITY AND CORPORATE COMPLIANCE

NAB DOMAIN 2A6: FINANCIAL REPORTING REQUIREMENTS (E.G., REQUIREMENTS FOR NOT-FOR-PROFIT, FOR-PROFIT, AND GOVERNMENTAL PROVIDERS); 2B4: COMPLIANCE PROGRAMS; 2B9: MANDATORY REPORTING REQUIREMENTS (E.G., INCIDENTS, ADVERSE EVENTS, ABUSE, NEGLECT, FINANCIAL EXPLOITATION, FRAUD)

Corporate Compliance: The Civil False Claims Act

Each facility is expected to appoint a person to be the corporate compliance officer. The Office of Inspector General of the U.S. Department of Health and Human Services enforces corporate compliance.

Over the past few years, the federal government has devoted substantial resources to investigating healthcare fraud and abuse. Healthcare providers can be found liable for submitting claims for reimbursement in reckless disregard or deliberate ignorance of the truth, as well as for intentional fraud. Because the False Claims Act authorized the imposition of damages of up to three times the fraud and civil monetary penalties of $11,000 per false claim, record-level fines, and penalties have been imposed against individuals and healthcare organizations that violate the law. Under the False Claims Act, the federal government has fined nursing facilities millions of dollars for seeking reimbursement for services for which residents do not qualify (Singh, 2016).

Each facility must appoint and empower a corporate compliance officer who has the authority to review all documents and other relevant information to comply with Medicare, Medicaid, and other laws. Compliance issues may range from simple overpayments to be returned to the payer to possible criminal violations. Perhaps the most challenging area for the corporate compliance officer in the nursing facility setting is monitoring the extent to which the facility is receiving all legally due reimbursement from Medicare, Medicaid, and other providers, but not claiming more reimbursement than permitted. For example, intentionally giving a resident a higher PDPM CMG score (reimbursement rate claim under Medicare) than is usual and customary (i.e., practiced as the industry norm).

Furthermore, each facility must devise its operational corporate compliance plan. If a facility chooses not to have one, and it is in violation, the Office of the Inspector General is more than happy to put one in place for the facility. Usually, these plans are very restrictive and nearly impossible to implement. Thus, almost all facilities today have a corporate compliance plan that they operate under—which they have devised themselves or has been passed down from corporate.

Sarbanes-Oxley Act of 2002

The Sarbanes-Oxley Act (SOX) requires publicly held companies to do the following:

1. Implement internal controls over their financial reporting, operations, and assets.
2. Evaluate the strengths and weaknesses of these internal controls in official documents filed with the Securities and Exchange Commission (SEC).
3. Make regular disclosures concerning the viability of these controls and potential fraud or losses that may affect the company's financial position.

This Act covers roughly 70% of U.S. nursing homes that are for profit. Compliance with the SOX of 2002 is more of a corporate concern than an individual facility concern. The goals of both the Office of the Inspector General of the U.S. Department of Health and Human Services for monitoring facility expenses and charges are of more immediate concern for the individual nursing facility administrator.

Terms Associated With Risk Management

NAB DOMAIN 2A8: INTERNAL FINANCIAL MANAGEMENT CONTROLS (E.G., SEGREGATION OF DUTIES, ACCESS); 2B: RISK MANAGEMENT

NAB DOMAIN 2B7: SCOPE OF PRACTICE AND LEGAL LIABILITY

NAB DOMAIN 3A3: SAFETY AND ACCESSIBILITY (E.G., ADA, SAFETY DATA SHEETS)

Civil liability. The three primary sources of healthcare malpractice suits are (a) failure to obtain effective consent before intervening in the life of the resident, (b) breach or violation of a contract or promise, and (c) the rendering of substandard, poor-quality care.

Claims-made policy. An insurance policy that pays for liability or other claims that occur only when the policy is in effect.

Occurrence policy. An insurance policy that pays liability or other claims for a lifetime, regardless of when the claim is reported, if the claim occurred while the insurance policy was in effect.

Tail coverage. Usually applicable to only claims-made policies. The addition of tail coverage to a policy extends the reporting period after the policy has been terminated. It essentially extends the initial coverage indefinitely.

NAB DOMAIN 2B7: SCOPE OF PRACTICE AND LEGAL LIABILITY

Durable power of attorney. Appointment of an agent empowered to act on behalf of the person creating the power in case of future incompetence (ordinary power of attorney ends when the person creating the power becomes incompetent).

Empty shell doctrine. Name for the view that the facility merely provides a workplace for health professionals and has no corporate liability for their actions. This concept was abandoned several years ago after the landmark Illinois case *Darling v. Charleston Community Memorial Hospital*, which was the first to hold a hospital facility liable for acts of staff.

NAB DOMAIN 1B1: PSYCHOSOCIAL NEEDS (E.G., SOCIAL, SPIRITUAL, COMMUNITY, CULTURAL); 1B13: DEATH, DYING, AND GRIEF

Euthanasia. A "good" or "easy" death. Active euthanasia in the nursing facility setting is the involvement of facility caregivers in the nonaccidental termination of a resident's life. Such practice is illegal in all but a few states and instances.

Assisted suicide. Suicide that is committed with the aid of another person, sometimes a physician. The "aid" is usually the provision of the means by which the individual ends their own life. Often synonymous with physician-assisted suicide (PAS) or physician-assisted dying.

NAB DOMAIN 1B7: CARE RECIPIENT DECISION-MAKING (E.G., CAPACITY, POWER OF ATTORNEY, GUARDIANSHIP, CONSERVATORSHIP, CODE STATUS, ADVANCE DIRECTIVES, ETHICAL DECISION-MAKING)

Guardianship. Appointment by a probate court of a substitute decision-maker for a person a judge has declared incompetent. Guardianship can reduce a person to the legal status of an infant, thus limiting a person's right to make healthcare and financial decisions and potentially preventing the person from voting, marrying, or entering contracts.

Malpractice system (purposes of). (a) The just financial compensation of innocent, injured residents and (b) the maintenance of a high level of care by deterring undesirable provider practices.

Palliative care. Alleviating suffering even when the underlying disease does not have a possible "cure."

Resident's rights—sources. (a) Judge-made (common) law based on society's values; (b) specific statutes of legislative law resulting in rules and regulations defining resident rights.

Standard of care. The duty to have and to use the degree of knowledge and skill that is usually possessed and used by competent, prudent similar healthcare providers in like or similar circumstances.

Substandard care. Four elements are required for a civil lawsuit: (a) duty owed, (b) breach or violation of that duty, (c) damage or injury, and (d) causation.

3.10.5 BUSINESS-RELATED CONCEPTS AND TERMS

In the healthcare field, the nursing facility industry is second in size only to the hospital industry in total dollars received and spent each year. The gross income of the larger nursing home chains is in the billions. The following is an introduction to some of the business vocabulary of running a $100 billion-plus industry.

Accounting Concepts (Additional)

Activity-based costing. An accounting method that assigns identifiable costs and allocates standard costs to specific facility activity areas, sometimes known as departmental area costing. This method allows the facility to identify the profit contribution of each activity or department. Similar to or the same as the step-down accounting method described previously.

Agency. A relationship in which one person acts on behalf of and under the control of another. The acts of the agent are binding on the person or business the agent represents. The nursing facility administrator is the facility's agent; thus, the facility is bound by the agreements the administrator makes on behalf of the facility.

Allowance for bad debts. A provision a facility makes for uncollectible accounts receivable. On the balance sheet, net receivables—the amount the facility realistically expects to collect from resident billings—are calculated by reducing the accounts receivable by allowing for bad debt.

American Institute of Certified Public Accountants (AICPA). A national organization of CPAs. This organization develops standards for its members and offers advice to such governmental agencies as the SEC. Decisions of this group usually become the standards of practice.

Annual report. A detailed statement of the facility's financial position at the end of its reporting year—either fiscal or calendar. Annual reports, as described previously, contain the facility's income statement, balance sheet, statement of cash flows, statement of owners or shareholder's equity, management's discussion and analysis of operations, notes to the financial statements, audit opinion, and other selected data. The Financial Accounting Standards Board (FASB) described subsequently also requires reporting on all other financial activities, for example, pharmacy holdings, or any other business activities that affect the facility's financial status.

Accounting rate of return (ARR). A method of measuring the potential profitability of an investment. ARR is calculated by dividing the net income by the investment amount (or average amount).

Audit. An examination of a facility's compliance with accounting standards and policies. There are four types of audits: financial, internal, management, and compliance. In the financial audit, an independent CPA examines the facility's financial records and gives an audit opinion. The internal audit utilizes an internal financial officer to study the financial records and ensure they meet facility policies. The management audit examines management's efficiency. The compliance audit determines whether the facility is meeting specific rules and regulations.

Audit opinion. A report performed by an independent CPA giving the auditor's opinion as to the reasonableness of the facility's financial statement.

Big Six. A term assigned to the six largest CPA firms in the United States. The rankings change over time, depending on criteria used, such as billings or number of staff.

Change in accounting estimate. A revision of an accounting forecast or assumption about the facility's expected or experienced performance.

Certified public accountant (CPA). A title given to accountants who pass the Uniform CPA examination administered by the AICPA and who satisfy the experience requirements of each given state (not unlike the licensing of nursing facility administrators through the NAB exam). CPAs are licensed to issue an audit opinion on a facility's financial statements.

Cumulative effect of a change in accounting principle. In accounting, the income statement account showing the impact of switching from one accounting principle to another. The cumulative effect shows the difference between the retained earnings reported at the beginning of the year under the old method and the retained earnings that would have been reported at the beginning of the year had the method never been changed.

Extraordinary item. In accounting, an economic item that is both unusual and infrequent (such as the replacement of the emergency power generator, which might occur once every 15 years).

Financial Accounting Standards Board (FASB). The independent institution that establishes and disseminates the GAAPs and recording practices. The AICPA and the SEC both recognize the statements of the FASB. All practicing CPAs are required to adhere to FASB guidelines.

Materiality. In accounting, the relative importance of an accounting error or omission in a facility's financial statements. A $200 error in an earnings statement of $2 million income would be immaterial, whereas a $500,000 error would clearly be material.

Qualified opinion. An auditor's report of a facility's financial statement pointing to some limitation; for example, the inability of the CPA to obtain objective evidence of a certain transaction that might directly or adversely affect the facility's financial standing.

Unqualified opinion. Sometimes known as a clean opinion; that is, the report meets all the GAAP requirements.

Asset-Related Terms

Brandmark. The portion of a brand that is a symbol, design, or distinctive coloring or lettering; also called a logo. Examples: One large nursing facility chain has a caregiver standing over a person in a wheelchair; another has a rose or flower symbol above its name.

Intangible asset. An item or right that has no physical substance and provides an economic benefit. The reputation of a nursing facility as the best caregiver in the community is a valuable intangible asset, for example.

Liquidity. The ability of current assets to meet the financial obligation of current liabilities. Having high liquidity enables a facility to take advantage of investment opportunities and borrow capital or receive a line of credit at a more favorable rate.

Long-term asset. An asset with future economic benefits that are expected to maintain for some years. Long-term assets are reported on the balance sheet as noncurrent assets and include buildings and equipment. A new central building for a life care community may have a long-term expected asset value for perhaps 40 or more years to come.

Net present value. In corporate finance, the present value (i.e., the value of cash to be received in the future expressed in current dollars) of an investment above the initial amount invested. The idea should perhaps proceed when a proposed project, such as building a new wing, has a positive net present value. If a proposed wing shows a negative net present value, it should possibly be delayed or abandoned.

Note receivable. A contract to receive money at a future date. Notes receivable are reported on the balance sheet as either current assets (less than 1 year) or non-current assets (more than 1 year).

Off-balance sheet. An item not reported in financial statements that nevertheless has an impact on the operations of a facility. An example might be an estimate of the monetary value of a strong reputation for the quality of a recently purchased facility.

Present value. The current value of a future payment or stream of payments. Present value is calculated by applying a discount (capitalization) rate to future payment(s). This method is sometimes referred to as the discounted cash flow method or the discounted earnings method. Its purpose is to estimate the fair market value of a potential investment.

Competition/Risk-Related Terms

Attachment. A legal procedure where a defendant's property is seized by court order pending the outcome of a claim against the defendant. The purpose is to gain control over property to satisfy payment of a judgment if the plaintiff's suit is successful.

Bad faith. Generally, implies a design to mislead or deceive another. Good faith means being truthful and faithful to one's obligations in business dealings.

Bankruptcy. Inability to pay one's debts; insolvency. It also refers to the legal process authorized under several chapters of the federal Bankruptcy Code, where assets of the business or individual(s) are liquidated, creditors paid, and the debtor is given a fresh start. In a Chapter 11 reorganization, the dominant form, the debtor's assets are not liquidated. Instead, the business continues to run, but their debt structure and company are rearranged, creditors are paid back in part or full under a "plan." Under Chapter 7, the conventional form under the Bankruptcy Reform Act, all the assets must be auctioned or sold to pay creditors. A court-appointed trustee gathers all assets, liquidates them, and then distributes the proceeds to the creditors. In most bankruptcy cases, debts remaining after liquidation distribution are discharged. Generally, debtors at the bottom of the creditor ranking receive little or nothing. Attorneys usually refer to a Chapter 7 bankruptcy as "straight" bankruptcy.

Better-off test. A method of evaluating the strategic impact of an acquisition or business venture on the facility's financial standing. The better-off test stipulates that the new venture must either (a) gain a significant competitive advantage through its functioning or (b) offer a significant competitive advantage to the facility.

Cannibalization. The reduction of income from the sale of a product due to the same facility or company introducing another similar product. For example, a facility may offer newer forms of physical therapy that reduce the use of currently used physical therapy methods. If the total combined income using the latest physical therapy method and the diminished use of the old process yields a higher final income, cannibalization is justified.

Caveat emptor. The Latin expression for "let the buyer beware." The purchaser buys at their own risk. In recent years, consumer protection laws and the Uniform Commercial Code have implied certain warranties in most purchases unless the goods are bought "as is."

Competitive advantage. The elements within a facility's operations providing an edge over its competitors. Building a new enlarged outpatient physical therapy wing might give Facility A a competitive advantage over its competitors. If, however, the competing Facility B counters by creating an even larger and more attractive state-of-the-art outpatient physical therapy wing, Facility A is placed at a competitive disadvantage. These are calculations used in developing the corporate strategy to be followed by Facility A.

Competitor analysis. The evaluation of the intent and actions of one's competitors as part of corporate strategy. The information gained in a competitor analysis is used to estimate the probable future actions of competitors based on their future goals and assumptions about the marketplace.

Cost of entry test. A method of evaluating the strategic impact of the acquisition or start-up of a new business venture for the facility. This test specifies that the cost of entering the new venture must not exceed the future profits generated by that venture.

Debt-to-assets ratio. A measure of the relative obligations of a facility. Generally, the lower the debt ratio, the more financially sound the facility is believed to be. The ratio is calculated by:

$$\frac{\text{Current liabilities} + \text{Noncurrent liabilities}}{\text{Total assets}}$$

Differentiation. A facility places emphasis on some significant product benefit or set of benefits valued by the entire market but not offered by the competition. Numerous facilities sought to differentiate themselves by being the only facility to offer, for example, subacute care or an Alzheimer's unit. These competitive advantages through differentiation are usually short-lived as competitors emulate and begin to provide the same services.

Externality. Any incidental by-product or by-products (both positive and negative) associated with a particular course of action chosen by a facility. A positive externality for a facility that decides to admit difficult-to-place patients from local hospitals might be an increased census. A negative externality associated with this course of action would be the necessity to hire additional staff and provide additional training for present staff.

Inflation. An increase in the general price level. Inflation can be viewed as an increase in the cost of doing business or erosion of the value of the facility's income. Higher inflation rates usually force facilities to offer higher salary increases.

Management's discussion and analysis of operations. A section of the facility's annual report required by the SEC summarizing the reasons for changes in operations, liquidity, capital resources, and working capital available to the facility. The purpose is to assist readers of the financial statements and in understanding the effects of changes in activities and accounting procedures.

Perfect competition. A market that is so competitive that all its participants have virtually no control over the price. Characteristics of an ideal market are thought to be (a) a large number of relatively small buyers and sellers, (b) easy entry and exit from the market, (c) a standardized product, and (d) complete information about market price. Few, if any, healthcare markets meet these requirements.

Price elasticity of demand. The effect price change has on income, calculated by:

$$\frac{\% \text{ change in quantity demanded(sales)}}{\% \text{ change in price}}$$

In setting its rates for private paying residents, each facility must calculate the impact of census on any rate increases. Potential private paying persons might go to a competitor if rates at facility A are raised significantly above rates at facility B, other things being equal.

Return on investment (ROI). A measure of the earning power of a facility's assets. A high ROI is desirable whether the facility is a for-profit or a not-for-profit operation. ROI is broadly thought of as net income divided by investments but may be calculated using three different figures: return on assets (ROA), return on equity (ROE), and return on invested capital (ROIC).

ROA is calculated by dividing the net income after any taxes by the average total assets:

$$\frac{\text{Net income after any taxes}}{\text{Average total assets}}$$

(Average total assets is calculated by adding the ending balance of total assets of the previous year and the ending balance of total assets for the current year and dividing by 2.)

Return on equity (ROE). Measures the return that a facility has earned on the funds invested in it. These funds may be invested by shareholders (public or private) or may be, for example, the funds invested by a church in its facilities. The ratio is calculated by dividing net income after any taxes by investor's equity:

$$\frac{\text{Net income after any taxes}}{\text{Investor's equity}}$$

Return on invested capital (ROIC). Tells how well a facility has used the funds given to it for an extended period. Invested capital equals noncurrent liabilities plus owners' equity.

$$\frac{\text{Net income after any taxes}}{\text{Noncurrent liabilities} + \text{Owners' equity}}$$

Benefits/Pensions

Accumulated benefit obligation (ABO). The present value of the amount a facility would owe to its pension plan if its eligible employees retired during that accounting period.

Charter. A document issued by a state or other sovereign government establishing a corporate entity (same as articles of incorporation).

Defined benefit pension plan. A program of pension benefits employees will receive when they retire. Typically, benefits are based on a formula involving years of service and compensation levels as employees near retirement. Whenever a facility establishes a defined benefit pension plan, it must ensure that its pension fund has enough assets to pay the promised benefits. Delivering promised health benefits has become a significant liability to pension plans in recent years because of the escalation of healthcare costs. Many companies are moving to reduce and/or eliminate this type of obligation.

Defined contribution pension plan. A program designating the annual dollar amount an employer contributes to a pension plan. Under a defined benefit pension plan, specific benefits such as dollar amounts and other benefits are promised. In contrast, under a defined contribution pension plan, the employer makes no guarantee of future benefits beyond the value of the dollar amount of the funds set aside in the pension fund each year. This approach is now the favored pension plan among U.S. businesses, preferring 401(k)s, individual retirement accounts, and the like as a replacement for a defined benefit.

Employee stock ownership plan (ESOP). An employee benefit plan that gives employees shares in the facility. These may be voting shares, but more often are a special class of nonvoting common stock. ESOP rules change with revisions to the tax code. Employers are allowed a tax deduction for part or all of their donations to ESOPs. Sometimes ESOPs are used as the acquiring mechanism, via bank loans to the ESOP, to achieve management buyout of part or all of a company. ESOPs may borrow from banks and acquire additional shares in the company.

Minimum pension liability. In accounting terms, an obligation is recognized when the ABO of a pension plan is greater than the fair market value of plan assets. This difference must be shown on the balance sheet as a pension liability. American corporations utilized this loss to such an extent that in recent years, the FASB instituted a new rule for accounting for pensions, resulting in companies making millions/billions of "losses" on their balance sheets to show this obligation.

Pension funds. The money set aside by an employer to meet the obligations under the pension plan. A pension fund is administered by trustees who pay the retirement benefits.

401(k). An employee retirement plan that can be called a salary reduction plan. This plan allows employees to set aside up to a government- and company-specified percentage of their salary in a specific retirement investment account. The IRS does not count contributions to a 401(k) plan as income. Contributions and earnings accumulate tax-free until they are withdrawn. Early withdrawals (before age 59 1/2) are subject to full taxation plus a 10% withdrawal penalty. Companies sometimes match contributions. Some long-term care chains use 401(k) plans instead of a defined pension plan as a cost-saving device. A drawback to the 401(k) approach is that workers often cash in their 401(k) plan for present needs, especially when changing companies.

NAB DOMAIN 2B13: CONTRACTED SERVICES (E.G., ROLES, RESPONSIBILITIES, OVERSIGHT, BACKGROUND CHECKS); 4B4: BUSINESS DEVELOPMENT (E.G., SALES, MARKETING, PARTNERSHIPS, ACOs, CONTRACTS AND AGREEMENTS, NEGOTIATIONS)

Contract. An agreement between two or more persons creating legally enforceable rights and remedies. Contracts must have the following elements:

- Competent parties (of majority age and of sound mind). In the case of some nursing facility residents, the courts decide on their competence to enter into a contract.
- Consideration—something of value given in return for the performance of an act or the promise to perform an act. A commitment to refrain from an act, that is, giving up a legal right, may qualify as consideration.
- Mutuality of agreement—the parties must agree willingly. Often stated as a "meeting of the minds."
- Mutuality of obligation—all parties are bound to some reciprocal performance. A promise by one person to do something at the will of another person without any consideration (benefit) to the first person is not a contract.
- An oral contract is an enforceable agreement that is not in writing or signed by the parties. Oral contracts are enforceable but are subject to limitations. Various state statutes impose monetary limits on oral contracts for the purchase of goods, and almost every agreement dealing with real estate must be in writing to be enforceable.
- Typically, no punitive damages are available for breach of contract. A person or facility suing for breach of contract can recover only what would have been received had the contract been fulfilled. Generally, the nonbreaching party can recover money damages but cannot command the performance of actual work. Ordinarily, attorney's fees cannot be recovered by the successful party.

Contractor. One who agrees to do work for another and retains control over the means, method, and manner the work is done. Concerning building, a general contractor is one who contracts with the owner of a property to accomplish agreed-on construction. A subcontractor is one who deals only with the general contractor for the performance of some portion of the work to be performed by the general contractor.

Coordination and Oversight of Contracted Services

NAB DOMAIN 2B13: CONTRACTED SERVICES (E.G., ROLES, RESPONSIBILITIES, OVERSIGHT, BACKGROUND CHECKS); 4B4: BUSINESS DEVELOPMENT (E.G., SALES, MARKETING, PARTNERSHIPS, ACOs, CONTRACTS AND AGREEMENTS, NEGOTIATIONS)

Understanding and managing contracted services are key to managerial success for the nursing facility administrator. Nearly all services provided by nursing facilities can be—and often are—contracted out to others. Contracted services should be an area of special concern for the administrator. Persons working under contracts with the facility are not direct hires whom the administrator can direct and control.

Nevertheless, under the concept of *respondeat superior*, the facility's administration is as legally responsible for the acts of contractors as for acts of full-time employees. The administrator is responsible for their actions from a regulatory standpoint.

For these reasons, the administrator must pay special attention to the contracted services. Depending on corporate policies, local facilities may enter contracts, such as hospice, transportation, or maintenance services. The alternative is for the corporate office to execute contracts and give the local administrator a copy. The local administrator needs to read and understand the entire contract terms and conditions in either case. The administrator must know contract details to understand what is expected daily. When the inevitable dispute arises, lawyers focus on each word in the contract. So must the administrator.

If the local administrator initiates a contract, it is crucial to obtain the opinion of a person knowledgeable in the subject area before signing. Before signing a hospice contract, the administrator might want the nursing service and the business office to review the proposed terms. Many corporations may allow the administrator to sign a contract but only after it has been reviewed and approved by legal counsel.

Contracts can affect much of the daily life of a facility. Medical direction and pharmacy are normally contracted services. Often physical, occupational, and recreational therapy are contracted. Food service providers and dietitians are contractors; sometimes, the entire dietary department is a contracted service. It is prevalent for housekeeping and laundry to be contracted services. Contracts similarly may govern maintenance and pest control services.

In all these cases, it falls to the administrator to ensure that contracted services are coordinated and supervised on an ongoing basis.

Additionally, it is the administrator's responsibility to ensure that written agreements between the care recipient and service providers protect the rights and responsibilities of both parties. Residents' rights are carefully specified in the *federal regulations*. State regulations differ in many jurisdictions and need to be met.

Cost-Related Terms

Acceptable quality level (AQL). The actual percentage, specified by the administration, of goods in many incoming materials that a facility will allow to be defective and still accept the lot as "good." This method applies to such areas as dietary where large deliveries of items, such as baked goods or canned goods, are received.

Alternative work schedules. A method of increasing worker flexibility by offering several different job scheduling options. Job sharing by two or more employees is such an option. Nurses have for some years been offered plans such as the "Baylor Plan" under which a nurse may work long hours over an entire weekend and receive a regular "week's" pay (e.g., three 12-hour shifts for 40 hours of income).

Cost–benefit analysis. A method of determining whether the results of a particular proposed course of action are sufficient to justify the cost of the undertaking. If a facility wished to purchase a similar facility 50 miles away, a cost–benefit analysis would assist in deciding whether it should undertake the purchase.

Default. A failure to perform any act or obligation. A typical example is a default on mortgage payments due.

Deferred expense. An expense incurred in one accounting period that will benefit future accounting periods; also called a *deferred charge*. Prepaid insurance, as mentioned previously, is a good example.

Economic order quantity (EOQ). A method of determining the optimum amount of materials to be ordered regularly. The costs of possession (storing, pilferage, becoming too old to use) are compared with the cost of acquisition.

Just-in-time (JIT). An approach to dealing with materials inventories that emphasizes the elimination of all waste and the continual improvement of the production process. Toyota Motor Company developed this concept in Japan to ensure that materials are replenished precisely when needed and not before or after. JIT is so widespread that traditional materials and supplies inventory are sometimes referred to as "just in case." In the nursing facility, however, nursing supplies for wound care, IVs, oxygen tanks, and the like are of critical importance with availability when needed.

Marginal cost. The increase or decrease in the TCs that results from the output of one more unit or one less unit; also called the *incremental cost*. For example, a nursing facility adding one more bed might trigger a state requirement for an additional RN, dramatically increasing the marginal cost of adding that one more bed to a wing.

Materials requirements planning. A system of materials or supplies management designed to reduce or eliminate the need for excessive inventories of supplies by analyzing product needs and lead times.

Methods–time measurement (MTM). A system for measuring individual motions called micromotions, such as reach, grab, and position. One process of changing a resident's bed may take significantly less time than a second method, for example. Or designing a facility to have no bed further than "x" feet from a nursing station might reduce care time.

Price controls. The use of government powers to keep the price either above or below its equilibrium point. When the government tries to keep what is paid for a product above the equilibrium, it establishes a "price floor," such as the price paid for a bushel of wheat being set to ensure that farmers continue to raise wheat. In the nursing facility situation, however, the government has sought to keep the price of a product below its equilibrium level, that is, a "price ceiling." The government establishes a price ceiling by Medicare paying only the lesser charge between usual and customary care or the actual healthcare charges. This payment method normally results in cost-shifting from Medicare or Medicaid residents' costs to charges made to private-pay residents.

Queue time. The time a job or activity must wait before a particular facility is available. The amount of time it takes housekeeping and nursing to "turn a room" to make it available for the next resident to move into it is a queue time that affects a facility's occupancy rate.

Financing: Forms and Terms

Arm's-length transaction. A business transaction at market-established prices between two unrelated parties. For example, a chain establishes and operates its own pharmacy to provide drugs to its facilities. To be reimbursable as an arm's-length transaction, that chain must sell drugs to other nursing facility chains and disinterested other purchasers at the same price it "sells" drugs to itself.

Commercial paper. Short-term securities (2–270 days) issued by corporations, banks, and other borrowing institutions to raise short-term working capital. Investors buy commercial paper as a very short-term investment. Commercial paper is unsecured debt that can be sold at a discount or bear interest.

Disclosure. A necessary explanation of a company's financial position and operating results. Impending lawsuits and other liabilities must be part of the disclosure.

Federal Trade Commission Act of 1914. The Act establishing the Federal Trade Commission (FTC) and giving it responsibility for promoting free and fair competition in interstate commerce in the interest of the public through the prevention of price-fixing agreements, boycotts, combinations in restraint of trade, unfair acts of competition, and unfair and deceptive acts and practices.

Letter of credit. A bank instrument stating that a bank has granted the holder the amount of credit equal to the face amount of the letter of credit (L/C). This transfers collection risk from the seller to the bank. A "standby L/C" cannot be drawn on unless the payee fails to perform or pay as agreed in the contract.

Leverage. In accounting and finance, the amount of long-term debt a company has in relation to its equity.

Leveraged buyout (LBO). Purchase of a controlling interest in a company using debt collateralized by the target company's assets to fund most or all of the purchase price. This technique has allowed small nursing facility chains to purchase much larger nursing facility chains.

Leveraging. The advantage gained by using debt financing to create asset appreciation. This method is used by most purchasers or builders of nursing facilities, which cost upward of $12 million for a 120-bed facility in today's market. Someone buying a condominium with a small down payment and a large mortgage is leveraging, as are persons buying a nursing facility or facilities with a small amount of cash and a large loan.

Securities and Exchange Commission (SEC). The federal agency responsible for regulating financial reporting. The SEC monitors accounting principles, trading activities, and auditing practices of publicly held companies.

Bonds. A debt obligation of a facility or corporation, or other body to pay a specific amount on a stated date. Facilities usually issue bonds to raise capital for building or renovation projects. Not-for-profit facilities may often be allowed to issue tax-free bonds. Issuing bonds usually involves the creation of a very detailed and expensive prospectus conforming with SEC information and disclosure requirements. Junk bonds are debt securities rated below investment grade by credit-rating agencies. *Long bonds* are 30-year U.S. Treasury bonds or other bonds that mature beyond 10 years. Interest charges used to measure the market in corporate bonds are reflected in basis points: 100 basis points equal 1% point of interest.

Capital. The amount on the balance sheet representing ownership in a business also called *equity* or *net worth*. It also refers to available funds or cash, as in working capital, financing, or "raising capital."

Capital asset. An asset purchased for use rather than resale, including land, buildings, equipment, goodwill, and trademarks.

Capitalize. To classify an expense as an asset because it benefits the facility for more than 1 year.

Capital market theory. A set of complex mathematical formulas that strive to identify how investors should choose common stocks for their portfolios under a given set of assumptions.

Cost of capital. The rate of return available in the marketplace on investments comparable in terms of risk and other characteristics such as liquidity and other qualitative factors.

- **Additional paid-in capital.** An accounting concept of the excess amount over par value that shareholders pay for a company's stock usually treated as a donation.

- **Borrowing base.** The facility assets used as collateral to secure short-term working capital loans from banks and other lenders.

- **Recapitalization.** The revision to a company's capital structure. May involve exchanging debt obligations for equity interests or exchanging one type of debt for another. Some reasons to recapitalize are to reduce debt service allowing additional borrowing, to clean up a balance sheet before a sale or merger, or to increase tax deductions (by for-profit facilities) by substituting interest payments for dividends.

Leases

- **Capital lease.** A lease in which the lessee acquires substantial property rights.

- **Finance lease.** A long-term rental commitment by both lessor and lessee that usually runs for the entire useful life of the asset. Usually, the total of the payments approximates the purchase price plus finance charges. Most leases are net leases, under which the lessee is responsible for maintaining the property, taxes, insurance, and the like. In the nursing home industry, most leases are net, net-net, or triple-net leases. The lessor's role is strictly that of a financier whose responsibility extends solely to finance the facility, assuming no liability from the operating of the facility.

- **Leasehold improvement.** Any refurbishment made to the leased property, for example, painting, reroofing, and redoing the interior. Leasehold improvements (if a for-profit facility) must be amortized over the life of the improvement.

- **Sale/leaseback.** A transaction where a facility sells some or all of its hard assets to a leasing company for cash and then enters a lease for that property. This contract allows for raising immediate capital while retaining control over the assets. A cash-poor small chain might, for example, use this mechanism to obtain money to purchase additional facilities.

Mortgage. A borrowed amount of money to purchase a specific property by promising to repay the debt on a scheduled basis. The interest rate on most mortgages is set based on the prime rate, the interest rate established by money center banks as a measuring base against which to calculate customer interest charges. Banks define the prime rate as the rate of interest charged to their best commercial customers.

Note. Borrowing of money for a purpose agreed on between a lender and a borrower. A *demand note* is a promissory note with no set maturity date; the holder may require payment at any time. Notes spell out the principal amount of the loan and the interest rate and may identify a final date for liquidation of the note. Promissory notes with a term of 5 to 6 years are regarded as medium-term notes.

Stocks

Stock companies own the majority of nursing facilities in the United States. How well the company's stock is doing may directly impact the availability of funds for next year's budget.

Arbitrage. The process of simultaneously buying a stock, currency, or commodity on one market and selling it in another. The price difference between the two markets gives the arbitrageur their profit.

Blue-chip. Common stock with a long history of dividend payments and earnings.

Book value per share. The assets of a company available to common shareholders; that is, what each share is worth based on the historical stockholders' equity costs maintained in a company's accounting books.

Capital stock. The shares representing ownership of a company.

Common stock. Certificates that represent ownership in a corporation. A variety of types of stock exist and are used by most nursing facility chains, such as common stock and preferred stock.

Common stock equivalent. A security that is not currently in common stock form but can be converted to common stock. Executives, for example, are often given stock options, that is, the right to purchase stock at a stated price over a specific time, as a benefit.

Convertible security. Stocks and bonds that can be converted into capital stock at a future date.

Debenture. An unsecured bond, generally in a subordinated position. Debentures often have convertible features or warrants attached that permit the holders to exchange their debenture or the warrants for common stock on a stated date or when specified events occur.

Garnishment. A legal process through which a plaintiff can obtain goods or money belonging to a defendant, held by a third party, that are due or will become due to the plaintiff. Garnishment is similar to attachment.

A person who receives notice to retain assets belonging to a defendant is the garnishee. Thus, the nursing facility may be the garnishee when a court directs the nursing facility to pay over a portion of an employee's salary to a plaintiff to repay a portion of an employee's debt.

Grandfather clause. Provision whereby persons already engaged in a business or profession receive a license or entitlement without meeting all the conditions new entrants would have to meet.

Option. A right that is granted in exchange for an agreed-on sum to buy or sell property; for example, a set amount of stock during some specified period.

Penny stocks. Stocks of young public companies that are not listed on any stock exchange and typically sell at a low price ranging from pennies to $10 per share.

Preferred stock. A type of capital stock giving its holder preference over common stock in the distribution of earnings or rights to the company's assets.

Price/earnings (P/E) ratio. A measure of the company's investment potential; literally, how much a share is worth per dollar of earnings:

$$\frac{\text{Market price per common share}}{\text{Primary earnings per common share}}$$

Reverse split. A procedure whereby a company "buys back" a portion of its outstanding stock. One major nursing facility chain, in the mid-1990s, reduced the number of outstanding shares dramatically by giving one new share for every four old shares held, thereby increasing the value of each remaining share.

Stock dividend. A dividend consisting of stock rather than cash paid to shareholders.

Stock exchanges. There are three major U.S. stock exchanges: the New York Stock Exchange (NYSE), the National Association of Securities Dealers Automated Quotation (NASDAQ) system, and the American Stock Exchange (ASE). The minimum listing requirements for the NYSE are (a) publicly held shares of $1 million, (b) market value of $16 million for those shares, (c) annual pretax net income of $2.5 million, (d) at least 2,000 shareholders, and (e) net assets of $18 million. In addition, the company listed must engage a registrar and a transfer agent in New York City.

The ASE requires (a) 300,000 publicly held shares, (b) market value of $2.5 million for those shares, (c) annual pretax net income of $750,000, (d) 900 shareholders of which 600 must own 100 shares or more, and (e) net assets of $4 million.

The minimum listing requirements for the NASDAQ are (a) 100,000 publicly held shares, (b) minimum of 300 shareholders, (c) net assets of $2 million, (d) net worth of $1 million, (e) two or more market makers, and (f) annual fee of $2,500 or $.0005 per share.

These stock listing requirements are provided because most nursing facility chains strive to move up the ladder to the NYSE. It is not uncommon for nursing facility chains to be initially on the ASE but to work diligently to become listed on the NYSE, which affords them more status and net-worth growth potential.

Treasury stock. Shares of common stock that have been issued to the general public but are repurchased by the issuing company. A nursing facility chain might choose to repurchase some of its stock to increase the value of its remaining shares.

Income-Related Terms

Consider as the Administrator . . .

- *A company's reported income may not be a reliable yardstick as to how that company is doing. Why?*

Annual percentage rate (APR). A measure of the actual cost of credit. APR yields the ratio of the finance charge to the average amount of credit used during a loan term or when money is owed to the facility in accounts receivable. The facility uses this rate to charge interest after a specified due date.

Cash cow. A facility or product that generates cash. The Boston Consulting Group coined this term as an element of its growth/market share matrix. For instance, the outpatient physical therapy department may be a cash cow for the facility if a large volume of private-pay patients uses the facility.

Cash equivalent. Any asset, such as a bond or stock, held as an investment that can easily and quickly be converted to cash.

Cash flow. The cash receipts less the cash disbursements from a given operation or set of operations for a specific period. If a facility has $300,000 cash income from accounts receivable for a month and operating costs of $275,000, there is a $25,000 cash flow for that month.

Contribution margin. The amount by which sales exceed the variable of a service's costs, such as supplies and labor. The resulting money left over is available to cover fixed costs, such as mortgages, insurance, and the like. A contribution margin can be calculated for each income-producing area of the facility.

Lien. A claim on the property of another person(s) as security for a debt owed. A lien does not give any title (ownership) to the property; instead, it is a right of the person holding the lien to have a debt satisfied out of the property to which the lien applies. Suppose a general contractor building a nursing facility is not paid under the terms of the contract. In that case, they may seek to have a lien placed on the facility until the indebtedness is satisfied. Similarly, if not paid within a specified period, regular creditors of the nursing facility might seek to have a lien placed against the facility.

Perceived value pricing. A pricing approach based on the buyer's perception of value rather than the seller's cost. A facility with a strong reputation for quality care may choose to price daily room rates higher than the prevailing market rate in its community.

Profit margin. The ratio of income to sales. There are two types of profit margin: gross profit margin and net profit margin. The gross profit margin shows the percentage return that the facility is earning over the cost of providing services. It is calculated as:

$$\frac{\text{Gross profit}}{\text{Sales}}$$

Net profit margin (also known as return on services rendered) shows the percentage of net income generated by each service billed dollar in for-profit facilities. It is:

$$\frac{\text{Net income after tax}}{\text{Sales}}$$

Rate of return. The annual percentage of income earned on an investment. There are numerous ways to calculate the rate of return. These are variously termed ROI, ROE, return on total assets, or return on sales. The rate of return on fixed-income securities is usually calculated as the current yield, which is the annual interest or dividend payments divided by the price of the security. For example, a bond may have been purchased below the face value and then provides an additional payout at maturity to match the total face value. That extra payment is the *yield to maturity* rate of return.

Ownership: Types and Forms

NAB DOMAIN 4A5: GOVERNANCE (E.G., BOARD OF DIRECTORS, GOVERNING BODIES, CORPORATE ENTITIES, ADVISORY BOARDS)

Articles of incorporation. The instrument that creates a corporation under the laws of a state.

Business combination. The process of associating two or more different companies. There are three forms of business combination: statutory merger, statutory consolidation, and acquisition. A statutory merger occurs when two separate companies combine so that one of the companies will no longer exist: $X + Y = X$. A statutory consolidation happens when two or more companies combine to form a new company: $X + Y = Z$. An acquisition occurs when two separate companies combine so that both keep their individual identities: $X + Y = X + Y$.

Core competence. The capabilities of a company separating it from competitors and serve as the basis for growth or diversification into new lines of business. For example, a nursing facility chain may be particularly successful in attracting and maintaining a large share of the private-pay patient market in the communities it serves, possibly being that company's core competence.

Corporation. An association of shareholder(s) (even one shareholder) created by statute and treated by the law as a "person." In effect, it is an artificial person with a legal existence entirely separate from the individuals who compose it. A corporation may have perpetual existence; buy, own, and dispose of property; sue and be sued; and exercise any other powers conferred on it by statute.

Typically, a stockholder's liability is limited to the corporation's assets; thus, stockholders avoid personal liability for their corporation's acts. Corporations are taxed at special rates, but stockholders usually pay an additional tax on any profits received from the corporation (dividends).

A small corporation earning a modest profit may elect to be taxed as a partnership. Stockholders, in this case, avoid personal liability for the acts of the corporation and avoid double taxation. A corporation choosing to pay federal taxes as a partnership is called an "S" corporation. For tax purposes, all income and losses of a corporation pass through to its shareholders.

To qualify for S status, a corporation and its shareholders must meet the following criteria: (a) be a domestic corporation and not part of an affiliated group of corporations; (b) not own 80% or more of the stock of another corporation; (c) not have more than 35 shareholders; (d) have no nonresident aliens as shareholders; (e) shareholders must be individuals, estates, or some trusts, not corporations or partnerships; and (f) issue only one class of stock. Voting and nonvoting shares of stock are permitted.

Each state enacts independent corporation laws. Some states, such as Delaware, give the officers and board of directors more freedom from minority shareholder controls, thereby attracting more groups to incorporate under their state's laws.

De facto corporations are those that exist in fact (de facto) without actual authorization by the law. Three conditions must be met: (a) a statute exists under which it could be incorporated, (b) it behaves in such a way as to appear to be functioning as a corporation, and (c) it assumes some corporate privileges.

Public corporations are created by authorization of the federal government and the states to accomplish specific purposes. They include towns, counties, water and sewage districts, and radio and television stations. The U.S. Postal Service and the Corporation for Public Broadcasting are two such entities.

Private corporations are corporations created by private individuals for non-governmental purposes.

Professional corporations are professional associations of one or more professionals, for example, physicians, dentists, physical therapists, nurses, who form themselves into a corporation.

Courts may choose to ignore the protection provided to stockholders from personal liability, typically when it can be shown that the purported corporation is found to be the "alter ego" of a principal (person). Suppose a purported corporation does not hold stockholder meetings or generally ignores the duties and activities associated with operating a corporation, neglecting corporate formalities. In that case, the courts may disregard the stockholders' usual immunity from personal liability and assign personal liability to the stockholders for acts of the corporation. If the incorporation itself was undertaken to defraud, the courts might hold the stockholders and officers personally liable for acts of the corporation.

Decentralization. The diffusion of authority, responsibility, and decision-making power throughout different levels of a company. Some nursing facility chains have regionalized the country, and each region has its own decision-making ability while being overseen by the corporate headquarters.

Horizontal integration. A growth strategy in which a company buys a competitor at the same level of services. We see this when nursing facility chains begin to buy up competitors, thus increasing the industry's horizontal integration.

Joint venture. A legal form of business organization between previously separate companies where there is a cooperation between entities toward achieving common goals. A *contractual joint venture* is a joint venture not created as a separate legal corporate entity. It is an unincorporated association set up to attain specific objectives over a specified period. An *equity joint venture* has two or more partners based on forming a legal corporation with limited liability and the joint management of it by the partners. Profits and losses are shared based on their equity in the joint venture. There are, in addition, *hybrid joint ventures* that take a variety of forms.

Limited liability company or limited liability corporation. Limited liability companies or corporations provide the flexibility of a partnership with the same kind of financial protection offered by a C corporate structure. Wyoming passed the first state law allowing this form, and many other states have followed suit. The IRS has ruled that it will treat limited liability companies as partnerships for tax purposes. The limited liability company provides liability protection for its owners like a corporation but allows the limited liability corporation or company to be taxed as a partnership.

Limited liability partnership. A new form of partnership used by professional groups such as physicians, nurses, and physical therapists to limit a partner's liability to the partnership's general contractual debts, the partner's individual malpractice, and the wrongful acts of persons acting under the partners' direct supervision. Unlike the standard partnership, there is no individual liability for the malpractice of the other partners. Many states have adopted this business formation. In some states, protection extends even to the partnership's contractual debts exceeding the partner's interest value.

Merger. A combination of two or more companies. The combination may be accomplished by exchanging stock, forming a new company to acquire the assets of the combining companies, or purchasing a company outright.

Minority interest. An ownership interest of less than 50%. In consolidated financial statements, minority interests are shown as a line item in the noncurrent liability section of the balance sheet.

Partnership. A contract between two or more persons to pool resources and efforts for the purposes of conducting a business operation. Usually, partnership status requires an agreement to divide profits and assume indebtedness in some proportionate share. Unlike stockholders in a corporation, the partners do not have limited liability unless it is a limited partnership—an entity in which one or more persons are designated general partners (who assume unlimited personal liability for the acts of the partnership). One or more persons are designated limited partners (whose liability is limited to their investment). Limited partners do not share in the management of the partnership.

Privately held company. A company whose ownership shares—unlike publicly held companies—are not publicly traded. A privately held company may choose one of many forms, including corporations, partnerships, proprietorships, limited partnerships, joint ventures, and limited liability corporations. The same accounting principles apply to privately held companies as to publicly held companies. However, reporting requirements of regulatory agencies such as the SEC and public stock exchanges do not apply to them. Hence, in most reports on nursing facility chains and ownership, privately held companies' financial statements are usually not shown because they choose not to make them available to the public at large. Privately held companies do make their financial statements available to lenders, private investors, and, as required, some state agencies.

Sole proprietorship. Ownership of a business by one individual. Before incorporation became popular among physicians, most of them were the sole proprietors of their office practices.

Vertical integration. Expansion by moving forward or backward within an industry. For example, nursing facility chains frequently integrate backward by owning and operating their pharmacies or therapy companies. Some chains are integrating forward by owning and operating home health agencies.

3.10.6 INSURANCE TERMS

NAB DOMAIN 2A5: REVENUE AND REIMBURSEMENT (E.G., PDPM, PDGM, ACOs, HMOs, MEDICAID, PRIVATE PAYORS); 2B10: INSURANCE COVERAGE (E.G., LIABILITY, PROPERTY)

Actuary. A person who computes insurance costs, usually to determine rates to be charged—a crucial function for the continuing care retirement communities that take lifetime responsibility for their residents.

Annuity. A fixed amount of money payable periodically by an insurer under the terms of an insurance contract. Normally, the annuitant (the person receiving the payments) has no rights other than entitlement to payments for a fixed period. Often, nursing facility residents have insurance annuities that can be applied to their costs of care.

Beneficiary. The person named in an insurance policy to receive the proceeds or benefits under the policy.

Binder. A contract for temporary insurance until a permanent policy can be issued.

Coinsurance. A division of responsibility for losses or risks between the insurer and the insured. The insured individual might agree to pay, for example, the first $50 of any claim.

Life insurance. Insurance that may be one of several types. Whole life insurance policies can build cash value (i.e., the insured can turn in cash) and usually pay dividends (i.e., interest on the cash value). Term insurance, in contrast, has no cash value; hence, no dividends. When term insurance expires, no value is left. Whole life insurance costs more than term insurance. Today, an almost infinite variety of policies are offered as variations on these two basic forms of life insurance.

Types of Insurance

- Fidelity or bond coverage of key employees
- Pharmacy
- Vehicle and driver
- Workers' compensation
- Property damage—coverage against fire, flood, earthquake damage to buildings, furniture, fixtures, building contents
- Furnace and machinery
- Business interruption
- Accounts receivable—protection against loss of income from the destruction of financial records
- Comprehensive general liability or casualty against losses sustained by residents, visitors, others resulting from negligence not related to the rendering of professional services
- Directors' and officers' coverage for acts done in their official capacities
- Malpractice or professional liability coverage protecting against losses sustained by others, resulting from negligence related to the rendering of professional services

3.10.7 TERMS ASSOCIATED WITH ADVANCE DIRECTIVES, WILLS, AND ESTATES

NAB DOMAIN 1B7: CARE RECIPIENT DECISION-MAKING (E.G., CAPACITY, POWER OF ATTORNEY, GUARDIANSHIP, CONSERVATORSHIP, CODE STATUS, ADVANCE DIRECTIVES, ETHICAL DECISION-MAKING)

Advance directives are increasingly important for nursing facility residents. Each state regulates the legal status and processes associated with advance directives. It is essential that on admission, each resident set up an advance directive regarding such matters as end-of-life care and whether to be a code (send the resident to the hospital when it is needed) or a no-code (give only palliative care). An advance directive must clearly state who has control over care under varying circumstances and how the resident views the directive, for example, whether a no-code means do not send me to the emergency department or hospital for my primary diagnosis (i.e., emphysema), but do send me for other events or some other version of the care desired. Approximately 65% of nursing facility residents have advance directives on file (Jones et al., 2011). The resident has a right to participate in determining their code status. Furthermore, the competent resident has a right to change their code status any time at will, verbally.

Administrator. A person appointed to transfer the property of one who dies *intestate* to those who succeed in ownership. To die intestate is to die without leaving a will. The estate (or property) of persons who die testate (with a will) is administered by an *executor* of the estate, usually named in the will.

Codicil. *See* Will.

Competence. The capability of a person to make a will. A person is judged capable or competent if they understand the nature and extent of their property, the identity of the property owned, and the consequences of the act of making a will.

Decedent. The person who has died.

Estate. A term that originally referred to land ownership but now refers broadly to all real and personal property a person owns or leaves at death.

Incompetence. Inability to function within limits judged normal by a court of law. If a person is found to be incompetent, a guardian must be appointed. The guardian must handle the incompetent person's affairs until the court determines that competency has returned, in which case the guardian is discharged.

Probate. The process of proving that an instrument presented as a will is the valid and duly executed will of the deceased person. Some states have special courts, called probate courts, to conduct these procedures.

Will. A person's declaration about how they wish their real and personal property to be disposed of after death. A will may call for actions desired by the decedent (testator) but must dispose of some property, real or personal, to be valid. Originally "will" referred to real estate and "testament" to personal property. "Last will and testament" refers to the most recent valid will left by the decedent.

A holographic will. An entirely handwritten will. In some states, a will may be handwritten and need not be witnessed to be valid. A *codicil* is a supplement or amendment to a will. *Codicil* literally means "to say along with." A codicil must meet the same formal requirements as the will.

Living will. Some nursing facility residents make a "living will," which governs the type(s) of treatment to be given the resident in the event the resident becomes comatose or in a similar condition. Several states have passed laws establishing living wills as valid legal instruments. A living will has nothing to do with the disposition of property.

WHAT WOULD YOU DO?

You are the administrator of Golden Arms Care Home. You recently became the administrator a few weeks ago. You are approached by a resident who asks you when they are going to get their $45 from their Social Security check (referring to what is left for a Medicaid patient after they pay their resident responsibility). You state that they should be getting this at the beginning of the month after all Social Security checks are received and deposited. The resident tells you that they have not gotten that money in 8 months, "since that new business office manager started." You tell them that you will look into it.

You then go to the business office manager and ask to see the reconciliations and statements for the resident trust fund for the facility. The business office manager is very questioning of your intentions and why you need to see this information, as those books are theirs. You inform the business office manager that all books are open ones, especially the ones that you are directly responsible for, and that the resident trust fund is one of those accounts. The business office manager tells you that they will need time to reconcile these books and that you need to give them a week or so to get all this information in order for your review. You rightly refuse this after their sketchy behavior and request that they produce them immediately in whatever form they currently exist. The business office manager refuses your request and yells for you to get out of their office.

What do you do next?

As you are new to the facility, you call your regional director and tell them of the situation and that your business office manager has not only refused to show you the resident trust fund ledgers but they have thrown you out of their office as well. You request that the regional director send down corporate support to investigate this resident complaint. Your regional director agrees. You also tell your director that you believe that this has moved to a concern of misappropriation of property at this time and that you would like to suspend the business office manager pending investigation. It is agreed on.

You then go and get your director of nursing to witness the event. You discuss the situation with your business office manager, tell them that there is a formal complaint regarding them and that despite your previous efforts to investigate this their lack of cooperation has required you to move this situation to not only corporate but also to a state reportable event. The business office manager explodes in a fountain of emotion and begins to yell at you for singling them out. You redirect them and

(continued)

state that the same would go for any employee who has a formal complaint against them. You will investigate and inform them of the investigation. They continue to be emotional, grab their keys, and begin to collect records and ledgers, throwing it all into a box to take home with them.

1. What would you do from here?
2. Can the business office manager take things with them?
3. Is it in your rights to physically lock your manager out of their office?
4. Can you request their keys and corporate belongings?
5. Should you disable their computer logins?
6. Are you within your rights to call the police should they not cooperate?

WHAT WOULD YOU DO?

As the administrator, you are very diligent in processing your accounts payable. The invoices come to your desk, you personally process them, and you ensure that the corporate entity pays them. You began as the administrator at Falling Leaves Nursing about 3 months ago. Your food vendor calls you up from their accounts receivable department wanting to know when you were going to bring your account up to date. You tell them that you have processed each and every invoice they have sent to you and that they have been paid in 15-day terms or less. You offer to provide them a tally of invoices, payments, and check numbers. They agree and you send over the information. You go on about your business for another month. Your account representative calls you up telling you that they are about to cut off your account due to outstanding invoices. You tell them the same story you did their accounts receivable department and supply them with proof of your excellent work. Another month goes by and your rep calls you up again requesting a meeting between you, them, and their corporate compliance officer. You agree to the meeting.

At this meeting, you are handed 6 months' worth of unpaid invoices. They are requesting payment, but begin asking you if you serve prime rib, prawns, lobsters, crown roasts, and other expensive items at your facility. You state that you do not; you use their menu plan. You and they look at the invoices and notice that each of the invoices was produced at "will call" at their facility and are signed by your dietary manager. They inform you that the entire stack of these are all will-call invoices and that they are not processed as normal invoices, as will call is used for emergencies in usual circumstances when someone forgets to order something that they need immediately. You thank them for their time and inform them that you will further investigate this situation and see where it leads you.

You scan all the invoices in and send them to your regional director. There is nearly $60,000 of unpaid invoices over the last 6 months. You and your director discuss the situation, and your director asks you if you knew that the dietary manager had a catering business on the side or not.

(continued)

1. What would you do from here?
2. Can you assume that the dietary manager was stealing food from the kitchen, as the consumables are nothing that your facility would order or use?
3. Is this activity illegal?
4. Was it wrong of you to find your dietary manager's Facebook page and print off their menus from their catered events, noting that their offerings matched exactly the invoices and dates?
5. Is termination your only remedy here?
6. Do you pay the invoices?

REFERENCES

Berger, S. (2014). *Fundamentals of health care financial management* (4th ed.). Jossey-Bass.

Brigham, E. F., & Houston, J. F. (2019). *Fundamentals of financial management* (15th ed.). Thompson Higher Education.

Centers for Medicare & Medicaid Services. (2017). *State operations manual. Appendix PP: Guidance to surveyors for long-term care facilities (Rev. 173, 11-22-17).* https://www.cms.gov/Regulations-and-Guidance/Guidance/Manuals/downloads/som107ap_pp_guidelines_ltcf.pdf

Chies, S. (2021). *Pratt's long-term care: Managing across the continuum* (5th ed.). Jones & Bartlett.

Cole, G. A., & Kelley, P. (2020). *Management theory and practice* (9th ed.). Cengage Learning.

Harrington, C. H., Carillo, H., Garfield, R., Musumeci, M., Squires, E., & Kaiser Family Foundation. (2018). *Nursing facilities, staffing, residents, and facility deficiencies, 2009 through 2016.* Kaiser Family Foundation.

Jones, A., Moss, A., & Harris-Kojetin, L. (2011). Use of advanced directives in long-term care populations. *National Center for Health Statistics.* https://www.cdc.gov/nchs/products/databriefs/db54.htm

Singh, D. A. (2016). *Effective management of long-term care facilities* (3rd ed.). Jones & Bartlett.

Zelman, W. N., McCue, M. J., Glick, N. D., & Thomas, M. S. (2020). *Financial management of health care organizations: An introduction to fundamental tools, concepts, and applications* (5th ed.). Jossey-Bass.

PART 4

Learning the Continuum of Long-Term Care

What You Will Learn in Part 4

In this section, you will learn how the following shape the nursing facility context:

- *Origins of the current nursing facility industry*
- *The Social Security Act*
- *Overview of the nursing facility industry*
- *Overview of the long-term care continuum*
- *The Older Americans Act*
- *Roles of Medicare and Medicaid*
- *An overview of labor and management*
- *Workplace safety*
- *Fire safety and the Life Safety Code*
- *The Americans with Disabilities Act (ADA) and accessibility guidelines*
- *The Affordable Care Act*
- *Patient Driven Payment Model (PDPM)*
- *Value-based care*
- *Pay for performance (P4P)*

Consider as the Administrator . . .

- *To what extent is the nursing facility population dictated by the system players like hospitals, home healthcare, Medicare, and Medicaid?*

4.1 ORIGINS, OVERVIEW, AND CURRENT PROFILE OF THE NURSING FACILITY INDUSTRY

Section Concepts

- *Understanding the history of the industry helps to make sense of current-day changes and regulations*

Consider as the Administrator . . .

- How much of this history do you believe governs what we do in the facility today? Are we paying the price for past sins? Are we just endeavoring to do things better?

NAB DOMAIN 3A3: SAFETY AND ACCESSIBILITY (E.G., ADA, SAFETY DATA SHEETS); 3B1: FEDERAL HEALTHCARE LAWS, RULES, AND REGULATIONS; 3B2: GOVERNMENT PROGRAMS AND ENTITIES (E.G., MEDICARE, MEDICAID, WAIVERS); 3B3: CERTIFICATION AND LICENSURE REQUIREMENTS FOR THE ORGANIZATION

The care given in the nursing facility takes place as part of the continuum of long-term care and the broader healthcare system.

The purpose of this chapter is to provide background on the nursing facility industry and information on several of the laws of which the administrator must be aware while operating a facility. The nursing facility is part of a continuum of caregiving. Information about other providers in the healthcare field is found here. The everyday life of the facility takes place within the rules set by Medicare and Medicaid, labor laws, occupational safety laws, the Life Safety Code, and the Americans with Disabilities Act (ADA) Accessibility Guidelines for facilities

4.1.1 ORIGINS: LONG-TERM CARE—A 400-PLUS-YEAR TRADITION

NAB DOMAIN 1: CARE, SERVICES, AND SUPPORTS

Long-term care administration is not a new phenomenon. As is sometimes perceived, it did not suddenly spring into existence after the passage of Titles 18 and 19 amending the Social Security Act more than 50 years ago.

Every nation has its tradition of providing care for the aged, chronically ill, and disabled that reflects the demands of the culture. Like other American institutions, the U.S. healthcare system was modeled on the English system, just as our legal system has its foundation in English common law.

EARLY NURSING FACILITY ADMINISTRATION

Throughout most of English and American history, until about 1850, little distinction was made between the long-term care facility and the hospital. Long-term care facilities in England were called hospitals. The functions of these facilities were similar to what is now considered those of a nursing facility. From the 12th through the 15th centuries, nearly 700 shelters for the aged, the destitute, and pilgrims were built in England. These institutions housed populations similar to those deemed long-term (or custodial) residents in today's nursing facilities: the aged, those without means of support in their own homes, and the disabled.

State Medicaid officials are concerned about the inappropriate or unnecessary placement of persons in nursing facilities. Appropriate placement is a concern today, as it was throughout history. Before 1453, all these facilities were associated with monasteries. They were administered by individuals appointed jointly by the king and the local bishop. Did administrators receive training for their jobs in those days? Probably so, in an apprenticeship system not unlike our administrator-in-training programs of today.

In 1536, King Henry VIII closed all the monasteries and their healthcare facilities simultaneously in a dispute with the Catholic Church. One of the most famous, St. Bartholomew's "hospital" (St. Bart's as it was called) in London, had been operating since 1123 CE. However, there are no records that St. Bart's had any medical staff during those first 400 years. Pressures to provide care for the poor forced the king to allow St. Bart's to be reopened 10 years later (1546). The king removed responsibility for management from the bishops and appointed local citizens to direct such facilities throughout England. In this process of removing healthcare from the Church's charge, the king appointed what is believed to be the first recorded board of citizen directors of a public hospital, consisting of 30 leading citizens. This board decided that the reopened St. Bart's could accommodate 400 aged and 650 "decayed" householders, 200 idle vagabonds, 350 poor men overburdened with children (no mention of women), and 20 sore and sick persons.

In sum, the board viewed the "hospital" as providing 99% long-term care and 1% acute care. The shift from chronic to acute care slowly evolved over the next 400 years.

During those years, physicians had little or no contact with what were being called hospitals. Medical care, such as it was, was provided on a solo practitioner basis to those who could afford to pay. In essence, physicians primarily served the upper classes in the patients' homes or their private clinics. Today, most nursing facility patients are recipients of Medicaid assistance. They are aged, chronically ill, and poor, and they have lost the ability to earn an income to support themselves or did not save enough during their lifetimes to sustain themselves in old age. We see those who are more financially stable remaining in their homes or moving to a continuing care retirement community (CCRC) or assisted living–type arrangement.

Nursing facilities, like the hospitals, gained the ability to "cure" or offer effective restorative care to patients in the same way as hospitals did during the late 19th and early 20th centuries.

HOME HEALTHCARE VERSUS INSTITUTIONAL CARE: A 400-YEAR-OLD DEBATE

For the average person in most societies, living to be very old or suffering from a chronic illness is to be without a steady income eventually. These conditions are becoming ever more closely linked. It is as much an economic condition as one of health.

An issue hotly debated in the U.S. Congress and the state legislatures regards the efficacy of nursing facilities versus home healthcare. Which is better? Which is less expensive for the state? Is healthcare provided to older and chronically ill persons in their own homes better and less costly? Or is it more frugal and at least as desirable to institutionalize them in a long-term care facility and pay for their care where economies of scale prevail?

This controversy has its roots in the Elizabethan Poor Law of 1601. The first Queen Elizabeth required each local community to care for its poor by providing cash and in-kind help to remain in their own homes. In the century that followed, the primary mode of assistance to older adults, the chronically ill, and the disabled was a program to allow them to stay in their own homes as long as possible.

Our present-day state legislatures and Congress are now concerned that the onslaught of baby boomers could bankrupt federally funded programs and state treasuries. When faced with the same issue early in the 18th century, the English government and our colonial predecessors decided to provide public welfare and health assistance only in institutional settings. In 1722, England enacted a new Poor Law that established almshouses, or workhouses. It was hoped that the aged, chronically ill, and disabled and other persons receiving assistance could be cared for less expensively. This system was emulated in Philadelphia (1722), New York City (1734), and Charleston, South Carolina (1735).

1830 TO 1930: NURSING FACILITY CARE IS OUT—HOME HEALTHCARE IS IN

During the early 19th century, the pendulum swung back toward providing in-home assistance to the aged, chronically ill, and the poor. In England, this was known as the Speenhamland System, in which a minimum annual income was guaranteed to everyone. But this program was expensive, and the potential to be abused by persons who are not genuinely needy existed. As a result, the pendulum swung back toward a requirement that individuals who needed assistance move into institutional settings. It was believed that institutionalization was less expensive and less subject to abuses of the system.

Between 1830 and 1930, when America was a land of great economic opportunity for all, the predominant mood was to insist that aid to the aged, chronically ill, and disabled be available only in what were called public workhouses. These institutions fostered two trends that are important in the history of long-term care in the United States. First, they had infirmaries for the ill among their population that were the origins of the early public hospitals in this country. Second, as care for subpopulations in the workhouses moved steadily toward specialization, the basis for the current long-term nursing facility population was established.

SEPARATING LONG-TERM CARE FROM ACUTE CARE: PRECURSORS OF THE 20TH-CENTURY NURSING FACILITY IN THE UNITED STATES

To understand the process by which long-term care facilities and acute care hospitals evolved from the same institution, let us consider the Philadelphia Almshouse (1734). Its operations included an infirmary from its inception. It was not until 19 years later that the first American private or voluntary hospital, the Pennsylvania Hospital, was opened in the same city. By 1795, 114 of the 301 residents of the Philadelphia Almshouse were classified as sick. Medical functions were finally recognized in 1935. At that time, a reorganization was undertaken, and the name changed to Philadelphia Hospital and Almshouse (read: long-term care facility in place of almshouse). In 1903, the hospital section became the Philadelphia General Hospital.

By 1920, the Philadelphia Almshouse and the Philadelphia General Hospital were officially separated. Two separate institutions had emerged from the original combined facility: an acute care hospital and a long-term care organization.

Emergence of Specialization

The Public Workhouse of New York City (1734) illustrates the slow emergence of healthcare services specialization from an early nonspecialized long-term care facility. It had been established in 1734, thus predating the New York Hospital, which opened in 1769. By 1825, the medical functions of the workhouse infirmary, until then without medical personnel, had been given administrative recognition when the first resident physician was appointed to its staff. The name was simultaneously changed to Bellevue Hospital. Then began a process of specialization of care leading to the current structuring of our nursing facility long-term population. In 1831, the blind were removed to specialized care; in 1848, the hospital assumed care of the acutely ill and responsibility for the intellectually disabled, children, the insane, epileptics, the infirm, the aged, and the chronically ill. Subsequent removal of specific categories of patients to facilities delivering specialized care occurred in the second half of the century. By 1900, Bellevue Hospital had evolved into an institution providing care to those with infectious diseases, the aged, the chronically ill, and the infirm.

20TH CENTURY

The dual functions of (a) short-term acute care and (b) long-term care for the aged and chronically ill had evolved as the primary functions remaining from what had begun nearly two centuries earlier as the public almshouse. This process laid the groundwork for the dual development of short-term acute care hospitals and long-term care institutions in the 20th century. This change was a response to the great strides in clinical medicine in the early 20th century. When physicians could cure their patients of many diseases, separating short-term acute care and long-term care into distinct facilities seemed indicated.

The first specific remedy in the pharmacopeia of modern 20th-century medications—Salvarsan, for the infection syphilis—was discovered by Paul Ehrlich in 1907. In 1912, a physician observed that a random patient encountering a random physician with a random disease had, for the first time, a better than even chance of profiting from the encounter. Astonishing progress was to be made over the next century.

SEPARATING LONG-TERM CARE FROM SHORT-TERM CARE: 20TH CENTURY

Suddenly, Everyone Is Living Longer

From 1900 to 1954, the age-adjusted death rate in the United States fell by 57%. This decrease occurred in three identifiable stages: from 1900 to 1919, engineering and preventive measures accounted for a 1% drop per year; from 1920 to 1935, mortality decreased 0.7% per year; and between 1936 and 1954, with the introduction of sulfonamides and antibiotics, the rate of decline became 1.5% per year.

With the capacity to cure many common diseases, the typical hospital rapidly evolved into an institution focused primarily, if not exclusively, on short-term acute care. Some hospitals specialized in long-term care, and some assigned a wing to long-term care, but the time had come for a fuller separation of the functions.

During these years, deaths due to infection were reduced from 33% to 4%, with dramatic implications for channels of healthcare delivery. Until the appearance of AIDS in 1981, the health community thought infectious diseases, in the United States at least, had been conquered (Halter et al., 2017).

GENESIS OF THE CURRENT NURSING FACILITY INDUSTRY: FEDERAL GOVERNMENT REIMBURSEMENT

With hospitals focusing more and more exclusively on short-term acute care, pressures mounted for long-term support for the aged, the chronically ill, and the disabled. In response, the United States once more tried giving financial support to persons in their homes instead of having them occupy a nursing facility or other institutional bed. It began when the New York Old Age Security Act of 1930 was enacted under the leadership of (then governor) Franklin Delano Roosevelt.

Like its federal successor, which would not appear until 1935, the New York Act provided cash income to persons in need of economic support in their old age—but it excluded those in public and private institutions. Similarly, its healthcare provisions emphasized short-term acute episodic care to exclude direct payments for long-term care in institutions. Persons needing such care were expected to pay for this out of direct cash assistance made to them through the Act. The expectation was a step in the right direction, but these cash payments were usually insufficient to support the resident in a full-time institutional setting. In any case, few institutions at the time were able to deal with this population.

Short-term hospital beds were far more available than long-term ones. More and more acute care beds were being built to match the ever-increasing capacity of the medical profession to effect cures. Little concern was given to the needs of patients with chronic diseases.

Their care had traditionally been the responsibility of the states and the cities and counties within those states. As life expectancy increased, so did pressures to develop a care system for this burgeoning population sector (Halter et al., 2017).

The states, cities, and counties were unwilling to assume the economic burden generated by this development. They searched for resources other than their tax bases to meet the cost of this care. A partial solution was to come through judicial interpretations of a seemingly minor provision of the federal Social Security Act passed in 1935.

The Social Security Act of 1935

As a response to the growing numbers of aged persons who could not afford to pay the costs of living out of their savings, Congress passed the Social Security Act of 1935. It amounted to an old-age insurance policy. If they chose, older adults could use the cash to pay for the first small nursing facilities that sprang up. Today, this legislation, primarily through Title 18 and Title 19 amendments, provides a substantial proportion of the cash flow that supports the modern nursing facility industry.

Like the New York Old Age Security Act, after which it was in part patterned, the U.S. Social Security Act sought to enable the aged, and subsequently the chronically ill and disabled, to stay in their homes through funding to support them. It also helped them choose to enter the small "mom and pop" nursing facilities that became available. In its earliest form, the Act was almost entirely a cash assistance program. The monthly Social Security check was to be the extent of federal governmental participation. This explains why, like the New York legislation, the framers of the federal act excluded payments to institutionalized persons. Similarly, no home health program, such as exists currently, was set up or envisioned.

LEGISLATIVE AND JUDICIAL ORIGINS OF TODAY'S NURSING FACILITY INDUSTRY

By limiting Social Security payments to noninstitutionalized persons, the federal Social Security Act left the onus of paying for long-term institutional care for the aged, chronically ill, and disabled to the states, counties, and cities. This seems to have been the intention of Congress. However, the Act did make federal dollars available for up to half of the costs of noninstitutionalized care for the long-term care population. Under pressure to assist in institutional care, local officials sought ways of making this community sector eligible for federal dollars, despite the original intent of the federal lawmakers.

BACKING INTO THE CURRENT SOLUTION

The solution (for the state and local officials) came in a series of court cases concerning persons in need of long-term institutionalization, whom local officials had placed in private homes for care. Often these were the homes of retired nurses or other persons seeking supplemental income. The courts ruled that these private homes/boarding houses were "nonpublic" institutions and therefore eligible for federal reimbursement. In this way, state and local officials successfully shifted a significant portion of long-term care costs from the local and state governments to the federal government.

THE 21ST CENTURY

Since the beginning of the 21st century, we have seen some amazing changes in the industry. We have seen a focus on new reimbursement methodologies. We have seen a focus on moving residents out of the facility in a variety of ways, to utilize home health or the Money Follows the Person (MFP) program. We have watched Medicaid change in reimbursement and in settling with estates after a resident's passing. We have watched the old-age assistance (OAA) be amended to work to decrease the incidence of institutionalization. We saw the Affordable Care Act (ACA) roll out in 2010, which began to incentivize care in the nursing facility. In 2011, we watched the first baby boomers turn 65. We embraced the overhaul of the Five-Star Quality Rating System. We realized a changed focus of Medicare on quality and its incentivization for high-quality facilities.

Moreover, we saw an unbelievable change in the types of residents we were expected to care for. Gone are the days of the resident just needing some help. Today's nursing facility expects operations to be on the level of subacute care. Hospitals discharge quicker and sicker, and nursing facilities are expected to make that work, understanding that readmissions are for the most part unacceptable.

The facility of the 20th century no longer exists today. We are in a new world, operating with new expectations. It is time to embrace the change!

COMMON PITFALLS IN PRACTICE
- Sadly, new administrators often go into facilities that time has seemingly forgotten. The new administrator *must* embrace change and champion it. When we do not embrace this change, we get left behind, and we are not able to meet the needs of the communities in which our facilities operate.

4.1.2 OVERVIEW/CONTEXT OF THE NURSING FACILITY INDUSTRY

Consider as the Administrator . . .

- The profile of the residents we serve is ever changing—often from year to year. How do you embrace this change and make it work for your success?

PROFILE OF THE CURRENT NURSING FACILITY INDUSTRY

Every day more than 10,000 Americans celebrate their 65th birthday and join the "elderly" sector of the population. In 1900, 4% of the population were aged 65 years or older; in 1980, 11.2% were in that group; in 2020, 12.7%; in 2030, 30.2%; and in 2060, 35.9% are expected to be 65 years or older (see Table 4.1).

TABLE 4.1 U.S. Population 65 Years of Age and Older and Percentage of Total Population: Selected Years and Projections, 1950–2060

Year	65 and Older (thousands)	% of U.S. Population
1950	12,397	8.1
1970	20,087	9.9
1980	24,927	11.2
2000	31,822	12.2
2010	34,837	12.7
2020	79,313	23.8
2030	107,588	30.2
2040	125,711	33.7
2050	133,144	34.2
2060	145,201	35.9

Source: U.S. Census Bureau. (2017). *2017 National population projections tables: Main series.* https://www.census.gov/data/tables/2017/demo/popproj/2017-summary-tables.html

INCREASED LIFE EXPECTANCY

Increased life expectancy accounts for much of the change in the older adult population that is of the most direct concern to the administrator. Since 1900, life expectancy has increased from 46 years to 79 years and more. A more significant number of people are reaching age 65 years. Life expectancy in the United States ranked 40th overall among nations, 41st for men, and 43rd among nations for women in 2020 (Roser et al., 2019).

Increased Proportions of the "Old-Old"

As a group, older adults are growing older all the time. The 64- to 74-year-old cohort (the "young-old") increased at approximately the general population rate during the 1980s and the 1990s. The number of those 74 to 84 years and 85 years and older is growing exponentially. See Tables 4.2 and 4.3. The striking increase in healthcare needs of the age group 85 years and older is dramatically changing the face of the nursing facility population. Active life expectancy continues to rise. However, in the last few years, there has been a slight decrease in overall life expectancy.

Fewer Men, More Women

As the older adult population grows older, their age group becomes more and more dominated by women. In 1900, men in all age groups outnumbered women 102 to 100, but by 1975 the ratio had reversed, with fewer men than women: 69 men for every 100 women. In the 1990s, this was even further reduced to 66 men for every 100 women. The preponderance of women is even more pronounced in the 75-plus-year age group: the ratio of men to women for 1900 in this age group was 96 men for every 100 women; in 1975 this had decreased to 58 men per 100 women; and in 2000, even fewer—54 men are expected to be alive for every 100 women. Currently, it is no wonder that most of the residents in nursing facilities are women.

However, we see an interesting change in projections over the next 30 years as the numbers will flip to where we have more men than women in nursing facilities (45 women for every 100 men) by 2050 (see Tables 4.2 and 4.3).

TABLE 4.2 Percentage Increases in U.S. Population for 10-Year Intervals, by Age Groups: Selected Years and Projections, 1950–2060

Year	All Ages	65–74 Years	75–84 Years	85 Years and Older
1950–1960	18.7	30.1	41.2	59.3
1970–1980	8.7	23.4	14.2	44.6
1990–2000	7.1	−2.6	15.6	29.4
2000–2010	9.1	8.5	9.5	7.7
2010–2020	9.3	6.7	−1.5	8.2
2020–2030	9.4	8.3	3.2	7.4
2030–2040	9.5	−1.1	8.3	6.3
2040–2050	9.6	9.3	−1.1	7.7
2050–2060	9.6	8.7	9.2	9.8

Source: U.S. Census Bureau. (2011). *Age and sex composition: 2010.* https://www.census.gov/library/publications/2011/dec/c2010br-03.html; U.S. Census Bureau. (2017). *2017 national population projections tables: Main series.* https://www.census.gov/data/tables/2017/demo/popproj/2017- summary-tables.html; U.S. Census Bureau. (2021). *ACS demographic and housing estimates.* https://data.census.gov/cedsci/table?d=ACS%205-Year%20Estimates%20Data%20Profiles&tid=ACSDP5Y2010.DP05

TABLE 4.3 Total Population and Older Population: Selected Years, 1950–2060 (Rounded)

Year	All Ages	65 Years and Older	75 Years and Older
1950	150,000,000	12,000,000	4,000,000
2004	284,000,000	36,000,000	18,000,000
2010	304,000,000	38,000,000	18,000,000
2020	333,000,000	56,000,000	23,000,000
2030	355,000,000	73,000,000	34,000,000
2040	374,000,000	81,000,000	44,000,000
2050	389,000,000	86,000,000	47,000,000
2060	404,000,000	95,000,000	51,000,000

Source: U.S. Census Bureau. (2017). *2017 National population projections tables: Main series.* https://www.census.gov/data/tables/2017/demo/popproj/2017-summary-tables.html

AGING BABY BOOMERS: THE 21ST CENTURY'S MAJOR CHALLENGE TO THE U.S. HEALTHCARE SYSTEM

Baby boomer refers to the generation of individuals born in the post–World War II era between 1946 and 1964. They are sandwiched between the "silent generation," from 1928 to 1945, and "generation X," from 1965 to 1980. For context, the baby boom generation consists of the individuals who lived through some of the most tumultuous histories of the United States, including counterculture, the building and fall of the Berlin Wall, hippie culture, Woodstock, the sexual revolution, the Cold War, the Cuban Missile Crisis, the assassination of President John F. Kennedy, the Civil Rights movement, the lunar landings, the Vietnam War, and many other significant points along the way. We expect to see a dramatic increase in the number of these individuals entering the healthcare arena over the next several years. By 2029, all baby boomers will be aged 65 years and older.

The aging of the population has significant consequences for the healthcare system, especially nursing facilities. As the older population increases, more services will be required to treat and manage chronic and acute health conditions. Providing healthcare services needed by Americans of all ages will be a significant challenge in this 21st century. Many concerns surround the ultimate quality of life for this generation of individuals. Many of this population and many legislators have a "wait and see" attitude when it comes to finding financing for healthcare via Medicare and the ultimate viability of the Social Security program. Much of the available information surrounding these two areas seem better left to guesswork than any empirical conclusions.

MEDICAID SPENDING TRENDS

NAB DOMAIN 1A5: ACTIVITIES OF DAILY LIVING (ADLs) AND INSTRUMENTAL ACTIVITIES OF DAILY LIVING (IADLs); 2A5: REVENUE AND REIMBURSEMENT (E.G., PDPM, PDGM, ACOs, HMOs, MEDICAID, PRIVATE PAYORS)

Consider as the Administrator . . .

- *To what extent will Medicaid spending trends determine the future of the nursing facility industry?*

As illustrated in Table 4.4, Medicaid, the primary funding source for nursing facility care days, is shifting its focus away from institutional spending, down from 61% in 1985 to 32% in 2019 for nursing facilities. Conversely, there is an opposite shift from 7% to 59% for home- and community-based services (HCBS) during that same timeframe.

INCREASING DEPENDENCY LEVELS AMONG THE AGED

As individuals age, they become susceptible to chronic conditions. Therefore, it is no surprise that older Americans also dominate the dependent population. Seven out of 10 individuals who require assistance with their activities of daily living

TABLE 4.4 Need for Institutional- and Community-Based Long-Term Care: Medicaid Spending Trends

Service Type	1985 (%)	1990 (%)	1995 (%)	2000 (%)	2005 (%)	2010 (%)	2014 (%)	2019 (%)
Institutional LTSS	93	87	82	73	63	52	47	42
Nursing Facilities	61	57	53	52	44	37	36	32
ICF/IID	25	24	17	13	12	10	7	7
HCBS	7	13	18	27	37	48	53	59

HCBS, home- and community-based services; ICF/IID, Intermediate Care Facilities for Individuals with Intellectual Disabilities; LTSS, long-term services and supports.

Source: Data from Kaiser Family Foundation. (2021). *Distribution of fee-for-service Medicaid spending on long-term care.* https://www.kff.org/medicaid/state-indicator/spending-on-long-term-care/?dataView=1&currentTimeframe=0&sortModel=%7B%22colId%22:%22Location%22,%22sort%22:%22asc%22%7D; Wenzlow, A., Eiken, S., & Sredl, K. (2016). *Improving the balance: The evolution of Medicaid expenditures for Long-Term Services and Supports (LTSS), FY 1981-2014.* Truven Health Analytics.

EXHIBIT 4.1 Definitions of Activities of Daily Living (ADLs) and Instrumental Activities of Daily Living (IADLs)

ADLs	Eating, bathing, dressing, getting to/using bathroom, getting into/out of bed, mobility, continence
IADLs	Keeping track of personal finances, preparing meals, light housework, telephone use, taking medications, accessing transportation, caring for pets

TABLE 4.5 Estimated Percentage Increase in the Need for Care in Long-Term Care Institutional Settings: 2010, 2020, and 2040

	2010	2020	2040
Nursing homes	10	20	30
Assisted living facilities	20	30	40
Multiunit senior housing	15	25	50

Source: Based on Centers for Medicare & Medicaid Services OSCAR estimates of current capacities and projected increases in proportion of persons 65 years of age and older in the U.S. population.

(ADLs) are older adults. ADLs (Halter et al., 2017) include eating, bathing, dressing, getting to and using the bathroom, getting in or out of a bed or chair, and mobility in general. Persons more able to care for themselves are described in the concept of instrumental activities of daily living (IADLs; Exhibit 4.1).

Older adults have higher dependency rates than the nonaged population, and aged women are much more likely to have a dependency in mobility and personal care than aged men. Old-old non-White females are especially hard hit. Their dependency rates are double those for White males and triple those of non-White males. The population at risk for institutionalization is most probably those older adults who need personal care assistance. Studies have shown that nearly 20 times as many nursing facility residents need this type of assistance than those needing mobility assistance.

Over the next few decades, there will be a dramatic need for all types of senior housing, both institutional and noninstitutional, as illustrated in Table 4.5.

ABILITY TO PERFORM THE ACTIVITIES OF DAILY LIVING

The nursing facility resident population is heavily dependent on the nursing facility staff, especially the nursing assistants (Halter et al., 2017). Over time, we are seeing increasing statistics in the number of ADLs with which residents require assistance within the facility.

COMMON PITFALLS IN PRACTICE
- Many administrators have placed their focus and trust in an increasing baby boomer population, hoping that this would cure many census ails. This has not been the case to date. It is crucial that the administrator find their niche market and not focus on a potential bump in population that may never occur.

4.1.3 NURSING FACILITIES

Section Concepts

- *There are many parts of the long-term care continuum of which a resident may take advantage*
- *Knowing your market and your competition assists in success*

Consider as the Administrator . . .

- *Where will you find your niche? How can you possibly succeed in a market which has better or newer facilities than yours?*

NAB DOMAIN 2A6: FINANCIAL REPORTING REQUIREMENTS (E.G., REQUIREMENTS FOR NOT-FOR-PROFIT, FOR-PROFIT, AND GOVERNMENTAL PROVIDERS); 4A1: ORGANIZATIONAL STRUCTURES (E.G., DEPARTMENTS, FUNCTIONS, SYSTEMIC PROCESSES); 4A5: GOVERNANCE (E.G., BOARD OF DIRECTORS, GOVERNING BODIES, CORPORATE ENTITIES, ADVISORY BOARDS); 4A6: PROFESSIONAL ADVOCACY AND GOVERNMENTAL RELATIONS

FACILITY CHARACTERISTICS: DO SIZE AND OWNERSHIP MATTER?

In a few words, not much. Researchers have been unable to establish a strong correlation whether size or ownership affects process and outcomes in terms of quality of care (Table 4.6). Many researchers have unsuccessfully attempted to demonstrate that not-for-profits deliver consistently better care.

We know that nonprofits generally receive fewer citations during a survey; however, a direct correlation as to why is still somewhat a mystery.

OVERVIEW OF THE LONG-TERM CARE CONTINUUM

The American long-term care system, insofar as it can be called a system, is loosely interconnected. Various pieces of legislation separately authorize each agency and program. No single agency or program is approved, or indeed able, to coordinate the various efforts on behalf of older adults. Although the Older Americans Act calls for and

TABLE 4.6 Percentage of Distribution of Long-Term Care Services by Type of Provider

	Nursing Facility	Hospice	Home Health
Government and other	7.2	14.1	4.6
Nonprofits	23.5	22.8	14.8
For profits	69.3	63	80.6

Source: Adapted from the National Center for Health Statistics. (2019). *Long-term care providers and services users in the United States, 2015-2016.* https://www.cdc.gov/nchs/data/series/sr_03/sr03_43-508.pdf

authorizes coordination, in reality, officials of the Older Americans Act have not been empowered to bring this about.

As of 2016 in the United States, there were an estimated 4,600 adult day-services centers, 12,200 home healthcare agencies, 4,300 hospices, 15,600 nursing facilities, and 28,900 residential care communities (National Center for Health Statistics [NCHS], 2019). Of these, approximately 65,600 regulated, long-term care service providers. This number includes 7.0% adult daycare centers, 18.6% home healthcare agencies, 6.6% hospice, 23.8% nursing facilities, and 44.1% residential care communities (NCHS, 2019).

Use Rate for Long-Term Care Services

In 2012, the daily use rate for persons aged 65 years and older for every 1,000 persons aged 65 years and older was 26 per 1,000 for nursing facilities, 15 per 1,000 for residential care communities, and 4 per 1,000 for adult daycare services centers.

A result has been that older adults must largely fend for themselves in seeking services in most communities. One proposed remedy for this situation is called "case management," which is the assignment of each elderly person in need of an assistance program to a specific caseworker who will help that individual plan and carry out a care program composed of services from several different agencies. Case management is what employees in departments of social services and the Area Agencies on Aging (AAAs) attempt to do. However, funds are insufficient to employ enough staff to assist all older Americans who need this type of assistance, and most of them are left to fend for themselves. In any event, case management can usually occur if the clients can reach or come under the guidance of an agency in the first place.

Exhibit 4.2 describes the primary sources of services available to older Americans, moving from the least restrictive to the most restrictive.

The nursing facility plays at least two significant roles in this continuum. First, it may be simultaneously providing rehabilitative services to almost anyone receiving a combination of long-term services. It is estimated that 25% of all older persons

EXHIBIT 4.2 Overview of the Long-Term Care Continuum

Meals on Wheels	Congregate meals	Group personal homes
Chore workers	Senior citizens centers	Personal care homes
Homemakers	Community mental health	Foster care
Home health aide	Adult daycare	Domiciliary care
Social worker visits	Geriatric day hospitals	Rest homes
Protective services	Respite care	Congregate housing with meals
Home rehabilitation		Congregate housing with social services
Home health		Congregate housing with medical services
Hospice		Congregate housing with housekeeping
		Life care communities
		Continuing care retirement communities
		Nursing facilities
LEAST RESTRICTIVE ---------------------------->		**MOST RESTRICTIVE**

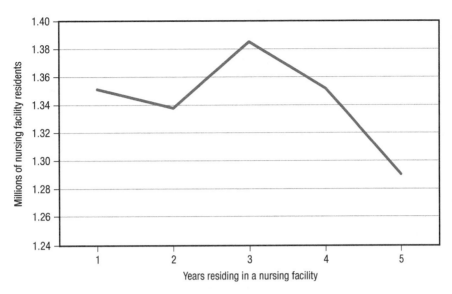

FIGURE 4.1 Trends in numbers of nursing facility residents.

use the services of a nursing facility at some point. Second, the nursing facility is the primary provider of intensive services for persons who no longer can care for themselves and need nursing care on a 24-hour basis. It is estimated that 5% of all the elderly are residents in nursing facilities at any one point in time.

The need for nursing facility beds remains in question over the coming decades, primarily due to the COVID-19 pandemic. We saw a significant drop in the number of nursing facility residents in 2020, and this number remains fluid at the moment (Figure 4.1).

NAB DOMAIN 1C: ANCILLARY SERVICES

HOME- AND COMMUNITY-BASED LONG-TERM CARE OPTIONS

There are many different types of home- and community-based care options. There are most likely more types of an informal fashion than this text can discuss. Exhibit 4.3 provides an overview of some of the various services offered under HCBS.

HOME-BASED OPTIONS

Friendly Visiting

Both the Area Agency on Aging and local volunteer groups arrange regular visits to older adults living alone. These visits offer both needed social contact and continuous monitoring of these individuals.

Meals on Wheels

Title 3C of the Older Americans Act and many other local sources pay for home-delivered meals under the Meals on Wheels program. To qualify, an organization must deliver meals (usually only the noon meal) on each of 5 days or more per week and meet specific standards, including providing one third of daily nutritional

EXHIBIT 4.3 Examples of Home- and Community-Based Services

Case Management
Assists beneficiaries in getting medical, social, educational, or other services
Personal Care
Includes bathing, dressing, ambulation, feeding, grooming, and some household services such as meal preparation and shopping
Adult Daycare
Includes personal care and supervision and may include physical, occupational, and speech therapies
Respite Care
Provides relief to the primary caregiver of a chronically ill or disabled beneficiary. Allows the primary caregiver to be absent for a time. Often a nursing facility will admit a person over a weekend, thus providing respite care.
Homemaker
Assists beneficiaries with general household activities and may include cleaning, laundry, meal planning, grocery shopping, meal preparation, transportation to medical services, and bill paying

requirements. As a rule, the Area Agency on Aging contracts with groups to deliver these meals. Nursing facilities frequently offer Meals on Wheels, both as a public service and a contact mechanism with potential applicants. The dietary department of the nursing facility automatically meets the various requirements of the program by preparing food for its residents.

Chore Worker and Homemaker

Area Agency on Aging subcontractors offer persons to come into older persons' homes and perform specific tasks. Chore workers usually do window washing or other less routine tasks. The homemaker visits on a more regular basis and performs housekeeping tasks such as dusting, dishwashing, and laundry.

Home Health Aide

In contrast to the homemaker and chore worker, the home health aide can perform only health-specific tasks, such as administering medicines, changing bandages, and the like. The home health aide is paid from Medicaid or Medicare funds, not the Area Agency on Aging. A home health agency can send such an aide if the older person is receiving Medicare services in the home for a specific illness or injury. Over the past few years, local Medicaid offices have increasingly been permitted to use Medicaid funds to pay for services designed to prevent or postpone the institutionalization of older persons. Initially, these were called Title 19 waivers, for which states had to apply.

The U.S. Department of Health and Human Services (DHHS) authorizes all Medicaid programs to offer various services similar to those available under the Older Americans Act if they were conducive to postponement or prevention of institutionalization. Usually, these services are funded up to three quarters of the costs of institutionalizing the client.

Social Worker Visits

Under Title 20 or other authorizations, the local department of social services is permitted to pay for social worker visits to the homes of older adults. This arrangement is similar to a social worker or caseworker visiting any other client.

Protective Services—Home Rehabilitation Services

The Area Agency on Aging or its subcontractor is authorized to assist older adults in bringing their homes up to minimum standards and providing added security measures to reduce the possibility of break-ins.

Home Healthcare

Home healthcare agencies are affording increasing competition to freestanding nursing facilities (Table 4.7). Since the mid-1960s, the federal government has fueled exponential growth in nursing facilities through funding legislation. Currently, federal (and state) support results in increasing numbers of home healthcare agencies on the assumption—probably erroneous—that they can provide care more inexpensively than the nursing facility.

An older person can receive home healthcare through one of the three programs under the Social Security Act: Medicare Part A, Medicare Part B, or Medicaid (Pratt, 2016).

Services Under Medicare Part A

Unlimited home healthcare visits at no cost are available to any Medicare recipient hospitalized under Part A and evaluated to need posthospital home healthcare for the final diagnosis-related group (DRG) diagnosis.

Services Under Medicare Part B

Unlimited visits, at 80% of the cost, are available to persons covered by Medicare Part B who are found to need part-time healthcare in the home for the treatment of an illness or injury. No prior hospitalization is required, but four conditions must be met:

TABLE 4.7 Home Healthcare Medicare-Certified Providers and Suppliers

1975	2,290
1990	6,461
2000	7,099
2005	8,090
2010	10,914
2015	12,149
2019	11,157

Source: Statista. (2021). *Number of Medicare home health agencies in the U.S. from 1967-2019.* https://www.statista.com/statistics/195318/number-of-medicare-home-health-agencies-in-the-us/

1. The care must include part-time nursing care, physical therapy, or speech therapy.
2. The client must be confined to their home.
3. A doctor must diagnose the need and design the plan.
4. The agency must participate in Medicare.

Medicare does not cover general household services, meal preparation, shopping, assistance in bathing or dressing, or other home assistance to meet personal, family, or domestic needs. Thus, to keep an ailing older adult who requires various types of home assistance functioning, several agencies with different priorities and interests must be coordinated by the client or by a friend or a caseworker on the client's behalf. Home healthcare agencies are increasingly caring for persons who are nearly as disabled as those cared for in the skilled nursing facility (SNF). A cost-effectiveness study found that at least 41% or more persons studied could be effectively managed outside the nursing facility. There has been a steady movement toward increasing the utilization of home healthcare. Since 1995, there has been an American Academy of Medical Administrators division for home healthcare executives, further recognizing the maturation of this field. We have seen exponential growth in this field since then.

Although home healthcare will remain a significant competitor for the nursing facility patient, the growth of this field is difficult to predict. The COVID-19 pandemic has caused a widespread change in healthcare, and we have recently seen a drop in the number of home healthcare agencies. It is impossible to forecast what the future holds for this particular part of the long-term care continuum. One change to this field is increasing regulations. Home healthcare generally has had weak regulations to protect patients; however, these regulations has increased over time. The regulations surrounding home healthcare have grown exponentially since inception.

Medicaid Services

Suppose a Medicaid recipient is found apt to need full-time institutional care. In that case, Medicaid can pay for nearly any type of in-home services available through either Medicare or the Area Agency on Aging. The economic rationale of this program is to reduce public expenditures by offering services that allow people to function in their own homes where they, or often their family, will be sharing the financial burden, thus reducing public costs. The care rationale to encourage them to remain at home is based on the positive psychological and emotional benefits and outcomes.

COMMON PITFALLS IN PRACTICE
- Many administrators simply do their best to accept all potential residents to their facilities. This does not serve these individuals well, nor does it serve the facility well. Ensure that placement is appropriate for your facility.
- Today's focus is largely on "heads in the beds." Understandably, as you get paid only for filled beds. Filling beds with inappropriately placed residents can cost you big money in the long run.

HOSPICE CARE

NAB DOMAIN 1C1: HOSPICE AND PALLIATIVE CARE

NAB DOMAIN 1B13: DEATH, DYING, AND GRIEF

Hospice care is provided only to persons usually believed to be at the end of their lives, with perhaps 6 months or less to live, who mainly seek alleviation from pain rather than intensive technological medical treatment. It, however, is not unheard of for hospice patients to "graduate" from the program to be released from hospice entirely when their health has improved. Hospice care is often provided at home. However, we often see hospice agencies attending residents in nursing facilities. Hospice is also offered in freestanding hospice centers for inpatients and patient wards in hospitals designated as hospice units and individual patients on other wards.

Medicare Part A pays for hospice care if three conditions are met:

1. Medical certification that the patient is terminally ill.
2. The patient's choice is to receive care from a hospice instead of the standard Medicare benefits.
3. A Medicare-certified hospice must provide the program.

People who choose hospice can be given Medicare Part A hospitalization care for events unrelated to their terminal illness, for example, a bone broken during an accidental fall.

The Centers for Medicare & Medicaid Services (CMS), which administers Medicare and Medicaid, defines hospice as a public agency or private organization primarily engaged in providing pain relief, symptom management, and supportive services to terminally ill people and their families. Medicare pays 100% of all hospice services except for 55% of outpatient drugs and respite care.

Conventional wisdom suggests that Medicare is wasteful, spending about 30% or more of its total on people in the last year (or last days) of their lives, most of it during their final month. However, a Medicare program self-study of those expenditures compared with costs for survivors differed little over a 12-year study period. Perhaps, we will see a change with the baby boomer population. Payments during the last month do not vary as dramatically as believed. Evidence that people in the final year of life account for a larger share of expenditures than younger beneficiaries seems inconclusive. One study suggests that when all medical services are included, the "older-old" costs might be somewhat less during their last year of life.

Palliative care is resident- and family-centered care that optimizes quality of life by anticipating, preventing, and treating suffering. Palliative care throughout the continuum of illness involves addressing physical, intellectual, emotional, social, and spiritual needs and facilitating patient autonomy, access to information, and choice.

Palliative care is often utilized in substitution for hospice care. We often see resident families who choose not to use hospice care or who have inappropriate expectations about utilizing palliative care through the nursing facility.

The following features characterize palliative care philosophy and delivery:

- Care is provided, and an interprofessional team coordinates services
- Residents, families, and palliative and nonpalliative healthcare providers collaborate and communicate about care needs

- Services are available concurrently with or independent of curative or life-prolonging care
- Resident and family hopes for peace and dignity are supported throughout the course of illness, during the dying process, and after death

Often, the facility contracts with a local hospice provider to serve individual residents. However, palliative care does not require this.

Many facilities have palliative care programs (eliminating hospice). When in place, hospice contracts must carefully detail the responsibilities of the facility staff and the responsibilities of the hospice caregivers who enter the facility. Generally, the facility staff remains fully responsible for the care of the resident. Hospice caregivers are supplementary to the care given by regular facility staff.

THE GRIEVING PROCESS

NAB DOMAIN 1B13: DEATH, DYING, AND GRIEF

Typically, the nursing facility provides end-of-life care for the majority of its residents. Persons at the end of life who need 24-hours-a-day nursing care may be in some stage of the grieving process as the end of life approaches and their dependency on others for the ADLs increases. The best-known model of the grieving process was developed by the American psychiatrist Elisabeth Kübler-Ross in her book *On Death and Dying* (Kübler-Ross, 1993). There are five stages of grief, according to her observations.

The Kübler-Ross model, or the five stages of grief, is a series of emotional stages experienced when faced with impending death or the death of someone. The five stages are denial, anger, bargaining, depression, and acceptance. Kübler-Ross noted that these stages are not meant to be a complete list of all possible emotions that could be felt and can occur in any order. Her hypothesis holds that not everyone who experiences a life-threatening or life-altering event feels all five of the responses, as reactions to personal losses differ among people.

Stages

The stages, popularly known by the acronym DABDA, are as follows:

1. *Denial.* As the reality of loss is hard to face, one of the first reactions to follow the loss is denial. The person tries to shut out the truth or the magnitude of their situation and develops a false, preferable reality.
2. *Anger.* Once in the second stage, the individual recognizes that denial cannot continue. Because of anger, the resident is tough to care for due to misplaced feelings of rage and envy. The resident in question can be angry with themselves, or with others, or with a higher power, especially those close to them. Specific psychological responses of a person undergoing this phase would be "Why me? It's not fair!" "How can this happen to me?" "Who is to blame?" and "Why would God let this happen?"
3. *Bargaining.* The third stage involves the hope that the resident can somehow undo or avoid a cause of grief. Usually, an extended life is negotiated with a higher power in exchange for a reformed lifestyle. Other times, residents will

use anything valuable as a bargaining chip against another human agency to extend or prolong the life they live. In essence, the individual cannot accept yet acknowledges that what has happened cannot be undone. Residents facing less severe trauma can bargain or seek to negotiate a compromise. For example, one may say, "Can we still be friends?" when facing a breakup. Bargaining rarely provides a sustainable solution, especially if it is a matter of life or death.

4. *Depression.* "I'm so sad. Why bother with anything?" "I'm going to die soon, so what's the point?" "I miss my loved one. Why go on?" During the fourth stage, the grieving person begins to understand the certainty of death. Much like the existential concept of The Void, the idea of living becomes pointless. Things start to lose meaning to the griever. Because of this, the resident may become silent, refuse visitors, and spend much of the time crying and sullen. This process allows the grieving resident to disconnect from objects of love and affection, possibly to avoid further trauma. Depression could be referred to as the dress rehearsal for the "aftermath." It is a kind of acceptance with emotional attachment. It is natural to feel sadness, regret, fear, and uncertainty when going through this stage. Feeling those emotions shows that the person has begun to accept the situation. Frequently, this is the ideal path to take, to find closure and make one's way to the fifth step, acceptance.

5. *Acceptance.* "It's going to be okay"; "I can't fight it. I may as well prepare for it." In this last stage, residents begin to come to terms with their mortality or inevitable future, or that of a loved one, or other tragic events. This stage varies according to the resident's situation. Individuals dying can enter this stage a long time before the people they leave behind enter it toward their own stages of grief. This typically comes with a clear, retrospective view for the individual and a stable mindset.

Typically, nursing facility staff themselves become attached to residents and experience phases of the grieving process as each resident passes through the experience of dying.

COMMON PITFALLS IN PRACTICE

- Many believe that hospice is something that a resident goes on to die. While this might be the case, hospice has a long history and track record of helping residents get better as well. Hospice is not a death sentence. Hospice is a service that can assist in the dying process or assist with certain diagnoses over time.

COMMUNITY-BASED LONG-TERM CARE

NAB DOMAIN 1B18: COMMUNITY RESOURCES, PROGRAMS, AND AGENCIES (E.G., MEALS ON WHEELS, HOUSING VOUCHERS, AREA AGENCIES ON AGING, VETERANS AFFAIRS)

Congregate Meals at Nutrition Sites and Senior Citizen Centers

Under Title 3c of the Older Americans Act, an effort has been made to make congregate meal sites available to as many older adults as possible in urban and rural areas.

The AAAs contract with many thousands of groups who serve meals 5 days or more a week under the meals program. Often these nutrition sites, as they are called, are rural schools or churches, which are usually centrally located. Transportation is generally provided, and counseling, nutrition education, recreation, and referral services are provided at the same site and time.

Senior Citizen Center Activities and In-Center Services

The AAAs provide various activities and services at these centers and usually congregate meals.

Community Mental Health Centers

Over the past two decades, mental health legislation has resulted in establishing an extensive network of community mental health centers to which older persons may refer themselves or be referred. However, the utilization rate of these centers has tended to be disproportionately low among older adults.

Adult Daycare

An adult daycare program is a community organization providing daytime health or recreational services to groups of impaired older adults in a centralized protective environment, often for long periods. Nursing facilities are uniquely positioned to offer adult daycare programs, and some do. We have seen a decreasing number, however, in recent years. Payments for adult daycare can come from various sources, including federal revenue-sharing programs, Title 4 of the Older Americans Act, Title 6 of the Social Security Act, and Medicaid.

People enter an adult daycare program for various reasons, such as the need for the caregiver to be at work during the day. Its primary function is to allow older persons with various disabilities to remain in the home setting longer.

Often the adult daycare participant in a nursing facility eventually becomes a resident there. This earlier exposure to the environment reduces the trauma usually involved in the transition to institutional care.

Adult daycare began in the mid-1970s. The National Institute of Adult Daycare was established in 1979. The average daycare program cares for about 22 persons between 9 a.m. and 3 p.m. Daycare programs typically offer a structured day, including social interaction, exercise, and a hot noontime meal. Some offer case management, health assessment, nutrition education, and therapeutic diets. The National Center for Health Statistics (2021) estimates that there were 4,600 adult daycare services centers in the United States in 2016, serving 286,300 persons daily.

Many adult daycare centers are located in nursing facilities. The majority of such participants are functionally dependent, older adult White women. Most are unmarried, and about a third are mentally impaired. Overall, nursing facility residents tend to be younger, are less dependent, and have less mental impairment. Few, if any, adult daycare programs are physically located in a hospital.

Geriatric day rehabilitation hospitals are a medical model of the adult daycare program. Adult daycare programs range from offering recreation with no healthcare to nearly complete health services similar in intensity to those of the nursing facility. Several studies have concluded that stand-alone adult daycare centers and daycare hospitals achieve the same outcomes. We also see many "daycare" programs surrounding specific diagnoses, often mental health related.

Adult Foster Care

This form of care is typically defined as care for no more than six unrelated persons in a community-based residence. Twenty-four–hour supervision and care are offered. Sponsorship can be individuals or public or similar agencies. There are no accurate estimates of how many such facilities exist.

Respite Care

Respite care is a short-term inpatient stay that provides temporary relief to the person who regularly assists with home care.

Under Medicare, respite care is available only to caregivers of hospice patients. Medicare will pay 95% of the costs and eventually 100% of the costs after the patient has paid a specified number of dollars of coinsurance. Medicare limits inpatient respite care to stays of no more than 5 consecutive days.

Depending on occupancy level, nursing facilities have offered respite care over the years. Some organizational obstacles to nursing facilities' ability to provide respite are (a) costs involved in the extensive paperwork required at each admission and discharge, regardless of whether the patient is a regular or a hospice resident, and (b) costs associated with keeping beds empty for hospice-type admissions, which, by definition, are of short duration and therefore incur higher administrative costs to the facility.

Recently, Congress authorized the Lifespan Respite Care Act, which reimburses family members (not just unrelated persons) who provide care for the first time.

Informal Caregiving

As of 2015, an estimated 17.7 million individuals in the United States act as informal caregivers (*Morbidity and Mortality Weekly Report*, 2020); generally, this assistance to older adults is unpaid and provided in-home.

This type of care can have many benefits for the elderly recipient; however, it can have many adverse effects for the caregivers, including depression, lower quality of life, and issues with their health.

INSTITUTION-BASED CARE

Low-Intensity Institution-Based Arrangements: Housing

An almost infinite range of housing options faces older adults attempting to decide where and how to live out their final years. Numerous group housing arrangements exist. These are variously called group homes, family homes, personal care homes, foster care homes, domiciliary care homes, or, often, rest homes. The number of older adults involved varies from three or four in a group or foster home to several hundred in a "rest" home. The primary source of public support for these housing arrangements is the local department of social services that administers the Medicaid program. A new variety of caregiving for older adults is emerging, variously named but often referred to as assisted living. Definitions vary confusingly from state to state.

Congregate care housing arrangements exist in many forms. These usually are publicly supported housing sites for older adults and disabled persons. Support can come from numerous public sources, including local tax monies.

These housing arrangements range from no services to a progressive array that includes meals, social services, housekeeping, and medical care. Often these are high-rise buildings or small complexes that offer the low-income person an approximate equivalent to the services provided to middle- and upper-income Americans in life care or continuing care communities.

Life care communities or CCRCs are a relatively new phenomenon, at least on the scale they are now being offered. This type of setting can be a microcosm of the community at large with its various services.

CONTINUING CARE RETIREMENT COMMUNITIES

This text focuses on the nursing facility. However, professional preparation as a nursing facility administrator offers simultaneous preparation for becoming the administrator of a CCRC.

The original CCRCs, often called life care communities, were usually set up and managed by religious organizations. In return for all their worldly possessions, participants were promised care for the rest of their lives. Today, the typical resident pays a one-time entrance fee plus monthly fees.

The CCRC that offers life care is, in essence, an insurance pooling. The entry and monthly fees are set based on actuarial calculations to cover the expected lifetime costs of each resident. In exchange for the entry and monthly fees, residents of life care communities are guaranteed care no matter how long they live, even if one's personal funds run out. Not every resident will need expensive nursing facility care, but the fees paid by all residents pay for those who do. As with an insurance annuity, those who live longer receive more benefits than those who die earlier.

Typically, the new resident initially occupies either a detached (garden) apartment or moves into an apartment building. As the need arises for more protected or assisted living, residents may move progressively from a detached unit to an attached apartment to "sheltered" care (assisted living) and, as needed, to full-time nursing care (if necessary).

Array of Facilities

A broad array of financial arrangements have emerged. Three types of CCRCs are identified in the literature:

- Type A or all-inclusive (about 33% of CCRCs) guarantee fully paid nursing care for as long as needed at no extra cost beyond the resident's monthly fee. Many services are "bundled" or included in the monthly fee (e.g., two or more meals each day, cleaning, laundry, linen, utilities, and recreation facilities). Fees vary by geographical area and size of the living unit, averaging $70,000 to well over $700,000 entry fees and $900 to well over $6,000 monthly fees.

- Type B or modified CCRCs (about 26% of facilities) usually offer nursing care at no substantial monthly fee increase but include fewer services. Fees, for example, may be charged for cleaning or laundry, and only one or two meals may be included. Residents in this type of community assume some of the financial risks of extended nursing care costs. Entry and monthly fees are commensurably reduced.
- Type C or fee-for-service CCRCs (about 38% of CCRCs) usually offer no meals or personal care service in the monthly fee. Access to nursing care, on-site (usually) or off-site, is guaranteed, but the resident using the service bears the total costs.

With today's competitive market, we have seen many changes in the financial arrangements and the fees, refundability, and many other intricacies of the business. Undoubtedly, we will continue to see changes as we move forward into the coming years.

Regulation

Resident contracts vary in CCRCs. Some states regulate through the insurance department, others through the health department, offices on aging, or even departments that supervise securities and corporations.

Successfully building and operating a CCRC is a complex business venture. The most common reason for failure is the low occupancy rate, as major costs are fixed.

COMMON PITFALLS IN PRACTICE
- Helping a resident get placed in your facility is just as important as helping them get placed in the correct level of care. *Both* of these actions can build your census over time. Turning away a resident because they are not sick enough for you helps build community confidence in you as a provider of long-term care.

HOSPITAL TRENDS: UNDERSTANDING THE CHANGING NURSING FACILITY CASE MIX

Hospitals may be regarded as the weathervane showing where healthcare industry providers such as nursing facilities and home healthcare agencies may be heading. This idea tends to be true because, ultimately, the behavior of the healthcare industry is driven by cost and new technologies. Generally, to understand hospital trends is to understand nursing facility trends.

Changes in the Wind

These hospital data reveal many trends in the healthcare field, most of which impact the nursing facility (Table 4.8). From 1965 (federal Medicare reimbursement legislation) until 1985 (federal Diagnostic Related Group reimbursement legislation), hospitals simply billed the federal government whatever they wished and were reimbursed. Beginning in 1984, hospitals were paid a fixed fee on a per-admission basis based on what the federal government was willing to pay for the admitting diagnosis, no matter whether the patient stayed 2 days or 10

TABLE 4.8 U.S. Hospital Trends, 1975–2015

	1975[a]	1990	2000	2005	2013	2015	2021[b]
Number of all hospitals	7,156	6,649	5,810	5,756	5,686	5,564	6,090
Federal	382	337	245	226	213	212	208
Community (all inclusive)	5,875	5,384	4,915	4,936	4,974	4,862	5,141
Community nonprofit	3,339	3,191	3,003	2,958	2,904	2,845	2,946
Community for profit	775	749	749	868	1,013	1,034	1,233
Occupancy rate of all hospitals (%)	76.7	69.5	66.1	69.3	64.7	65.5	NA[c]
Federal	80.7	72.9	68.2	66.0	64.5	64.9	NA
Community (all inclusive)	75.0	66.8	63.9	67.3	62.9	63.6	NA
Community nonprofit	77.5	69.3	65.5	69.1	64.5	65.3	NA
Community for profit	65.9	52.8	55.9	59.6	56.2	57.5	NA

[a]Data from Centers for Disease Control & Prevention. (2018). *Health, United States, 2017.* https://www.cdc.gov/nchs/data/hus/hus17.pdf
[b]Data from American Hospital Association. (2021). *Fast facts on U.S. hospitals, 2021.* https://www.aha.org/statistics/fast-facts-us-hospitals
[c]Data unavailable.

days. Today, we see a focus around equal billing but incentives and penalties surrounding admissions and discharges. There are incentives for hospitals that meet and exceed specific metrics. There are conversely penalties for readmissions of patients for the same issue (thus, ideologically not being corrected during the first admission, and to disincentivize early discharges). This shift in how hospitals were paid for their services changed how they also cared for patients. This shift trickled down to nursing facilities receiving discharged hospital patients (sooner and sicker).

Today, nursing facilities are expected to take much more acute residents and provide a much more significant level of care. Gone are the days of nursing facilities being "rest homes." Today, our focus has become one of subacute care and skilled nursing.

Number of Hospitals, Ownership Changes

From 1975 to 2021, the total number of hospitals in the United States has dropped from 7,156 to 6,090. However, it is essential to note the peaks and valleys in those numbers as presented in Table 4.8. During times of significant changes in billing, we saw drops in the number of hospitals in the United States. We see a trend up in numbers from 2015 to 2021 from 5,564 to 6,090.

This changing trend is undoubtedly in response to expectations surrounding baby boomers coming into the healthcare system. Considering ownership of hospitals, little has changed compared to nonprofit versus for profit, which we would expect. Nonprofit entities have always provided the most care. We are, however, seeing a steady trend in the number of for-profit hospitals increasing from 775 in 1975 to 1,233 in 2021. Many reasons for this are postulated in the literature; however, demand for high-touch, high-tech healthcare has been driving significant increases in recent years. Patients want cutting-edge technology, and both they and their insurance companies are willing to pay for it.

Where Is the Money Going?

It is essential to consider where the money is going today when considering business models and places we are caring for patients. As a country, we spent a mere $27.2 billion on healthcare in 1960. Spending jumped to $1,369.2 billion in 2000 and a whopping $3,649.4 billion in 2018. These numbers are interesting to see trends; however, they are unadjusted for "today's dollars." Making adjustments for inflation since 1960, that $27.2 billion is worth $240.9 billion today. This dollar figure is tiny compared to today's expenditures of $3,649.4 billion, but do consider the level of healthcare we have today. Commonplace procedures today were unheard of in 1960. The first successful cardiopulmonary bypass surgery was in 1961. The previously controversial procedure became somewhat common in the 1970s. The first coronary stent was placed in 1977. The approval to use these stents to treat acute myocardial infarction did not occur until 1994. Consider, before these revolutionary techniques, a heart attack was often a fatal diagnosis. Today, it seems to be an arbitrary concern with thousands of these types of procedures done daily. We could not do many of the surgeries we have today, nor did we have the technology to back them. Today, we have both, and that ability costs money.

Changes in How Hospitals Do Business

With lowered federal reimbursement and improving technology and drugs, hospitals began emphasizing outpatient surgery instead of the traditional inpatient model. We have seen an increase in outpatient surgeries from a low number of 16% of surgeries in 1975 to 64% or more today. Many of these patients simply show up to the hospital or an ambulatory surgery center, have surgery, and go home.

We have also seen an exciting trend in hospital surgeries surrounding a much quicker discharge. For many older adult patients, this means at least three midnights in a hospital after a surgery or event. Then they are whisked off to an SNF for therapy or continued treatment that used to be provided in the hospital. Hospitals are essentially not in the business of delivering subacute care anymore.

What Is the Least Expensive Level of Care?

Healthcare system usage is cost driven. Hospital care costs *thousands* of dollars per day; nursing facility care costs *hundreds* of dollars per day. Healthcare payers, whether government entities or private entities, prefer lower daily rates for healthcare. The acuity level in nursing facilities increases in response to the dramatically high cost per hospital day of stay.

Occupancy Rates as Behavioral Influences

Hospitals and home healthcare agencies are vying for many of the same residents the freestanding nursing facility seeks. As a result of occupancy rates, hospitals are adding hospital-based nursing facilities at an alarming rate. The trend for hospitals to build and operate their own nursing facilities is continuing. The economic incentive for hospitals to own nursing facility beds is simple—it begins a new and otherwise unavailable flow of cash to the hospital for nursing facility care days (hundreds of dollars per day). Moving the patient to a nursing facility bed also quickly ends the acute care stay where the payment was based on a single reimbursement rate. In many cases, it also expedites an otherwise slow discharge process to the nursing facility. Another aspect of this is the difficulty many hospitals have in placing their patients in nursing facility beds. Many hospitals find difficulty placing patients with only Medicare, with only Medicaid, or especially Medicaid pending. There is also concern with discharge time from the hospital, where it seems nursing facilities simply drag their feet on admissions. It is not unheard of in the hospital arena for a patient to go unassessed for days or for admissions to occur only on weekdays. There are often no nursing facility representatives available to assess the patients for admission over a weekend. If you believe this to be a significant issue, you are correct. You can be the hero to the hospital, your corporation, and your bottom line by focusing on admissions (especially over the weekends). Potential residents sitting for days in the hospital equate to missed opportunities to build census.

Note: The total picture is much more complex, as Medicare and Medicaid, with their fixed reimbursement rate per admission, are not the only providers that pay for hospital days of care. The reality is that most non-Medicare/Medicaid providers negotiate reimbursement rates to hospitals based primarily on published Medicare and Medicaid reimbursement rates. The effect on the nursing facility case mix is thus similar: Patients discharge from hospitals to the nursing facility quicker and sicker to lower the daily cost of care to the payers such as Medicare and Medicaid.

ROLES OF THE NURSING FACILITY IN THE LONG-TERM CARE CONTINUUM

Physicians prescribe institutional nursing care for persons in a stable or unstable condition who require continuing medical supervision and services of licensed nursing personnel around the clock.

COMMON PITFALLS IN PRACTICE
- Understand the place of your facility in the field—you are the step-down provider from the hospitals today for many residents. It is time for the industry to step up to meet this need and bolster the services that we offer.
- All too many administrators refuse to work together with their neighboring hospitals. This should be a very open relationship between you and the hospital. The well-prepared administrator who builds census on a daily basis is a phone call away from the hospital discharge planner.

OUTSIDE RESOURCES OF THE NURSING FACILITY

NAB DOMAIN 1B18: COMMUNITY RESOURCES, PROGRAMS, AND AGENCIES (E.G., MEALS ON WHEELS, HOUSING VOUCHERS, AREA AGENCIES ON AGING, VETERANS AFFAIRS); 1C: ANCILLARY SERVICES

The nursing facility staff alone is physically and emotionally incapable of meeting its residents' complete psychosocial and medical needs. Churches, schools, and other community groups, along with individual volunteers, are a necessary part of caregiving within the facility.

Outliving one's peers is one of the more difficult adjustments in old age. For persons living to the age of 80 years and beyond, the deaths of most of one's friends and peer family members is a saddening reality. There is a portion of the resident population in every facility with no one left interested in their welfare.

There is not enough money in the average nursing facility budget to staff at a level sufficient to provide all the human contact and caring the residents need. Even when there are funds, there remains a qualitative difference between care offered by a paid staff member and what a volunteer from the community can offer. If the nursing facility experience is to be fully humanized, this will occur only when there is sufficient contact between the residents and the community.

MAJOR ORGANIZATIONS IN THE LONG-TERM CARE FIELD

The following are some of the outside groups and organizations that may directly or indirectly impact the lives of nursing facility administrators:

- AARP—membership of more than 33 million Americans aged 50 years and older. Represents aging Americans' interests on a number of dimensions. https://www .aarp.org/
- American College of Health Care Administrators (ACHCA)—the only professional organization specifically for nursing facility administrators. Student memberships, student mentorship programs, and many other resources are available for both students and administrators. Offers the ability to become a fellow (FACHCA) in the industry. https://www.achca.org/
- American College of Health Care Executives (ACHE)—the professional organization focused upon hospital administrators and other acute care executives. Offers the ability to become a fellow (FACHE) in the industry. https://www.ache.org/
- Administration on Aging (AOA)—part of the Association for Community Living today, focused on advancing older Americans' concerns and interests. This is the principal organization that carries out provisions of the Older Americans Act. https://acl.gov/about-acl/administration-aging
- Alliance for Retired Americans—focused on ensuring that all seniors and retirees can live a life of dignity and retirement security. Affiliated with trade unions. https://retiredamericans.org/
- American Federation for Aging Research—focused on advancing the science of healthy aging through research. https://www.afar.org/

- American Geriatrics Society—a nationwide nonprofit society of geriatrics health-care professionals dedicated to improving older people's health, independence, and quality of life. https://www.americangeriatrics.org/
- American Health Care Association/National Center for Assisted Living (AHCA/NCAL)—the largest association in the United States representing long-term and postacute care providers. Focused on improving the lives of the millions of frail, older adults and individuals who receive long-term or postacute care in member facilities. https://www.ahcancal.org/Pages/default.aspx
- American Society on Aging—broadly representative of professionals interested in the aging field. Focused on optimizing the quality of life for older adults in America. https://www.asaging.org/
- Argentum—a national trade association serving companies that own, operate, and support senior living communities in the United States. https://www.argentum.org/
- Gerontological Society of America—a large, interdisciplinary organization focused upon cultivating excellence in research and aging to advance innovations in practice and policy. https://www.geron.org/
- LeadingAge—a national industry group that represents members from all areas of the long-term care continuum. https://leadingage.org/
- National Institute on Aging—part of the National Institutes of Health. Overall focus is on supporting aging research, developing research and clinician-scientists in aging, and disseminating information via its website. https://www.nia.nih.gov/
- National Association of Long-Term Care Administrator Boards (NAB)—the NAB develops and administers national testing programs for state licensure qualification for Health Services Executives, Nursing Home and Assisted Living Administrators, and Home and Community-Based Services Managers (the "NAB exams"). The NAB also provides administrator continuing education (CE) tracking through NAB's CE Registry and approves continuing education offerings accepted in all states requiring continuing education. NAB offers administrator in training (AIT) resources and training, as well as AIT preceptor resources and training. The NAB is the accreditor of academic programs for Health Services Executives. The NAB's Health Service Executive Qualification designation supports state licensure qualification in multiple lines of service in states that have adopted the NAB Health Service Executive (HSE) standard. NAB also develops and maintains the Domains of Practice for the profession. https://www.nabweb.org/
- National Council on Aging—nonprofit group, helping community service organizations enhance older adults' lives. https://www.ncoa.org/

COMMON PITFALLS IN PRACTICE
- Many new administrators believe that it is "me against the world," and this is far from the case. Get involved in your professional organizations (ACHCA) and get the professional support you need, mentorship, and a keen ear on the industry by being involved.

4.2 THE SOCIAL SECURITY ACT: MEDICARE AND MEDICAID

Section Concepts

- *Reimbursements from Medicare and Medicaid account for well over half of the typical nursing facility cash flow*
- *The Social Security Act (Medicare and Medicaid), for example, Medicare Parts A, B, C, and Plan D*
- *Medicaid concepts such as spend down and buy-in agreements*

Consider as the Administrator . . .

- *Is it possible to manage the Medicare and Medicaid admissions in such a way that these residents are a source of profit rather than a source of potential loss to the facility?*

NAB DOMAIN 3B1: FEDERAL HEALTHCARE LAWS, RULES, AND REGULATIONS; 3B2: GOVERNMENT PROGRAMS AND ENTITIES (E.G., MEDICARE, MEDICAID, WAIVERS); 3B3: CERTIFICATION AND LICENSURE REQUIREMENTS FOR THE ORGANIZATION

4.2.1 THE SOCIAL SECURITY ACT: MEDICARE

Consider as the Administrator . . .

- Knowing some of this history will help you understand the origins of the industry and how we got to where we are today. It will also help explain some of those changes that will inevitably happen as you begin your career!

The nursing facility industry is molded by the Social Security Act and owes the large scale of its economic existence (passing the $172 billion mark in 2019; Martin et al., 2020) to this original legislation and its later amendments. This one Act is mainly responsible for generating financial support for older persons, enabling the nursing facility industry to become the second-largest segment of the healthcare industry, after hospitals.

ORIGINS OF THE SOCIAL SECURITY ACT

When the Social Security Act came into existence in 1935, it responded to a fundamental societal change in American life: our evolution from an agrarian to a highly industrialized form of society. Growing old suddenly became visible nationally during the shift from an agricultural form of society in which the aged were customarily cared for by the family in the home to a society where the workplace was a factory. Economic conditions beyond their influence often control the socioeconomic status of workers. Urbanization and industrialization brought increased problems to the aged, such as unemployment and economic survivorship concerns. This became especially true for the dependents when the primary wage earner died.

The event that brought these problems to the attention of America in dramatic terms was the Great Depression of the 1930s. By 1935, 50% of the aged were indigent. Within 5 years, the proportion had grown to 66%.

ASPECTS AFFECTING THE NURSING FACILITY INDUSTRY

The nursing facility industry owes its size to Social Security checks and reimbursement by Medicare and Medicaid for residents' bills.

The Original Social Security Act and Its Amendments

The original Social Security Act, as passed in 1935, consisted of 11 titles enacting the program, authorizing the necessary taxes, and establishing the administrative mechanisms of the Act. Numerous amendments have been added to the Social Security Act over the years. Only those more directly affecting the nursing facility industry are mentioned here.

In 1950, permanently disabled persons, who might need nursing facility care, were added as beneficiaries. In that same year, federal matching money was made available to states to pay for medical care for persons on public assistance—a precursor of Medicaid, which was to come in 1965. States were required to establish licensing programs for nursing facilities. Some already had done so.

By 1956, the Social Security program was known as OASDI—old age (OA), survivors (S), and disabled (D) insurance (I). It was not until 1960 that the H (for health) was added, and it became OASDHI. The next step toward the Medicaid program, so critical to the nursing facility industry, came in 1960 with the Kerr-Mills Act, which amended the Social Security Act to provide medical assistance to the aged (MAA). This amendment offered 50% to 84% in matching funds to states, depending on the per capita income of each state. However, during the following 5 years, only 25 states implemented this program to assist their aged.

The major amendments affecting the nursing facility industry were added in 1965, with the passage of Title 18, known as Medicare, and 1 year later, Title 19, known as Medicaid. These are discussed in the following pages.

Amendments called for the licensure of nursing facility administrators and recognized the category of "intermediate care facility." The amendments established the definition of the SNF and dropped the term "extended care facility" (ECF), which had been causing some confusion. In 1990, the federal designations "intermediate care nursing facility" (ICF) and SNF were replaced by the single term *nursing facility*.

Title 20 was added, supporting, among other things, in-home services to older adults. In 1977, antifraud amendments were passed to minimize abuse of the program. Numerous additional amendments were passed during the 1980s. For the past 50 years, the primary focus has been the containment of costs rather than expanding services. In general, it appears that from 1935 to about 1975, the federal government sought to expand benefits under the Social Security Act. In contrast, since 1975, the thrust has reduced the rate of cost increases and the service units for which payment is made.

THE "CONDITIONS OF PARTICIPATION"

After an extended implementation period and several additional amendments (described subsequently), the Social Security Administration (SSA) prepared an extensive set of rules or minimum conditions required for any nursing facility receiving federal funds to meet. Proposed rules were published in the *Federal Register* on July 12, 1973. The SSA received so many comments that the usual 30-day period for public comment was extended to 60 days, ending September 13, 1973. Officials made several changes in response to public comments and published final rules on January 17, 1974 (*Federal Register*, 39(12), Part 3, pp. 2238–2249). These rules still govern day-to-day life in nursing facilities.

Importance to the Nursing Facility Industry

Federal rules are of overriding importance to the nursing facility industry because, directly or indirectly, most nursing facilities must comply with them, especially if they expect to be reimbursed for services to Medicare or Medicaid patients. The states license nursing facilities. However, most states relied very heavily on the earlier federal conditions of participation in drawing up their standards for licensing nursing facilities. The net effect is that nearly every nursing facility, directly or indirectly, is obligated to comply with federal standards.

These new rules did bring some clarity to the industry. Nomenclature for the various levels of nursing care facilities had been a source of confusion at the federal level (and still is at the state level). States use different designations for nursing facility levels of care. To further complicate matters, the development of CCRCs and the concept of "assisted living," which is used in many states, suggests that we have moved into a period of multiple designations for nursing facility-like services.

Using federal money in part, states conduct on-site inspections of nursing facilities to determine whether they meet state, and usually, federal requirements. It is important to note that the federal government can also come in and inspect any facility that receives federal funding as a means of payment (read: Medicare and Medicaid).

Not many months after the 1974 conditions were published, the Department of Health, Education, and Welfare (currently designated the DHHS) commissioned "Operation Common Sense." This operation involved a group of federal regulation writers who committed themselves "to revise and recodify (these) regulations to produce clear, readable and helpful documents." In making the regulations more easily understood, these federal employees attempted to introduce "needed" policy changes simultaneously.

By 1976, a drive called the "Long-Term Care Facility Improvement Campaign" was on within the Department of Health Education and Welfare. It began by issuing a monograph supporting the idea of a comprehensive patient assessment mechanism.

Out of this grew a 3-year project called the Patient Care Evaluation Project (PACE). PACE staff tested two versions (PACE I and PACE II). Criticisms were that the instrument brought "burdensome paperwork," that it put "too much emphasis on the medical model" (for the nursing facility), and that "evidence was lacking that PACE produced either cost-effectiveness or benefit." However, the federal government was preparing to move.

As a response to complaints, the CMS (the federal agency that administers Medicare and Medicaid) published a general notice in the June 8, 1978 *Federal Register* that it planned to revise these federal regulations. It invited public comment.

The response by 1,200 organizations, individuals, and providers was impressive. Hearings were held in California, Georgia, the District of Columbia, Maryland, and Illinois. In addition, 620 written comments were received. Most comments were focused on the CMS easing regulatory burdens. In the summer of 1980, the CMS published what it assumed would be the new requirements destined to replace the long-criticized 1974 amendments.

The CMS officials ran into heavy seas. During the Carter administration, all of these changes had been proposed by the CMS. President Carter lost the election to Ronald Reagan, who rejected the proposed revisions, using the Tax Equity and Fiscal Responsibility Act as his vehicle.

Several years of unrest followed. To deflect congressional criticism, the executive branch suggested that the Institute of Medicine appoint a 20-person panel to study facility care. This panel issued a 400-page report. They found the quality of care and quality of life in nursing facilities "unsatisfactory" and called for a new federal government regulation effort. The panel members sought to strengthen the federal requirements, with a new emphasis on inspections based more on the quality of patient care delivered, that is, a focus on care outcomes. Patients' rights, they argued, should be given more attention.

A coalition of more than 40 concerned long-term care organizations successfully lobbied for new legislation that embodied much of the 200-page Institute of Medicine report. Medicare and Medicaid long-term care amendments were passed in the 1987 Omnibus Budget Reconciliation Act. This legislation, and new federal requirements proposed by the federal CMS in the February 2, 1989 *Federal Register* were implemented during 1989 and 1990. This new legislation ended 15 years of stagnation, during which the federal regulations (called Conditions of Participation) remained static despite constant attempts at reform. In 2010 and subsequent years, the CMS constantly updates the Guidelines to Surveyors throughout the year.

We turn now to an examination of the essential components of the Medicare and Medicaid legislation, after which we examine several other pieces of legislation that affect and constitute what may be called the long-term care continuum.

MEDICARE

Part A

Everyone receiving Social Security is automatically covered under Part A.

Hospital Costs

Covered hospital-related costs are paid on the following basis:

- Patient paid deductible for each benefit period
- Days 1–60: $0 coinsurance for each benefit period
- Days 61–90: $371 coinsurance per day of each benefit period
- Days 91 and beyond: $742 coinsurance per each "lifetime reserve day" after day 90 for each benefit period (up to 60 days over your lifetime)
- Beyond lifetime reserve days: All costs are the responsibility of the patient (CMS, 2021a, 2021b)

Nursing Facility Costs

Covered SNF-related costs are paid on the following basis:

- Covered *skilled* care is under Part A benefits, on a short-term basis
- Conditions must be met to begin coverage
  - Patient has Part A and has benefit days left in their benefit period to use
  - Patient must have a qualifying hospital stay (otherwise known as the three-midnight rule)
  - Physician-made decision that patient needs daily skilled care
- Payment is covered as follows:
  - Days 1–20: $0 for each benefit period
  - Days 21–100: $185.50 coinsurance per day of the benefit period
  - Days 101 and beyond: Resident pays all costs
- What skilled care entails:
  - Semi-private room
  - Meals
  - Skilled nursing care
  - Physical therapy
  - Occupational therapy
  - Speech therapy
  - Social services
  - Medications
  - Medical supplies and equipment (durable medical equipment [DME])
  - Ambulance transportation
  - Dietary counseling
  - Swing bed services (CMS, 2021b, 2021c, 2021d, 2021e)

Home Healthcare Costs

Covered home health services–related costs are paid on the following basis:

- Only eligible services are covered:
  - Part-time or intermittent skilled nursing care
  - Physical therapy
  - Occupational therapy
  - Speech therapy
  - Social services

- Part-time or intermittent home health aide services
- Injectable osteoporosis drugs for women

- Conditions must be met to begin coverage:
  - Patient must be under the care of a physician and getting care under a plan of care created and reviewed regularly by a physician
  - Physician must certify:
    - The need for intermittent skilled nursing care
    - The need for and expected improvement from utilizing physical therapy, occupational therapy, and/or speech therapy services
  - Patient must be homebound, and this must be certified by a physician
- Payment is covered as follows:
  - $0 cost to the patient for home healthcare services
  - 20% cost to the patient of the Medicare-approved amount for DME (CMS, 2021f)

Part B

Part B covers only medically necessary services and preventive services. The focus is physicians' services and testing, outpatient care, home healthcare services, durable medical equipment, and preventive services.

Services pertinent to nursing facilities are as follows:

- Ambulance services (some and limited)
- Clinical laboratory services, bloodwork
- Diabetes screenings
- Physician services
- Durable medical equipment
- Emergency department services
- Flu shots
- Home healthcare services
- Mental health services (outpatient)
- Testing (other than lab testing—x-ray, others; DHHS, 2014)

Payments Under Part B

Currently, under Part B, after the patient pays their yearly deductible, they typically pay 20% of the Medicare-approved amount for the following:

- Most physician services (inpatient and outpatient)
- Outpatient therapy
- DME (CMS, 2021c, 2021f)

Excluded From Coverage

Many healthcare costs associated with older adults are excluded from payment by Medicare Parts A and B. These exclusions are why many patients opt for supplemental insurance or to take part in Part C Advantage plans. Neither Part A nor Part B will pay for the following:

- Long-term care (custodial care)
- Most dental care
- Eye exams related to prescribing glasses
- Dentures
- Cosmetic surgery
- Acupuncture
- Hearing aids and exams for fitting them
- Routine foot care (CMS, 2021b)

Part C

Part C plans are referred to as Medicare Advantage plans. These are alternatives to traditional Medicare and are offered by private insurance companies, which Medicare approves. Essentially, these Advantage plans are "bundled" plans that include Part A (hospital insurance), Part B (medical insurance), and Part D (drug coverage). The other benefit to these plans is that they offer things that traditional Medicare does not cover, such as vision, hearing, and dental. Many other covered services are included in the Advantage plan, which differs from company to company offering the insurance. Each plan has stipulations on what is covered, levels of coverage, the use of network providers, and many others, making this particular coverage difficult for some older adults to navigate and use.

Part D

Part D coverage is the Medicare drug plan, implemented in 2006, after many years of concern surrounding older adults not being able to afford their medications. This coverage primarily assists patients outside nursing facilities. The nursing facility absorbed many prescription drug costs (all costs in the case of Part A residents, some costs for all other payers).

SOME DEFINITIONS

Medicare Administrative Contractors

Medicare administrative contractors (MACs) are private entities that process medical claims for Medicare beneficiaries. Initially, these entities were called intermediaries (for Part A billing) and carriers (for Part B billing). These terms are often still used in the field and are included here as a clarification.

Assignment

Assignment refers to the agreement by doctors, providers, and suppliers to accept the Medicare-approved amount as full payment for covered services. They cannot charge additional for any services, and patients would still be required to pay any coinsurance or deductible amounts that they have outstanding at the time of the claim.

COMMON PITFALLS IN PRACTICE
- Spend time learning the ins and outs of Medicare and other payment method-ologies. It will help you, and it will help your residents and families. You will be viewed as the resident expert on all this as the administrator.

4.2.2 TITLE 19: MEDICAID

Consider as the Administrator . . .

- Understand that Medicaid is a federal program which is provided by the individual states. Many administrators live close to state lines or work in multiple states; thus, they will have to understand specific intricacies of the Medicaid program where they are working.

Medicaid and Medicare were both passed as amendments to the Social Security Act. Medicare has been essentially an insurance program for recipients of Social Security benefits. Medicaid has not been insurance; as designed, it has been medical aid for persons receiving assistance (formerly referred to as "welfare") and for comparable groups of persons defined as medically indigent.

Although Medicare was a federally run program, Medicaid was a program of federal grants to the states to enable them to provide medical assistance to four categories of persons:

- Families with dependent children (AFDC)
- The aged—persons receiving Old Age Assistance (OAA)
- The blind—aid to the blind (AB)
- Persons permanently and totally disabled (i.e., persons receiving federally aided public assistance)

Comparable groups of medically indigent persons, not currently on medical assis-tance but who fall into the preceding four categories, are medically needy when medical expenses reduce their income below the Medicaid eligibility level.

SPEND DOWN

Research suggests that the majority of nursing facility residents were, at entry, either already financially qualified or would have been so immediately had they been institutionalized. It is estimated that:

1. One in four persons admitted as private payers stayed long enough to become Medicaid recipients
2. Approximately one in three persons eventually covered by Medicaid were not eligible when admitted
3. About 30% to 40% of Medicaid expenditures on nursing facility care is attribut-able to individuals who spent down

The idea of "spend down," as applied to a nursing facility resident, is that they spend down their assets during a prolonged stay to the point where they qualify for Medicaid.

THE MEDICAID LOOK-BACK PERIOD

A concern of Medicaid applicants is qualifying for coverage. Medicaid assumes financial need. Over the years, the program has seen many inventive ways to take advantage of proving a financial need. In fact, at one time, families would simply transfer assets out of the name of the individual applying for Medicaid and then apply. Medicaid has had a "look-back period" for many years to deal with this system abuse. The stipulations often change with congressional years; however, at this time, the period applies as follows:

- Applicant cannot have assets above the asset (resource) limit.
- All asset transfers are reviewed which occur within the look-back period, should there be a violation of the rules, there is a penalty period of Medicaid ineligibility.
- Currently, 48 states and the District of Columbia have look-back periods that are 60 months.
- California and New York have a look-back period of 30 months.
- Each state has specific guidelines associated with look-back periods, acceptable expenditures, and so forth.

THE QUALIFYING INCOME TRUST

These types of trusts go by many names—qualifying income trusts (QITs), Miller's Trusts, Income Only Trusts, Income Diversion Trusts, and a few others.

These trusts are wildly controversial and are viewed by many as diverting money away from care that the resident should be responsible for to the state. However, these trusts have rather specific uses associated with them.

They are intended for those who fall into the odd area between having too much income for Medicaid qualification and not enough income to pay for long-term care. They are also used to allow one spouse to maintain their lifestyle in the community while another spouse resides in a nursing facility. As a result, the QIT can be put into place to "protect" assets, allowing an individual to qualify for Medicaid while not qualifying for it. The QIT diverts the income over the maximum asset (resource) limits into a restricted funds account each month. The QIT, when in place, is irrevocable.

As a result of these financial workarounds, many states have departments collecting any available funds after a Medicaid resident's death. These Medicaid Estate Recovery Programs (MERPs) have the option to exercise their right to get any monies paid out on behalf of a resident back from their estate. Most will not collect any amount greater than the amount spent on the resident while alive and a Medicaid recipient. Such action may seem harsh; however, it is essential to understand that many Medicaid recipients have estates, assets, and other tangibles worth millions of dollars. These MERPs are simply tasked with collecting any monies due to the state when an estate is liquidated.

FACILITY BEDS BY CERTIFICATION CATEGORY

Licensed nursing facilities may apply to be certified for participation in the Medicare and/or Medicaid program voluntarily. Facilities may participate in (a) the Medicaid only (Title 19) program, (b) the Medicare only (Title 18) program, or (c) in the Medicare/Medicaid dually certified (Title 18 and 19) program. Since 1991, the Medicare program classified facilities as SNFs, whereas the Medicaid-certified facilities were designated as nursing facilities. Federal Medicare certification allows all or part of a facility to be certified.

RESIDENTS BY PAYER SOURCE

Who Pays for Nursing Facility Care?

NAB DOMAIN 1B18: COMMUNITY RESOURCES, PROGRAMS, AND AGENCIES (E.G., MEALS ON WHEELS, HOUSING VOUCHERS, AREA AGENCIES ON AGING, VETERANS AFFAIRS); 2A5: REVENUE AND REIMBURSEMENT (E.G., PDPM, PDGM, ACOs, HMOs, MEDICAID, PRIVATE PAYORS)

For many years now, Medicare and Medicaid have been the predominant payers for nursing facility care given in the United States.

The predominant payer has been and is likely to remain Medicaid. Medicare reimbursement policies, together with Medicaid reimbursement policies, typically determine the profitability of the average facility. The number of private payers has been slowly increasing but not as quickly as expected with the number of baby boomers. Long-term care insurance has not become a significant payer source due to its high annual premiums, limited availability, and confined benefits. Persons in their 50s or 60s purchase most policies as they anticipate retirement and increasing healthcare costs.

The primary problem with long-term care insurance is that as a general rule, those who can afford it probably could pay for care without it, while those who cannot afford it would likely need such insurance. In one sense, long-term care insurance to date has been purchased by persons who wish to insure every eventuality and to help ensure that their life savings do not end up as payments for long-term care. When long-term care insurance was introduced, the proportion of private-pay residents in nursing facilities was expected to rise from a steady 5% to a significantly increased proportion of private payers. But this has not happened and is unlikely to happen. Most residents who are private payers would pay privately with or without long-term care insurance. As some long-term care insurance policies now cover assisted living, that segment of the long-term care industry benefits most.

Facilities often have other sources of revenue. The proportion of private-pay residents is typically less than 10%, although a few (perhaps only a few hundred) nursing facilities are 100% private pay. In this case, the facility must inform the resident before and at admission that should the resident become eligible for Medicaid, the resident must move out of the facility. Additional sources of revenue include the Department of Veterans Affairs and hospice payments. Additionally, most facilities have service-related sources, such as soda machines and similar vendor income, income from beauty services, and the like. Often facilities offer allied health services, such as various therapies such as physical therapy, occupational therapy, and speech therapy. Facilities are generally free to provide other healthcare-related services to the public should they choose to do so. A facility might, for example, decide to offer x-ray services through a subcontractor who brings the machine to the facility on stated days.

CASE STUDY

Long-Term Care Insurance?

While making administrator "rounds" one afternoon in your facility, Ms. Brown's son stops you in the hall. He asks for your advice about whether to join a long-term care insurance program by a mutual life insurance company that his employer has just announced. Mr. Brown and his wife are each 55 years old, both working and in good health. He says he understands that only about 3% to 5% of Americans have elected to take out long-term care insurance for one or both spouses and wonders how to make his decision. Could you help?

He hands you a sheet with the following information:

Sample of the Monthly Premium Payments			
Daily Maximum Benefit Options			
Monthly Premium			
Age (years)	Option 1 ($75/day)	Option 2 ($150/day)	Option 3 ($200/day)
35	$17.94	$23.57	$28.66
45	$23.66	$33.95	$43.26
55	$31.58	$50.72	$60.56
65	$57.43	$101.60	$145.78

Option 1: $115,000 maximum lifetime benefit
Option 2: $205,000 maximum lifetime benefit
Option 3: $295,000 maximum lifetime benefit
Waiting period: 120 days of continuous service
Types of covered services: Nursing facility care, home healthcare, adult daycare, and respite care
Qualifications for benefits: Benefits will be paid when the insured individual has met the following requirements:
- Has been certified as unable to perform at least two of the following ADLs independently: bathing or dressing, eating, toileting, transferring from bed to chair, maintaining continence
- Has incurred expenses for covered services
- Has completed the required waiting period
Prior hospitalization is not required to be eligible for benefits.

(continued)

Case management: The services of a case manager will be provided to all insured. The case manager will review information to determine ADL dependency; if necessary, arrange for a visiting nurse to assess functional dependency; recommend the type of site and level of care; and help arrange for care.

The case manager's recommendations for the type of site and level of care are for your consideration only. You are not required to follow these recommendations. However, the recommendations can be cost-effective as they provide you with information on the level of care that may be best for you. Avoiding a more intensive level of services than is necessary may increase the length of the period over which you receive benefits.

Coverage: Alzheimer's disease, senile dementia, and other degenerative illnesses are covered under the plan. Self-inflected injury and a condition caused by attempting to commit a felony are not covered. Alcoholism and drug addiction treatments are not covered.

Cost adjustments: Nursing facility and home healthcare costs will be reviewed every 3 years using the Consumer Price Index (CPI) or other indicators. If costs increase, you will be allowed to increase your benefit amount. The premium for this increase will be based on your age at the time of the offering. However, the premium for the originally selected benefit amount will continue to be based on your age when you enrolled in the program.

Mr. Brown seeks your recommendations about joining the plan and which option to select if you recommend joining the plan. He says his main concern is that he might not even qualify to collect under the plan.

- *What is your recommendation to your resident's son? What is the basis for your advice?*

COMMON PITFALLS IN PRACTICE
- New administrators often find that they need to be very well versed in business office operations. Helping families navigate Medicare, Medicaid, and other payer sources will help to ensure your success in the field.

4.3 OLDER AMERICANS ACT

Section Concepts

- *The Older Americans Act has far-reaching effects on older Americans, both inside and outside the facility*

Consider as the Administrator . . .

- Whereas the Older Americans Act has little to do with residents in a facility, your knowledge of it can certainly assist your discharged residents' transition back into the community.

The Older Americans Act can be characterized as Congress's response to noninstitutional, primarily nonhealthcare needs of older adults. Medicare and Medicaid mainly provide this group's institutionalized healthcare needs (home healthcare being the exception). Title 20 of the Social Security Act is also a response to the primarily noninstitutional needs of older adults.

The Older Americans Act authorizes payment for almost any activity that may lead to an improved quality of life for persons 60 years and older (with some programs, e.g., "reemployment" programs, for persons 55 years and older). The funds and agencies authorized and generated by the Older Americans Act play significant roles in shaping the long-term care industry in the United States. For this reason, some of its more essential features are explored here.

PRECURSORS OF THE OLDER AMERICANS ACT

Events that laid the foundation for the passage of the Older Americans Act began about 1945, when the first state, Connecticut, set up a commission concerned with the needs of older individuals. That same year, a White House conference on aging was held, at which lobbyists brought heavy pressure for a federal role in addressing the needs of older adults. Years later, President John F. Kennedy sent a message to Congress titled "Elderly Citizens of Our Nation." He recommended federal help for older individuals who do not need institutional care but are encountering the expected increase in the difficulty of successfully performing ADLs, such as bathing, dressing, and toileting. Continued lobbying for federal aid for the functional older adult led to the passage of the Older Americans Act.

GRAND OBJECTIVES: TITLE 1

Title 1 states the goals of the Older Americans Act: Equal opportunity of every older individual to the full and free enjoyment of the following:

- Adequate income
- The best possible physical and mental health science can offer, without regard to economic status
- Affordable, suitable housing
- Full restorative services for those needing institutional care
- Employment
- Retirement in health and dignity
- Pursuit of the widest civic, cultural, educational, and recreational opportunities
- Efficient community services (low-cost transportation, choices in living arrangements, coordinated social service assistance)
- Immediate benefit of technological developments
- Freedom, independence, and the free exercise of individual initiative in planning and managing their own life

Other portions of the Older Americans Act authorize the Commissioner on Aging, the Older Americans Act administrator, to pay for virtually any service or activity that will foster these broadly stated goals. The goals and authorizations are sweeping; however, the economic realities of the level of funding have prevented the implementation of large-scale programs to achieve these goals.

OTHER TITLES

Title 2 established the AOA within the Office of Human Development Services (OHDS), which is within the federal DHHS. A Commissioner on Aging, appointed by the president and confirmed by the Senate, is empowered to administer the Older Americans Act and reports directly to the secretary of the DHHS.

Title 3 authorized grants to the states to create Planning and Service Areas within which the local AAAs function. Title 3b is concerned with social services, Title 3c1 with congregate nutritional services for those 60 years or older and their spouses, and Title 3c2 with home-delivered meals. Title 4 deals with research and training. Title 5 creates the Senior Community Services Employment Program (SCSEP) for those 55 years or older with limited incomes (usually 125% of poverty). Title 6 addressed grants to Native American (Indian) tribes. Title 7 authorized a health education and training program for older individuals.

COMPREHENSIVE SERVICES SYSTEM

Another major assignment to the states and their local AAAs is to foster the development of comprehensive and coordinated service systems for older adults. This assignment is accomplished by establishing numerous supportive services, nutrition programs, and multipurpose senior centers.

DEFINITION OF SUPPORTIVE SERVICES

The local AAAs have legislative approval to engage in all the following extensive range of activities:

- Health services, including education, training, welfare, information, recreation, homemaker, counseling, and referral to specialists
- Transportation to and from supportive services
- Services to encourage the older adults to use supportive services
- Help older persons to obtain housing, repair and renovate to minimum housing standards, adapt homes to individual's disabilities, and introduce modifications to prevent unlawful entry
- Services to avoid institutionalization, including institutional evaluation and screening and legal services such as tax and financial counseling
- Physical exercise services
- Health screening
- Career counseling
- Ombudsperson services for long-term care complaints
- Unique disabilities services
- Job counseling
- Other services necessary for the welfare of older individuals

In sum, the local AAAs are empowered to engage in various activities on behalf of older persons in the community. Generally, however, funding has been at a modest level.

Effectiveness of the Act

The extent to which the Older Americans Act has achieved its goals is debatable. The local AAAs have been given a mandate that could cost billions of dollars if implemented and awarded a shoestring budget for accomplishing these tasks. Whether the services under the Older Americans Act would be available without a means test to every older adult is also in question.

One of the most significant burdens of growing old is the loneliness resulting from losing friends and family members of the same generation. For many individuals, participating in the congregate meal is a primary source of social contact with other people, regardless of income level.

Have the AAAs been successful in establishing a coordinated service system for long-term care in their communities? Generally, no. They have had neither the funds nor the administrative authority to bring together and organize the long-term care providers in the communities. Despite the meager funding levels and lack of control, however, there is a network of services in place for all older Americans who need assistance to remain outside an institution. This network is a significant improvement over the decades before the 1960s when such services did not exist at all. This network and the nutritional assistance to all older Americans have become integral to the long-term care system in which nursing facilities are active participants.

COMMON PITFALLS IN PRACTICE

- As the administrator, you are the community resource expert. Much of the Older Americans Act applies to things outside the facility. The more you know about this, the more people you can help. When you are the referral source for Older Americans Act services in the community, you often see referrals coming back your way! Be in the know.

4.4 LABOR AND MANAGEMENT: LAWS AND REGULATIONS

Section Concepts

- *Labor laws directly impact the daily operations of every facility. Here you will learn some background on labor law:*
  - *What is permitted and forbidden in dealing with labor unions*
    - *How the following laws affect the facility:*
    - *Consumer Credit Protection Act*
    - *Equal Employment Opportunity Act (EEOA)*
    - *Pregnancy Discrimination Act*
    - *Equal Employment Opportunity Commission (EEOC)*

- *Americans with Disabilities Act (ADA)*
- *Patient Self-Determination Act*
- *Safe Medical Devices Act*
- *Clinical Laboratory Improvement Act*
- *Civil Rights Act*
- *Family and Medical Leave Act (FMLA)*
- *Health Insurance Portability and Accountability Act (HIPAA)*
- *The Lifespan Respite Care Act*

- *You will also learn about compensation regulations covering such areas as minimum wages, overtime, exempt and nonexempt employees, equal pay, workers' compensation, and unemployment compensation*

Consider as the Administrator . . .

- *What rights do nursing facility administrators have when employees in the facility are seeking to form a union? What rights do the employees have? What are the basic laws and regulations governing the managers' dealings with employees?*

NAB DOMAIN 2C: HUMAN RESOURCES; 2C14: LABOR RELATIONS (E.G., UNION, COLLECTIVE BARGAINING [CBA], CONTRACT/POOL STAFF)

NAB DOMAIN 3B1: FEDERAL HEALTHCARE LAWS, RULES, AND REGULATIONS

This section provides a framework to enable the reader to begin to answer these questions.

4.4.1 EARLY MANAGEMENT: LABOR RELATIONS IN THE UNITED STATES

During most of the earlier years of its history, the government of the United States strongly supported management in its dealings with employees. It was not until 1935 that American workers won government sanction of the right to form trade unions.

The passage of the National Labor Relations Act (better known as the Wagner Act) in 1935 was the first nationwide American labor legislation to favor the growth of trade unions. This passage was the culmination of a long, slow process.

MANAGEMENT PREFERENCES

Most managers would prefer not to have to deal with organized labor. Unionization is perceived as intensifying the difficulty of the administrator's responsibilities. There is a natural tendency for what organizational theorists call the "we/they" phenomenon to occur in the relationship between labor and management. Workers often perceive their interests as different from those of managers, whose task is to operate cost-effectively, that is, to produce the best results for the least cost.

The administrator would be happy to pay nurses and nurse's aides the premium wages that will attract the most competent workers available, but pressures to keep costs down and low reimbursements do not often permit this. The result is that most nursing facility workers, especially the nurse's aides and the kitchen and housekeeping staff, are paid at prevailing rates in the particular geographical area, which are usually close to the required minimum wage levels (Cole & Kelley, 2020). Understandably, these workers, many of whom hold a second full-time job to make ends meet, seek to increase their incomes from the nursing facility and obtain the best working conditions on their jobs. Tensions between managers and workers are inevitably built into the situation. How do they deal with them? What are the manager's rights? What rights do the employees have?

THE COLONIAL PERIOD

So powerful were the managers in the colonial period that workers contented themselves with forming "fraternal unions" to help each other cope with personal economic adversity but certainly not to act collectively for improved working conditions and more pay. Employers were able to prevent effective unionization. At their discretion, employers could fire any worker seeking to organize a union, refuse to negotiate with any union representative, and require each new employee to sign a "yellow dog" contract by which the worker agreed not to join a union.

During the 19th century, the U.S. courts consistently sided with management. In 1806, a federal court ruled that workers who sought to combine to exert pressure on managers were participating in a "conspiracy in restraint of trade," which in effect meant that such grouping was to be treated as criminal activity. The first hint of rights for workers did not appear until 1842, when the Massachusetts Supreme Court ruled that unions that did not resort to illegal tactics were not guilty of criminal conspiracy. Still, managers could fire any worker at will for union activity, impose yellow-dog contracts, and (when all else failed) obtain a court injunction against threatened strikes. The managers still retained nearly all of the power. Despite this, the union movement grew. By 1886, skilled workers, such as machinists, bricklayers, and carpenters, formed the American Federation of Labor (AFL).

It was not until 1935 that another major labor force, the Congress of Industrial Organizations (CIO), emerged; in 1955, it merged with the AFL. It was a slow process because the government did not substantially back labor until the Wagner Act was passed in 1935.

The federal government had given American workers some negotiating rights earlier in the century to keep the nation's railroads running. The Railway Labor Act of 1926 was the first federal legislation sanctioning union organizations and the right to bargain collectively with management.

The first national effort to define workers' and managers' respective rights came just 6 years later. In 1932, the Norris-LaGuardia Act, also called the Anti-Injunction Act, limited the powers of federal courts to side with management through issuing injunctions, court decrees to stop or restrict union efforts to picket, boycott, or strike. Yellow-dog contracts were prohibited.

4.4.2 MAJOR LEGISLATION AFFECTING EMPLOYER/EMPLOYEE RELATIONSHIPS

THE WAGNER ACT

The Wagner Act of 1935 is the landmark law that defined workers' rights for the first time in federal legislation. The Wagner Act limited the freedom of employers to give their views on proposed unionization. The Wagner Act also guaranteed employee bargaining rights: "Employees shall have the right to self-organization, to form, join, or assist labor organizations, to bargain collectively through representatives of their choosing, and to engage in concerted activities, for collective bargaining or other mutual aid or protection."

The Wagner Act created the National Labor Relations Board (NLRB; see https://www.nlrb.gov/about-nlrb/who-we-are/our-history).

THE TAFT-HARTLEY ACT, 1947

In the provisions of the Taft-Hartley Act, unions were prohibited from the following actions:

1. Restraining or coercing employees in exercising their right to join a union or not (unless an agreement existed with management that every worker must be a union member). Union members could not physically prevent other workers from entering a facility, act violently toward nonunion employees, or threaten employees for not supporting union activities.
2. Causing an employer to discriminate against an employee for antiunion activity, nor could unions force employers to hire only workers acceptable to the union.
3. Bargaining with an employer in bad faith. They could not insist on negotiating "illegal" provisions, such as the administration's prerogative to appoint supervisors.
4. Participating in secondary boycotts or jurisdictional disputes. Unions may not picket a nursing facility in an attempt to force it to apply pressure on a subcontractor (e.g., a food service contractor) to recognize a union, nor can a union force an employer to do business only with others, such as unionized suppliers, nor can one union picket for recognition when another union is already certified for a nursing facility.
5. Charging excessive or discriminatory membership fees. They may not charge a higher initiation fee to employees who did not join the union until they negotiated a union contract.
6. Coercing or restraining employees in the selection of the parties to bargain on management's behalf. The manager is free to hire the best labor lawyer available to represent the facility.
7. Forcing managers to hire employees when they are not needed (called featherbedding).

However, certain employee rights were retained when the Wagner Act was amended by this pro-management act (the Taft-Hartley Act). Managers may not:

1. Interfere with, restrain, or coerce employees in the exercise of their rights. Managers may not, for example, give wage increases timed to discourage employees from joining a union or threaten with loss of their jobs employees who vote for a union.
2. Interfere with or attempt to dominate any labor organization or contribute financial or other support to a labor organization. For example, managers cannot take an active part in union affairs or permit a nursing facility supervisor to participate actively in a union, or show favoritism toward one union over another.
3. Discriminate in hiring or giving employees tenure or setting employment terms to encourage or discourage union membership. For example, they cannot fire an employee who urges others to join a union or demote an employee for union activity.
4. Fire or discriminate against any employee who files charges or gives testimony under the Wagner Act.
5. Refuse to bargain collectively with the duly chosen representatives of its employees. For example, the nursing facility administrator must provide financial data to a union if the facility claims to be experiencing financial losses, bargain on mandatory subjects such as hours and wages, and meet with union representatives duly appointed by a certified bargaining unit (Singh, 2016).

An essential consideration for nursing facility administrators is the denial of legal protection to supervisors seeking to form their own unions, thus keeping the management roles of these persons (usually department heads in nursing facilities) managerial in function and identification.

The most critical provision of the Taft-Hartley Act for nursing facility administrators is the restoration of the right of managers to express their views regarding unions and unionizing efforts. This verbiage means that administrators are free to express their opinions about their employees voting for a union in the workplace and judgments about unions in general. Administrators are prohibited from threatening, coercing, or bribing employees concerning their union membership or their decision to join or not to join a union.

THE NATIONAL LABOR RELATIONS BOARD

A significant aspect of the Wagner Act was creating the NLRB, which plays a dominant role in U.S. labor/management relations. It has the following responsibilities:

- To determine what the bargaining unit or units within an organization shall be. A unit contains employees who are represented by a particular union and are covered by its agreement.
- To conduct representation elections by secret ballot to determine which union shall represent the employees within a unit.
- To investigate unfair labor practice charges filed by unions or employees and prosecute any violations revealed by such investigations.

The board is empowered to initiate action against illegal strikes or unfair labor practices by unions. In a typical month, as many as 4,000 new cases are filed with the NLRB.

One of the more controversial features of the Taft-Hartley Act is a provision allowing the president of the United States, through the office of the Attorney General, to seek an injunction for a period of 80 days against strikes or walkouts affecting the nation's welfare or health. Some labor leaders have called this "slave labor."

THE LANDRUM-GRIFFIN ACT OF 1959

Officially designated as the Labor–Management Reporting and Disclosure Act of 1959, the Landrum-Griffin Act seeks to protect the interests of the individual union member against possible union abuses. Specifically, the Act gives each union member a right to the following:

- Nominate candidates for union office
- Vote in union elections
- Attend union meetings
- Examine required annual financial reports by the union to the Secretary of Labor

In addition, employers must report any payments or loans made to unions—the officers or any members—to eliminate what were called "sweetheart contracts," under which union officials and the managers benefited, but the rank-and-file union members did not.

SPECIAL DISPUTE-SETTLING RULES FOR NURSING FACILITY AND HOSPITAL (HEALTHCARE) ADMINISTRATORS

The NLRB had jurisdiction over healthcare institutions. However, until 1974 the Board was expressly forbidden by the original Taft-Hartley Act to hear cases in the nonprofit sector. As the vast majority of nursing facilities and hospitals operating in the 1950s and 1960s were nonprofit, most of the healthcare industry was not subject to these labor laws.

In 1973, Congress began talking of having the law apply to not-for-profit nursing facilities and hospitals. Nursing facilities and hospitals pressed for the following benefits:

- Special protection against strikes
- Priority for rapid NLRB action on disputes
- Mandatory mediation requirements
- Limit on the number of bargaining units to one each for professional, technical, clinical, and maintenance and service workers

On the whole, the nursing facilities and hospitals were successful.

In 1974, Congress amended the Taft-Hartley Act to bring nursing facilities and hospitals under its regulations. However, special provisions were made:

- A nursing facility, hospital, or union must give to the other party 90 days notice of a desire to change an existing contract (this is 30 days more notice than required of others).

- The Federal Mediation and Conciliation Service (FMCS) must be given 30 days notice if an impasse occurs in bargaining for an initial contract after the union is first recognized.
- A nursing facility or hospital union may not picket or strike without 10 days prior notice to allow the facility to make provisions for continuity of care (no prior notice is required of other unions).
- The FMCS may appoint a board of inquiry to mediate the dispute if it decides that a strike would imperil the welfare or health of the community. Neither the nursing facility nor the union is obliged to accept the Board's recommendations, but they must provide any witnesses or information sought by the Board.

For-profit nursing facilities benefited from the 1974 amendment to the Taft-Hartley Act because of these four special labor relations rules.

THE BARGAINING UNIT

Labor unions must seek recognition as representing the majority of persons in a specific bargaining unit of a nursing facility. As indicated earlier, nursing facilities and hospitals sought to limit bargaining units in negotiations to professional, technical, clinical, and maintenance and service workers.

During most of the decade after the 1974 amendments to the Taft-Hartley Act, the NLRB ruled that service and maintenance workers, clerical staff, licensed practical nurses (LPNs), registered nurses, and security guard units constitute appropriate bargaining units in nursing facilities and hospitals. Then the NLRB issued a new ruling. In *St. Francis Hospital (Memphis, Tennessee) v. International Brotherhood of Electrical Workers Local 474*, the NLRB ruled that a group of 39 maintenance workers did not constitute an appropriate bargaining unit. After that, healthcare workers had to represent either "all professionals" or "all nonprofessionals" rather than the particular interest groups allowed during the previous decade.

The effect of this NLRB ruling is to make the union organization of nursing facility employees much more difficult. A far more diverse group of workers must be approached than before for purposes of union representation in elections. The Service Employees International Union (SEIU), at that time, argued that this ruling made it extremely difficult for healthcare workers to unionize.

Decisions favoring either labor or management are reflections of the political administrations in power. Nursing facilities and hospitals had initially wanted to keep the number of bargaining units to no more than four. The NLRB, under more liberal (pro-labor) auspices in Washington, had permitted five. Under the more management-oriented administrations, the number of allowable bargaining units was cut back to two, which could ease matters considerably for nursing facility administrators.

The unionization of nursing facilities is a complicated affair. Several unions have undertaken vigorous attempts to unionize nursing facilities over recent years. As of 2022, we see healthcare worker unionization in about 16.8% of all facilities nationwide (Dean et al., 2022).

All regions of the United States have unionized nursing facilities. From "most unionized" to "least unionized" were the Mid-Atlantic, followed by the West Coast, New England, the Midwest, the Southeast, and the South-Central states. We are seeing an increased interest in unions today. Increased union activity is especially apparent in acute care in the post-COVID-19 world. Many nurses and service line employees feel that their safety was not considered by management and that they did not receive the support necessary from employers during the pandemic. Many employees also did not receive the required medical care when they were struck by COVID-19, as employers stated there was no proof they got it while on the clock. The belief was that the employee could have contracted the disease anywhere, even while working on COVID-19 units with minimal personal protective equipment. It is easy to see why employees are much more interested in union representation today.

The SEIU has been the most active union seeking to organize nursing facility workers. The largest proportion of nursing facilities with unions are in the SEIU, which is an AFL-CIO member. Sadly, the SEIU chose to not make available any current information at the time of this publication. As such, the authors have simply mentioned it here as an entity to increase awareness.

Typically, employees in nursing, dietary, housekeeping, and laundry are the most likely to be unionized. A growing number of employers, particularly the larger chains, attempted to prevent unionization of nurses by arguing that all nurses (RNs and LPNs) are statutory supervisors and thereby excluded from labor law protection to join a union. The employers insisted that because all nurses supervise nurse's aides, all nurses are therefore supervisory personnel and thus not covered by labor laws. In a setback for unionization of nursing facility workers, the United States Supreme Court, by a 5-to-4 decision, agreed and ruled that nurses who supervise lesser-skilled employees are not protected by the National Labor Relations Act (*NLRB v. Health Care & Retirement Corporation of America*). The U.S. Supreme Court, in *NLRB v. Kentucky River Community Care, Inc.*, again confirmed that professional employees, such as nurses, who direct other employees are supervisors and thus ineligible for union membership.

2020: STATE OF THE UNION

Conventional wisdom in the nursing facility industry is that facilities are unionized when employee–management/employee communication is low and focuses more on dissatisfaction with working conditions than on pay levels.

In 2020, approximately 14.3 million U.S. employees were in unions (USA Facts, 2021). There was a significant decrease in the number of union members of 321,000 from 2019 to 2020. Most likely, this decrease was associated with the pandemic. Quite intriguingly, when we look at union membership among healthcare and social assistance workers between 2000 and 2020, we see no change as the percentage of these unionized employees remained firmly at 7.1% (USA Facts, 2021).

NONUNION WORKERS

Nearly 90% of the total labor workforce in this country is not unionized. There are 27 states currently that are "right-to-work" states which affect union membership. These states prohibit requiring employees to join a union to get or to keep a job. There are both positive and negative aspects to this status. However, what of the rights of the nonunionized employee? Over the years, the federal government has enacted legislation establishing and protecting workers' rights in general. Several of these laws are discussed next.

EQUAL PAY ACT OF 1963

The Equal Pay Act requires that men and women performing equal jobs receive equal pay, thus protecting against wage discrimination based on sex. In effect, the act protects both men and women in all forms of compensation. Employees have the right to file discrimination claims under this Act to the Equal Employment Opportunity Commission (EEOC), which enforces the policies (EEOC, 2021a, 2021b).

CIVIL RIGHTS ACT

Title VII of the Civil Rights Act of 1964 prohibits employers and others from discriminating against employees based on race, color, religion, sex, gender, pregnancy, or national origin (EEOC, 2021a, 2021c). Title VII also prohibits discrimination concerning employment conditions, including hiring, firing, promotion, transfer, and admission to training programs. Many of the prohibited questions during an interview are based on ensuring that Title VII is not violated. The Pregnancy Discrimination Act of 1978 amended Title VII to afford pregnant women the same rights as other disabled employees. The Act makes it illegal to discriminate based on pregnancy, childbirth, or related medical conditions in hiring, promoting, suspending, or discharging pregnant women. In addition, the employer is required to pay medical and hospital costs for childbirth to the same extent it pays for other conditions.

CONSUMER CREDIT PROTECTION ACT

Title III of the Consumer Credit Protection Act limits the amount of an employee's earnings that may be garnished and protects employees from being discharged for any indebtedness. In general, an employee's earnings may be garnished by the lesser of 25% of disposable earnings or the amount by which disposable earnings are greater than 30 times the federal minimum wage. The Act does allow for garnishment of up to 50% or 60% of wages for past-due taxes and child support (U.S. Department of Labor [DoL], 2021a). Other conditions apply. The DoL's Wage and Hour Division administers and enforces Title III. Violations can require back pay, reinstatement, and fines up to $1,000 or imprisonment for not more than 1 year or both.

What Is Discrimination?

Discrimination itself today is a hotly debated topic. Ultimately, discrimination itself is where someone treats another person differently or less favorably than others. Discrimination is largely defined by issues surrounding race, color, religion, sex (which includes pregnancy, sexual orientation, and gender identity), national origin, disability, age (40+), or genetics. Without question, this is quite a large number of things an employer needs to consider in their actions in the workplace, with current employees and with potential employees as well. Issues with discrimination often stem from unfair treatment, harassment, denial of workplace changes, improper questions about employees, improper required disclosure of genetic or medical information, or retaliation.

Discrimination Based on Sex

Few situations exist that justify discrimination based on sex. The only legitimate basis for discrimination based on sex may be that the employee must use body organs specific to their sex to accomplish the job requirements. However, this definition is currently evolving as our society begins to recognize further classifications outside traditional male versus female roles. However, understand that sex discrimination extends to much more than simply gender. Sex discrimination includes pregnancy, gender identity, and sexual orientation. Understanding the nuances of sex discrimination can help ensure that it does not occur. This is a quickly changing area and one that requires awareness surrounding all the change. The terms for lesbian, gay, bisexual, queer, transgender, and others are also evolving quickly. It is important to be well versed in these terms and what they refer to. GLAAD offers a Media Reference Guide that one can utilize to stay aware of the most current terminology. The guide is available here: https://www.glaad.org/reference/

Sexual Harassment

Sexual harassment has been defined in the EEOC guidelines as follows:

> Unwelcome sexual advances, request for sexual favors, and other verbal or physical conduct of a sexual nature constitutes sexual harassment when (a) submission to such conduct is either explicitly or implicitly a term or condition of an individual's employment, (b) submission or a rejection of such conduct by an individual is used as a basis for employment decisions affecting such individual, or (c) such conduct has a purpose or effect of unreasonably interfering with an individual's work performance, or creating an intimidating, hostile, or offensive working environment. (Guidelines on Discrimination Because of Sex, 2016)

In recent years, two general categories of cases have emerged: quid pro quo and hostile work environment. In quid pro quo (something-for-something) instances, the harassment is not only a demand for sexual favor(s) but also the adverse employment decision that results from the rejection of those demands. A hostile work environment case requires evidence of pervasive offensive conduct of a sexual nature; for example, proof that obscenities and sexual gestures, remarks, or touching were commonplace. Some "environment" cases have involved nude or partially nude women as proof of discrimination.

The facility can be held strictly liable for the acts of department managers who are found to be sexually harassing employee(s). A written policy against sexual harassment containing procedures available to employees is an advisable step for facility management to take. Sexual harassment laws apply equally to people of all genders, gender identities, gender expressions, sexual orientations, sexual characteristics, and other groups. Sexual harassment laws generally are aimed at superior/subordinate relationships but may also apply to peer relationships and those between residents and employees.

EQUAL EMPLOYMENT OPPORTUNITY COMMISSION: ENFORCING THE EQUAL EMPLOYMENT OPPORTUNITY COMMISSION'S LAWS

The EEOC was established by the Civil Rights Act. The Commission is responsible for enforcing federal laws that make it illegal to discriminate against job applicants or employees because of their race, color, religion, sex (including pregnancy, transgender status, and sexual orientation), national origin, age (40 and older), disability, or genetic information (EEOC, 2021a). Amendments gave the Commission additional authority to bring lawsuits against employers in the federal courts. The EEOC has enforced the Age Discrimination in Employment Act (ADEA), the Equal Pay Act, Section 501 of the Rehabilitation Act, and the ADA. The laws apply to most employers with 15 or more employees and include decisions around hiring, firing, promotions, harassment, training, wages, and benefits.

Between 1997 and 2020, there was an average of 18,859 age discrimination filings per year. However, employers have generally been successful in finding creative ways to shed older workers without being prosecuted.

Even so, the commission still cannot directly issue enforceable orders, as do other agencies such as the Environmental Protection Agency. Hence, the EEOC cannot order an employer to discontinue discriminatory practices, nor can it order back pay to victims of discrimination. It must seek action through the courts.

The backlog of cases for the EEOC runs approximately 20,000 to 30,000. It is not possible to handle all of them, of course. Only a tiny percentage of charges are eventually resolved by EEOC or by the courts. Nevertheless, the EEOC's legal history is being made, and its presence is felt in employment practices.

Equal Employment Opportunity Commission Procedures

Step 1. The EEOC has the power to require employers to report employment statistics on federal forms.

Step 2. If the EEOC feels that the charges are justified, it authorizes its pre-investigation division to review the complaints.

Step 3. The investigation division then interviews all parties concerned.

Step 4. If there is substance to the case, the EEOC seeks an out-of-court settlement.

Step 5. If the parties cannot be reconciled, the EEOC can sue the employer.

In cases settled by court decisions, the courts have required such actions as back pay, reinstatement of employees, immediate promotion of employees, hiring quotas, abolition of testing programs, and the creation of special training programs. Some settlements have cost employers millions of dollars.

Specifically, the EEOC may seek any or all of the following:

- Back pay (all)
- Hiring, promotion, reinstatement, benefit restoration, front pay, and other affirmative relief (Title VII, ADA, ADEA)
- Actual pecuniary loss other than back pay (Title VII, ADA)
- Liquidated damages (ADEA, Environmental Protection Act [EPA])
- Compensatory damages for future monetary losses and mental anguish (Title VII, ADA)

- Punitive damages when an employer acts with malice or reckless disregard for federally protected rights (Title VII, ADA)
- Posting a notice to all employees advising them of their rights under the laws that EEOC enforces and their right to be free from retaliation (all)
- Corrective or preventive actions taken to cure the source of the identified discrimination and minimize the chance of its recurrence (all)
- Reasonable accommodation (ADA)
- Stopping the specific discriminatory practices involved in the case (all)

COMMON PITFALLS IN PRACTICE

- Laws and regulations change quickly in the world of the administrator. Definitions change even more quickly today in our society. Ignorance of knowledge does not make violating current expectations acceptable, ever. It is important to monitor changes, even the tiny ones, in every area discussed in this textbook. The administrator is always responsible for the knowledge.

LAWS AFFECTING FEDERAL CONTRACTORS AND SUBCONTRACTORS

NAB DOMAIN 2B13: CONTRACTED SERVICES (E.G., ROLES, RESPONSIBILITIES, OVERSIGHT, BACKGROUND CHECKS)

NAB DOMAIN 4B4: BUSINESS DEVELOPMENT (E.G., SALES, MARKETING, PARTNERSHIPS, ACOs, CONTRACTS AND AGREEMENTS, NEGOTIATIONS)

Several laws and executive orders (orders issued by the president of the United States under the authority vested in them) govern hiring and job practices of firms that hold federal contracts of over $50,000. Although it is unlikely that any nursing facility would be directly affected by these regulations, many contractors working for them are subject to these regulations.

EXECUTIVE ORDER 11246

This order by the president of the United States requires written affirmative action programs of all contractors. It prohibits them from discriminating based on race, color, religion, sex, sexual orientation, gender identity, or national origin. The Office of Federal Contract Compliance Programs (OFCCP) was established to enforce this executive order. The OFCCP was later given responsibility for administering laws protecting veterans.

REHABILITATION ACT

The Rehabilitation Act requires federal government contractors to mount affirmative action programs for the disabled. The OFCCP enforces it. The Act also provides a measure of federal support for programs to assist in training the disabled. The Act extends to hiring, retaining, and promoting individuals with disabilities; preventing discrimination against individuals with disabilities; and electronics/information technology that must be developed, procured, maintained, or used must be accessible to people with disabilities.

VIETNAM-ERA VETERANS READJUSTMENT ASSISTANCE ACT

> **NAB DOMAIN 2C1: FEDERAL HUMAN RESOURCES LAWS, RULES, AND REGULATIONS (E.G., ADA, FMLA, WAGE AND HOUR, FLSA)**

The Vietnam-Era Veterans Readjustment Assistance Act (VEVRAA) requires discrimination in employment against protected veterans and requires employers to take affirmative action to recruit, hire, promote, and retain these individuals.

VEVRAA extends to *any* protected veterans, not just those who served during the Vietnam War.

THE AMERICANS WITH DISABILITIES ACT OF 1990

Title I of the ADA prohibits facilities from discriminating against qualified individuals with disabilities in job application procedures, hiring, firing, advancement, compensation, job training, and other terms, conditions, and privileges of employment.

An individual with a disability is a person who:

- Has a physical or mental impairment that substantially limits one or more major life activities (e.g., walking, reading, bending, communicating, different physiological functions of the body)
- Has a history or record of such an impairment (e.g., has been treated for a mental illness)
- Is perceived by others as having such an impairment (e.g., a person who has extensive scars from burns)

The ADA applies to any qualified individual with a disability who can perform the position's essential functions with or without reasonable accommodation. Individuals who have HIV or AIDS are considered disabled within the meaning of the ADA. Current users of illegal drugs are not protected as disabled persons. The facility may not limit, segregate, or classify a disabled job applicant or employee in any way that adversely affects their opportunities. Facilities may not fire or refuse to hire disabled persons for any cause that a reasonable accommodation could eliminate.

Reasonable Accommodation

The required accommodation may include the following:

- Making existing facilities freely accessible to disabled persons
- Supplying readers or interpreters
- Modifying policies, examinations, or training manuals
- Restructuring jobs or changing work schedules
- Reassigning the individual to a vacant position
- Acquiring or modifying equipment for use by the disabled individual

Employers are required to provide reasonable accommodations to qualified employees with disabilities unless doing so would pose an undue hardship. Examples of reasonable accommodations include the following:

- Modification of desks, desk height, providing screen magnifiers, providing deaf telecommunications
- Changing work structure from 5 days a week to 4 days a week at 10 hours per day
- Reasonable amounts of unpaid leave for medical treatment
- Other unlimited possibilities

"Undue Hardship"

The facility is required to make an accommodation to the known disability of a qualified applicant or employee if doing so would not impose an "undue hardship" on the facility. *Undue hardship* is defined as an action requiring significant difficulty or expense when considered in light of factors such as a company's size, financial resources, and the nature and cost of the proposed accommodation. Undue hardships are too costly to implement, too extensive, or too disruptive to the workplace.

Standards

The facility is not required to lower quality or production standards to make an accommodation or to provide personal-use items such as glasses or hearing aids.

Medical Examinations

The facility may not ask job applicants about the existence, nature, or severity of a disability. Applicants may be asked about their ability to perform specific job functions. A job offer may be conditioned on the results of a medical examination if the examination is required for all entering employees in similar jobs. Medical examinations of employees must be job-related and consistent with the employer's business needs. Medical tests must contain only "normal" medical test aspects given to all preemployment applicants and include no features that could be construed to be testing for or testing of a disability.

Suppose an applicant is not hired because of post-offer medical examination results. In that case, the reason must be given, and a statement made that no reasonable accommodation was available that would have enabled the applicant to perform the essential job functions or that accommodation would impose an undue hardship.

An employer may seek information about an employee's medical condition when it is "job-related and consistent with business necessity" only.

The employer must have a reasonable belief that the employee will be unable to perform the essential functions of their job or that the employee will pose a direct threat because of their medical condition.

Employee/Applicant Rights

Employees and applicants are entitled to appeal decisions to the EEOC. If the applicant is successful, the EEOC may require that the person be placed in a position where the discrimination had never occurred. This action might entitle the applicant to hiring, promotion, reinstatement, back pay or other remuneration, or reasonable accommodation, including reassignment. The successful complainant may also be entitled to damages for future money losses, mental anguish, and inconvenience. Punitive damages may also be imposed on the facility if the EEOC feels that it acted with malice or reckless indifference. The complainant may also be entitled to attorney's fees.

CIVIL RIGHTS ACT OF 1991

This Act expanded the 1964 Civil Rights Act. The 1964 Civil Rights Act only permitted back pay, and perhaps attorney's fees, to successful litigants. The 1991 Act allowed awards of compensatory damages such as money lost, emotional pain and suffering, and loss of enjoyment of life. Punitive damages, meant to discourage other employers from similar practices, were also allowed by providing payments to the plaintiff beyond actual damages suffered. This payment schema applied to the Civil Rights Act, the ADA, and the ADEA. Maximum punitive damages per incident were set at between $50,000 for smaller employers to $300,000 for employers with more than 500 employees.

THE FAMILY AND MEDICAL LEAVE ACT

Under the Family and Medical Leave Act (FMLA), a covered employer must allow up to 12 workweeks in a 12-month period of unpaid leave connected with the following:

- The birth of a child and care for the newborn child within 1 year of birth
- The placement with an employee of a child for adoption or foster care, within 1 year of placement
- To care for the employee's spouse, child, or parent who has a serious health condition
- A serious health condition of the employee's that make them unable to perform the functions of their job
- Any qualifying exigency arising out of the employee's spouse, son, daughter, or parent being a covered military member of "covered active duty"
- Additionally, FMLA provides, in the case of a servicemember, 26 workweeks of leave in a 12-month period to care for a covered servicemember with a serious injury or illness if the employee is the servicemember's spouse, son, daughter, parent, or next of kin (DoL, 2021b)

BENEFITS IMPROVEMENT AND PROTECTION ACT

The Benefits Improvement and Protection Act (BIPA), focused mainly on Medicare, Medicaid, and SCHIP benefits, has consequences for nursing facilities. This Act is responsible for the requirement of the staffing posting with which nursing facilities must comply. This requirement extends to SNFs and nursing facilities and states that they must at the beginning of each shift (in real-time) post the facility-specific shift schedule for the 24-hour period upcoming. Numbers must reflect employed or contracted nursing staff and licensed and unlicensed nursing staff directly responsible for resident care.

Direct care staff are RNs, LPNs/LVNs, and CNAs.

HEALTH INSURANCE PORTABILITY AND ACCOUNTABILITY ACT/ HEALTH INFORMATION TECHNOLOGY FOR ECONOMIC AND CLINICAL HEALTH ACT

NAB DOMAIN 2B11: HEALTHCARE RECORD REQUIREMENTS (E.G., CONFIDENTIALITY, DISCLOSURE, SAFEGUARDING, HIPAA, HITECH)

Protected health information (PHI) is highly regarded today, and the Health Insurance Portability and Accountability Act (HIPAA) is an important part of daily business in the facility. There are essentially three parts to HIPAA, as follows:

1. The Privacy Rule—defines which organizations must follow the HIPAA standards and defines what PHI is for each. It further defines how organizations can use and share PHI and resident rights surrounding PHI.
2. The Security Rule—sets the standards for the protection of PHI (both written and electronic) and defines which organizations must follow the security rule. It also explains which information is protected under the security rule and what safeguards must be in place to protect the PHI. PHI must be kept confidential, and integrity and availability must be ensured.
3. The Breach Notification Rule—defines what acceptable PHI usage is and how to report breaches of the use of PHI that are not permitted under the rule. When necessary, breaches must be reported to the affected individuals, the DHHS, and the media.

Considerations for the nursing facility are such requirements as follows:

- A policy against emailing patient records
- A written information security plan
- Assurance that third-party vendors and contractors are compliant with HIPAA
- Written record that all residents in the facility are informed about all the ways their records are being used
- Written record that all residents have been allowed to refuse to allow the facility to share their medical information

It is illegal for any person to gain access to personal medical information for any reason other than healthcare delivery, operations, and reimbursement. Information can be shared on a need-to-know basis with other healthcare professionals, such as doctors, nurses, and other allied health professionals. Healthcare information can be used for obtaining reimbursement and facilitating such activities as transferring the resident to another healthcare provider. Privacy includes all transfer formats such as electronic records, paper records, or orally. The facility must provide each resident with a statement of how the facility handles PHI, including all individually identifiable health information relating to the resident's past, present, and future physical and mental health provisions. A resident can restrict uses, and no disclosures of healthcare information may be done without their written informed consent. The facility's PHI policy must be given to the resident or guardian at admission, with a written acknowledgment of receipt of the information placed in the resident's records. The PHI policies must also be prominently displayed in a public area of the facility.

The Health Information Technology for Economic and Clinical Health (HITECH) Act was signed into law to further strengthen HIPAA regarding electronic health records. The HITECH Act was enacted to encourage the use of electronic health and medical records and clarify HIPAA and how it applied to electronic health records. The HITECH Act increased penalties for inappropriate disclosures of PHI and increased accountability of everyone involved with the medical record itself, from the facility to vendors to the manufacturers of software.

The HITECH Act closed many loopholes, which were in the original HIPAA legislation. Both HIPAA compliance and HITECH Act compliance are vast and evolving topics. We can assume that we will continue to see changes in both areas as software and technology evolve. It is imperative to the administrator to stay abreast of changes in these topics and to ensure that both they and their staff are well educated in these areas.

FACILITY GUIDELINES INSTITUTE AND AMERICAN INSTITUTE OF ARCHITECTS: 2018 GUIDELINES

These two entities periodically issue guidelines surrounding the design of health and residential care facilities. Often, we see nursing facility guidelines tending to follow behind the guidelines which are issued for acute care. We see many new facilities today mimicking these guidelines in new construction.

LIFESPAN RESPITE CARE ACT OF 2006

This Act was designed to assist those caregivers who are taking care of their loved ones at home. The Act allows for home caregivers to seek respite care for their loved ones while they are given some temporary relief from the burden of direct care. Respite services can be provided for caregivers in various settings, including the home, adult daycare centers, or residential care facilities.

COMMON PITFALLS IN PRACTICE
- As you have seen here, there are many laws that exist that govern what we do in nursing facilities outside of our already voluminous regulations. It is imperative that you are aware of, and abide by, all these other laws as well.
- Despite some of these laws dating from well over 50 years ago, they are still in effect and are being enforced. Just because they "look old" does not mean that they are any less effective today than they once were.

4.4.3 REGULATION OF COMPENSATION

Section Concepts

- *The laws surrounding compensation are vast and ever-changing*
- *This section provides a primer of current regulations surrounding compensation*

Consider as the Administrator . . .

- *Your knowledge of how you can pay your employees, and the legal intricacies of the differences, is imperative knowledge for your success.*

NAB DOMAIN 2C1: FEDERAL HUMAN RESOURCES LAWS, RULES, AND REGULATIONS (E.G., ADA, FMLA, WAGE AND HOUR, FLSA)

Compensation regulation is an area of interest for the administrator, as this can change from state to state. Whereas the Fair Labor Standards Act (FLSA) has explicit provisions for labor, overtime, and other areas, it is essential to realize that state laws can supersede these laws (this happens most often, as states have more stringent measures in place).

FAIR LABOR STANDARDS ACT

The FLSA was initially passed in the 1930s, but it has been amended many times. The FLSA establishes minimum wage, overtime pay, recordkeeping requirements, and youth employment standards for employers.

Minimum Wage Rates

Today, the federal minimum wage is $7.25 per hour (as of this writing). However, many states have their own minimum wage laws today. Even some localities have minimum wage laws, and many employers publicize their own minimum wage guidelines. Much of this has been spurred forth by the "living wages" movement we often see in the news today.

What Is Work?

Preparatory activities integral to the employee's job may be considered work time. Suppose an employee performs work that is prohibited with the knowledge or acquiescence of management. In that case, the employee must be paid, even if the work is away from the facility. If the employer believes the work is being performed, payment for that time is required. On-call or waiting time may be considered work if the employee is "engaged" by the employer to wait for the work. Travel associated with or required by the job is compensable. Bonafide meal periods are not compensable, must be 30 minutes in duration, and free the employee from performing any work. If meal periods are frequently interrupted, as often happens in a nursing facility setting, the whole meal period may be considered compensable work time. Rest periods and coffee breaks are compensable. There are many facets to what is considered work and what is not by the FLSA. Understanding all the intricacies associated with this is imperative for success.

The minimum wage rates are significant to nursing facilities because many pay nurse's aides, housekeeping, and maintenance employees at or just above the minimum wage.

Overtime

The FLSA requires overtime for more than 40 hours per week to be paid at one and one-half times the regular pay rate. In the past (before 2009), healthcare had different rules to follow regarding overtime; however, this is not the case anymore. Nonexempt employees must make at least the federal minimum wage for all hours worked and overtime pay for hours worked over 40 in a work week.

Exempt/Nonexempt

FLSA overtime rules do not apply to employees who are considered exempt from minimum wage and overtime pay. These employees are usually executive, administrative, or professional (administrator, director of nursing, department heads, supervisors) or outside sales representatives. Most nurses prefer to work as nonexempt employees because this permits them to receive overtime pay. A September 19, 2019, Fact Sheet #17 N: Nurses and the Part 541 Exemptions Under the FLSA, indicates that nurses qualify as learned professionals if they are paid $455 per week. Nurses who are paid on an hourly basis should receive overtime pay. However, RNs registered by the appropriate state examining board generally meet the duties requirements for the learned professional exemption. If paid on a salary basis of at least $455 per week, they may be classified as exempt. Only RNs can qualify for the learned professional exemption. LVN/LPNs and other similar healthcare employees do not qualify for this controversial exemption. A word of caution: Many a facility has lost qualified RN workers due to exempting floor RNs under this rule. Be sure to exempt employees only when appropriate.

Enforcement of the Fair Labor Standards Act

Records may be subpoenaed without a warrant at offsite locations. Usually, a warrant is required for onsite inspections. Violations are subject to a penalty of up to $1,000 per violation. Injunctions may be issued regarding minimum wage, overtime, child labor, and record-keeping violations. Criminal proceedings may be brought by the Department of Justice. Willful violations may be prosecuted criminally, and fines can be up to $10,000. Second offenders may be fined and subject to imprisonment. Violations of child labor laws are subject to penalties of up to $10,000 per employee affected. Wage and hour inspectors are liable to show up unannounced. In general, the word of the employee is taken most seriously by these inspectors. If an employee said they worked 2 hours per week "off the clock" for the previous year, the facility might be required to pay that employee for 2 hours of overtime per week for that past year. The burden of proof is on the employer, in a strict sense.

Child Labor

Child labor laws are split across two areas, agricultural and nonagricultural. Nonagricultural laws apply to nursing facilities, and permissible employment is as follows:

1. Youth 18 and older may perform any job, hazardous or not, for unlimited hours.
2. Minors 16 and 17 may perform any nonhazardous job, for unlimited hours.
3. Minors 14 and 15 may work under significant hours and conditions restrictions imposed by the FLSA. These conditions should be checked before employees of this age group are hired.

EQUAL PAY ACT

The FLSA was amended by the Equal Pay Act. Under this amendment, no employer shall discriminate between employees on the basis of sex by paying wages to employees less than the rate at which they pay wages to employees of the opposite sex for equal work on jobs that require equal skill, effort and responsibility, and similar working conditions (EEOC, 2021b).

The equal-pay provision of the FLSA is of particular concern to nursing facility operators, who may employ both male and female nurses, male and female aides, and male and female maintenance and laundry persons. Today, this is less clear as traditional male/female roles are not as clearly defined as they once were.

COMMON PITFALLS IN PRACTICE
- Compensation and the FLSA are areas that are easily overlooked or violated. When looking at anything in this area it often helps to consider it from an outsider's perspective. "Would this be the right decision if someone were looking over my shoulder?" This thought process often spurs questions on your decision-making process that can assist you.

4.4.4 WORKER'S COMPENSATION: ASSISTANCE FOR ON-THE-JOB INJURIES

Section Concepts

- *Worker's compensation and on-the-job injuries are always a concern for the administrator*

Consider as the Administrator . . .

- *Is it better to have an employee at home recovering or back at work on light duty? What happens to the probability of an employee coming back to work fulltime after months of at-home recovery?*

NAB DOMAIN 2B2: WORKERS' COMPENSATION

Workers' compensation laws are based on the principle that employees themselves should not have to pay costs associated with injuries that occur at work. On-the-job injuries, the lawmakers have reasoned, are a cost of doing business and should be passed on to the consumer.

Overall, there are no federal regulations that require workers' compensation insurance; however, most states do have laws regulating the need for such insurance by an employer. Previously, several states allowed employers to be "self-insured"; however, this practice is all but gone in a couple of states. Otherwise, employers must participate in a state-sponsored or state-approved program.

Under most state laws, workers are paid a percentage of their regular wages while recovering from an injury on the job. States typically set limits to benefits and specify how long they must be paid.

Hospitalization and other medical costs are also usually covered by workers' compensation insurance funds. There are usually death benefits for the worker's family. States establish commissions that handle any claims that are in dispute. Generally, the result is little cost to the injured worker and reasonably rapid assistance.

States usually take one of two basic approaches to funding workers' compensation insurance. Sometimes the state operates its own insurance system in which employers are generally obliged to participate. In other states, employers are allowed either to self-insure or to join a private insurance company program.

One characteristic of most worker accident compensation plans is that the amount the employer must pay per month is based on experience. Under this system, employers with good safety records pay less than those with large numbers of claims. In some states, benefits to the injured worker are reduced if the worker is willfully negligent in following safety procedures.

In 2019, employees in nursing and residential care facilities suffered work-related illnesses and injuries at an incident rate of 29.8 nonfatal injuries and illnesses per 100 full-time employees (U.S. Bureau of Labor Statistics, 2019). This number includes *all* different settings in the long-term care continuum; however, the result here is staggering. Nursing facilities have some of the highest statistics when it comes to employee injuries. There are many reasons for this, but primarily the jobs in nursing facilities are difficult ones, which often involve heavy labor to complete. As a result, we see many cases of back injuries, strains, sprains, musculoskeletal disorders, slip and fall injuries, and many other causes.

Many states have enacted safe patient handling legislation to cut workers' compensation insurance costs, which has done much to decrease employee injuries. Nursing facilities are also a focus of the Occupational Safety and Health Administration (OSHA) due to these large numbers. Nearly all employers are focused on safe lifting, proper ergonomics, and proper techniques in handling residents to decrease these numbers and to increase employee safety.

UNEMPLOYMENT COMPENSATION

NAB DOMAIN 2C3: COMPENSATION AND BENEFITS PROGRAMS (E.G., TIME OFF, HEALTHCARE INSURANCE, EMPLOYEE PAY AND PAYROLL)

Employees who participate in the Social Security Act program are eligible for unemployment compensation when laid off by their employer. The Social Security Act covers nearly all nursing facility employees.

Unemployment compensation is available for up to 26 weeks through the state employment agency if the worker registers and accepts any suitable comparable work offered through the agency. Unemployment compensation is funded by a federal payroll tax based on the wages of each employee up to a certain maximum. The federal government turns these monies over to the states for disbursement.

A separate record is kept for each employer. Once a company has paid an account equivalent to the required reserve, its rate of taxation is reduced. In actual practice, this means that nursing facilities with few unemployment compensation claims against them pay at a lower tax rate than those with a large number of such claims.

Experience has shown that, despite being discharged or let go for valid reasons (unrelated to a lack of work), the facility must have excellent documentation on the circumstances of the dismissal. Otherwise, employees may be successful in claiming unemployment compensation (even when not deserved). When this happens, the costs of the unemployment compensation paid by the state are allocated to that individual nursing facility's account. It is crucial for the administrator to know their employee handbook and policies and procedures and educate their staff on the same. When the unfortunate circumstance of termination needs to happen, proof that employees knew these policies would be required, as well as a large volume of documentation leading up to the termination.

Many employers today have progressive discipline policies. There should be clear and resounding proof that employees violated company policy and that the employer followed their policy on discipline. The burden of proof is truly on the employer for unemployment claims.

Extensive information on many of these labor-related topics can be accessed at https://www.dol.gov/ or through your state-specific sites.

4.4.5 RETIREMENT

Consider as the Administrator...

- We often hear about the idea of "forced retirements"; however, this can present a host of legal concerns.

AGE DISCRIMINATION IN EMPLOYMENT ACT

The ADEA protects employees from being discriminated against based on age. It is intended to prevent companies from replacing older employees with younger ones, whether to achieve a younger average age among the working force, to decrease payroll costs, or to avoid paying pension benefits. There are some exceptions, such as certain occupational groups and employers with fewer than 20 employees. However, the practical effect is that no employees in the typical nursing facility can be forced to retire against their wishes solely based on age.

Congress investigated pensions for American workers and discovered that for a variety of reasons, up to one half of American workers covered by pension plans would never receive any benefits. The most significant problem was the failure of businesses to fund their pension plans adequately. Workers were similarly failed when leaving a company, as they often lost any pension benefits. The EEOC is the primary agency responsible for enforcing this Act through the Employee Retirement Income Security Act (ERISA).

THE EMPLOYEE RETIREMENT INCOME SECURITY ACT

In reaction, Congress passed ERISA. This Act sets minimum funding levels for pension funds, requires certification every 3 years of the actuarial soundness of the plan, and requires vesting of the employee's equity in the pension fund. Employers are not required, under ERISA or any other law, to provide a private pension fund for their employees.

As part of its regulation, ERISA set up the Pension Benefit Guaranty Corporation (PBGC), which is supported by premiums from employers to ensure that employees will eventually receive retirement funds. Companies that decide to withdraw from the plan must make substantial payments into the corporation before being permitted. This provision and other elements of the Act create hardships for employers who otherwise are committed to providing pension benefits for employees.

One major drawback to the ERISA legislation is that its rules are so demanding that many employers choose not to offer pension plans. Upon implementation of the Act, many employers decided to withdraw their plans rather than comply with the law. Another unfortunate result is that many employees elect to receive their accumulated "retirement" benefits when they leave the organization. Studies have documented that all too often, these pension benefits never find their way into 401(k) or similar retirement mechanisms.

In place of regular company-created and maintained pension plans, many employers have opted to offer employees participation in what is known as 401(k) and similar plans, under which employees contribute money on a tax-deferred basis for retirement purposes. The major drawback for the employee is that on leaving the company, they often receive the 401(k) contributions in a lump sum. Employees can roll over these 401(k) funds to similar tax-deferred investments within a specified number of days and retain them for eventual retirement purposes. Sadly, the temptation to use the funds for current expenses is too great for many employees, and these funds are never reinvested.

4.5 WORKPLACE SAFETY: THE OCCUPATIONAL SAFETY AND HEALTH ACT

Section Concepts

- *Nursing facilities have one of the highest accident rates of any industry*
- *Occupational Safety and Health Act (OSHA) rules affect how every nursing facility interacts with its employees*

Consider as the Administrator . . .

- *Which employee should be responsible for OSHA compliance? Can this be a "one person only" job, or is it a group effort?*

NAB DOMAIN 3A3: SAFETY AND ACCESSIBILITY (E.G., ADA, SAFETY DATA SHEETS)

NAB DOMAIN 2B1: OSHA RULES AND REGULATIONS

NAB DOMAIN 3B1: FEDERAL HEALTHCARE LAWS, RULES, AND REGULATIONS

NAB DOMAIN 3A4: FACILITY MANAGEMENT AND ENVIRONMENTAL SERVICES

ORIGIN AND PASSAGE

For the first seven decades of the 20th century, state governments were responsible for safety in the workplace. During that period, organized labor became less and less satisfied with the enforcement of state laws, variation in laws among the states, and often the absence of any safety laws. In the half decade before the passage of federal legislation, job-related accidents were causing up to 2.5 million disabilities and 14,000 deaths annually.

After 3 years of intense lobbying by employees and the unions, Congress passed OSHA (Public Law No. 91–596; https://www.osha.gov/laws-regs/oshact/completeoshact). OSHA applies to nearly all employees and includes all of those working in nursing facilities.

FEDERAL IMPLEMENTATION

Two federal agencies have been set up to implement OSHA. The Act is administered by the Occupational Safety and Health Administration (also known under the acronym

OSHA) in the Department of Labor. The National Institute of Occupational Safety and Health (NIOSH) was established to conduct research and develop standards.

A primary goal of the Act has been to turn workplace safety enforcement back to the states with a strengthened work safety law. States have been encouraged to establish their own inspection programs and industrial safety laboratories. Some states are referred to as a "state-plan" state, where the state has its own occupational health and safety programs; other states are not, but they have methods of inspection of OSHA concerns through various state agencies.

In addition to meeting all standards, OSHA imposes on employers a general duty to provide each employee a safe workplace, free from recognized hazards causing or likely to cause death or serious physical harm. OSHA invoked the "general duty" obligation when inspecting nursing facilities. This further impacts facilities today when considering COVID-19, tuberculosis (TB), and other growing infections and workplace hazards such as lack of personal protective equipment.

THREE OCCUPATIONAL SAFETY AND HEALTH ACT IMPACT AREAS

OSHA directly affects the operations of nursing facilities in at least three main areas:

1. Meeting the standards set by OSHA
2. Cooperating in OSHA inspections of the facility
3. Keeping the necessary records on job-related accidents and illnesses

SOURCES OF STANDARDS

OSHA standards may originate from a variety of sources. The Secretary of Labor may issue and revise standards at will. This may be done on the secretary's own initiative, on the recommendation of NIOSH, or at the urging of interested parties such as labor unions or groups of affected employees.

Adopting Standards of Other Organizations

OSHA has adopted several national consensus standards developed by other groups, including the National Fire Protection Association's Life Safety Code and the Standards for the Physically Handicapped of the American National Standards Institute. OSHA also provides an interpretation of the ADA and aids in enforcement of it.

DEFINITION OF "STANDARD"

OSHA safety standards are "practices, means, operations or processes, reasonably necessary to provide safe . . . employment." Each employer is responsible for knowing OSHA standards in their facility (either federal or a combination of federal and state). These standards can be permanent or temporary ones based on industry needs. Currently, there is a temporary emergency standard to protect healthcare workers from COVID-19 (https://www.osha.gov/coronavirus/ets).

Despite the minutiae and length of the current volume, each manager is responsible for knowing applicable standards and is subject to both fines and imprisonment if found to violate them. Note the imprisonment verbiage carefully. Despite most administrators working for a corporation, the licensed administrator is ultimately responsible for local enforcement of standards.

SOME OCCUPATIONAL SAFETY AND HEALTH ACT REQUIREMENTS

OSHA bulletins have listed the following as among OSHA's requirements.

Employers

Every employer must furnish a workplace free from recognized hazards that are causing or are likely to cause death or serious harm to employees. Employers must also comply with OSHA standards and display the required OSHA poster, "Job Safety and Health—It's the Law" that informs employees of their rights and responsibilities and compiling annual figures on work-related illnesses and accidents (https://www.osha.gov/publications/poster).

Employees

Each employee shall obey all OSHA requirements. However, the facility is held responsible for worker violation of OSHA standards. The employer has the choice of dismissing such a worker, but there are no punishments for the worker who willfully ignores OSHA requirements. Willful disregard of OSHA rules is, however, grounds for termination permitted under federal law and applicable employee handbook policies.

Any employee may lodge a complaint with OSHA. The complaint must be in writing and signed with a description of the hazardous condition. The signed complaint is submitted to the OSHA regional director and the employer. It is submitted unsigned if the employee wishes to remain anonymous.

Inspections

OSHA inspectors will visit at times of their choosing, or at the invitation of any employer, union, or employee. Employees requesting an inspection need not be identified.

The employer and the employees must each designate a representative to accompany the OSHA inspector(s). If the employees do not do so, the OSHA compliance officer must consult several employees during the visit. This officer must hold an opening conference to discuss the scope and reason for the inspection and a concluding conference presenting findings to the employer.

Employers must not discriminate against any employee or employees who ask for an OSHA safety or health inspection. Any employee may file a complaint with the nearest OSHA office within 30 days for any such alleged discrimination.

OSHA inspectors examine the premises for compliance with regulations and the records of illnesses and injuries to employees.

Citations

Citations may be issued at the end of the inspection itself or later by mail. Any citation issued must be posted at or near the site of violation for 3 days or the duration of the violation, whichever is longer. One citation must be issued for each serious and nonserious violation found and a time limit specified for its correction.

OSHA compliance officers may categorize employer violations as follows:

1. *Willful*—can close operations down; the employer is aware that hazardous conditions exist, knows that it violates a standard, and makes no effort to correct. Penalties are associated.
2. *Serious*—the substantial probability that death or serious physical harm will result from the condition that exists unless the employer did not and could not have known about the violation. Penalties are associated.
3. *Other-than-serious*—a violation in which a direct and immediate relationship exists between the condition and occupational health but not such as to cause death or serious physical harm. Penalties are associated.
4. *De minimis* (small violation)—employer implements a safety measure different from what is specified in the standard, but the situation does not pose any immediate threat to safety or health. No penalties are associated.
5. *Failure to abate*—the employer has failed to correct a violation OSHA has already cited, and the abatement date has passed. Penalties are associated.
6. *Repeated*—past violations are found to be out of compliance during subsequent visits. Penalties are associated.
7. In every case, a time period is specified within which the violation must be corrected. Depending on the type of violation, the penalties are different.

Penalties

Penalties are imposed for the following:

- $13,563 per violation—*Serious, Other-than-serious, Posting requirements*
- $13,563 per day past the abatement date—*Failure to abate*
- $136,532 per violation—*Willful, Repeated* (OSHA, 2021)

Record Keeping

The area that most directly affects nursing facility administrators daily is keeping standardized records of illnesses and injuries from which ratios must be calculated. This record is the OSHA form called "Log and Summary of Occupational Injuries and Illnesses," which must be kept by each facility (https://www.osha .gov/recordkeeping).

Accidents and illnesses that do not have to be reported require only first aid and do not result in any work time lost. Accidents and illnesses that do have to be reported are those that result in death(s), disabilities that cause the employee to miss work, and injuries that require treatment by a physician. Reporting requirements have been tightened in recent years. Fatal or serious multiple cases (three or more employees hospitalized) must be reported to the OSHA regional director orally, by telephone, within 8 hours, a time period that begins as soon as any facility representatives become aware of the situation. Also, these incidents must be reported if death or hospitalization occurs within 30 days of the incident. Other cases must be recorded within 6 days and reported on standard forms as requested by OSHA.

Occupational illness is a definition of particular relevance to the nursing facility setting. An occupational illness is any abnormal condition or disorder other than one resulting from an occupational injury caused by exposure to environmental factors associated with employment. It includes acute and chronic illnesses or diseases caused by inhalation, absorption, ingestion, or direct contact. OSHA defines an occupational injury as any injury, such as a cut, fracture, sprain, or amputation, resulting from a work accident or an exposure involving a single accident in the work environment. There are even more stringent regulations surrounding COVID-19 at this time.

Each time a recordable case is entered in the log mentioned earlier, a "Supplementary Record of Occupational Injuries and Illnesses" must be completed, giving information on what the employee was doing, which part of the body was affected, and the identity of the employee.

Another OSHA form, "Summary of Occupational Injuries and Illnesses," must be submitted annually and posted where employees can easily see it (e.g., near the time clock) at least during January and February of every year.

The Current and Emerging Situation

Completing, submitting, and posting accident and illness forms as required will remain a continuing requirement for nursing facility administrators, but the inspection issue is another matter. After years during which few, if any, nursing facilities were being inspected in the various states, OSHA inspectors have begun showing up to perform routine inspections of nursing facilities. In many locales, OSHA inspectors will, at the invitation of the facility, perform "dry run" inspections for an employer, advising on any "violations" and providing an opportunity for correction before any official inspection. This review can be an invaluable service to the facility.

OSHA WEBSITE

OSHA offers an extensive nursing facility-specific website filled with excellent resources for the administrator. Information on standards, enforcement, hazards and solutions, and safety and health programs are available. Refer to this website: https://www.osha.gov/nursing-home.

EMPLOYEE HEALTH AND SAFETY

NAB DOMAIN 2C1: FEDERAL HUMAN RESOURCES LAWS, RULES, AND REGULATIONS (E.G., ADA, FMLA, WAGE AND HOUR, FLSA); 2C2: SELECTION AND HIRING PRACTICES (E.G., EEOC, INTERVIEWING, ADVERSE IMPACT, PROTECTED CLASSES, OCCUPATIONAL QUALIFICATIONS); 3A3: SAFETY AND ACCESSIBILITY (E.G., ADA, SAFETY DATA SHEETS)

Preemployment Screening

Screening can include any of the following:

- Immunization review
- Employment physical
- Drugs/alcohol screening
- Latex allergy screen (history; if positive, blood test)
- Screen for active TB symptoms; if positive, chest x-ray, sputum
- Latent TB (tuberculin skin test or impaired fasting glucose rate blood test)
- Mask fit test clearance
- Personal protective equipment (PPE) fit tests
- Counseling: pregnant women, immunocompromised

Evaluation of Employees With a Potentially Communicable Disease

- Infectious disease exposures
- Determination of exposure and risk of disease transmission
- Evaluate for postexposure prophylaxis
- Consider need for work restrictions
- Communicate with infection control if patients exposed
- Monitor other occupational hazards in the nursing facility setting

Infections

- Viral respiratory diseases
- Aerosol-transmitted diseases: TB, pertussis
- Bloodborne pathogens: percutaneous, mucous membrane
- Contact-transmitted diseases: syphilis, Methicillin-resistant *Staphylococcus* aureus (MRSA), norovirus, rotavirus

Injuries

- Work-related (e.g., fall, strain, sprain) and ergonomic (e.g., strain, sprain, repetitive motion)
- Dermatitis (related to latex gloves, antiseptics)
- Psychosocial stress

Recommended Vaccines for Healthcare Workers in the Long-Term Care Setting

Recommended by the Centers for Disease Control and Prevention (CDC):

- Hepatitis B
- Influenza (flu)
- MMR (measles, mumps, rubella)
- Varicella (chickenpox)
- Tdap (tetanus, diphtheria, pertussis)
- COVID-19

Needlestick Injuries Management

- Test source for hepatitis B (HBsAg), hepatitis C, and HIV
- Provide hepatitis B prophylaxis, if indicated
- Provide follow-up for hepatitis C, if indicated
- If the source is HIV-positive or at "high risk" for HIV exposure confirmed, offer employee HIV prophylaxis per CDC protocol
- Maintain confidentiality: separate records, labs, and pharmacy requisitions sent with code number

COMMON PITFALLS IN PRACTICE
- Workplace safety is an easy area in which to ensure compliance; however, many facilities have little monitoring in this area. It is not unheard of for a safety data sheet book to be firmly mounted to a wall with an inch of dust on top of it or to have eyewash stations that are inoperable or hooked up to hot water. These are easily correctable situations.
- OSHA is not necessarily an entity to fear. With corporate blessings, calling them out for a preemptive strike session at your facility can easily let you know what needs to be corrected.

4.6 FIRE SAFETY: THE LIFE SAFETY CODE

Section Concepts
- *Fire safety is of special concern to the nursing facility because a significant proportion of residents cannot independently leave the fire area or the building in case of a fire*

Consider as the Administrator . . .
- *Is it possible to adequately protect all the residents from the effects of a fire?*

NAB DOMAIN 1B4: CARE RECIPIENT SAFETY (E.G., FALL PREVENTION, ELOPEMENT PREVENTION, ADVERSE EVENTS)

NAB DOMAIN 3A4: FACILITY MANAGEMENT AND ENVIRONMENTAL SERVICES

NAB DOMAIN 3A3: SAFETY AND ACCESSIBILITY (E.G., ADA, SAFETY DATA SHEETS)

NAB DOMAIN 3B1: FEDERAL HEALTHCARE LAWS, RULES, AND REGULATIONS

The basic principles of creating a safe physical environment for care recipients are contained in the Life Safety Code (Section 4.6) and the ADA Accessibility Guidelines (see Section 4.7). The basic principles of creating a safe emotional environment are set forth throughout the Federal Requirements and Guidelines to Surveyors, especially F550 through F586: Resident Rights and F675 through F680: Quality of Life. These principles are further expanded in F684 through F700: Quality of Care.

The National Fire Protection Association was founded in 1896 as a nonprofit organization focused on eliminating injury, property, and economic loss due to fire, electrical, and related hazards. It is widely known for their codes and standards of all types, which apply to many industries. It is not a governmental agency, nor does it write federal regulations.

However, it maintains, updates, and publishes the Life Safety Code, which current nursing facility regulations enforce as law. NFPA 101: Life Safety Code is used in every state and is fully adopted in 43 states. NFPA 101 addresses minimum building design, construction, operation, and maintenance requirements to protect residents from dangers that may be caused by fire, smoke, or toxic fumes. The Life Safety Code discusses at length building codes, means of egress, and other safety features of nursing facilities.

The NFPA 101: Life Safety Code is an all-encompassing volume that changes yearly, or more often if necessary. Changes must happen due to current findings or situations that present themselves. It is a living, breathing document meant to keep people safe. As such, it is impossible to include specifics about it in this textbook, as it would quickly be out of date. The CMS often updates the version of NFPA 101, which is required for enforcement, as do many states often require more current editions. New construction is usually held to the most current version of NFPA 101 by the states.

The administrator needs to be well versed in the requirements and regulations for their respective states.

Information from the National Fire Protection Association on the Life Safety Code is available at https://www.nfpa.org/.

Furthermore, facilities are also required to comply with:

- NFPA 13, Standard for the Installation of Sprinkler Systems
- NFPA 25, Standard for the Inspection, Testing, and Maintenance of Water-Based Fire Protection Systems

- NFPA 72, National Fire Alarm Code
- NFPA 99, Health Care Facilities Code
- Tentative Interim Amendments and other required codes

4.7 AMERICANS WITH DISABILITIES ACT ACCESSIBILITY GUIDELINES FOR FACILITIES

Section Concepts

- *Every nursing facility should be handicapped accessible*

Consider as the Administrator . . .

- *How can an accessible route be maintained 24/7?*

NAB DOMAIN 1B4: CARE RECIPIENT SAFETY (E.G., FALL PREVENTION, ELOPEMENT PREVENTION, ADVERSE EVENTS)

NAB DOMAIN 3A4: FACILITY MANAGEMENT AND ENVIRONMENTAL SERVICES

NAB DOMAIN 3A3: SAFETY AND ACCESSIBILITY (E.G., ADA, SAFETY DATA SHEETS)

As discussed in previous sections, the ADA has specific requirements for nursing facilities with specific Standards for Accessible Design, which are available for use. Current expectations are based on the *2010 Standards for Accessible Design* available here: https://www.ada.gov/2010ADAstandards_index.htm

Many of the 2010 Standards are based upon the American National Standards Institute (ANSI) works and its publication ICC A117.1, *Accessible and Usable Buildings and Facilities*. The current document is available here: https://webstore.ansi .org/Standards/ICC/ICCA1172017?source%20=%20blog&_ga=%202.87300824 .1793379845.1627680202-997835409.1627680202.

Each of these documents is important for the administrator to know and understand so that they can ensure ongoing compliance with the ADA requirements. Most specifically, nursing facilities are using the *2010 Standards for Accessible Design* as the standard of expectation.

As both of these documents are subject to constant and immediate change, including specifics from them is outside the scope of this textbook, as any information provided here would be out of date.

4.8 VOLUNTARY OPERATING STANDARDS: THE JOINT COMMISSION

Consider as the Administrator . . .

- Voluntary accreditation has many advantages, but it also comes with many costs as well. This is not a one-sided decision to pursue; always involve corporate or ownership in such decisions.

Long-term care facilities that meet specific requirements are eligible to apply for accreditation from The Joint Commission (TJC). Accreditation by the TJC is voluntary, and currently less than 10% of long-term care facilities have applied for it.

There has long been controversy that having TJC accreditation may substitute for state and/or federal inspections. This is incorrect. TJC accreditation has several advantages for the facility, but it is not treated differently for annual or complaint surveys.

THE JOINT COMMISSION ACCREDITATION BENEFITS

Slightly more than 1,000 long-term care facilities are members of the Joint Commission on Accreditation of Healthcare Organizations (JCAHO). As there are about 16,000 facilities in the United States today, it is clear how having TJC accreditation might give one provider a competitive advantage over another. TJC accreditation may also lower liability insurance rates and assist in quality and performance improvement for the individual facility. The TJC also offers a very comprehensive library of educational offerings to increase the quality of resident care through education and the advancement of operations. With today's focus on quality improvement, TJC can be a great help to facilities in meeting metrics.

4.9 THE AFFORDABLE CARE ACT

Consider as the Administrator...

* The ACA has changed how we do business and where our focus is. It changes even further with each Congressional session. Ensure you stay ahead of what is happening with this Act.

NAB DOMAIN 3B1: FEDERAL HEALTHCARE LAWS, RULES, AND REGULATIONS

The Patient Protection and Affordable Care Act (PPACA), which is commonly called the ACA or "Obamacare," is a U.S. federal statute that was signed into law by President Barack Obama on March 23, 2010. Together with the Health Care and Education Reconciliation Act, it represents the most significant regulatory overhaul of the U.S. healthcare system since the passage of Medicare and Medicaid in 1965.

The ACA was enacted to increase the quality and affordability of health insurance, lower the uninsured rate by expanding public and private insurance coverage, and reduce healthcare costs for individuals and the government. It introduced several mechanisms to increase coverage and affordability, including mandates, subsidies, and insurance exchanges. The law also required insurance companies to cover all applicants within new minimum standards and offer the same rates regardless of preexisting conditions or sex. Additional reforms were introduced to reduce costs and improve healthcare outcomes by shifting the system toward quality over quantity through increased competition, regulation, and incentives to streamline the delivery of healthcare.

The ACA continued a trend of shifting Medicaid and Medicare spending toward greater HCBS care and away from skilled nursing care reimbursement. States were able to shift more monies toward noninstitutional-based eldercare using a section 1915(c) waiver for Medicaid reimbursements and a 2005 program titled MFP. MFP programs were recently reauthorized as part of the Consolidated Appropriations Act of 2021 and are focused on expanding community living opportunities for those who are disabled. The program helps those in nursing facilities be set up in the community so that they can leave the institutional setting and move home. The ACA bolstered another 1915(c) program titled Community First Choice, allowing additional monies to flow toward home- and community-based care. The offerings are similar in all states, but the benefits are state-specific as it is a Medicaid outreach program.

Other key provisions of the ACA that had direct effects on nursing facilities include the following:

- Implementation of Quality Assurance Performance Improvement (QAPI) programs, which study care continuously in nursing facilities and improve it based on best practices
- More publicly available information on nursing facilities to include enhanced data on Nursing Home Compare, staffing data through Payroll Based Journaling (PBJ) data collected by the CMS, and further information about survey results to include 2567s and civil monetary penalties
- Special focus facility programs
- Enhancements to nurse's aide training education programs
- Enhanced criminal background checks under the coupled Patient Safety and Abuse Protection Act

4.10 THE ELDER JUSTICE ACT

Consider as the Administrator . . .

- We see many "hidden" laws buried in legislation today. The Elder Justice Act was one of these such laws. There is no way around your involvement in the political process anymore; it is a daily part of the administrator's job!

NAB DOMAIN 3B1: FEDERAL HEALTHCARE LAWS, RULES, AND REGULATIONS

The Elder Justice Law was passed by Congress in 2010 and incorporated into the ACA. Among other provisions, this law requires nursing facilities to prevent or respond to elder abuse, neglect, or exploitation. The most important feature for the nursing facility is a requirement that both the federal DHHS and local law enforcement authorities be notified of any suspicions of abuse, regardless of whether that suspected abuse results in bodily harm. Facilities and employees can face fines of up to $300,000 for noncompliance.

TRENDS

Incentive payments for quality (as defined by the federal DHHS) were incorporated into the ACA. The federal government constantly evolves incentives toward improved quality care. The CMS is evolving new definitions of quality care and incentivizing facilities to achieve improved quality. These strategies are frequently referred to as pay for performance (P4P) or value-based purchasing (VBP). Such an approach has already been implemented for incentivizing hospitals that are being reimbursed or penalized for not achieving goals set by the CMS, such as attaining a CMS-specified low rate of readmission for Medicare patients who receive hospital care (Singh, 2016). The CMS is incentivizing hospitals to collaborate with nursing facilities in reducing unplanned readmissions by allocating dollars to hospitals that achieve lowered readmission rates in collaboration with nursing facilities (Singh, 2016). There are significant impacts on reducing hospital readmissions from nursing facilities, and this will continue to be a focus area into the future (Mileski et al., 2017). In some situations, a readmission to the hospital from the nursing facility can come with significant financial penalties.

GAINING THE FIVE-STAR RATING

The CMS was enabled to upgrade and update the Nursing Home Compare website to include a "Five-Star Quality Rating System," which allows consumers to easily compare side-by-side information about facilities in choosing the best one for their needs. Five-Star ratings are based on the ability of the nursing facility to meet metrics surrounding health inspections, staffing (PBJ), and quality measures. Quality measures are pulled from Minimum Data Set (MDS) data being collected by the facility on its residents. Some opponents of the Five-Star system feel that it penalizes certain nursing facilities for taking certain types of residents (wound care, behaviors, infections, as a few examples), as those numbers would count negatively against the facility in this measure.

COMMON PITFALLS IN PRACTICE

- Knowing what things in your facility you can influence to make changes to your Five-Star rating is very important. This changes quite often, so staying ahead of the curve on this can only help you in the long run.
- The Five-Star rating is not only *your* job. It is everyone's job in the facility. When you make it a focus as the administrator, it becomes a focus for everybody.

4.11 PATIENT DRIVEN PAYMENT MODEL

Consider as the Administrator . . .

- At one time, the administrator had to be concerned only over RUG scores and how they fit into reimbursement. PDPM is yet another change in the Medicare model, which we expect to continue to change as we forge forward.

NAB DOMAIN 2A5: REVENUE AND REIMBURSEMENT (E.G., PDPM, PDGM, ACOs, HMOs, MEDICAID, PRIVATE PAYORS)

The Patient Driven Payment Model (PDPM) refers to a new case-mix classification model that began on October 1, 2019, for classifying SNF residents covered in a Part A stay. PDPM is part of the SNF Prospective Payment System (PPS), which has gone through many changes over the years. PDPM is the most current of the changes and how SNFs are now getting paid for skilled care. The change to PDPM was enacted due to what some believed were inappropriate financial incentivization of services under the prior payment plan. Under the old methodology, reimbursement was mainly driven by the number of therapy minutes provided. Today, under PDPM, payment is based on the resident's clinical characteristics from an overall standpoint.

PDPM is proposed to improve payment accuracy and appropriateness by focusing on the resident, not the number of services. It is expected to be able to reduce the administrative burden on providers. Finally, PDPM is expected to improve SNF payments to underserved residents without increasing overall Medicare payments (CMS, n.d.). PDPM itself consists of five case-mix adjusted components: physical therapy, occupational therapy, speech therapy, nursing, and nontherapy ancillaries. PDPM additionally includes a variable per diem adjustment that is included in the reimbursement calculation. All this is being done to allow the facility to focus on a more individualized model of care for each resident instead of the prior scramble for therapy minutes and specific types of care used to maximize RUG-IV payments.

This is a very generalized look at the PDPM system, which replaced the previous RUG-IV system of reimbursement. The PDPM system is still based upon the use of the MDS 3.0 for resident assessment and classification. It is more critical today than ever to have a highly skilled MDS nursing team to oversee the accuracy of this documentation. PDPM truly changes the playing field when it comes to Medicare reimbursement. The highly qualified administrator will be well versed in this relatively complicated system. Do understand that certain insurance companies are still using the RUG system for reimbursement purposes at this time. As an effective administrator, you will need to understand both PDPM and RUGS.

COMMON PITFALLS IN PRACTICE

- PDPM is changing as you are reading this sentence. This is a new system, and we will continue to see constant change and revision as the months move forward. This is another area for which you should stay ahead of the curve, as what you do today can affect your billing months from now.

4.12 VALUE-BASED CARE AND PAY FOR PERFORMANCE

Consider as the Administrator . . .

- With VBP and P4P, your relationships with local hospitals are more important than ever before. Get out into your market, meet your colleagues, and help meet their needs and yours!

NAB DOMAIN 2A5: REVENUE AND REIMBURSEMENT (E.G., PDPM, PDGM, ACOs, HMOs, MEDICAID, PRIVATE PAYORS)

Beginning with the ACA, there has been a more significant focus on quality than ever before. The CMS has been at the heart of this quality effort and has done many different things to drive quality in the facility. The Skilled Nursing Facility Value-Based Purchasing (SNF VBP) program is one of these things. This program rewards high-performing facilities with an incentive payment based on the quality of care that they provide. This quality is ultimately based on specific measures surrounding hospital readmissions. The SNF VBP is a part of the Social Security Act, which was added to by the Protecting Access to Medicare Act of 2014 (PAMA). PAMA required the SNF VBP program to come into existence. Under the SNF VBP, SNFs can expect the following:

1. Evaluations for performance on specific hospital readmission measures
2. Scoring for both improvement and achievement
3. Feedback via quarterly reports concerning performance
4. Incentive payments based on performance (CMS, 2021e)

Overall, the purpose behind this program is to incentivize and assist nursing facilities in making a transformation toward a high-quality atmosphere and product that is being provided to residents. P4P stresses quality over quantity of care and provides financial benefits for those who do so. There is a financial benefit for the CMS and other entities here. If this is done correctly, we should see decreases in rehospitalizations and decreases in overall care costs. As with all pros, however, there are cons. It is believed that this type of program will simply penalize those facilities that cater to differing populations, particularly those who are already socioeconomically disadvantaged. This population is already poorer and, as a result of this, has struggled to maintain health, healthcare, medications, and follow-up care. These individuals will come to a nursing facility already sicker and in need of more care. This predisposition would reflect poorly on P4P programs, and disincentivize providers from accepting these residents, as they would most likely be a financial drain due to their already precarious health concerns.

COMMON PITFALLS IN PRACTICE

- P4P has been around for a while now. One way to help yourself is to help others in this area. Be on a first-name basis with your neighboring hospital administrators. Be on the speed dial of your doctors. Make this an area of priority for your residents. When you care, the others who care for your residents will see this and will be willing to work with you on a much more amicable level.

 CASE DISCUSSIONS

Long-Term Care Insurance?

There is no "answer" to this case. Most people conclude that long-term care insurance is too expensive. This is why few residents in facilities will be private

(continued)

payers using long-term care insurance policies. Medicare and Medicaid will continue to be the major payers.

It can be argued that if you can afford long-term care insurance, you probably don't need it. That is, you have enough assets in place to pay for long-term care out of pocket. To the extent this is true, long-term care insurance insured residents would have been able to pay out of pocket anyway.

WHAT WOULD YOU DO?

You identify several residents in your facility who are early risers (4 a.m. to 5 a.m.). Your night-shift staff gets them up and out of bed as they are ready to start their day (and it makes day shift easier for those who work it as well). You have a weekend activities aide who comes home from college to work each week. This aide realizes that there are residents who are up very early. Their normal shift started at 7 a.m. each Saturday and Sunday. They ask for authorization to come in at 6 a.m. to do something with these early risers, and they receive it.

The aide puts together a "toastest with the mostest" program starting at 6 a.m. This program consists of them providing coffee in the morning along with toast in the activities room (directly across from the nurses' station). During this time the aide also reads certain articles in the local newspaper and holds discussions of the content with the residents.

Your early-riser residents are in love with this program and have asked you to do it during the week, as well as on the weekends. In fact, you have more early-riser residents now than ever—just so they can attend this early morning activity.

1. What would you do from here?
2. Should you be happy about this program?
3. Should your day-shift certified nursing assistants (CNAs) be happy about this program?
4. Might this program cause any issues on your night shift with your staff?
5. Quite often, you are entering the facility around 5 a.m. to do rounds. What might you leverage from this program if you were the person doing it on a daily basis?

REFERENCES

American Hospital Association. (2021). *Fast facts on U.S. hospitals, 2021.* https://www.aha.org/statistics/fast-facts-us-hospitals

Centers for Disease Control and Prevention. (2018). *Health, United States, 2017, with special feature on mortality.* U.S. Department of Health and Human Services. https://www.cdc.gov/nchs/data/hus/hus17.pdf

Centers for Medicare & Medicaid Services. (n.d.). *SNF PPS: Patient driven payment model.* https://www.cms.gov/Medicare/Medicare-Fee-for-Service-Payment/SNFPPS/Downloads/MLN_CalL_PDPM_Presentation_508.pdf

Centers for Medicare & Medicaid Services. (2020). *National health expenditures.* https://www
.cms.gov/Research-Statistics-Data-and-Systems/Statistics-Trends-and-Reports/National
HealthExpendData/NationalHealthAccountsHistorical.html

Centers for Medicare & Medicaid Services. (2021a). *Inpatient hospital care.* https://www.medicare
.gov/coverage/inpatient-hospital-care

Centers for Medicare & Medicaid Services. (2021b). *What's not covered by Part A & Part B.*
https://www.medicare.gov/what-medicare-covers/whats-not-covered-by-part-a-part-b

Centers for Medicare & Medicaid Services. (2021c). *Part B costs.* https://www.medicare.gov
/your-medicare-costs/part-b-costs

Centers for Medicare & Medicaid Services. (2021d). *Skilled nursing facility (SNF) care.* https://
www.medicare.gov/coverage/skilled-nursing-facility-snf-care

Centers for Medicare & Medicaid Services. (2021e). *The Skilled Nursing Facility Value-Based Purchasing (SNF VBP) program.* https://www.cms.gov/Medicare/Quality-Initiatives-Patient
-Assessment-Instruments/Value-Based-Programs/SNF-VBP/SNF-VBP-Page

Centers for Medicare & Medicaid Services. (2021f). *Home health services.* https://www.medicare
.gov/coverage/home-health-services

Chies, S. (2021). *Pratt's long-term care: Managing across the continuum* (5th ed.). Jones and
Bartlett.

Cole, G. A., & Kelley, P. (2020). *Management theory and practice* (9th ed.). Cengage Learning.

Dean, A., McCallum, J., Kimmel, S. D., & Venkataramani, A. S. (2022). Resident mortality and
worker infection rates from COVID-19 lower in union than nonunion US nursing homes,
2020–21. *Health Affairs, 41*(5), 751–759. https://doi.org/10.1377/hlthaff.2021.01687

Guidelines on Discrimination Because of Sex. 45 C.F.R. § 1604.11. (2016).

Halter, J. B., Ouslander, J. G., Studenski, S., High, K. P., Asthana, S., Supiano, M. A., & Ritchie,
C. (2017). *Hazzard's geriatric medicine and gerontology* (7th ed.). McGraw Hill.

Harrington, C.H., Carillo, H., Garfield, R., Musumeci, M., Squires, E., & Kaiser Family
Foundation. (2018). *Nursing facilities, staffing, residents, and facility deficiencies, 2009 through
2016.* Henry J. Kaiser Family Foundation.

Kane, R. L., Ouslander, J. G., Abrass, I. B., & Resnick, B. (2013). *Essentials of clinical geriatrics*
(7th ed.). McGraw Hill.

Kübler-Ross, E. (1993). *On death and dying.* Scribner.

Martin, A. B., Hartman, M., Lassman, D., & Catlin, A. (2020). National healthcare spending in 2019: Steady growth for the fourth consecutive year. *Health Affairs, 40*(1). 14–24.
https://doi.org/10.1377/hlthaff.2020.02022

Meals on Wheels America. (2021). *What we deliver.* https://www.mealsonwheelsamerica.org
/learn-more/what-we-deliver

Mileski, M., Topinka, J. B., Lee, K., Brooks, M., McNeil, C., & Jackson, J. (2017). An investigation of quality improvement initiatives in decreasing the rate of avoidable 30-day, skilled
nursing facility-to-hospital readmissions: A systematic review. *Clinical Interventions in
Aging, 12*, 213–222. https://doi.org/10.2147/CIA.S123362

Morbidity and Mortality Weekly Report. (2020). *Characteristics and health status of informal unpaid caregivers—44 states. District of Columbia, and Puerto Rico. 2015-2017.*
https://www cdc.gov/mmwr/volumes/69/wr/mm6907a2.htm

National Center for Health Statistics. (2019). *Long-term care providers and services users in
the United States, 2015-2016.* https://www.cdc.gov/nchs/data/series/sr_03/sr03_
43-508.pdf

National Center for Health Statistics. (2021). *Adult day care centers.* Centers for Disease
Control and Prevention. https://www.cdc.gov/nchs/fastats/adsc.htm

Occupational Health and Safety Administration. (2021). *OSHA penalties.* https://www.osha
.gov/penalties

Robbins, S. P., & Coulter, M. (2018). *Management* (14th ed.). Pearson.

Roser, M., Ortiz-Ospina, E., & Ritchie, H. (2019). *Life expectancy.* Our World in Data. https://ourworldindata.org/life-expectancy

Singh, D. A. (2016). *Effective management of long-term care facilities* (3rd ed.). Jones & Bartlett.

Topol, E. (2015). *The patient will see you now: The future of medicine is in your hands.* Basic Books.

U.S. Bureau of Labor Statistics. (2019). *Injuries, illnesses, and fatalities.* https://www.bls.gov/web/osh/summ1_00.htm

U.S. Census Bureau. (2011). *Age and sex composition: 2010.* https://www.census.gov/library/publications/2011/dec/c2010br-03.html

U.S. Census Bureau. (2017). *2017 national population projections tables: Main series.* https://www.census.gov/data/tables/2017/demo/popproj/2017-summary-tables.html

U.S. Census Bureau. (2021). *ACS demographic and housing estimates.* https://data.census.gov/cedsci/table?d=ACS%205-Year%20Estimates%20Data%20Profiles&tid=ACSDP5Y2010.DP05

U.S. Department of Health and Human Services. (2014). *What does Part B of Medicare (medical insurance) cover?* https://www.hhs.gov/answers/medicare-and-medicaid/what-does-medicare-part-b-cover/index.html

U.S. Department of Labor. (2019). *Fact sheet #17N: Nurses and the Part 541 exemptions under the Fair Labor Standards Act (FLSA).* https://www.dol.gov/agencies/whd/fact-sheets/17n-overtime-nurses

U.S. Department of Labor. (2021a). *Fact sheet #30: The Federal Wage Garnishment Law, Consumer Credit Protection Act's, Title III.* https://www.dol.gov/agencies/whd/fact-sheets/30-cppa

U.S. Department of Labor. (2021b). *Family and medical leave act.* https://www.dol.gov/agencies/whd/fmla

U.S. Equal Employment Opportunity Commission. (2021a). *Overview.* https://www.eeoc.gov/overview

U.S. Equal Employment Opportunity Commission. (2021b). *The Equal Pay Act of 1963.* https://www.eeoc.gov/statutes/equal-pay-act-1963

U.S. Equal Employment Opportunity Commission. (2021c). *Title VII of the Civil Rights Act of 1964.* https://www.eeoc.gov/statutes/title-vii-civil-rights-act-1964

USA Facts. (2021). *Labor union membership.* https://usafacts.org/articles/labor-union-membership/

PART 5

Building Your Resident Care Skills

- *Each person ages differently and hence has different needs to be met by the facility*
- *Research on aging is a new and imprecise science*

Consider as the Administrator . . .

- *Do the differences in functions of the 75-year-old person compared to the 30-year-old person matter?*
- *How much clinical acumen do you need as an administrator? Do you need skills to speak to and understand doctors and nurses?*

5.1 AGING PROCESS

Section Concepts

- *Aging is an individualized process*
- *How we define the aging populations and their needs changes with age*

Consider as the Administrator . . .

- *If aging is a "use it or lose it" situation, how do you keep your residents on the "use it" side of the situation?*

NAB DOMAIN 1A: QUALITY OF CARE; 1B: QUALITY OF LIFE; 1B1: PSYCHOSOCIAL NEEDS (E.G., SOCIAL, SPIRITUAL, COMMUNITY, CULTURAL)

How many Americans die of old age each year? Our answer is "no one." Old age is not a disease process.

At one time, we used "old age" as a diagnosis for a resident passing. However, this is far from the truth. The body is made to operate for a long time and can do so, barring any disease or pathological processes. The problems associated with these diseases and pathological processes can accelerate death. Without the issues that come from these diseases, the body could keep going on for quite some time. Unfortunately, we see acute and chronic disease processes that often cause death. These acute and chronic processes result from lifestyle, a lack of exercise, diet, genetics, activity levels, environmental exposure, and other causes (Fabiani-Longo et al., 2017). A newer influence has been COVID-19, which has been shown to reactivate dormant diseases. There has been a significant change in common causes of death today from what they have traditionally been for many years.

Every older person, just as every young one, dies of specific causes. Generally, one or more body systems (described later) become overwhelmed (known as a loss of homeostasis) due to a disease or an injury, resulting in death. It is important to understand that age-related changes are not diseases but a natural loss of function (Bengtson & Settersten, 2016; Saxon et al., 2022).

RESEARCH ON AGING

The two groups that study aging individuals are physicians and gerontologists. Physicians specializing in treating older adults are called geriatricians. Professionals who study the problems of the aging population in society are called gerontologists.

Tremendous amounts of research have been conducted and published over the last 20 or so years on aging. Society has begun to focus on aging, understanding that baby boomers were coming into the healthcare system with specific health issues. Luckily, we realized this early and began to address these issues in earnest, knowing that the baby boomer population would change healthcare as we know it.

GENERAL OBSERVATIONS

The aging population is quickly growing due to the baby boomers and their entry into the healthcare landscape. We have always focused on the aged as three split populations, as each of these populations has different needs, different concerns, and different physiology. These three populations are the "young-old" (65–74 years of age), the "middle-old" (75–84), and the "old-old" (85+).

The services each of these populations requires are significantly different because as people grow older, their needs change significantly. The young-old often need services that help them reintegrate into their previous life, whereas the old-old often need services that provide support and protective services (Saxon et al., 2022). For example, the young-old would be the population a facility would focus on for short-term rehabilitation services to home after an event. As a resident moves into middle-old and eventually into old-old, they might still receive some rehabilitative services in a facility but likely would transition from there into custodial care within the facility after rehabilitation plateau during a Medicare Part A stay. An important thing to note regarding the population characterized as "elderly" is that each person's experience with aging is unique and will require individualized care for their needs. Geriatricians are physicians specially trained to meet the diverse needs of this population.

Many aging individuals have succumbed to a "use it or lose it" situation. The body is meant to move. Keeping the body healthy requires exercise, proper nutrition, and appropriate stress management (Saxon et al., 2022). Without these things, acute and chronic diseases can set into the body quickly. Unfortunately, we often see issues with these areas, especially as people age. Multiple conditions increase difficulty with being able or motivated to perform such functions leading to worsening issues with the body and the homeostasis. The body begins to lose "reserve capacity" over time. Reserve capacity is the body's ability to deal with issues that might occur. As the body ages, the available reserve capacity decreases, allowing disease processes to progress (McGarrigle et al., 2019; Saxon et al., 2022; Schöllgen et al., 2012).

5.1.1 OVERVIEW OF SOME APPEARANCE AND FUNCTIONAL CHANGES ASSOCIATED WITH AGING

Section Concepts

- *The body systems can change significantly as the body ages*
- *Changes in the body can become cumulative in many systems over time*

Consider as the Administrator . . .

- *Knowing that the body changes as it ages, how can you use this information to provide a better quality of life for your residents?*

NAB DOMAIN 1A: QUALITY OF CARE; 1B: QUALITY OF LIFE; 1B1: PSYCHOSOCIAL NEEDS (E.G., SOCIAL, SPIRITUAL, COMMUNITY, CULTURAL); 1B2: PERSON-CENTERED CARE AND COMPREHENSIVE CARE PLANNING

The following observations are discussed at greater length under the headings of the 10 body systems described later in this chapter. The phenomena discussed here are generalizations that can be applied to the aging population.

- *Changes in collagen.* Collagen is one of the most abundant proteins in the body, and it undergoes biomechanical and structural changes with aging (Van Gulick et al., 2019). Collagen loses elasticity over time and can account for the sagging appearance of the skin (Aldwin et al., 2017; Saxon et al., 2022).
- *Reduced reserve.* All organ systems can experience a decrease in their reserve capacity with aging. This reduced capacity can account for the body slowing down with age, disease processes, and the ability to do things "how they used to" (Coll, 2019; Saxon et al., 2022).
- *Gradual changes in the immune system.* The primary purpose of the immune system is to recognize what belongs in the body and what does not. Upon recognition of something foreign, the body rejects these cells. As the body ages, one theory holds that a progressive weakening of the immune response increases one's susceptibility to respiratory and other illnesses (Aldwin et al., 2017; Halter et al., 2017; Kane et al., 2018).
- *Temperature response changes.* A reduction of capacity to maintain proper body temperature leads to diminished shivering and sweating responses. The decreased response can lead to temperatures ranging to dangerous levels and may result in death during heat or cold waves (Fabiani-Longo et al., 2017). This lack of adaptability is an excellent example of decreased reserve capacity.
- *Postural imbalances.* The balancing mechanisms appear to function less well, resulting in some persons aged 65 years and older being progressively at risk of tripping and falls. Balance and posture are regulated mainly by the cerebellum and the proprioceptors in the body. Neural changes, brain shrinkage, and decreased numbers of neurotransmitters available in the brain contribute to issues with posture (Aldwin et al., 2017; Saxon et al., 2022).
- *Decalcification of the bones.* As the body ages, bone formation and remodeling slow. As a result, there is a loss of bone matrix and density over time. Many older persons are at increased risk of bones breaking, especially if they fall (Aldwin et al., 2017; Halter et al., 2017; Saxon et al., 2022).
- *Decreased bone and muscle mass.* This process may result in a stooped posture, reduced height, spontaneous fractures, loss of muscle power, misshapen joints, and limitations in mobility (Saxon et al., 2022).
- *Urinary system.* Multiple issues simultaneously occur in this system, with a decrease in kidney size and function, bladder capacity, and the ability to filter blood appropriately (Saxon et al., 2022). These concerns lead to an overall lessened capacity of the renal system to operate correctly.
- *Decreases in bowel function control.* As the central nervous system (CNS) tends to function less and less well in some older persons, the ability to control the bowels lessens (Aldwin et al., 2017).

- *Frequent anorexia.* Anorexia (loss of appetite) among some older adults leads to skipping meals and a reduced level of nutrition (Saxon et al., 2022). This anorexia is often linked to a decline in the taste sense (Aldwin et al., 2017).
- *Hearing and vision.* Both hearing and vision are often reduced among aged persons (Kane et al., 2018).
- *Skin.* With the loss of some subcutaneous fat, an older person may feel colder, and the skin may wrinkle. Some pigment (color) cells of the skin enlarge with age, resulting in the pigmented plaques often seen on the skin of aged persons. The skin is also largely responsible as a first-line defense for immunity. As the skin ages, the compromises in the skin can also affect the body's immune processes (Aldwin et al., 2017; Saxon et al., 2022).
- *Memory.* Decreases in brain capacity can lead to overall memory issues. Recall of names and information takes longer, learning new information is more difficult, and processing information takes longer (Aldwin et al., 2017).

5.1.2 SOMATIC THEORIES OF AGING

Section Concepts

- *The differing theories of aging*
- *The effects of exercise on aging persons*

Consider as the Administrator . . .

- *Should nursing facility residents be required to exercise?*
- *Can you hide exercise in otherwise unobtrusive activities?*

NAB DOMAIN 1A: QUALITY OF CARE; 1B: QUALITY OF LIFE; 1B1: PSYCHOSOCIAL NEEDS (E.G., SOCIAL, SPIRITUAL, COMMUNITY, CULTURAL)

Most investigators of the causes of aging agree that no one theory thoroughly explains the biological aging phenomenon. Somatic theories are specific to the body and its potential changes with aging. Generally, there are stochastic theories (those that result from adverse changes in cells) and nonstochastic theories (those that result from repeated errors in cells and may be programmed; Eliopoulous, 2018). There are quite a variety of theories that take from both types. Additional theories continue to arise as more research is completed. We discuss a few of the more popular and well-known theories here. However, the breadth of discussing even the somatic theories alone is far outside the scope of this textbook.

Because no one knows why specific changes occur with aging, there are several theories instead of one generally accepted explanation. Theorists increasingly suspect that the forces that produce age changes are different from those that drive longevity determination.

WEAR AND TEAR THEORY

The wear and tear theory postulates that cells and tissues have vital parts that simply wear out, which results in aging (Jin, 2010). Simply, the body parts as we know them wear out from repetitive use over time. These cellular parts fail, which compromises tissues that begin to fail and eventually leads to the body failing. Wear and tear is still a very popular theory today, despite parts of the theory being outdated. We know that the body does improve from use, lifestyle changes, and other outside influences. Certain research identifies that the body can be improved—go against the wear and tear theory—to bring back the body to previous resilience (Mitteldorf, 2010).

CROSS-LINKING THEORY

The cross-linking theory postulates that an accumulation of cross-linked proteins can cause damage to cells and tissues, which slows down body processes over time, resulting in aging (Bjorksten, 1968; Jin, 2010). These cross-linked proteins consist of collagen and elastin, which change with aging leading to a lack of flexibility and optimal tissue operation (Saxon et al., 2022).

FREE RADICAL THEORY

The free radical theory postulates that superoxides and other free radicals damage cell components, causing accumulated damage to the cells, resulting in eventual organ damage and eventual failure (Harman, 1956; Jin, 2010). Free radicals are normal metabolic by-products of cellular metabolism (body operations) that may also derive from the environment (Bengtson & Settersten, 2016; Saxon et al., 2022). The body normally neutralizes free radicals; however, as the body ages, the ability to perform this function efficiently decreases (Beckman & Ames, 1998).

DNA/RNA DAMAGE THEORY

The DNA/RNA damage theory postulates that DNA and RNA damage occurs continuously in cells during copying. The damage accumulates over time as cells lose the ability to correct errors (Jin, 2010; Park & Yeo, 2013). The lack of corrections to errors in gene copying results in cellular damage, then tissue deterioration, and eventual organ failure (Saxon et al., 2022). The ability to repair DNA or RNA damage is directly proportional to the life span as its repairability is impaired with aging (Bohr & Anson, 1995).

PROGRAMMED AGING/LONGEVITY THEORY

This theory postulates that aging is the result of a sequential switching on and off of certain genes (Davidovic et al., 2010; Jin, 2010). Aging is programmed into the body at the time of birth by a biological or genetic clock that drives the aging process (Hayflick & Moorehead, 1961; Saxon et al., 2022). This programing results in a preprogrammed life expectancy (Troen, 2003).

ENDOCRINE THEORY

This theory of aging that lifetime pacing is set by a biological clock governed by hormones (Jin, 2010). Aging impairs the hypothalamus, pituitary gland, and endocrine systems (Park & Yeo, 2013). Recent research has strengthened this theory as it has been demonstrated that certain hormonal pathways play key roles in the hormonal regulation of aging (Tatar et al., 2003; Van Heemst, 2010).

IMMUNOLOGICAL THEORY

The immunological theory stipulates that the immune system is programmed to decline over time, resulting in increased vulnerability to disease and death (Jin, 2010). The immune system is most effective at puberty and gradually declines until death (Cornelius, 1972). Recent research has linked issues with immune response to cardiovascular disease, Alzheimer's disease, inflammation, and cancer (Rozemuller et al., 2005).

COMMON PITFALLS IN PRACTICE
- With so many theories for just about everything in the nursing facility or surrounding the resident, no one answer or theory always applies. Consider all these theories different tools in your toolbox and pull the best fit for your situation.

5.1.3 RESIDENT EXERCISE AND FITNESS

Section Concepts

- Aging accumulates over time, and working with residents to stop this accumulation can lead to a higher quality of life

Consider as the Administrator . . .

- We know that physical activity and health are connected, but how can you meet this need?

NAB DOMAIN 1A3: DISEASE MANAGEMENT (E.G., ACUTE VS. CHRONIC CONDITIONS); 1A5: ACTIVITIES OF DAILY LIVING (ADLs) AND INSTRUMENTAL ACTIVITIES OF DAILY LIVING (IADLs); 1B17: THERAPEUTIC RECREATION AND ACTIVITY PROGRAMS

Much of what happens in the aging body appears to accumulate over time, with one issue leading to another. Degradation in cardiovascular function interferes with the supply of nutrients and oxygen to the cells as aging occurs (Kane et al., 2018). This starvation damages the tissues and organs in the body, leading to the decline of organ function (Halter et al., 2017). Many studies demonstrate that physical conditioning can improve the cardiovascular system, the respiratory system, the musculature, and the body composition of older persons. Even moderate exercise is important to the cardiovascular system of aged persons (Michel et al., 2017; Walter & Chang, 2020). The notable Paffenbarger et al. (1978) Harvard Alumni Health Study, more broadly known as the Harvard Study, attributed 1 to 2 years of increased longevity to 80-year-old men who had exercised moderately over the years. The Harvard Study is ongoing and has found even more conclusive results that total physical activity and vigorous activities show substantial reductions in coronary heart disease risk (Sesso et al., 2000).

All tissues in the body depend on oxygen and nutrients transported by the blood. Exercise increases the blood flow, improving supplies of oxygen and nutrients, leading to improved organ and cell status (Michel et al., 2017; Walter & Chang, 2020). This physiology gives credence to the claims for the benefits of exercise in older adults. There are additional perceived benefits on depression as well as a reduction in the risk of developing heart disease, improved oxygenation and oxygen transport, greater protection against deterioration of glucose tolerance, and denser bone mass (Saxon et al., 2022; Walter & Chang, 2020; Yu et al., 2018).

Considering noncommunicable diseases (heart disease, stroke, cancer, diabetes, and chronic lung disease), one of the top four causes is a lack of physical activity (World Health Organization, 2021a). Sedentary lifestyles and poor physical fitness are thought to be responsible for some of the typical nursing facility symptoms such as headaches, constipation, joint pain, backaches, insomnia, and fatigue (Walter & Chang, 2020). A lack of physical activity results in insufficient energy expenditure of the body, leading to obesity, type 2 diabetes, cardiovascular diseases, and other chronic diseases (Hallal et al., 2012). Living in a nursing facility can contribute to a lack of physical activity, as residents are often institutionalized due to a lack of ability to participate in activities of daily living (ADLs). Thus, working with our residents to provide some level of physical activity is essential to improving their overall health status and quality of life.

Reduced risk of chronic diseases and a decreased risk of premature death are primary benefits of physical activity (Mora & Valencia, 2018; Yu et al., 2018). Physical activity in nursing facility residents improves physical and cognitive functions while decreasing depressive symptoms and psychiatric concerns (Brett et al., 2016; Lok et al., 2017; Northey et al., 2018; Pitkälä et al., 2013).

While there is a proven link between physical activity and health, a disconnect commonly occurs in the facility's ability to provide it. Many of our residents are unable to take part in routine physical activity. Other residents cannot identify or understand cues for such activities (Huang et al., 2020). Finding a way to "sneak" physical activities into the daily work of the activity director, involving the therapy department, and innovation are required to provide exercise to residents. Adaptability is also crucial, as the resident base is continually changing, and they arrive "quicker and sicker" from the hospitals. Their higher acuity level confounds their ability to participate in even the most basic physical activity or exercise.

The inclusion of aerobic exercise (exercise sustaining the heart rate at an elevated level, delivering increased oxygen for a specified minimum period each week) matched to each resident's capabilities should be included in their plan of care (Ferrini & Ferrini, 2012; Michel et al., 2017; Walter & Chang, 2020).

5.2 MEDICAL AND RELATED TERMS

5.2.1 MEDICAL SPECIALIZATIONS

Section Concepts

- *The names of the medical specializations the administrator may deal with in the day-to-day functioning of the facility*

Consider as the Administrator . . .

- *Who better serves your resident population? Should residents be seen by a geriatrician, specialists in various body systems, or a combination of both?*
- *Can a physician team be interdisciplinary as well?*

NAB DOMAIN 1A12: BASIC HEALTHCARE TERMINOLOGY

By professional custom, physicians usually place only "MD" or "DO" after their names, omitting any reference to certification they may hold as a specialist. A "specialization" requires a physician's complete and additional training program after medical school. This additional training can occur during their residency or with an added fellowship and can take anywhere between 3 and 12 years, depending on the specialty.

A nurse practitioner (NP), also called an advanced practice registered nurse (APRN), is a highly trained nurse who specializes and is certified in a clinical area and population (Mileski et al., 2020). The NP role as independent providers with full practice rights in nursing facilities is quickly growing. NPs are not physicians. Their training includes an immersive clinical practicum focusing on their certification population while in school, and scope varies by state. Some states still require physician oversight of NPs to practice within the scope of their license. However, the national trend is moving toward more states giving full practice rights. This trend also promotes the doctoral preparation of NPs, as some state laws provide a preferential scope of practice to this level of education. The administrator is responsible for knowing each professional's scope of practice according to their professional board.

The following is a focused list of specialists commonly covering residents in the nursing facility:

- *Cardiologist.* A physician specializing in diagnosing and treating cardiac and vascular diseases.
- *Chiropodist.* See podiatrist.
- *Dermatologist.* A physician who diagnoses and treats diseases of the skin.
- *Endocrinologist.* A physician who specializes in disorders affecting the endocrine system. This system includes the pituitary, thyroid, pancreas, adrenal, and other glands that secrete hormones into the bloodstream.
- *Exodontist.* A dentist who specializes in the extraction of teeth.
- *Family medicine specialist or practitioner.* In 1879, 80% of physicians were general practitioners (GPs), and 20% were specialists. With the proliferation of

medical knowledge, the reverse is true today: 80% of physicians are specialists, and 20% are GPs. GPs are a specialty requiring 3 years of residency beyond medical school. They provide the bulk of care in nursing facilities and specialize in diagnosing diseases and making appropriate referrals to specialists.

- *Gastroenterologist.* A physician who treats and diagnoses diseases of the digestive tract.
- *General surgeon.* A physician who specializes in operative procedures to treat illnesses or various injuries.
- *Geriatrician.* A physician who concentrates on treating older adults, usually a subspecialty with education past residency or fellowship (geriatric psychiatrists, cardiogeriatricians, geriatric neurologists). The Society for Post-Acute and Long-Term Care Medicine/American Medical Directors Association offers extensive education to physicians wishing to enter this field.
- *Gerontologist.* A professional who studies the problem of the aging population in society. The gerontologist is often not a medical doctor but holds PhD or master's-level preparation.
- *Internist.* A physician who specializes in diagnostic procedures and treatment of nonsurgical cases.
- *Neurologist.* A physician who diagnoses and treats diseases of the brain, nervous system, and spinal cord.
- *Ophthalmologist.* A physician who diagnoses and treats eye diseases and disorders, performs eye surgery, refracts the eyes, and prescribes corrective eyeglasses and lenses. The focus here is much higher-level treatment or surgical intervention than the optometrist (discussed later) can provide.
- *Optician.* Not a physician; a technician trained to grind lenses and fit eyeglasses.
- *Optometrist.* A doctor of optometry examines, diagnoses, and treats diseases and disorders of the eye. They also prescribe corrective eyeglasses and lenses.
- *Orthopedist.* A physician specializing in diseases and injuries to bones, muscles, joints, and tendons. An orthopedic surgeon is a physician who specializes in surgical procedures relating to the bones, muscles, joints, and tendons.
- *Osteopath.* A doctor of osteopathy (DO) is a primary care physician, different in training but similar in scope to an MD. MDs and DOs are on equal footing in the nursing facility. DOs specialize in family medicine, internal medicine, and many other fields, and many act as geriatricians in the nursing facility.
- *Physiatrist.* A physician specializing in physical medicine, body movements, and conditioning, much like a physical therapist's focus, and is often associated with sports medicine.
- *Podiatrist.* A doctor of podiatric medicine (DPM) is a physician who treats the foot, ankle, and leg. We often see them providing care of the feet, including clipping of toenails for diabetics and treating ailments such as corns and bunions in the nursing facility. Many also provide oversight and treatment of diabetic skin issues, stasis ulcers, and other skin integrity issues involving the feet.
- *Proctologist.* A physician specializing in diagnosing and treating the large intestine, particularly the rectum and anus.
- *Psychiatrist.* A physician who specializes in the diagnosis and treatment of mental disorders.

- *Psychoanalyst.* A psychiatrist who specializes in the use of a psychoanalytic therapy technique.
- *Psychologist.* A practitioner who studies the function of the mind and behavioral patterns and administers psychological tests. The psychologist is often a PhD-trained practitioner.
- *Pulmonologist.* A physician specializing in the treatment of the lungs and respiratory conditions.
- *Radiologist.* A physician specializing in medical diagnostic imaging such as x-ray, MRI, and CT scans.
- *Rheumatologist.* A physician who specializes in the treatment of rheumatic and arthritic diseases.
- *Urologist.* A physician specializing in diagnosing and treating diseases of the kidney, bladder, and reproductive organs.

5.2.2 MEDICATIONS/THERAPEUTIC ACTIONS OF DRUGS

Section Concepts

- *The extent of drug use in facilities*
- *Route of drug administration*
- *Basic actions of drugs*
- *Use of* pro re nata *or "prescribe as needed" (PRN) in the facility*
- *Antianxiety and antipsychotic medications*
- *Vitamins and minerals*
- *Analgesics*
- *Cardiovascular agents*
- *Respiratory agents*
- *Controlled drug schedules*
- *The therapeutic actions of drugs*

Consider as the Administrator . . .

- *Is polypharmacy a concern in the facility? Do you, as the administrator, have any control over the number of medications your residents receive?*

NAB DOMAIN 1A2: MEDICATION MANAGEMENT AND ADMINISTRATION

It is important to note that daily safe and appropriate medication administration is a crucial part of care in the nursing facility. Nurses usually administer medications, but many states allow administration by certified medication aides (specially trained nurse's aides). The individual giving the medications must assess the resident each time before a drug is given to ensure that administration is safe, appropriate, and effective (Ernstmeyer & Christman, 2020).

ROUTES USED IN DRUG ADMINISTRATION

Drugs must be absorbed in the body for them to be effective. Absorption occurs after the drugs enter the body when they enter the circulatory system. There are various ways for medications to enter the body:

- Oral (PO—by mouth)
- Intramuscular (IM—injection into a muscle)
- Subcutaneous (SC—injection into the fatty tissue beneath the skin)
- Inhalation (breathing in medications from inhaler or nebulizer)
- Topical (creams or ointments directly on skin, membranes, or other tissues)
- Transdermal (patches)
- Sublingually (held under the tongue)
- Rectal (PR—suppositories and creams into the rectum)
- Enteral (deposited directly into the gastrointestinal tract [GI] via nasogastric [NG] or percutaneous endoscopic gastrostomy [PEG] tube)

Once the medication is administered, it is absorbed into the bloodstream and may require metabolic breakdown to be converted to its active form. This breakdown is referred to as drug metabolism. Medications eventually become inactivated in the liver, kidneys, or intestines and are removed from the body via the urine or feces (Ernstmeyer & Christman, 2020; Halter et al., 2017; Michel et al., 2017).

INJECTIONS AND INTRAVENOUS THERAPY

Facilities provide injections and intravenous (IV) therapy for a variety of reasons. Injections do not undergo the same barriers to absorption due to avoiding the stomach and intestines and, in some cases, allow prolonged bioavailability. IV therapy is fully available to tissues once it enters the bloodstream, offering complete bioavailability and much more immediate effects than other administration routes (Ernstmeyer & Christman, 2020; Michel et al., 2017).

Injections and IV therapy are commonplace in nursing facilities today, a change from previous standards. This ability is now expected as residents often have higher acuity due to earlier hospital discharge. Each facility needs nurses trained on IV therapy according to its state's nursing scope of practice.

FIVE BASIC DRUG ACTIONS

The following are the five basic types of actions drugs will produce:

- Blocking nerve impulses
- Stimulating nerve impulses
- Working directly on living cells
- Working to replace body deficiencies
- Any of these in combination

Every person is affected by drugs differently because of individual body chemistries, so every resident must be monitored to determine the appropriateness of each medication and its dosage (Michel et al., 2017).

As a result of age-related changes in the liver, kidney, and body fat composition altering the drug concentration, bioavailability, and metabolism, older adults are at a greater risk of adverse drug reactions. They may also experience an increase in side effects commonly associated with most medications. Unintended drug interactions, side effects, and adverse effects all require active monitoring of patient reactions.

POLICY IMPLICATIONS

Nursing facility residents are more likely to suffer from multiple diseases and use multiple medications, and these drug combinations can produce dangerous drug interactions (Michel et al., 2017). This risk, combined with altered metabolism of drugs, means the nursing facility administrator must ensure that the consulting pharmacist appropriately monitors drug regimens in the facility with proper in-depth periodic reports to the facility management. Polypharmacy is a common occurrence in nursing facilities due to the acuity of residents and the number of medications used for treatment (Cadenas et al., 2021). Special precautions can be mounted to prevent the consequences of illness or disability from drug reactions.

The increased use of electronic health records (EHRs) in nursing facilities is causing a move toward bedside systems with handheld devices for staff to scan patient bracelet bar codes or enter information at mobile workstations while providing medications. This bar code medication administration (BCMA) is used in many hospitals today to prevent medication errors by real-time verification of the "five rights" of medication administration—right resident, right dose, right drug, right time, and right route before administration (Nolen & Patton, 2009; Shah et al., 2016). BCMA systems compare medication records in the EHR to what is being given at the bedside, and they can create real-time warnings or approvals for those administering the medication. They also facilitate care by automatic documentation in the medication administration record (MAR) of the EHR system.

Beers Criteria/Boxed Warnings

The American Geriatrics Society maintains the Beers Criteria for Potentially Inappropriate Medication Use in Older Adults to combat medication administration issues in older adults. Published in the *Journal of the American Geriatrics Society* after every 3-year update, it lists which drugs should be avoided by older adults in most circumstances or under specific situations (American Geriatrics Society Beers Criteria Update Expert Panel, 2019). The most current update is always available for download through the American Geriatrics Society website.

Another type of medication warning is a "black box warning," which appears on prescription drug labels and is designed to call attention to serious or life-threatening risks of drugs. You will find a high correlation between black box warnings and inclusion in Beers Criteria for drugs. Nursing facilities need to be aware of medications being prescribed with black box warnings within the facility to avoid complications.

Use of Pro Re Nata Medications

Often physicians rely on what is commonly referred to as PRN (*pro re nata*, "as the thing is necessary") approaches. These "use as needed" orders allow nurses to use their discretion to determine when to administer a particular medication based on timing present in the order, assessment, and resident requests. PRN drugs are categorized as unscheduled medications that can be given alone or in addition to routine medications (Vaismoradi et al., 2019). These PRN drugs allow nurses to address known physical or mental symptoms instead of calling the physician each time a patient requires intervention (Baumann & Greif, 2017; Douglas-Hall & Whicher, 2015). Common PRN medications are used for analgesia, GI distress, psychotropic, anxiolytic, or sedative purposes (Vaismoradi et al., 2019). Physicians do not want to be called for these occurrences repeatedly, and we often see a set of standardized PRN medications ordered upon admission.

As these medications are utilized on an as-needed basis, there is a potential for inappropriate use by nurses or residents (Nyborg et al., 2017). Additionally, there is an unfortunate potential for these drugs to be used without the resident's consent or request (Moermans et al., 2018). The indiscriminate use of these drugs can result in chemical restraint, unintended side effects, or disguising a drug diversion. Therefore, a process must be in place to monitor PRN drug utilization.

Polypharmacy

Polypharmacy is a complication of increased side effects arising from too many medications prescribed for a person, often resulting in duplication of goal or even medications working in opposition. A policy involving the facility pharmacy consultant, medical director, and the nursing staff in constant monitoring of drug regimens and reactions is a significant step toward appropriate usage of all medications. Increasing concern has been generated regarding polypharmacy (too many drugs) being given to older adult patients (Michel et al., 2017; Walter & Chang, 2020). Polypharmacy is associated with many negative health outcomes, including adverse drug reactions, cognitive decline, hospitalization, and increased mortality (Lalic et al., 2016; Onder et al., 2019; Vetrano et al., 2018). However, closer and more active monitoring seems appropriate since undesirable drug interactions are a significant ongoing concern to nursing facility administration (Halter et al., 2017).

Pharmacies are required to review and evaluate Medicaid recipients' drug profiles for possible therapeutic duplication, drug interaction, and incorrect dosage. As a result of this requirement and other concerns with drug regimens, many nursing facilities utilize pharmacies that specifically cater to the resident populations we serve. Part of filling prescriptions also includes reviews of all medications to decrease polypharmacy and adverse reactions.

The Five Rights

The five rights of medication administration include identifying:

- The right medication
- The right dose
- The right time for administration
- The right route (oral, injection, etc.)
- The right patient (a picture with the medical administration record [MAR] is always a good idea)

The "five rights" of medication administration are essential to policies to ensure the correct usage and administration of drug regimens. Medication errors are a concern in nursing facilities, ranging between 16% and 27% of all residents experiencing some error level (Ferrah et al., 2017). Research surrounding medication error cause and prevention is often conflicting. Still, policies to decrease the potential for errors and use of EHR and BCMA technologies can reduce medication errors. The five rights are certainly the right place to start in every facility.

GENERIC AND BRAND NAMES

Familiarity with both the generic (chemical) and brand (manufacturing) names of commonly prescribed medications can be helpful. The following discussion mentions frequently prescribed medications with first generic names and brand names following in parentheses. Health professionals often use brand names unless many companies produce a particular drug (e.g., aspirin).

ANTIANXIETY AND ANTIPSYCHOTIC (PSYCHOACTIVE) MEDICATIONS

Antianxiety and antipsychotic medications act on the central nervous system (CNS) to enable residents to deal with changes in their behavior or stressful and anxiety-provoking changes in their environment. The precise mechanism behind this action is unknown. The two major classes of this type of drug are tranquilizers and sedatives/hypnotics.

These medications act directly on the primary control center—the brain—and should be administered very cautiously. The administration of these drugs can be significantly deleterious in the older adult population. Again, we can reference the Beers Criteria. Older adult patients with dementia-related psychosis are at an increased risk of death due to cardiovascular complications or infection when being administered antipsychotics (Ernstmeyer & Christman, 2020).

Commonly prescribed tranquilizers and sedatives/hypnotics used in the nursing facility are thioridazine and chlordiazepoxide. Thioridazine (Mellaril) is a major tranquilizer and antipsychotic drug prescribed for mild to moderate anxiety relief. This medication has been used for long-term alcoholics to control their illness. Chlordiazepoxide hydrochloride (Librium) is a minor tranquilizer prescribed to relieve anxiety.

The following side effects are associated with these medications:

- Death
- Drowsiness, dizziness, disorientation (Michel et al., 2017)

- Impaired motor function (issues with walking or moving)
- Neurotoxicity (weakness, lethargy, confusion, fever, nervous system symptoms)
- Tardive dyskinesia (involuntary contraction of oral and facial muscles often causing tongue thrusting actions or movements of the extremities)
- Neuroleptic malignant syndrome (a life-threatening syndrome that includes high fever, unstable blood pressure, and myoglobinemia)
- Extrapyramidal symptoms (involuntary motor symptoms similar to Parkinson's disease; Ernstmeyer & Christman, 2020)

VITAMINS AND MINERALS

Vitamins and minerals are very commonly prescribed for residents in the facility. These are prescribed for their specific nutritional benefits or at the family's request. There is controversy over providing vitamins and minerals as many of them can exhibit drug/nutrient interactions with negative results for the resident (Goorang et al., 2015). But research also shows benefits when combatting deficiencies (Williams & Williams, 2020).

Side effects can also occur from supplement use. For example, iron supplements can irritate the GI tract, causing stomach upset or constipation. Supplement use is under constant research, and knowledge is growing continually. COVID-19 showed the importance of vitamin D and zinc in our resident populations (Griffin, 2020).

ANALGESICS

Analgesics are often administered for pain relief. Acetylsalicylic acid (ASA), or aspirin, may be relatively safe, except for residents with kidney or bleeding problems and ulcers. Aspirin may also act as an anti-inflammatory agent for arthritic patients by reducing the amount of damage to the joints and lessening the painful side effects of the inflammatory process. It is important to note that ASA is listed in Beers Criteria for bleeding. ASA has an anticoagulant action, which increases bleeding risk when coupled with other anticoagulants.

Some of the side effects of aspirin include stomach upset, ringing in the ears, deafness, dizziness, confusion, bleeding, and irritability.

Acetaminophen (Tylenol) is an analgesic similar to aspirin but without anti-inflammatory properties, and hence, it may serve only as a pain reliever and fever control. Some side effects are redness and itching of the skin and possible liver damage. The risk of liver damage is higher in the older adult population as many of our residents already have compromised liver and other organ concerns.

Nonsteroidal Anti-Inflammatory Drugs

Nonsteroidal anti-inflammatory drugs (NSAIDs; e.g., ibuprofen) are widely used for treating arthritis and chronic pain. NSAIDs provide fast and effective pain relief (Kane et al., 2018). However, adverse effects are experienced in older adult nursing facility residents. NSAIDs inhibit cyclo-oxygenase (COX) enzymes, resulting in life-threatening GI ulcers with bleeding and decreased kidney function (Walter & Chang, 2020; Halter et al., 2017).

Narcotics

Another group of much more potent analgesics is narcotics. Federal regulations require that they be kept under lock and key in a safe place because of their potential for abuse (double lock and key in many states). A dangerous side effect of these drugs is the potential to depress breathing and respiratory functions controlled by the CNS. A decrease in consciousness or blood pressure may also occur and may be cumulative. Some of the more commonly prescribed narcotic analgesics include codeine (methylmorphine), meperidine (Demerol), morphine sulfate, fentanyl, hydrocodone, methadone, and oxycodone (Percodan).

Additionally, there is a concern for drug diversion with narcotics. A large percentage of drug diversions occur by healthcare workers' actions (Protenus, 2021). The most diverted drug is oxycodone, followed by hydrocodone and fentanyl. The administrator must continue to monitor for this significant issue.

LAXATIVES AND GASTROINTESTINAL AGENTS

GI agents are among the most prescribed medications for nursing facility residents. This category includes suppositories like glycerine, stimulants such as bisacodyl (Dulcolax), bulk laxatives like psyllium (Metamucil), and stool softeners, such as milk of magnesia and docusate sodium.

Often these agents are prescribed with other medications to neutralize their irritating effects on the GI tract. Unfortunately, antacids, one of the most indicated for this purpose, may also cause side effects such as diarrhea. Milk of magnesia is also frequently prescribed for GI problems.

CARDIOVASCULAR AGENTS

Many different drug classes, with various actions, are used to treat heart or circulatory system conditions. These conditions can include arrhythmias, blood clots, coronary artery disease (CAD), hypertension, hypotension, heart failure, stroke, and many others. Cardioactive medications may work on the blood vessels (altering blood pressure), the heart (improving cardiac effectiveness), the kidneys (adjusting blood pressure), or the liver (lowering blood cholesterol and fat).

Antihypertensives

Combination drugs are commonly used to treat hypertension, often a diuretic with an inhibitor. Typical pairings are diuretics with thiazides (hydrochlorothiazide and lisinopril), angiotensin-converting enzyme (ACE) inhibitors with calcium channel blockers (amlodipine and benazepril), antiadrenergics with thiazides (chlorthalidone and clonidine), and beta-blockers with thiazides (metoprolol and hydrochlorothiazide). But there are other combinations used to meet the resident's specific needs.

Diuretics

Diuretics (also called water pills or fluid pills) work by forcing the body to excrete excess fluid via urination by affecting the salt and water balance in the kidney. The main classes of diuretics are loop diuretics, potassium-sparing diuretics, and thiazide diuretics. Diuretics treat fluid retention, heart failure, kidney failure, and other disease processes sensitive to blood volume. Furosemide (Lasix) and hydrochlorothiazide (Esidrix) are commonly prescribed. However, diuretic use may result in side effects, including electrolyte imbalance, muscle weakness, lethargy, and muscle cramping. Residents who use these drugs must be monitored to ensure appropriate actions to negate side effects are in place.

Those That Directly Work on the Heart

Other medications act directly on the heart muscle. Digoxin (Lanoxin) slows the heart rate by decreasing the speed of impulses traveling along muscle fibers. Carvedilol (Coreg) is a beta-blocker that blocks chemicals from increasing the heart rate. Some side effects from these medications include a loss of appetite, nausea, vomiting, confusion, blurred vision, and arrhythmias (irregular heartbeats).

Antianginals/Vasodilators

Antianginal medications alleviate the pain associated with vasospasm and decreased oxygen supply to the heart muscle. Nitroglycerin (NTG) is a vasodilator, relaxing and increasing the size of blood vessels, allowing increased oxygen delivery. This medication is often administered sublingually (under the tongue) and is used to treat angina, heart failure, and hypertension.

ANTIDEPRESSANTS

Antidepressants reduce symptoms associated with different depressive disorders by acting on neurotransmitter imbalances in the brain. Neurotransmitters are chemicals for communication between nerve cells. Antidepressants often inhibit the "reuptake" of neurotransmitters, causing the neurotransmitter to remain available for multiple stimulations of the receiving nerve. Neurotransmitters associated with depression are dopamine, serotonin, and norepinephrine.

ANTI-INFECTIVES

Anti-infectives kill or decrease the growth of infectious organisms, complementing the natural body defense mechanisms. These infectious organisms can include bacteria, fungi, helminths, protozoa, viruses, and other pathogens.

Antibiotics are one of the most notable groups of medications within this class. There are currently seven classes of oral antibiotics for use:

1. Penicillins (penicillin and amoxicillin)
2. Cephalosporins (cephalexin/Keflex)
3. Macrolides (erythromycin, azithromycin/Zithromax)
4. Fluoroquinolones (ciprofloxacin/Cipro, levofloxacin/Levaquin)
5. Sulfonamides (co-trimoxazole/Bactrim)
6. Tetracyclines (tetracycline, doxycycline/Vibramycin)
7. Aminoglycosides (gentamycin/Garamycin, tobramycin/Tobrex)

Seven classes of IV antibiotics are increasingly used in nursing facilities:

1. Carbapenems (meropenum/Merrem)
2. Cephalosporins (cefepime/Maxipime, cefazolin/Ancef, ceftriaxone/Rocephin)
3. Fluoroquinolones (ciprofloxacin/Cipro, levofloxacin/Levaquin)
4. Glycopeptides (vancomycin, daptomycin)
5. Nitroimidazoles (metronidazole/Flagyl)
6. Oxazolidones (linezolid/Zyvox)
7. Penicillins (piperacillin/tazobactam/Zosyn)

IV antibiotics are becoming essential as the only line of defense against some drug-resistant bacteria. Multidrug resistant organisms (MDROs) require powerful antibiotics to be eradicated, and in some cases, there are no stronger alternatives. Therefore, antibiotic stewardship is paramount for the administrator, as we are currently at our infection treatment limits.

MISCELLANEOUS MEDICATIONS

Respiratory Agents

Expectorants, both oral and inhaled, are used to break up and expel mucus from the respiratory tract. Infections of the respiratory tract in patients with chronic bronchitis are effectively treated by specialty anti-infectives: aztreonam, tetracycline, or ampicillin (Michel et al., 2017).

Optical Medications

Mydriatics decrease the fluid buildup in the eye resulting from glaucoma and are often used for residents. Common eyedrops in this category are pilocarpine and physostigmine. Some of the most common side effects are headaches, diarrhea, and sweating.

CONTROLLED DRUG SCHEDULES

Federal regulations require all drugs and biologicals to be stored in locked compartments. Separately locked, permanently affixed compartments are required for Schedule II drugs listed in the Comprehensive Drug Abuse Prevention and Control Act of 1970.

The federal government has classified drugs in the following five schedules:

- *Schedule I drugs.* Drugs with high abuse potential and no accepted medical use in the United States, including heroin, marijuana, LSD, and peyote.
- *Schedule II drugs.* Drugs with high abuse and dependency potential but also an accepted medical use in the United States, including morphine, codeine, methadone, cocaine, amphetamine, and barbiturates.
- *Schedule III drugs.* Drugs with less abuse potential than Schedule I and II drugs, including hydrocodone, Tylenol with codeine, Phenaphen with codeine, and ketamine.

- *Schedule IV drugs.* Drugs with less abuse potential than Schedule III drugs, including barbital, Librium, diazepam, Valium, and Dalmane.
- *Schedule V drugs.* Drugs with less abuse potential than Schedule IV drugs. These are typically compounds containing limited qualities of narcotics for antitussive (anticough) and antidiarrheal purposes. Examples are Lomotil, Phenergan expectorant with codeine, and Robitussin A–C syrup.

THERAPEUTIC ACTIONS OF DRUGS

NAB DOMAIN 1A12: BASIC HEALTHCARE TERMINOLOGY

- *Analgesic.* Reduces pain; for example, aspirin
- *Antacid.* Neutralizes the acid in the stomach; for example, Maalox
- *Antianemic.* Used in the treatment of anemia; for example, epoetin alpha, ferrous sulfate
- *Antibiotic.* Destroys microorganisms in the body; for example, penicillin
- *Anticoagulant.* Depresses (slows) the clotting of blood; for example, clopidogrel
- *Antidote.* Used to counteract poisons
- *Antiseptic.* Slows the growth but does not kill all of the bacteria; for example, hydrogen peroxide
- *Antispasmodic.* Relieves smooth muscle spasm; for example, diazepam (Valium)
- *Antitoxin.* Neutralizes bacterial toxins in infections; for example, tetanus antitoxin
- *Astringent.* Constrict skin and mucous membranes by withdrawing water; for example, salicylic acid
- *Carminative.* Reduces flatulence (gas) in the stomach or intestinal tract
- *Cathartic/Laxative.* Induces bowel movements; for example, bisacodyl
- *Caustic.* Destroys tissue by local application; for example, silver nitrate
- *Chemotherapeutics.* Chemicals used to treat illness; for example, sulfanilamide for streptococcal infection
- *Coagulant.* Stimulates clotting of the blood
- *Diaphoretic.* Used to induce perspiration
- *Disinfectant.* Destroys pathogenic organisms; for example, isopropyl alcohol
- *Diuretic.* Stimulates elimination of urine and reduce hypertension; for example, Lasix, hydrochlorothiazide
- *Emetic.* Induces vomiting; for example, ipecac syrup
- *Emollient.* Used to soften and soothe tissue; for example, lotions, petrolatum
- *Expectorant.* Increases bronchial secretion and facilitates expulsion (coughing); for example, Robitussin, guaifenesin
- *Hypertensive.* Raises blood pressure; for example, midodrine
- *Hypnotic.* Assists residents to fall asleep; for example, Ambien, Lunesta
- *Miotic.* Constricts the pupil of the eye
- *Mydriatic.* Dilates the pupil of the eye
- *Sedative.* Relieves anxiety and emotional tensions; for example, barbiturates and benzodiazepines
- *Tonic or stimulant.* Used to stimulate body activity; for example, Ritalin
- *Vasoconstrictor.* Causes blood vessels to narrow or constrict
- *Vasodilator.* Expands or dilates blood vessels
- *Vitamins.* Used in replacement or supplementation therapy; for example, vitamin C

COMMON PITFALLS IN PRACTICE

- Do not assume that because you are not a nurse you do not need to know about medications. You will field daily questions from residents, families, nurses, or pharmacy consultants requiring you to have some knowledge of drugs.

5.2.3 ABBREVIATIONS

Section Concepts

- *The most used abbreviations in resident charting, prescriptions, and other medical specialist speech and writing*

Consider as the Administrator . . .

- *Is there an unacceptable increase in the risk of misinterpretation by using so many abbreviations?*
- *Is there any reason to use abbreviations in charting in the era of electronic medical records? Or should staff be typing these things out in their notes instead to decrease confusion or inaccuracies?*
- *If present, should abbreviations follow an accepted standard (e.g., The Joint Commission [TJC], the Centers for Medicare & Medicaid Services [CMS])?*

NAB DOMAIN 1A12: BASIC HEALTHCARE TERMINOLOGY

@	at
<	less than
>	greater than
A&D	admission and discharge
Aa	of each
Abd	abdomen
Ad lib	as much as desired, at pleasure
ac	before meals
A/G	albumin/globulin ratio
AIDS	acquired immunodeficiency syndrome
aq	water
aq dist	distilled water
ASHD	arteriosclerotic heart disease
amp	ampule
amt	amount
BE	barium enema
BID	twice a day
BMR	basal metabolic rate
BP or B/P	blood pressure
BPM	beats per minute
BRP	bathroom privileges

c	with
Ca	carcinoma
CABG	coronary artery bypass graft (heart bypass)
CAD	coronary artery disease
caps	capsules
cath	catheter
CHD	coronary heart disease
CHF	congestive heart failure
CBC	complete blood count
cc	cubic centimeter
cf	compare
CNS	central nervous system
comp	compound
COPD	chronic obstructive pulmonary disease
CVA	cerebrovascular accident (stroke)
D5W	dextrose 5% in water
d/c	discontinued or discharge
decub	lying down
Diab	diabetic
Diag or Dx	diagnosis
Diff	differential blood count
Dil	dilute
Disc	discontinue
Dx	diagnosis
EEG	electroencephalogram
EKG or ECG	electrocardiogram
Exam	examination
FBS	fasting blood sugar
fl or fld	fluid
FUO	fever of unknown origin
Fx	fracture
GI	gastrointestinal
gm or g	gram
gr	grain
gtt or gtts	drop(s)
H or hr	hour
H_2O	water
H&H	hemoglobin and hematocrit
Hct	hematocrit
HDL	high-density lipoprotein
Hgb	hemoglobin
HIV	human immunodeficiency virus
HOB	head of bed
hs	at bedtime ("hour of sleep")
hypo	hypodermically (below)

I&O	input and output
IDDM	insulin-dependent diabetes mellitus
IM	intramuscular
inf	infusion
isol	isolation
IV	intravenous
KUB	kidney–ureter–bladder
l or **L**	liter
lab	laboratory
Lat	lateral
lb	pound
liq	liquid
MAOI	monoamine oxidase inhibitor
MAR	medication administration record
MDR-TB	multidrug-resistant tuberculosis
MDS	Minimum Data Set
mEq	milliequivalents
mg	milligram
MI	myocardial infarction (heart attack)
min	minute
mL	milliliter
mm	millimeter
MOM	milk of magnesia
MN	midnight
MRSA	methicillin-resistant *Staphylococcus aureus*
MS	morphine sulfate
MSDS	material safety data sheet (see also SDS)
N	noon
NIDDM	non-insulin-dependent diabetes mellitus
no	number
noct.	at night
NPO	nothing by mouth (nil per os)
NS	normal saline
NSAID	nonsteroidal anti-inflammatory drug
NV	nausea and vomiting
O&P	ova and parasite
O$_2$	oxygen
od	right eye
ORIF	open reduction/internal fixation
os	left eye
OT	occupational therapy
OTC	over the counter
ou	each eye
oz	ounce

p	pulse
pc	after meal
PERRLA	pupils equal, round, reactive to light, and accommodation
PFT	pulmonary function test
PO	by mouth (per os)
PPE	personal protective equipment
PR	per rectum (suppository)
PRN	as needed (pro re nata)
prog	prognosis
PROM	passive range of motion
pt	pint, patient
PT	physical therapy
PTSD	posttraumatic stress disorder
PVD	peripheral vascular disease
PX	physical examination
QD	every day
qh	every hour
qhs	each bedtime
qid	four times a day
qn	every night
qod	every other day
qs	sufficient quantity
RBC	red blood count, red blood cell
RD	registered dietitian
ROM	range of motion
ROS	review of systems
RPh	registered pharmacist
RUGS	Resource Utilization Group System
Rx	prescription
s̄	without
SDS	safety data sheet
SOAP	subjective data, objective data, assessment, plan
SOB	shortness of breath
sol	solution
sos	one dose, if necessary
spec	specimen
SS	soap solution
ss	half
supp	suppository
susp	suspension
stat	immediately
surg	surgery
T	temperature
tab	tablet
TB	tuberculosis
TF	tube feeding

THA	total hip arthroplasty
TIA	transient ischemic attack
tid	three times a day
tinct or tr	tincture
TO	telephone order
TPN	total parenteral nutrition
TPR	temperature, pulse, and respiration
u	unit
ung	ointment
URI	upper respiratory infection
UTI	urinary tract infection
VO	verbal order
vol	volume
VRE	vancomycin-resistant Enterococci
vs	vital signs
W/C	wheelchair
WBC	white blood cells
WNL	within normal limits
wt	weight
Zn	zinc

5.2.4 PREFIXES

Section Concepts

- *A basic medical word-building vocabulary will facilitate patient chart audits. Nurses, doctors, and other professionals document in patient charts. However, the administrator is ultimately responsible for the acceptability of the facility charts*

Consider as the Administrator . . .

- *Realize that understanding prefixes and suffixes will allow you to "know more than you know," as you will be able to figure out things based on your knowledge of this vocabulary.*

NAB DOMAIN 1A12: BASIC HEALTHCARE TERMINOLOGY

Prefixes are at the beginning of words and augment whatever comes next.

a-   *Without*; for example, anorexia (loss of appetite)

ab-   *From, off, away*; for example, abnormal (not normal)

ad-   *Toward, to at*

adeno-   *Gland*; for example, adenoma, a benign (noncancerous) epithelial (surface-covering) tumor in which the cells form recognizable glandular structures

an-	*Without*; for example, anoxia (the absence of oxygen to the tissues despite adequate tissue blood perfusion)
ambi-	*Both*; for example, ambilateral (relating to both sides)
ana-	*Up, toward*; for example, anabolism (building up metabolism)
angio-	*Relating to a vessel*; for example, angioedema (swelling of blood vessels under skin)
ante-	*In front of, before*; for example, ante cibum (before a meal)
arthro-	*Joints*; for example, arthropathy (any disease affecting the joints)
auto-	*Self, same*; for example, autoimmune (a person's immune system attacking normal tissue)
bact-	*Relating to bacteria*; for example, bacteriuria (presence of bacteria in the urine)
bi-	*Two*; for example, bilateral (relating to both sides)
bio-	*Relation to life*; for example, biopsy (the process of removing tissue from living residents for a diagnostic examination)
brady-	*Slow*; for example, bradycardia (a slow heart)
broncho-	*Relating to the trachea or windpipe*; for example, bronchoedema (swelling of the mucosa of the bronchial tube)
carcino-	*Pertaining to cancer*; for example, carcinogen (any cancer-producing substance)
cardio-	*Pertaining to the heart*; for example, cardioplegia (paralysis of the heart), cardiomyopathy (a generalized term denoting heart disease)
cata-	*Downward, against*; for example, catabolism (the breaking down of complex chemical compounds into simpler ones in the body)
celio-	*Pertaining to the abdomen*; for example, celiotomy (surgical incision into the abdomen)
cephalo-	*Head*; for example, cephalogram (an x-ray image of the structures of the head)
cervico-	*Neck or cervix*; for example, cervicogenic headache (headache arising from the neck)
chiro-	*Hand*; for example, chiroplasty (plastic surgery on the hand)
chole-	*Pertaining to bile*; for example, cholelithiasis (gallbladder stones)
circum-	*Around*; for example, circumcorneal (around or about the cornea of the eye)
com-, con-	*With, together*; for example, complication (a disease or adverse condition that arises from another disease or adverse condition)

contra-	*Against, opposite;* for example, contraindicated (not recommended, advised against)
counter-	*Against, opposite;* for example, counteraction (action of a drug or agent opposed to that of some other drug or agent)
cranio-	*Pertaining to the head;* for example, cranioplasty (surgical repair of the skull)
cysto-	*Bladder;* for example, cystitis (inflammation of the urinary bladder) or cystocele (hernia of the bladder)
cyto-	*Relation to a cell;* for example, cytolysis (the dissolution of a cell)
de-	*Down, away from;* for example, defibrillation (stopping fibrillation), or debridement (removal of foreign or contaminated tissue from healthy tissue)
derm-	*Skin;* for example, dermatitis (inflammation of the skin)
dextro-	*Toward or on the right side;* for example, dextrocardia (a heart pointing to the right side)
di-	*Double, twice;* for example, diarthric (relating to two joints)
dia-	*Through, apart;* for example, dialysis (blood through a filter)
dys-	*Painful, difficult;* for example, dysphasia (difficulty in talking) or dyspnea (difficulty in breathing)
ecto-	*Out, away from;* for example, ectopy (part of a heartbeat in the wrong place)
em-, en-	*In;* for example, embolic (pushing or growing in)
encephalo-	*Condition in the brain or head;* for example, encephalopathy (damage or disease of the brain)
endo-	*Within, inner;* for example, endocarditis (inflammation of the endocardium or lining membrane of the heart)
entero-	*Relating to the intestines;* for example, enterocolitis (inflammation of the mucous membrane of intestines)
epi-	*Above, upon, over;* for example, epidermititis (inflammation of the epidermis or the superficial layer of the skin)
eu-	*Good;* for example, euphoria (a feeling of well-being, commonly exaggerated and not necessarily well founded)
fibro-	*Pertaining to fiber;* for example, fibromyalgia (a condition characterized by fatigue, stiffness, and chronic pain in the muscles, tendons, and ligaments)
gastro-	*Stomach;* for example, gastrostomy (the establishment of an artificial opening into the stomach, usually for feeding purposes)
glyco-	*Relationship to sweetness (sugar);* for example, glycogen (the chief carbohydrate storage material in animals formed and stored mainly in the liver)

gyneco-, gyno-	*Pertaining to a female*; for example, gynecology (the science of diseases of women, especially those of the genital tract)
hemato-, hema-	*Pertaining to the blood*; for example, hemorrhage (bleeding, a flow of blood) or hematuria (blood in the urine)
hemi-	*Half*; for example, hemiplegia (paralysis of one side of the body)
hepato-	*Liver*; for example, hepatitis (inflammation of the liver)
histo-	*Tissue*; for example, histolysis (disintegration of the tissue)
hydro-	*Pertaining to water*; for example, hydrocyst (a cyst or sore with clear, watery contents)
hyper-	*Excessive*; for example, hyperesthesia (abnormal acuteness of sensitivity to touch, pain, or other stimuli)
hypno-, hypna-	*Relating to sleep*; for example, hypnotherapy (the treatment of disease by inducing prolonged sleep)
hypo-	*Deficiency, lack of*; for example, hypochondria (a false belief that one is suffering from some disease), or hypotension (low blood pressure)
hystero-	*Relating to the uterus*; for example, hysterogram (an x-ray of the uterus)
ileo-	*Relating to the ileum* (remote end of the small intestine); for example, ileocolitis (inflammation of the mucous membrane of both ileum and colon)
infra-	*Below, beneath*; for example, infracardiac (beneath the heart, below the level of the heart)
inter-	*Between*; for example, intercostal (between the ribs)
intro-, intra-	*In, into*; for example, intragastric (leading or passed into the stomach, e.g., a nasogastric tube for feeding)
kerato-	*Relating to the cornea or horny tissue*; for example, keratoconjunctivitis (inflammation of the conjunctiva of the eye)
labi-	*Relating to the lip*; for example, labial frenulum (connection from lip to gum)
macro-	*Large, long*; for example, macrocyte (a giant red cell)
mast-	*Relating to the breast*; for example, mastectomy (amputation of the breast)
mega-	*Large, oversize*; for example, megacardia (enlargement of the heart)
meta-	*After, beyond, transformation*; for example, metastasis (the shifting of a disease)
micro-	*Small*; for example, micro infarct (a very small infarct, i.e., death of tissue due to a lack of blood supply, due to obstruction of circulation in capillaries or small arteries)
multi-	*Many*; for example, multicellular (composed of many cells)

myel-	*Pertaining to the spinal cord*; for example, myeloplegia (spinal paralysis)
myo-	*Relating to muscle*; for example, myotrophy (muscular atrophy) or myocardial infarction (death of heart muscle due to lack of blood supply, a heart attack)
necro-	*Relating to death*; for example, necrotizing (causing the death of tissues)
nephro-	*Kidney*; for example, nephritis (inflammation of the kidney)
neuro-	*Nerves*; for example, a neurogenic bladder (urination controlled by the nervous system rather than voluntary control)
odont-	*Relating to the teeth*; for example, odontalgia (a toothache)
omo-	*Shoulder*; for example, omodynia (pain in the shoulder joint)
ophthalmo-	*Relating to the eye*; for example, ophthalmoplegia (paralysis of the motor nerves of the eye)
opto-	*Relating to vision*; for example, optometer (an instrument for determining the refraction of the eye)
ortho-	*Straight*; for example, orthostatic (standing upright from a sitting or reclining position)
osteo-	*Pertaining to the bones*; for example, osteoporosis (reduction in bone mass)
oxy-	*Sharp, acute*; for example, oxyesthesia (a condition of increased sensation)
pan-	*All*; for example, pancarditis (diffuse inflammation of the heart)
patho-	*Disease*; for example, pathogenesis (the origin or development of a disease)
per-	*Through*; for example, perfusion (pouring over or through, especially the passage of a fluid through the vessels of a specific organ)
peri-	*Around*; for example, peribronchitis (inflammation of the tissues surrounding the bronchial tubes)
phlebo-	*Relating to a vein*; for example, phlebitis (inflammation of a vein)
pneumo-	*Lung*; for example, pneumonia (infection of the lung)
poly-	*Many, much*; for example, polyarthritis (inflammation of several joints)
procto-	*Relating to the anus*; for example, proctitis (inflammation of the rectum)
pseudo-	*False*; for example, pseudodementia (a condition of indifference to one's surroundings without actual mental impairment)
psycho-	*Pertaining to the mind*; for example, psychotherapy (counseling help)

pyo-	*Signifying pus*; for example, pyoderma (an infection of or on the skin that contains pus)
rhino-	*Nose*; for example, rhinoplasty (a repair of the nose)
sub-	*Under*; for example, subcutaneous (under the skin)
syn-	*Loss*; for example, syncope (fainting, a temporary loss of consciousness)
tachy-	*Rapid*; for example, tachycardia (rapid beating of the heart)
thermo-	*Heat*; for example, thermophobia (morbid fear of heat)
uni-	*One*; for example, unicellular (composed of one cell)
uro-	*Relating to the urine*; for example, urosepsis (septic poisoning from retained and absorbed urinary substances)
vaso-	*Vessel*; for example, vasoconstriction (narrowing of the blood vessels) or vasodilation (widening of the blood vessels)

5.2.5 SUFFIXES

Suffixes come at the end of the word to augment the meaning.

-ac	*Pertaining to*; for example, cardiac (pertaining to the heart)
-algia	*Pain*; for example, neuralgia (nerve pain)
-cele	*Hernia*; for example, hepatocele (protrusion of liver through the abdominal wall)
-centesis	*Surgical puncture*; for example, paracentesis (a puncture of the body cavity for removing fluid)
-clysis	*Washing, irrigation*; for example, enteroclysis (enema of the intestines)
-cyte	*Cell*; for example, hepatocyte (liver cell)
-ectasia	*Dilation, stretching*; for example, gastrectasia (dilation of the stomach)
-ectomy	*Excision (cutting out) of*; for example, tonsillectomy (cutting out of the tonsils)
-emesis	*Vomiting*; for example, hyperemesis (excessive vomiting)
-emia	*Condition of the blood*; for example, glycemia (sugar in the blood)
-genesis	*Producing*; for example, carcinogenesis (the origin or production of cancer)
-itis	*Inflammation*; for example, dermatitis (inflammation of the skin)
-lith	*Stone*; for example, nephrolith (kidney stone)

-lysis	*Breakdown*; for example, hemolysis (the destruction of red blood cells)
-malacia	*Softening*; for example, osteomalacia (a disease characterized by gradual softening and bending of the bones)
-megaly	*Enlargement*; for example, cardiomegaly (enlargement of the heart)
-odynia	*Painful condition*; for example, cardiodynia (pain in the heart)
-oma	*Tumor*; for example, carcinoma (a malignant tumor)
-opsy	*Vision*; for example, biopsy (removing living tissue for microscopic examination)
-orexia	*Appetite, desire*; for example, anorexia (loss of appetite)
-orrhaphy	*Suture*; for example, gastrorrhaphy (the suture of a perforation of the stomach)
-orrhea	*Flow, discharge*; for example, gastrorrhea (excessive secretion of gastric juice or mucus of the stomach)
-ostomy	*To make a new opening*; for example, colostomy (the establishment of an artificial anus by diverting the colon)
-otomy	*Incision, to cut into*; for example, nephrotomy (an incision into the kidney)
-path	*Morbid or diseased*; for example, a sociopath (a person who feels no remorse or guilt about behaving in socially unaccepted ways, e.g., physically beating a roommate and feeling no guilt or remorse)
-pathy	*Disease*; for example, neuropathy (any nerve disease)
-penia	*Deficiency*; for example, leukopenia (total number of leukocytes—white blood cells— is less than normal)
-pepsia	*Digestion*; for example, dyspepsia (indigestion or upset stomach)
-phobia	*Fear*; for example, claustrophobia (fear of being closed in a small space)
-plasty	*Surgical repair*; for example, thoracoplasty (reparative or plastic surgery to the chest)
-pnea	*Breath*; for example, dyspnea (difficult or labored breathing)
-rhythmia	*Rhythmical*; for example, arrhythmia (any variation from the normal rhythm of the heart)
-sclerosis	*Hardening*; for example, arteriosclerosis (hardening of the arteries)
-stasis	*Arrest, control*; for example, cholestasis (an arrest in the flow of bile)
-tripsy	*Crushing*; for example, lithotripsy (the ultrasonic crushing of a kidney stone)

-trophy	*Development, nourishment*; for example, hypertrophy (an overgrowth or increase in the bulk of a body part or organ)
-uria	*Urine*; for example, proteinuria (the presence of protein in urine)

5.3 THE AGING PROCESS AS IT RELATES TO DISEASES COMMON TO THE NURSING FACILITY POPULATION

Section Concepts

- *To identify the 10 different basic body systems*
- *The difference between chronic and acute care*

Consider as the Administrator . . .

- *How well does the typical facility identify when a resident's chronic care condition morphs into an acute care situation?*
- *What methods might be used to increase the level of care for your residents based on their chronic conditions?*

NAB DOMAIN 1A: QUALITY OF CARE; 1B: QUALITY OF LIFE; 1B1: PSYCHOSOCIAL NEEDS (E.G., SOCIAL, SPIRITUAL, COMMUNITY, CULTURAL)

NAB DOMAIN 1A3: DISEASE MANAGEMENT (E.G., ACUTE VS. CHRONIC CONDITIONS)

It is helpful for the administrator to be familiar with biological processes, human anatomy, and basic physiology to understand what parts of the body are affected by the aging process. This knowledge allows the administrator to appreciate problems specific to the facility and its residents. Additionally, the administrator will understand basic medical terminology to improve professional communication with their clinical staff.

The body's physical processes change due to aging, including a decrease in the overall energy reserve, breakdown of some of the body functions, and an alteration of individual cell structures, ultimately affecting body tissue and organ functioning.

The systems referred to are groups of structures that perform a specialized function in the body. The following is a list of 10 body systems and the processes and structures most commonly categorized for each. Disease processes common to the nursing facility population affect these 10 systems.

Each system is highly interrelated by a process known as homeostasis. Homeostasis is a state of balance among all the body systems. When homeostasis is "off," disease processes often become apparent. Many nursing facility residents typically suffer from multiple chronic diseases that may affect combinations of body systems and challenge homeostasis mechanisms.

- *Cardiovascular/circulatory system.* The heart, arteries, capillaries, veins, and blood enable the body to transport oxygen to cells and tissues via blood circulation. Oxygen is carried by the red blood cells (RBCs; erythrocytes) from the lungs to the tissues, where it is exchanged for the metabolic waste product of carbon dioxide.
- *Respiratory system.* The trachea, lungs, bronchi, bronchioles, and alveoli exchange carbon dioxide and oxygen in the lungs. This mechanism is also responsible for the pH levels of blood.
- *Nervous system.* The brain, spinal cord, nerves, and sensory organs are responsible for the communication and coordination of the body systems to maintain homeostasis. It also controls body functions and regulates activities (heart rate, breathing, reflexes).
- *Endocrine system.* The glands in the body (thyroid, pituitary, adrenals) produce hormones released directly into the bloodstream to coordinate body functions.
- *Digestive system.* The mouth, pharynx, esophagus, stomach, small intestines, large intestine, liver, and gallbladder break down food into a form in which the nutrients may be used by the individual cells. Food is broken down into smaller nutrients and absorbed into the digestive bloodstream.
- *Integumentary system.* Skin, hair, and nails protect the body from damage, provide waterproofing, and are the first line of defense against foreign invaders (immunity).
- *Musculoskeletal system.* The bones, muscles, tendons, ligaments, and joints are used in body movement and blood production (hematopoiesis).
- *Urinary system.* Kidneys, ureters, bladder, and the urethra filter and transport waste from the blood out of the body.
- *Lymphatic system.* Bone marrow, spleen, tonsils, lymphatic fluid, and lymph nodes are responsible for immunity in the body and overall fluid balance within the body.
- *Reproductive system.* The uterus, ovaries, prostate, testicles, and other organs; in older adults, the focus is on sexuality.

CHRONIC VERSUS ACUTE

Chronic illness is thought of as a long-term or permanent illness that often results in disabilities that may require help with various activities. The nursing facility administrator typically cares for persons with chronic illnesses. Chronic illnesses are persistent conditions lasting over an extended period, often more than 3 months. Usually, these are diseases of slow progression and long duration. Acute illness, in contrast, is an illness characterized by an abrupt or rapid onset and usually of short duration.

The typical acutely ill person in the hospital is considered unstable and needs constant monitoring by physicians and nurses. In contrast, the typical nursing facility resident has exhibited one or more chronic illnesses that are thought to be in a stable state. The hospital focuses on acutely ill persons; the nursing facility focuses on chronically ill persons. As hospitals are discharging patients quicker and sicker, the acuity level of the nursing facility resident has increased. They often require higher-level nursing care due to their subacute condition.

Subacute residents are typical in today's nursing facility. They no longer require hospital-level care but are not ready to be sent home yet. Many of these residents are admitted to the nursing facility to continue their care, often at a higher level than family members or home healthcare could provide directly after discharge. Subacute residents need multiple therapies including respiratory therapy, IV antibiotics, or coordination of ongoing and underlying medical conditions.

5.3.1 CARDIOVASCULAR/CIRCULATORY SYSTEM

Section Concepts

- *How the cardiovascular system works:*
  - *Arteries*
  - *Veins*
  - *Lungs*
  - *The heart*
  - *Aging effects on the cardiovascular system*
  - *How to identify six common cardiovascular diseases and their treatment modalities:*
    - *Arteriosclerosis*
    - *Aortic stenosis*
    - *Atherosclerosis*
    - *Cerebrovascular disease*
    - *Peripheral vascular disease*
    - *Coronary artery disease*

Consider as the Administrator . . .

- *How aggressively should the facility team approach coronary problems in patients?*

NAB DOMAIN 1A: QUALITY OF CARE; 1A3: DISEASE MANAGEMENT (E.G., ACUTE VS. CHRONIC CONDITIONS; 1B: QUALITY OF LIFE

The circulatory system, also called the cardiovascular system, is an elaborate pump mechanism. It is powered by the heart, which pumps the blood throughout the body within a network of blood vessels (arteries and veins).

ARTERIES

Arteries are the vessels that carry blood rich in oxygen and nutrients away from the heart to the remaining body cells. Blood pressure is created by the force of the heart's left ventricle pumping blood into the arteries. The aorta is the largest artery in the body and comes directly off the left ventricle and distributes blood to other arteries and into the capillary bed. Capillaries are the smallest blood vessels and form a network connecting the smallest arteries to the smallest veins (Figure 5.1). The capillaries are where oxygen is exchanged for carbon dioxide and the distribution of nutrients occurs.

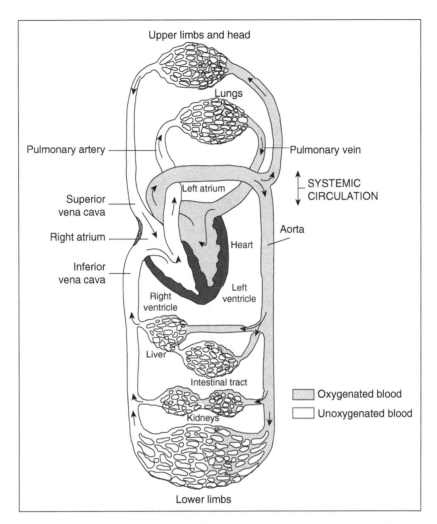

FIGURE 5.1 Representation of the circulatory and oxygenation process.

Oxygen is a colorless, odorless, gaseous chemical element in the air we breathe and is required for life. Oxygen enters the body in the lungs, where it is exchanged for carbon dioxide in the capillary beds. Carbon dioxide is produced as a regular product of the body's metabolic processes and is removed during exhalation.

VEINS

The veins are the other side of the capillary beds from the arteries and are not under any pressure, so they cannot be used to measure blood pressure. RBCs travel through the capillary beds exchanging their oxygen for carbon dioxide along the way. This blood exits the capillary bed into tiny venules and then into larger veins, eventually ending up in the two largest veins in the body, the superior (from the upper body) and inferior (from the lower body) vena cavas (Figure 5.1).

From the vena cavas, the blood then enters the top of the heart's right side. This chamber (right atrium) contracts, pushing the blood down to the lower chamber (right ventricle), which then contracts, pushing blood into the pulmonary arteries. The blood in the pulmonary arteries flows to capillary beds surrounding the alveoli in the lungs. As with tissues, these capillary beds are the site of oxygen and carbon dioxide exchange.

Carbon dioxide in veins is discarded and exchanged for oxygen within the lungs' alveoli. The carbon dioxide is then exhaled from the body, and oxygen is inhaled. The newly oxygenated blood returns to the left side of the heart (left atrium) by the pulmonary veins. When the atria contract, this blood is pumped into the heart's left lower chamber (left ventricle). The blood in the left ventricle is then pumped forcefully (the top number in blood pressure) out of the heart into the aorta. Arteries branch off from the aorta carrying oxygen-rich blood to the rest of the body. This process occurs with every heartbeat.

THE HEART

The heart itself is a complex organ with four chambers, two atria sit on the top of the heart, and two ventricles sit below them. The tricuspid valve separates the right atrium and ventricle. The bicuspid, or mitral valve, divides the left-side atrium and ventricle. The heart is a muscle composed of a particular type of muscle tissue and its own conduction system, facilitating coordinated blood flow. The heart requires oxygen to function and is supplied by a network of coronary arteries that stem from the aorta (Figure 5.2).

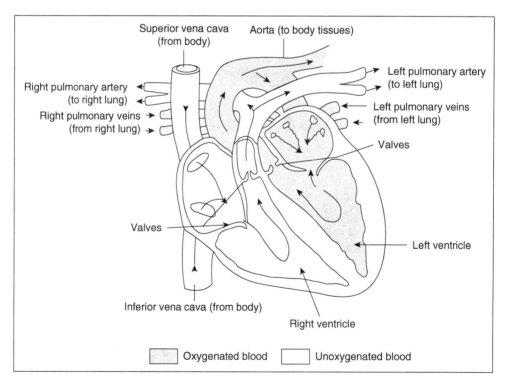

FIGURE 5.2 Schematic representation of blood flow through the heart.

AGING EFFECTS

The extent to which the aging process plays a role in this deterioration is still being argued. It is known that the cardiovascular system (heart and blood vessels) is not designed to last indefinitely. Cardiac cells are incapable of regeneration and are not replaced once damaged (Saxon et al., 2022). As such, we see some changes over time in the cardiovascular system. Whether these changes are simply age-related or related to disease processes is difficult to determine.

Decreased Elasticity

A specific age-related change in the heart may include a lessening of the force of contraction (pumping) due to the decreased elasticity of muscle. *Elasticity* is the ability of the heart muscle to stretch and return to normal size spontaneously. Too much stretch over time causes elasticity to decrease, which reduces the force of contractions of the heart (pumping) and diminishes the amount of blood pumped by the heart (also termed *cardiac output*). Changes to the elasticity of arteries are discussed later under "Blood Pressure Changes."

Decreased Cardiac Output

In addition to lost elasticity, reduced cardiac output may be caused by increased blood vessel resistance to blood flow from arteriosclerosis (stiffening of the arteries) or atherosclerosis (a type of arteriosclerosis due to plaque).

This decreased cardiac output decreases blood and oxygen delivered to all body tissues. Over time, we expect to see some decrease in cardiac output, and if mild, it may not cause significant effects to the body. However, a lack of oxygen coupled with other chronic disease processes may result in older adults tiring more quickly or lacking endurance (Saxon et al., 2022). The fatigue of older adult individuals is closely related to a diminished cardiovascular ability and can cause many symptoms secondary to blood pressure and gas exchange complications (Gecaite-Stonciene et al., 2021).

Blood Pressure Changes

The role of the aging process and its effect on blood pressure is currently under debate. The debate pertains to whether changes in the blood vessels result from aging or lifestyle choices. In many older adults, blood pressure increases from arteriosclerosis and loss of elasticity of large and *peripheral* vessels commonly associated with the aging process (Kane et al., 2018). The heart must pump harder to overcome any arterial resistance.

While arteries experience progressive stiffening, this causes resistance to blood flow throughout the body (peripheral vascular resistance), increased blood pressure, and may exacerbate decreased heart function.

The vein walls tend to weaken with increased deposits of fats, cholesterol, fibrin, platelets, cellular debris, and calcium over time. The capillary walls become thickened, thus decreasing their absorption of carbon dioxide and waste products with the cells. These changes result in a slower return of venous blood to the heart, which can cause other issues in the body (Halter et al., 2017; Saxon et al., 2022).

COMMON CARDIOVASCULAR DISEASES

Diseases that affect the heart are the leading cause of death in the United States (Centers for Disease Control and Prevention [CDC], 2021a). Diagnoses of any heart disease are significant as they often lead to life-changing consequences. The most commonly seen cardiovascular disease is CAD, which often leads to a myocardial infarction (MI; heart attack). Heart failure indicates that one or more ventricles are ineffective at pumping blood. More than 40% of heart failure patients are admitted to a skilled nursing facility at some point after diagnosis (Chamberlain et al., 2017).

Arteriosclerosis

Arteriosclerosis is a hardening of the arteries. Usually, arteries are smooth inside and can stretch to permit the passage of more blood and oxygen when needed. With arteriosclerosis, the blood vessels are less responsive. We see evidence of arteriosclerosis at all ages, even those we might consider the youngest and virile (McNamara et al., 1971). Almost half of long-term nursing facility residents manifest disease changes due to chronic arteriosclerosis. Two forms of this condition (aortic stenosis and atherosclerosis) account for much of the heart disease in older adults.

   Symptoms. A resident may experience sharp chest pain or pressure that might radiate to the neck or arm and shortness of breath with exertion. These symptoms should resolve with rest, and if they do not, immediate emergency medical attention is required.

   Treatment. While treatment may include intervention at the hospital, management at the nursing facility typically consists of a beta-blocker, ACE inhibitor, and a statin or other cholesterol-lowering medication.

Aortic Stenosis

Stenosis of a valve means the valve does not open fully to allow blood to pass. Aortic stenosis is the narrowing of the aortic valve, causing blood to be trapped in the left side of the heart instead of passing into the aorta. The valve resistance and trapped blood stimulate the left ventricle to pump harder and thicken over time. The pressure that builds up in the left side of the heart, combined with regular aging changes, places considerable stress on the cardiovascular system. It can result in heart failure, which is discussed at the end of this section.

   For many older adult residents, the stenosis is either the result of scarring from childhood rheumatic fever or calcified deposits on the valve.

   Symptoms. The symptoms of aortic stenosis are related to the blood held in the heart, causing difficulty breathing, dizziness, chest pain, and variable blood pressure.

Treatment. Treatment can consist of surgical correction, rest to decrease the work-load on the heart, and medication therapy.

Atherosclerosis

Atherosclerosis is the most common form of arteriosclerosis, caused by a progressive buildup of fat deposits (atheromas) on the inner lining of blood vessel walls. The disease does not usually manifest itself until the blood vessel becomes fully obstructed or causes markedly decreased blood flow. The symptoms can affect the body anywhere but is a leading factor of hypertension, MIs, strokes, and other vascular diseases. Treatment is usually directly related to the specific disease process which the atherosclerosis has caused or contributed to in the body.

Cerebrovascular Accidents (Strokes) and Transient Ischemic Attacks

There are two different types of strokes, ischemic and hemorrhagic. Ischemic strokes (occlusion-based) are the most common, with atherosclerosis being a leading cause of cerebrovascular accidents (CVAs). An atherosclerotic plaque causes a blood clot or thrombus to form, causing occlusion of the artery. Ischemic strokes can also be caused by an embolus circulating in the blood (air, fatty tissue, blood clot), which gets caught in an artery of the brain. A hemorrhagic stroke occurs when a blood vessel in the brain tears, thus causing a bleed and stopping blood delivery past the tear.

Resident conditions increasing the risk of CVAs include high blood pressure, previous history of heart disease, tobacco use, diabetes, and atherosclerosis. The specific symptoms of a CVA or transient ischemic attack (TIA) depend on the location of the brain affected. *TIAs* (also termed "mini-strokes") are caused by a temporarily diminished blood supply to the brain, with deficiencies improving within 1 hour and entirely within 24 hours (Halter et al., 2017). TIAs are viewed as an "early warning sign" of an impending major CVA, and immediate intervention can reduce CVA risk (Furie & Rost, 2021; Walter & Chang, 2020).

Symptoms. Generalized symptoms of cerebrovascular disease include slurred speech, blurred vision, dizziness, numb hands and fingers, and mental confusion. While symptoms could be easily attributed to the "aging process" rather than a CVA or TIA, immediate evaluation using the American Stroke Association F.A.S.T. acronym is required.

F.A.S.T.

- Face drooping
- Arm weakness
- Speech difficulty
- Time to call 911 (American Stroke Association, 2021)

Symptoms for CVA and TIA can be similar. Therefore any neurological change must be taken very seriously. When it comes to either of these disorders, the concept of "time is tissue" is imperative. "Time is tissue" refers to the idea that prompt, comprehensive care must occur to minimize tissue damage. Immediate treatment and recognition are necessary to increase survival and fewer lasting symptoms.

Cerebrovascular Accident Symptoms

- Sudden numbness, weakness, or paralysis of the face, leg, or arm; often one-sided
- Issues with speaking coherently or understanding others who are speaking
- Confusion
- Vision changes in one or both eyes
- Sudden issues with walking
- Dizziness or loss of coordination
- Sudden severe headache with no cause ("worst headache you ever had")
- Dysphagia, or trouble swallowing
- Facial droop; often one-sided

> **Treatment.** Immediate treatment is determined by the stroke type (hemorrhagic or ischemic) using a CT scan at an acute care facility. Upon admission or return to the nursing facility, the patient will be on preventive medications and require extensive physical, occupational, and possibly speech therapy.

Peripheral Vascular Disease

Peripheral vascular disease (PVD) describes a group of conditions that affect the veins or arteries of the extremities (arms and legs). The symptoms result from decreased blood flow to or from the affected area. Most commonly, the source is atherosclerotic disease, which leads to peripheral artery obstruction (Neschis & Golden, 2021).

> **Symptoms.** The most frequent symptoms are ones that are similar to what would be seen with vascular insufficiency (Neschis & Golden, 2021) and include the following:
> - No symptoms
> - Atypical pain on movement of an extremity
> - Pain that is chronic in a localized area
> - Intermittent claudication (discomfort in specific muscles induced by exercise and relieved by rest)
> - Cold, numb feet
> - Changes in skin integrity, such as ulcers or infections that are slow to heal
> - Other signs of ischemia (Halter et al., 2017; Neschis & Golden, 2021)
>
> **Treatment.** Symptom management medications related to wound healing, chronic pain, support/pressure stockings, and oral vasodilators.

Coronary Artery Disease

CAD is also known as coronary heart disease or ischemic heart disease. The condition occurs because the heart muscle itself suffers from a lack of oxygen due to blockages in the coronary arteries that usually supply it (CDC, 2021b; Michel et al., 2017). Most commonly, coronary arteries are caused by atherosclerosis plaque buildup over time (Kannam et al., 2021).

Symptoms. Often, the first symptom of CAD is a MI (heart attack), discussed later. For those who do not have an entirely blocked artery, CAD symptoms are as follows:

- Chest pain—commonly called *angina*—results from a lack of oxygen to some regions of the heart muscle. Pain may be located anywhere in the chest and radiate to the left arm or neck
- Weakness, lightheadedness, nausea, cold sweat
- Pain or discomfort in the arms, shoulders, neck, or mid-back
- Shortness of breath
- Pressure or tightness in the chest (an "elephant is standing on my chest")
- Fatigue
- Neck pain (CDC, 2021b; National Heart, Lung, and Blood Institute, 2021a)

Treatments. Treatments vary depending on disease severity. Initially, patients with only mild manifestations of the disease can be treated conservatively with restrictions on sodium and fat from their diet and increased exercise. Medications commonly used in the nursing facility are nitroglycerin (NTG), nitrates, beta-blockers, or calcium channel blockers.

NTG, the most common medication prescribed for angina, is administered sublingually by the resident holding the pill under the tongue while it dissolves. This drug lowers blood pressure by dilating the blood vessels, including the coronary arteries, to decrease resistance to blood flow and may cause a headache.

Angina is often relieved by angioplasty (percutaneous coronary intervention [PCI]). Stents are placed, or dilating balloons are deployed in the coronary arteries by a catheter that enters the body through the groin or wrist.

Myocardial Infarction

MI (literal meaning is heart muscle death) results when a large enough area of the heart muscle does not receive oxygen (Michel et al., 2017; Walter & Chang, 2020). With a massive MI, the heart can no longer act as a pump and may completely stop beating (cardiac arrest; Halter et al., 2017).

Symptoms. Except for a cardiac arrest, symptoms are as follow:

- The same as CAD, described earlier

It is worth noting that women often have different symptoms than men and may not experience any chest pain or angina. Instead, women often exhibit other symptoms listed for CAD, as well as the following:

- Dizziness
- Fatigue
- Nausea or pain around stomach mimicking acid reflux
- Chest pressure or tightness
- Stomach pain
- Back pain
- Neck and throat pain (Kannam et al., 2021; National Heart, Lung, and Blood Institute, 2021a)

There are two types of MI, ST-segment elevation myocardial infarction (STEMI) and non-ST elevation myocardial infarction (NSTEMI). The STEMI results from complete and prolonged occlusion of the coronary arteries by a blood clot and causes changes in the ST segment of an EKG. The NSTEMI results from coronary artery narrowing or occlusion by a platelet clot and does not cause ST changes in the EKG. Despite the difference in electrical current shown on an EKG, both types show similar changes in cardiac enzymes (Daga et al., 2011; Reeder and Kennedy, 2021). Both STEMI and NSTEMI are very serious and require emergency treatment, and both can result in admissions for rehabilitation in the nursing facility.

> **Treatments.** The most common treatment for any MI is revascularization. Initial intervention for a STEMI is PCI within 90 minutes of presentation to the ED. For an NSTEMI, PCI is usually performed after chemical anticoagulation, a delay of 12 to 24 hours. If the PCI is unsuccessful, a coronary artery bypass graft (CABG; commonly known as open-heart surgery) is performed. A CABG leaves the blocked vessels in place, and graft vessels are surgically attached to the artery to bypass the blocked sections (Reeder & Kennedy, 2021).

After appropriate interventions, the resident will have maintenance medications, including a beta-blocker, platelet inhibitor, blood thinner (warfarin sodium, apixaban, ticagrelor), and anti-lipid (statins). Lifestyle and dietary changes are also in order, and these residents are often placed on a low-salt and low-fat diet to assist with treatment and blood pressure.

CASE STUDY (AN ACTUAL CASE, DEIDENTIFIED)

Ms. Sims Leans Forward

Ms. Sims is a 73-year-old female who has been a patient at The Laurels for 2 years. She has a diagnosis of old CVA, hypertension, and a history of urinary tract infection (UTI). She has a documented right-sided weakness but can ambulate for short distances with a Hemi-walker and nursing assistance. She gets up daily with nursing assistance and spends her day in the main lobby cheerfully and clearly conversing with other patients and visitors (Halter et al., 2009, p. 975).

On Thursday, Ms. Jones, the receptionist, notices that Ms. Sims is leaning forward in her chair and is disoriented when Ms. Jones asks if she is okay.

As Ms. Jones wheeled Ms. Sims back to the nursing station, Ms. Sims began to cry because she could not remember what had happened to her. When they reached the nursing station, Ms. Sims stated, "I feel weak and felt like I have had another stroke."

Nurse Riley helped Ms. Sims back to bed and checked her blood pressure, which was 150/80. The nurse then told Ms. Sims, "Everything is just fine. If you had eaten your breakfast, you would not feel weak now." Nurse Riley then told the receptionist, "She is just getting more and more disoriented as she gets older. There is nothing to worry about." Nurse Riley then proceeded to complete the medication rounds.

- *How well do you think Nurse Riley handled this situation? As administrator of The Laurels, what policies could you institute to improve care?*

High Blood Pressure

High blood pressure/hypertension is diagnosed when the blood pressure measurement is consistently greater than 130/90 (Saxon et al., 2022; Walter & Chang, 2020).

The numbers 130/90 measure the amount of pressure the blood exerts on the walls of the arteries. The first number (130) measures the maximum pressure (systolic) exerted on the aorta by the cardiac output when the heart's ventricles are fully contracted. The second number (90) is the minimum pressure (diastolic) occurring when the heart's ventricles are dilated or fully relaxed. Part of the risk hypertension presents is that about 50% of individuals do not have adequate control of the disease (Basile & Bloch, 2021).

Blood pressure measurements and classifications are as follows:

- Normal blood pressure—systolic <120 and diastolic <80
- Elevated blood pressure—systolic 120 to 129 and diastolic <80
- Hypertension
  - Stage 1—systolic 130 to 139 or diastolic 80 to 89
  - Stage 2—systolic at least 140 or diastolic at least 90 (Basile & Bloch, 2021)

There are two types of disease: (a) primary (essential) hypertension and (b) secondary hypertension. The cause of primary hypertension is vague; however, it is believed that there are genetic and environmental factors at play (Basile & Bloch, 2021). Primary hypertension does not have a complete cure, but it can be successfully controlled by medication. Secondary hypertension is a symptom of underlying diseases, including anemia, fever, endocrine disease, hormonal disruption, arteriosclerosis, obstructive sleep apnea, and kidney disease (Basile & Bloch, 2021; Michel et al., 2017; Walter & Chang, 2020). These diseases place a greater demand on the heart and may cause the blood pressure to increase during the disease episode or permanently.

The effects of continued high blood pressure, regardless of the type, are harmful to various organs within the body, especially the heart, brain, kidney, and eyes. High blood pressure requires the heart to pump harder to circulate the blood throughout the body. As the heart works harder to compensate, it begins to fail after being overworked. This failure in the ventricles reduces the blood flow to the vital organs, damaging their function.

Symptoms. In many cases, hypertension has no symptoms at all. It is known as the "silent killer" due to a lack of symptomatology often associated with it. However, when symptoms do occur, we might see headaches, nosebleeds, irregular heart rhythms, visual changes, and buzzing in the ears of the resident. In severe cases, we may also see fatigue, nausea, vomiting, confusion, anxiety, chest pain, or muscle tremors (World Health Organization, 2021b).

Treatment. Nonpharmacological treatments of smoking cessation, weight loss, and diet therapy restricting salt and fat intake, such as the DASH (Dietary Approaches to Stop Hypertension), are part of all suggested management plans (Walter & Chang, 2020). Further recommended lifestyle changes include exercise and decreased alcohol intake (Basile & Bloch, 2021).

Adding pharmacological treatment is also common. The goal is to use as few drugs as possible to decrease hypertension. Many drug types help control hypertension, often including cardiac agents already prescribed to the resident. Diuretics are frequently used to reduce the heart's workload by removing extra blood volume through increased urination. ACE inhibitors act in the rennin angiotensin system to prevent angiotensin II and aldosterone formation. Stopping these two products prevents blood vessel constriction and prevents the kidneys from retaining sodium (which attracts water). Diuretics are often used with ACE inhibitors in single pill combination medications, such as hydrochlorothiazide and lisinopril. Beta-blockers act by reducing sympathetic fight or flight response in the heart and blood vessels, decreasing heart rate and blood vessel constriction. Calcium channel blockers work to decrease the amount of squeeze in the muscle of the ventricles to reduce cardiac output.

Heart Failure

Heart failure can be acute or chronic and occurs when the heart's ventricles cannot pump enough blood to meet the body's needs (National Heart, Lung, and Blood Institute, 2021b). Heart failure is most commonly caused by a condition that has damaged the heart (CAD, hypertension). The effect of insufficient blood flow ultimately results in illness as a progressively weakening heart fails to pump enough oxygen to the various tissues of the body (Kane et al., 2018). This failure of forward blood flow results in a congestion of blood backing up in the circulatory system. The backup causes fluid to leak from the bloodstream into surrounding tissues and organs. Right ventricle failure causes excess fluid to affect the legs, while left ventricle failure backs fluid into the lungs. These processes and symptoms create congestive heart failure (CHF; National Heart, Lung, and Blood Institute, 2021b; Michel et al., 2017). Ultimately heart failure can cause damage to other organs such as the lungs, liver, kidneys, or further heart damage (Colucci & Dunlay, 2021; National Heart, Lung, and Blood Institute, 2021b).

Symptoms.
- Pleural effusion (fluid around lungs)
- Pulmonary edema (fluid in lungs)
- Ascites (swelling of the abdomen)
- Edema (swelling of feet, ankles, legs)
- Trouble breathing
- Coughing
- Fatigue and weakness
- Bluish tint to lips, fingers, or fingernails
- Sleepiness and issues concentrating
- Unable to sleep lying flat
- Frequent urination
- Weight gain (Colucci & Dunlay, 2021; National Heart, Lung, and Blood Institute, 2021b)

Treatment. There is no cure for heart failure. Treatment includes lifestyle changes of energy conservation, daily monitoring weight (to guard against fluid retention), and diet therapy. Advised dietary changes include calorie-dense foods while reducing salt and fluid intake. Supplemental oxygen may be required due to less exchange area available in the lungs.

Medications are prescribed to increase cardiac output, reduce edema in the body, and include different cardiac drugs, antithrombotics, statins, vasodilators, and diuretics (Saxon et al., 2022; Colucci, 2021).

Some diuretics deplete the body's supply of essential electrolytes, such as sodium and potassium. Low potassium levels can be particularly dangerous for older adult residents, as they are especially vulnerable to such imbalances. Potassium supplements are frequently prescribed to increase the blood level of this naturally occurring mineral.

5.3.2 RESPIRATORY SYSTEM

Section Concepts

- *How the respiratory system works*
- *The oxygenation process: Age-associated changes*
- *Influences of the environment on the lungs*
- *Chronic respiratory disease*
- *Chronic bronchitis and emphysema*
- *Pneumonia and its specific dangers to the nursing facility population*

Consider as the Administrator . . .

- *How can the facility ensure that the facility's environment does not negatively affect residents who have respiratory problems?*

NAB DOMAIN 1A: QUALITY OF CARE; 1B: QUALITY OF LIFE; 1B1: PSYCHOSOCIAL NEEDS (E.G., SOCIAL, SPIRITUAL, COMMUNITY, CULTURAL)

NAB DOMAIN 1A3: DISEASE MANAGEMENT (E.G., ACUTE VS. CHRONIC CONDITIONS)

The chief function of the respiratory process is providing the body with oxygen while removing excess carbon dioxide. The exchange of these gases occurs during breathing when air enters and exits the body through the nose and mouth. The air that enters the body is rich in oxygen, necessary for many of the cells' essential chemical functions. Oxygen is exchanged for carbon dioxide in the capillary beds of the lungs. The respiratory and circulatory systems are interrelated in the oxygenation process.

THE OXYGENATION PROCESS

The circulatory system is responsible for the movement of blood within the body. The blood contains RBC (erythrocytes), which carry oxygen and carbon dioxide. As the RBCs leave the lungs and travel to the left atrium, they are oxygen rich. As they travel through the body, erythrocytes transfer oxygen to and remove carbon dioxide from the tissues in the capillary beds. The carbon dioxide–rich blood moves from the right side of the heart back to the lungs to repeat the cycle.

The body structures that allow the respiratory system to move oxygen and carbon dioxide include the mouth, nose, pharynx, larynx, trachea, bronchi, bronchioles, lungs, alveoli, diaphragm, and various accessory respiratory muscles (OpenStax College, 2021).

Air is inhaled through the nose or mouth, travels through the trachea to the bronchi of the lungs. The two bronchi divide and subdivide numerous times before forming the bronchioles (Figure 5.3). The bronchioles are the smallest airways in the lungs that terminate in numerous alveoli.

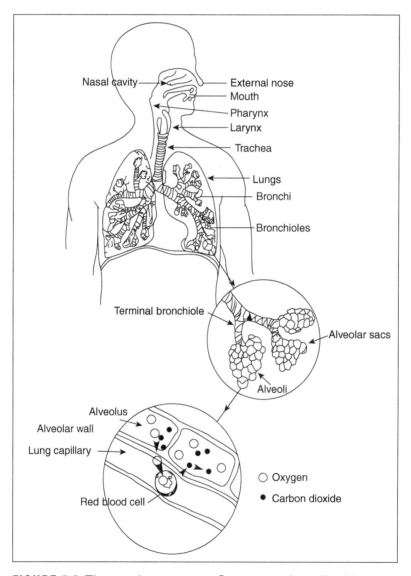

FIGURE 5.3 The respiratory tract. Oxygen–carbon dioxide exchange occurs at the alveolar walls.

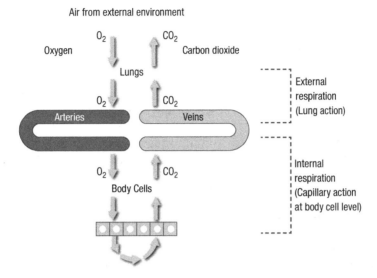

FIGURE 5.4 Diagram of events simultaneously occurring during respiration.

Alveoli are the many air-filled sacs enveloped by the capillaries in the lungs and are the site of the actual oxygen–carbon dioxide exchange (Figure 5.4). Here, oxygen is absorbed by the blood, and carbon dioxide is released into the air as the breath is exhaled. Much of the lung tissue volume is taken up by blood undergoing this stage of the oxygenation process.

Damage to either the cardiovascular or the respiratory system is likely to affect the other system directly. The diaphragm and secondary respiratory muscles aid the lungs in expanding and contracting with each inhalation and exhalation.

AGE-ASSOCIATED CHANGES

Some decreases in capacity and efficiency of the respiratory system occur with aging. However, without any significant disease, these changes should not prevent ADLs.

One reason for this resilience is that the lung, unlike the heart, has a remarkable ability to repair itself after infection or damage with only minor traces of previous damage. Age-related changes to the respiratory system include the following:

- Decreasing size (and therefore capacity) of the alveoli
- Loss of elasticity of lung tissue
- Stiffening of the rib musculature (requiring increased work for muscles to pump air in and out of the lungs)
- Calcification of rib cartilage decreases the chest's ability to expand during breathing
- Calcification of larynx or tracheal cartilage

- Reduced numbers of cilia in the respiratory tract decreasing mucus production
- Decreased ability to cough
- Changes in the shape of the chest (barrel chest)
- Reduced resistance to infection (Eliopoulos, 2018; Saxon et al., 2022; Walter & Chang, 2020)

The decreased capacity of the alveoli is not enough to cause dramatic changes but does reduce the efficiency of breathing and may lead to disability and respiratory problems over time.

Older adults are prone to infections. With lungs receiving foreign materials continuously from the outside air, it is not surprising that many older adults suffer from some form of lung disease.

INFLUENCE OF THE ENVIRONMENT ON THE LUNGS

Because the lungs are in almost direct contact with the air outside, the environment can play a role in developing lung disease as much as any other body system. Environmental exposure to a lung irritant over a prolonged period often produces changes that result in respiratory disease. Some examples are miners' exposure to coal dust, welders to asbestos and toxic fumes, and chronic cigarette smokers to tar and nicotine. Exposure to pathogens causing lung infection is a common cause of death among older persons. Before antibiotics were common, pneumonia (a lung infection) was known as the "old man's friend" as it led to a relatively quick and painless death.

CHRONIC OBSTRUCTIVE PULMONARY DISEASE

Chronic obstructive pulmonary disease (COPD) is a group of progressive diseases that cause issues with airflow and breathing, which worsens over time through three stages (CDC, 2021c). These diseases include chronic bronchitis, emphysema, and chronic obstructive asthma (Han et al., 2020).

COPD is common among those who were long-term smokers and those chronically exposed to secondhand smoke. However, COPD can also occur in those never exposed to nicotine smoke. It is believed that COPD may be caused by air pollution exposure, family history, history of respiratory infections, genetics, or occupational exposures to toxic materials (CDC, 2021c; National Heart, Lung, and Blood Institute, 2021c; Saxon et al., 2022).

Symptoms of COPD include the following:

- Coughing or wheezing
- Excess phlegm, mucus, or sputum
- Shortness of breath
- Problems taking deep breaths
- Orthopnea (a feeling of air hunger when laying flat)
- Dyspnea (trouble breathing) during exertion (Han et al., 2020; Saxon et al., 2022)

COPD's long-term symptoms include anorexia and weight loss due to COPD's physical toll on the body. Work of breathing required in advanced cases is extreme, and the energy expenditure by the resident is so significant that these symptoms can occur.

Treatment for COPD includes lifestyle changes where necessary. Smoking cessation is a crucial step to slow down further damage from occurring. As patients progress through the four stages of COPD, treatments are added to their regimen. At stage I, patients use short-acting (rescue) bronchodilators by inhaler (puffer) or nebulizer and add long-acting bronchodilators and pulmonary rehab at stage II. Many residents have progressed to stage III, which requires the addition of inhaled glucocorticoids (steroids). Bronchodilators and glucocorticoids open the airways and reduce inflammation in the respiratory tract. Pulmonary rehabilitation includes exercise training, health education, and breathing techniques to improve quality of life. At stage IV, the resident has become dependent on supplemental oxygen, usually delivered through a nasal cannula or mask (Global Initiative for Chronic Obstructive Lung Disease, 2021).

Chronic Bronchitis

As the name suggests, chronic bronchitis is caused by a continuing irritation of the bronchi (the two airways in the lungs). The insides of these airways swell and become clogged with mucous secretions, making it more difficult to breathe. This swelling may be due to an environmental irritation or a recurrent infection. Chronic smokers are most likely to develop bronchitis due to inhaled irritants. Chronic bronchitis is defined as a chronic productive cough for 3 months in each of 2 successive years when other causes of chronic cough have been excluded (Global Initiative for Chronic Obstructive Lung Disease, 2021; Han et al., 2020). Chronic bronchitis often exists with emphysema, making it difficult to distinguish between them in some (Saxon et al., 2022).

Emphysema

Emphysema is a loss of elasticity in the lung tissue, causing the alveoli to enlarge and their walls to be destroyed over time (Han et al., 2020). The damage accumulates slowly over time, eventually causing severe tissue damage. This destruction causes carbon dioxide to build up in the body, lessening the ability of the lungs to exchange carbon dioxide for oxygen. The increased carbon dioxide bound to blood cells causes the need for increased oxygen concentration in inhaled air, leading to the need for continuous oxygen therapy. Oxygen therapy reduces lung hypertension and promotes oxygenation of the blood and tissues.

The causes of emphysema are similar to chronic bronchitis, the most common being smoking. Other potential causes include secondhand smoke, air pollution, allergens, recurrent infections, and chronic irritant exposure to the lungs (Global Initiative for Chronic Obstructive Lung Disease, 2021; Han et al., 2020; Saxon et al., 2022). Emphysema is much more severe than bronchitis, and often residents with this disease die from heart failure due to prolonged stress on the cardiovascular system.

Emphysema symptoms are similar to most lung diseases: chronic cough, increased production of thick white mucus, and some shortness of breath. These symptoms result from the body attempting to rid itself of the respiratory irritation. The irritated inner lining of the respiratory tract causes increased mucus production to trap the offensive particle and assist in its excretion from the body.

A cough is another way the body rejects irritating particles. When this irritation is chronic, these mechanisms are continually being triggered.

Symptoms of long-term emphysema include the following:

- Cardiovascular system stress and an enlarged heart
- Heart failure
- Thick mucus plugs block the smaller airways within the lung
- Overinflated alveoli that eventually burst, decreasing space available for oxygen exchange
- Long-term or "smoker's" cough
- Barrel-shaped chest
- Poor appetite
- Weight loss
- Dizziness
- Continual fatigue

Treatments are focused on symptomatic relief. Bronchodilators and glucocorticoids minimize airway irritation, obstruction, and relax bronchi to improve airflow. Expectorants thin the mucus to improve coughing efficiency.

Asthma

Asthma is a chronic inflammatory disorder of the airways associated with recurring episodic wheezing, breathlessness, chest tightness, and coughing (Global Initiative for Asthma, 2021).

Asthma is a generalized reversible airway obstruction characterized by bronchial reactions to internal or external stimulants. Irritants can include environmental exposures to chemicals, insect parts, or dust. This disease may affect the aged population but is much more common among youth. Treatments for asthma are similar to other respiratory disorders discussed so far and include inhalers, dry powder inhalers, and nebulizer treatments.

Pneumonia

Pneumonia is an infection in the lungs caused by a virus, bacteria, or fungi. Residents with COPD are much more susceptible to this infection because these pathogens grow in stagnant areas like those where the mucus is collecting. Respiratory infections create difficulty breathing in older adults and cause disruptions in other systems. Common causes of pneumonia in resident populations include influenza, respiratory syncytial virus (RSV), and SARS-CoV-2 (COVID-19), and present more severe risks to that population (CDC, 2021d). Pneumonia is also often caused by the aspiration of food into the lungs by residents with compromised gag reflexes and swallowing issues due to sensory and motor nerve deficits (Saxon et al., 2022).

Symptoms of pneumonia include shortness of breath, cough, dizziness, confusion, weakness, and a fever. The cough may have sputum production, which is stained and cultured in a laboratory to determine the best treatment regimens.

Treatment generally includes antibiotic therapy when bacteria cause this infection, antifungals for fungi, and possibly antivirals for viral infections. Other treatment is supportive and focused on symptom abatement or comfort. Pneumonia is also a common reason for transfer to hospital for residents who cannot be managed locally at the nursing facility.

Newer to the nursing facility is pneumonia secondary to COVID-19 infection. As COVID-19 is a virus, it is complicated to treat, and recovery is challenging. COVID-19 uses the immune system in the lungs to spread through the lungs causing rampant inflammation and leaving damaged tissue behind (Grant et al., 2021). This method of infection contributes to a long duration of pneumonia and much more significant complications than what would be seen with "normal" pneumonia. As the infective agent is viral, little treatment is available to affect the virus directly. Treatment is focused on symptoms including respiratory failure, which can progress to adult respiratory distress syndrome (ARDS). Common things seen in the treatment of respiratory failure are proning (lying on the stomach), extracorporeal membrane oxygen (ECMO; a machine does the work of the heart and lungs, allowing them to rest), and mechanical ventilator support with intubation. COVID-19 is unlike anything we have seen before in healthcare, and treatment options are often experimental, with providers trying everything possible to assist those suffering from it. Recovered patients are sent to nursing facilities for significant rehabilitation after near paralysis from prolonged muscle wasting and respiratory failure (Kim & Gandhi, 2021).

Prevention has become the focus for nursing facility residents, including pneumococcal and annual flu vaccines. These are known to deter the potential for a resident to acquire both pneumonia and flu. Federal tag F883—Influenza and Pneumococcal Vaccinations must be adhered to very closely. Noncompliance can quickly find a facility in a substandard quality of care situation.

Chronic Tuberculosis

Tuberculosis (TB) is an infectious disease found among nursing facility residents because of their higher risk of infection due to multiple chronic conditions. The rate of TB is four times higher in nursing facilities versus the general population (Morbidity and Mortality Weekly Report, 1990).

TB may infect a person while young, but a healthy immune system often wards off the disease, which goes into a dormant state. As people age, they become immunocompromised, and the dormant disease may become active. Older adults are the largest reservoir for this disease in the United States (Hochberg et al., 2016; Khan et al., 2019).

Signs and symptoms are similar to those listed for COPD, except for night sweats and sputum containing the TB bacteria. The disease is infectious because it may easily be transmitted through the secretions or when a patient coughs.

One of the most important treatments is to isolate the person as long as they are coughing and producing sputum. Staff and visitors generally are required to wear masks, gloves, and gowns when in contact with the resident or in their room to prevent the spread of infection. Many facilities also employ negative pressure rooms for those residents with TB. These rooms exhaust room air to the atmosphere outside the facility instead of recirculating the air within the facility.

Pulmonary Rehabilitation

Many of those who survived COVID-19 have persistent symptoms after they have recovered from the disease. This process is known as "long COVID" and has symptoms such as dyspnea, headaches, fatigue, muscle weakness, depression, and other functional capacity impairments (Celli, 2021; Mikkelsen & Abramoff, 2021). Pulmonary rehabilitation (and cardiac rehabilitation) is indicated for these individuals. Recovery ranges from 2 to 12 months following discharge from the hospital in these residents, depending on their hospitalized interventions, which often include a tracheostomy (Mikkelsen & Abramoff, 2021). As such, we see the need for facilities to provide an increased level of service to meet the needs of these recovering individuals. Many facilities have used post-COVID-19 rehabilitation as a niche and built a census on it and their increased level of services. Proper pulmonary rehabilitation involves a team of individuals only partially seen in most nursing facilities. Pulmonary rehabilitation requires doctors, nurses, physical therapists, respiratory therapists, exercise specialists, dietitians, and an entire interdisciplinary team to be successfully offered (American Lung Association, 2021).

5.3.3 NERVOUS SYSTEM

Section Concepts

- *The components of the nervous system and the possible effects of aging*
- *Perceptual change attributed to aging*
- *The eye: Glaucoma, cataracts, vision problems among the facility population*
- *Hearing impairments*
- *Stroke: Causes and degrees of disability, including aphasia, dysarthria*
- *Parkinson's disease*
- *Frontotemporal dementia*
- *Alzheimer's disease: Stages and research*
- *Dementia: Its near omnipresence in the facility population*
- *How to distinguish delirium from dementia*

Consider as the Administrator . . .

- *Knowing that these disabilities affect a significant subset of the facility residents, what accommodations should the facility make?*

NAB DOMAIN 1A: QUALITY OF CARE; 1B: QUALITY OF LIFE; 1B1: PSYCHOSOCIAL NEEDS (E.G., SOCIAL, SPIRITUAL, COMMUNITY, CULTURAL)

NAB DOMAIN 1A3: DISEASE MANAGEMENT (E.G., ACUTE VS. CHRONIC CONDITIONS)

One of the body's most important mechanisms is the nervous system. It acts as its control center by coordinating functions and maintaining order. The brain is the control center, much like a computer system, with the nerves and spinal cord transferring input and output messages to and from each part of the body.

Some specific nervous system functions for control of the body include responding to events outside the body, interpreting input from the five senses, performing voluntary activities such as walking, and storing memories, ideas, and emotions to be used later for various thought processes. The nervous system also performs automatic activities and reflexes such as breathing, maintaining heart rate, and controlling temperature.

COMPONENTS OF THE CENTRAL NERVOUS SYSTEM

The CNS includes the brain and spinal cord. Some consider the brain to be the most important organ in the body because it is accorded a high level of priority among body functions. When the body is undergoing stress, organs reduce their nutrient intake to direct more nutrients to the brain.

The brain is protected by the skull and floats in a protective layer of cerebrospinal fluid. This organ is very specialized, with unique cell types grouped in specific areas, responsible for particular body functions. Because brain cells perform complex processes, they need large amounts of oxygen to function continually. A lack of oxygen to the brain causes the cells and tissues to die within minutes.

The brain consists of two cerebral hemispheres (left and right), connected by the corpus callosum, making up the bulk of the brain. There are four lobes in each hemisphere, the frontal, temporal, parietal, and occipital, and each has a specialized function. The frontal lobe has memory, retention, thinking, and speech functions. The temporal lobe manages hearing, with some contribution to speech. The parietal lobe interprets sensory information such as touch, temperature, or pressure. The occipital lobe houses the vision center (Saxon et al., 2022; Walter & Chang, 2020).

The cerebellum (or tiny brain) is located on the posterior of the brain under the cerebral hemispheres. The cerebellum allows for integrative functions such as reflexes, coordination of muscle tone, voluntary muscle movements, posture, and equilibrium, allowing balanced and coordinated actions.

The brainstem is at the base of the brain, with three parts. From the top down, they are the midbrain, pons, and medulla oblongata. The medulla oblongata extends from the spinal cord and has the essential functions of controlling motor activity or movement and the cardiac and respiratory centers. Special nuclei here also control swallowing, coughing, sneezing, vomiting, and other vital functions (Saxon et al., 2022; Walter & Chang, 2020).

The spinal cord extends directly from the bottom of the medulla oblongata through the vertebral canal for protection. The spinal cord transports information from the body to the brain and back, providing integrative functions for the body. It also locally acts as reflex centers at different spinal cord levels to help keep the body safe.

COMPONENTS OF THE PERIPHERAL NERVOUS SYSTEM

Structures related to the nervous system and not the brain or spinal cord (CNS) are peripheral nervous system (PNS) components. The PNS includes the cranial and spinal nerves.

Twelve pairs of cranial nerves arise directly from the brain and supply motor and sensory function and control to the head, face, neck, and special senses (including vision, taste, smell, and hearing). Thirty-one pairs of spinal nerves carry sensory and motor messages between the body and the CNS.

Each nerve is composed of many individual fibers encased in a fatty substance called myelin, much like coating electrical wires to conduct an electrical charge efficiently. The individual fibers are composed of nerve cells called neurons.

The nerve fibers form an intricate network that carries various messages to the brain as electrical impulses. Each impulse stimulates the appropriate area of the brain, triggering either an involuntary response reaction (reflex) or a thought (cognitive) process.

The nerve fibers form a complex series of pathways to carry impulses to the brain. It is vital to remember that the left side of the brain controls the functions on the right side of the body, while the right hemisphere controls the functions on the left side of the body.

POSSIBLE EFFECTS OF AGING

The effects of aging on the nervous system are believed to result from a reduced oxygen supply to the brain cells. This oxygen starvation can lead to permanent alterations of brain cells, which are extremely sensitive to the level of oxygen.

Brain mass decreases with age, possibly because of brain cell, nerve fiber, and supporting cell (neuroglia) loss (Aldwin et al., 2017; Saxon et al., 2022). Additionally, certain parts of the brain are more susceptible to aging. Gray matter tends to decline more slowly with age than white matter. It is believed that the faster decline in communicating white matter contributes to cognitive issues over time (Aldwin et al., 2017).

Sleep patterns also change with aging. Overall, it takes older adults longer to fall asleep, and they sleep for a shorter period going through multiple sleep and wake cycles throughout the night, resulting in needing naps during the day. These factors decrease sleep quality and contribute to health issues (Saxon et al., 2022).

PERCEPTUAL CHANGES

Perception and interpretation of sensations tend to decrease with age. One of the perceptual changes commonly attributed to the aging process is a reduced sensitivity to touch.

Visual changes associated with age include loss of vision for near objects and reduced clarity of vision due to decreased flexibility of the eye's lens (Michel et al., 2017). Common issues that occur with the eye include cataracts, glaucoma, and macular degeneration.

Among the general population, an increasing number of individuals have issues hearing as they get older. This loss often results from high-frequency sound loss. Speaking to residents in deep tones can help compensate for this loss.

In many older individuals, the taste buds appear to degenerate, and saliva production is diminished (dry mouth syndrome—xerostomia), reducing the ability to taste different flavors (Halter et al., 2017; Michel et al., 2017; Saxon et al., 2022). Taste reduction and dry mouth can also be side effects of medications (Baer & Sankar, 2020). The reduction of taste can result in the overuse of salt by patients to "improve" or increase taste sensations. The ability to taste sweets appears to be unaffected, which may explain the preference of many older adult residents for eating dessert first (Halter et al., 2017). The sense of taste may be further reduced by a loss in the sense of smell, as they are linked to each other (Saxon et al., 2022).

Odor detection is reduced by the age-related decrease in neurons responsible for the sense of smell. The drying of the nasal concha, where the olfactory nerves lie, from either normal aging or medication side effects, also causes a decreased sense of smell.

THE EYE

The eye is a complicated structure held in place by numerous muscles. The retina is the innermost eye layer and contains receptor cells that generate electrical nerve impulses when hit by light. The nerve fibers leave the retina and form the optic nerve, which carries the impulses to the brain. The region of the brain responsible for vision is the occipital lobe. The retina is protected by the lens covering the eye.

The lens is similar to layers of skin, but rather than discarding old layers, they are continually compacted within the eye. The aqueous humor is a fluid that bathes and protects the lens. Light enters the eye through the lens, passes through the iris, and then is projected on the retina, where it is converted to a nerve impulse sent to and processed by the brain. Issues can occur anywhere along the way, causing problems with vision.

Presence of Eye Problems

The number of people in the United States is expected to reach 359.4 million by 2030 (Statista, 2022), and approximately 7.7 million of these individuals are expected to be aged 65 and over with severe vision impairments (Meehan & Shura, 2016). We see anywhere between 29% to 62% of long-term care residents who experience some type of visual impairment (Elliott et al., 2010; Meehan & Shura, 2016). The higher percentages include those with moderately impaired vision (Meehan & Shura, 2016).

Glaucoma

Glaucoma is a chronic condition that occurs due to increased intraocular eye pressure from aqueous humor produced beyond what drains naturally, increasing pressure in the eye. This condition is severe and can lead to severe vision issues or blindness.

There are two main types of glaucoma, open-angle and angle-closure, each marked by an increased pressure within the eye (intraocular pressure; Glaucoma Research Foundation, 2020). Open-angle glaucoma, also referred to as primary or chronic glaucoma, is the most common type, accounting for more than 90% of all cases (Glaucoma Research Foundation, 2020; Saxon et al., 2022). Open-angle glaucoma is so named because it is caused by the drainage canals of the eye slowly becoming clogged, creating a wide and open angle between the iris and cornea. This glaucoma develops gradually over time and is a lifelong condition. Angle-closure glaucoma is a much less common form. It is an acute condition caused by suddenly blocked drainage canals, causing a sudden increase in intraocular pressure (Glaucoma Research Foundation, 2020). It has a closed or narrow angle between the iris and cornea and demands immediate medical attention.

The symptoms of glaucoma are often none until vision is affected, as the disease process is gradual. There are few warning signs or painful symptoms associated with open-angle glaucoma. In contrast, symptoms of closed-angle or late-stage open-angle glaucoma can include acute pain in the eye, elevated blood pressure, blurred vision, and halos seen around lights. Untreated glaucoma can lead to blindness.

Treatment varies with the form or state of disease, with the initial medical therapy promoting the drainage of excess fluids from the eye (Jacobs, 2021a). Medications are the first line of defense against glaucoma, followed by laser therapies, and then surgical interventions.

Cataracts

A cataract is a clouding of the lens, causing it to appear white, which blocks the light from reaching the retina (Jacobs, 2021b). Cataracts are a significant cause of blindness (Lee & Afshari, 2017). Causes of cataracts include increased age, malnutrition, metabolic abnormalities, sun damage, and medication (Jacobs, 2021b).

The primary symptom of cataracts is increasing blurred vision and "shadows," which can progress to blindness. The first choice treatment for cataracts is a surgical intervention where the damaged lens is entirely removed and replaced with a new, often prescription, lens (Jacobs, 2021b). This surgery is indicated when the resident can no longer meet their ADL needs due to a lack of visual acuity, and the newly implanted "prescription" lens may replace previously required glasses.

Importance of Vision Among Residents

When older persons with visual impairments receive vision improving interventions, they adapt better to their surroundings. Interventions can include providing large-type books, magazines, and newspapers; implementing color-coded boundaries and walkways to provide location and navigation assistance (painted baseboards or doors); and using large letters and numbers on doors, elevators, and clocks.

HEARING

The outer ear structures include the external ear, which directs sound waves down the tympanic canal to the eardrum (tympanic membrane). The tympanic membrane vibrates the three bones of the middle ear (the incus, malleus, stapes) that conduct sound waves to the inner ear. The inner ear contains the cochlea, which transforms sound waves to nerve impulses that travel down the vestibulocochlear (cochlear/auditory) nerve (the eighth cranial nerve) to the brain's auditory center. The vestibulocochlear (vestibular) nerve also serves the inner ear's semicircular canals that detect body movement.

Hearing Impairments

Presbycusis describes hearing impairment in old age (Blevins, 2020; Kane et al., 2017; Walter & Chang, 2020). Presbycusis affects approximately 43% of those aged 65 to 74, at least 50% of those aged 75 years, most adults older than 80, and nearly all adults who are 90 or older (Blevins, 2020). We see presbycusis more commonly in males than females, potentially due to higher occupational exposures to loud noise.

Hearing impairments are divided into two categories—conductive and sensorineural. Conductive impairments stem from issues that cause problems in transmitting sound from the external and middle ear to the inner ear. A common cause of conductive loss is cerumen impaction (earwax). Other causes include ear infections, damaged eardrums, or malformation of the outer or middle ear (American Speech-Language-Hearing Association, 2021a). Sensorineural hearing loss is caused by the inner ear's inability to turn sound waves into appropriate neural signals. A common misnomer calls this hearing loss "nerve deafness." However, this is incorrect as this hearing loss is due to the cochlea's inability to transmit to the nerve, not a deficiency of the nerve tissue (American Speech-Language-Hearing Association, 2021b; Blevins, 2021).

Symptoms. Symptoms of hearing impairment can include tinnitus (a persistent ringing in the ears), progressive hearing loss, increased inability to hear high-frequency sounds (including shouting, warning bells, or buzzers), or dizziness (Blevins, 2021; Walter & Chang, 2020).

Treatment. Depending upon the cause of the hearing loss, the treatment can include ear cleaning to remove built-up cerumen, antibiotics for common infections, or device intervention. Actual sensorineural loss may be treated with hearing aids, cochlear implants, assistive listening devices, and auditory rehabilitation (Blevins, 2021).

MOBILITY AND COMMUNICATION

A CVA, also known as a stroke, can be one of the most debilitating conditions for an older adult (Michel et al., 2017). CVA causes and treatment were discussed earlier under cardiovascular diseases. However, those who suffer from a stroke often have issues with mobility and communication, requiring rehabilitation and possibly resulting in permanent disability.

Degrees of Disability

The degree of disability resulting from a stroke may range from slight impairment to complete immobility and localized loss of muscle control. Affected areas of the body typically directly correlate to the injured area of the brain. Symptoms may include the following:

- Muscle weakness on one side of the body (hemiplegia)
- Complete loss of muscle control (quadriplegia)
- Paralysis of the body below the upper extremities (paraplegia)
- Difficulty standing or walking
- Poor balance
- Pain in arms and legs
- Fatigue
- Confusion
- Problems in spatial judgment, distortion
- Poor vision, including partial blindness
- Seizure
- Syncope (fainting)
- Migraine aura
- Difficulty speaking (aphasia; Furie & Rost, 2021; Halter et al., 2017)

Aphasia

Aphasia is a person's inability to produce or understand language, most often because the brain area responsible for speech is damaged during a stroke (Clark, 2021). This inability may be demonstrated as a slowed ability to retrieve vocabulary, inappropriate grammar or word choice, and difficulty comprehending spoken words (Halter et al., 2017; Singh, 2016).

Aphasia syndromes or progressive aphasias are classified by the effects on creating or understanding speech. Some types of aphasia cause an inability to express desired communication in words. Other aphasias cause inappropriate and sometimes vulgar language due to a lack of control over word choice. Common types of aphasias include Broca's aphasia, which affects the person's ability to speak complete thoughts but leaves language understanding intact, or Wernicke's aphasia, which creates difficulty in communication because the person's ability to understand spoken language is damaged (Clark, 2021).

Dysarthria

Dysarthria (literally imperfect articulation of speech) is a muscular issue preventing clear speech rather than a language or neural abnormality that may accompany paralysis, weakness, or a lack of coordination. The incidence of these disorders may exceed 50% of the long-term population in a nursing facility (Singh, 2016, p. 239). This deficit can be a frustrating experience for the resident who has all other mental capacities intact and often leads to emotional upset. The most critical need is addressing the resident's ability to communicate.

Treatment through individually tailored rehabilitative therapy is the most effective. The anticipated recovery from a stroke is best correlated with the location of the injury, with lower brainstem damage having a more favorable prognosis than an upper brain injury.

Rehabilitation therapy by physical and occupational therapists usually focuses on achieving ADLs, mobility, standing, and walking with a cane or other appliance. Speech therapy addresses rehabilitation of the specific musculature involved in the dysarthria and dysphagia. This work includes slowing down the speech, stressing speech clarity, and possibly utilizing electrical stimulation, which is a quite effective treatment (Tache-Codreanu & Cucu, 2020).

Parkinson's Disease

Parkinson's disease is a progressive neurodegenerative disease that eventually leads to complete disability. Parkinson's disease is a complex condition that includes motor, neuropsychiatric, and nonmotor symptoms (Chau, 2021; Langston, 2006). The disease involves many parts of the brain, spinal cord, and autonomic nervous system, causing many clinical signs and symptoms (Langston, 2006).

Parkinson's disease symptoms can include tremor of any limbs at rest, rigidity or muscle stiffness, and bradykinesia (slowness in body movements). These specific symptoms are commonly considered "parkinsonian symptoms." Additional symptoms may include the following:

- Stooped posture while standing
- Walking with short, shuffling steps
- Garbled speech
- Illegible handwriting
- Sad, lifeless facial expression
- Facial droop
- Mood swings
- Dementia (an impairment in intellectual ability)
- Rapid eye movement sleep disorder
- Olfactory dysfunction (problems with smelling)
- Constipation
- Cardiac sympathetic denervation (part of autonomic dysfunction)
- Depression
- Psychosis
- Dementia (Chau, 2021; Langston, 2006)

There is no cure for Parkinson's disease, so treatment aims to control symptoms and improve function. Often residents with Parkinson's disease suffer from mental disturbances similar to those seen in patients with Alzheimer's disease (Rodnitzky, 2020). The commonality between the two conditions causes difficulty for practitioners to diagnose either definitively.

Dementia

Dementia refers to a substantial decline from the person's previous baseline that interferes with independence in daily activities due to a significant acquired impairment in one or more cognitive domains (American Psychiatric Association, 2013). Dementia is not a disease but a symptom of many diseases covering a wide range of medical conditions. Disorders termed "dementia" are often caused by abnormal brain changes impairing thinking skills (cognitive abilities), as well as behaviors, changes in feelings, and changes in relationships (Alzheimer's Association, 2021; Brosch & Farlow, 2021).

Dementias are all caused by abnormal brain changes which can occur over time. Alzheimer's disease is the most common cause of dementia accounting for 60% to 80% of cases. Vascular dementia, caused by changes in the brain's blood vessels, is the second most common cause. The remaining common causes are Lewy body dementia, frontotemporal dementia, and other disease processes such as Huntington's disease or Parkinson's disease, which also cause dementia (Alzheimer's Association, 2021).

Signs of dementia or pathological brain processes may include the following:

- Issues with short-term memory
- Inability to pay bills correctly
- Failure to remember to eat or to prepare meals
- Failure to recall appointments or places to be
- Getting lost during travel in familiar places, such as a neighborhood where someone has lived their entire lives
- Issues with speech or with being able to form cohesive sentences
- Other memory concerns
- Personality changes
- Headaches
- Stroke-like symptoms (Alzheimer's Association, 2021; Brosch & Farlow, 2021)

There are numerous specific causes of dementia:

- Neurodegenerative dementias—the most common cause of a cognitive decline in dementia
  - Alzheimer's disease
  - Frontotemporal dementia
  - Neurodegenerative diseases related to tau protein accumulation
  - Lewy body dementia
  - Parkinson's disease dementia
- Vascular dementias
- Infectious diseases
  - Creutzfeldt–Jakob disease
  - HIV-associated neurocognitive disorder (HAND)
  - Neurosyphilis
  - Whipple's disease
- Inflammatory and autoimmune diseases
  - Multiple sclerosis
  - Different encephalopathies

- Neurometabolic disorders
  - Mitochondrial disease
  - Leukodystrophies
- Others
  - Chronic traumatic encephalopathy (CTE)—often resulting from sports, combat, or motor vehicle accidents
  - Alcohol abuse
  - Huntington's disease (Alzheimer's Association, 2021; Brosch & Farlow, 2021)

Diagnosis and Treatment

The diagnosis of dementia is a complex process of exclusion, requiring ruling out many other diseases before dementia can be a concluding diagnosis. However, it is often challenging for a provider to determine the exact cause as many of the issues listed earlier have overlapping symptoms.

Treatment of dementia depends on the source. Medications are currently the first line of dementia treatment to control symptoms and possibly reverse the disease process. However, most dementias are progressive and worsen over time, eventually leading to palliative care.

CASE STUDY (AN ACTUAL CASE)

Wandering California Hallways and Byways—On Haldol

Part A

Mrs. Annie Wood is a 69-year-old San Diego resident admitted to Desert Sands Nursing Center (a privately owned facility) 3 years ago. A brief medical history, current physician's orders, current care plan, and excerpts from recent nurse's notes follow.

Desert Sands Nursing Center is physically adjacent to the freeway (10-lane Interstate 15) just north of the San Diego city limits, near the Miramar Naval Air Station. Mrs. Wood, and nearly all of the 200 patients at Desert Sands, are private pay.

Although weakened by her recent heart episodes, Mrs. Wood remains physically vigorous, in part due to her years of outside activities. Mrs. Wood has led an active life, including years as an avid and competitive water-skier. She also played tennis and golf at her local club.

Three years ago, in a freak accident, Mrs. Wood fell from the roof of her hillside suburban home in San Diego. Her husband had left early one morning on a business trip, and there was no hot water coming from the solar panels on their roof. Mr. Wood usually went up on the roof and "tinkered with it," and it had always started working. Mrs. Wood decided to try this solution and climbed up on the front side of the roof. As soon as she moved to the steeper backside, she lost her footing on the red clay tiles, which were still covered with dew. She slid off the two-story roof onto the concrete back patio some 30 feet below. Several vertebrae were crushed.

(continued)

She did well following initial surgery at a Los Angeles neurosurgical center. But after a second surgery during which the surgeons removed bone fragments (but found it impossible to fuse or implant plates to support the lower spine), she lost her ability to walk, speak, or interact coherently with others.

Mrs. Wood roams the halls and patient rooms throughout Desert Sands most of the days, mumbling incoherently. Occasionally her only son visits with one of the grandchildren. During such visits, Mrs. Wood brightens, smiles a lot, and reminisces about the past in more or less coherent sentence fragments while eating her favorite snack, Fritos, brought by her son.

History: Cardiac catheterization 6 years ago, MI 3 years ago; admitted to San Diego General Hospital. History of syncopal episodes, gout, urosepsis

Diagnosis: Spinal cord injury (nonspecific); atrial fibrillation; coronary atherosclerosis; convulsions; alcoholic dementia; senile dementia

Current Physician Orders:

Cleanse area on L hip in NS then cover w. duoderm q 3 days PRN until healed
Macrodantin 50 mg PO BID 9 a.m., 9 p.m.
Haldol 2 mg PO at 8 a.m. and 12 noon
Haldol 1 mg PO at 8:00 q p.m.
Diltiazem 60 mg
PO q day q a.m.
A.S.A. 325 mg PO q day q a.m.
Dilantin 100 mg PO BID
Colace 100 mg PO BID
Isordil 20 mg PO TID
Weekly skin assessment on Tuesday
Routine vital signs
Up to W/C w/ lap cushion daily; lap cushion D/T poor standing balance HX of
  falls and inability to retain safety instructions.
May have side rails as enablers secondary to the patient's use for positioning and
  support
Prognosis: fair
Rehab potential: poor
PT to eval for least restrictive device

Current Plan of Care

Problem	Goal	Approach	Staff
Routine care needs	Caregiver be aware of individual preferences and care needs	Monitor percent of meals eaten and offer replacement if <50% eaten	DT
		Offer HS snack/ document	NA

(*continued*)

Current Plan of Care (*continued*)

Problem	Goal	Approach	Staff
		Shower/bath w/ ROM 7× week; fingernails and toenails cleaned and checked; shampoo as needed	NA
		Oral hygiene 2× day	NA
		Document bowel function	NA
		Requires total care with bathing and dressing every day; likes hats	NA
		Provide incontinence protection: incontinence briefs, none while in bed	NA
		Toilet before and after meals	NA
Trauma: potential for R/T internal factor: R/T wandering	Whereabouts will be known to staff as demonstrated by no incident reports due to leaving the facility	Side rails up when in bed at all times for safety and support and define parameters of bed	NA
		Administer medication as ordered (Haldol)	LPN
R/T external factor: falls R/T dementia R/T injury to others	Will remain free from falls through nursing intervention and prevention as evidenced by no falls	Safety device as ordered—lap cushion when out of bed in W/C	LPN
	Will have no injury to other residents	Monitor whereabouts when out of bed; ensure she stays out of other residents' rooms—intervene and redirect any altercations w/ other residents	All staff

(*continued*)

Current Plan of Care (*continued*)

Problem	Goal	Approach	Staff
		Consult medical doctor regarding medication taper	LPN
Verbal communication	Needs will be met as can be determined	Monitor closely to anticipate needs that cannot be verbalized or demonstrated	LPN/NA/SS/ACT/DT
		Provide care in relaxed, unhurried, nonjudgmental manner	LPN/NA
		Give clear and simple directions; likes to talk about animals	LPN/NA
Physical mobility impaired R/T paralysis—bilateral lower extremities	Will be able to transfer self to and from W/C with moderate assist	Transfer with two person-assist—encourage to assist w/ transfer	NA
	Will not develop complications of immobility, for example, bedsore, contractures, pneumonitis	Supervise activity to perform toileting, transfer, and hygiene tasks before and after meals	NA
		Pressure-relieving device to bed/chair; report any red or open areas	NA
		Pt. to be up in W/C with lap cushion restraint and with wheelchair anti-tip bars with cushion for pressure relief	NA
Seizure activity	Will be free from seizure-related injury	Monitor Dilantin levels	LPN
	Medication will be within therapeutic level	Meals as ordered, Dilantin	LPN

(*continued*)

Current Plan of Care (*continued*)

Problem	Goal	Approach	Staff
		Monitor for seizure—report any jerking movements to charge nurse	NA
Resident frequently propels self in and out of activity room and appears restless within group activities as evidenced by wheeling about with no rational purpose	When addressed by name, resident will re-establish attention to the group at least one time during each activity	Invite and directly guide resident into appropriate group activities; music groups	ACT/NA
		Gently attempt to redirect resident attention as necessary	ACT
Skin integrity impaired—actual—R/T Stage II pressure injury to (L) hip	Skin will be intact	Treat as ordered	LPN
	Stage II will improve	Monitor healing process or lack thereof; contact physician for condition update PRN and treatment change as needed	LPN
WT loss secondary to acute illness URI w/WT loss	Stabilize weight at 160–165 lb	Monitor percent of meals eaten	DT
		Take to dining room for all meals	NA
		Monitor PO intake, encourage intake, and assist as needed to complete meal	NA/LPN
		Weigh monthly	LPN/DT

ACT, activities; D/T, due to; DT, dietary therapist; HS, at bedtime; HX, history; LPN, licensed practical nurse; NA, nurse's aide; PO, by mouth; PRN, pro re nata (as needed); Pt., patient; R/T, related to; ROM, range of motion; SS, social services; tfr, transfer; UTI, upper respiratory infection; W/C, wheelchair; WT, weight.

(*continued*)

Excerpts from recent nursing notes:

6 months ago: Continues to require total assistance with personal care; lap belt when in W/C, soft roll belt in bed.

2 months ago: Discussed and reviewed at the monthly restraint committee meeting. Continue with a lap cushion to W/C due to HX of falls, poor standing balance, and inability to retain safety instructions. No falls noted past month.

1 month ago: Continues to be verbally aggressive and noted unprovoked agitation. Often wheels into staff/residents unknowingly. Some agitation when redirected.

3 weeks ago: Weekly skin measures obtained, wound base is red, area is granulating.

2 weeks ago: Resident found outside building on the ground beside W/C about 50 feet from the Interstate 15 fence.

1 week ago: Bruising or abrasion noted from fall (1 week ago). Continues to wheel self about throughout the facility. Continues to wander outside the building.

Your Turn:

1. Evaluate Mrs. Wood's plan of care, physician's orders, and nursing notes excerpts (from the point of view of the facility's administrator) for facility risk management, both from the point of view of OBRA (Omnibus Budget Reconciliation Act) requirements and potential for any litigation.
2. Consider the use of restraints with Mrs. Wood.
3. List the risks you perceive from the administrator's point of view and propose steps to address risks you identify.

Part B

At 2:15 p.m. on Saturday, a nursing assistant heard a commotion coming from Mrs. Brown's room. Upon quickly moving to Mrs. Brown's room, the nursing assistant found Mrs. Brown striking Mrs. Wood with the 18-inch-long metal grasping claw Mrs. Brown uses to pick up objects. By the nursing assistant's arrival, Mrs. Brown had inflicted 20 gashes at least 1 inch long on Mrs. Wood's arms, legs, head, and neck, 15 of which were bleeding profusely. Mrs. Brown showed no sign of abating her attack. The nursing assistant wrestled the grasping claw from Mrs. Brown's hand and backed the wheelchair-bound Mrs. Wood into the hallway, where four or five staff immediately began treating the bleeding gashes. The scalp wounds were bleeding the most extensively. Mrs. Wood, who seldom speaks coherently, was moaning, "I didn't do anything, I

(continued)

didn't do anything." Mrs. Wood was taken to the San Diego General Hospital's emergency department by emergency medical services (EMS) vehicle.

The administrator was reluctant to have law enforcement officers seen at the facility but felt he had no choice but to report the assault. A 911 call brought a San Diego County sheriff's deputy to the facility. The deputy questioned the staff and then talked with Mrs. Brown.

The administrator was anxious to get Mrs. Brown out of the facility. Mrs. Brown had been admitted only 2 weeks earlier, was fully ambulatory, and was scheduled to go home the following Wednesday. Mrs. Brown was fully functional; an earlier discharge would not in any way jeopardize her health (she had come for a course of physical therapy, which was already completed). Mrs. Wood's family would likely be visibly upset upon seeing her condition and the possibility of a lawsuit weighed heavily on the administrator.

The administrator asked the deputy to admit Mrs. Brown for a 48-hour psychiatric evaluation at the mental health wing of San Diego General Hospital. The deputy said his hands were tied. Under state and county California law, the San Diego County sheriff could not himself seek admission of Mrs. Brown to the hospital's psychiatric evaluation unit for evaluation and overnight observation. "Only a California licensed physician can do that," the deputy stated. The administrator asked the deputy to consider a charge of assault with intent to inflict bodily harm. The deputy replied that under nearly any other circumstances, he would, but Mrs. Brown was a nursing facility patient and no one ever put nursing facility patients into the county jail on any charge, as far as he knew. The deputy sheriff left after admonishing Mrs. Brown not to assault any additional patients.

The assistant director of nursing (ADON), who was doing weekend duty, attempted to call Mrs. Brown's physician but was informed that he was away on a fishing trip near Catalina Island. She then called the facility's medical director, whose response to her request that Mrs. Brown be sent to the hospital for a psychiatric evaluation was, "You people are paid to take care of this kind of older folks. I am not going to request an admission resulting in others having to perform your responsibilities."

Mrs. Brown's roommate was taken to the nursing station and asked if, for safety, she would like to be moved to another room. She replied, "No, she has never attacked me. I'll stay." The administrator asked Mrs. Brown why she attacked Mrs. Wood. Mrs. Brown replied that she had told Mrs. Wood to get out of her room "20 times" in the last week. She stated that she had warned the facility administrators to keep Mrs. Wood out of her room.

A nursing assistant was assigned to remain near Mrs. Brown's room in the hallway. About 5 p.m. that afternoon, the nursing assistant overheard Mrs. Brown state to another patient who had wandered into her room, "You saw what I did to Mrs. Wood this afternoon. If you don't get out of my room and stay out, I'll do the same thing to you."

(continued)

During the 1 hour 45 minutes following the attack on Mrs. Wood, the administrator's investigation found that Mrs. Brown had an extended history of committing physically violent acts against family members and others. Mrs. Brown appeared to be psychopathic (a person who inflicts damage on other persons and feels no remorse). The staff then contacted Mrs. Brown's family (responsible party), who was scheduled to take her home the following Wednesday. The family said they could not take responsibility for Mrs. Brown and would not come to the facility to take her home.

Distressed, the administrator again called the county sheriff's office. The same deputy responded to the call, arriving within a few minutes. The administrator sought to have Mrs. Brown removed from the facility in light of the 5 p.m. threat by Mrs. Brown that she would similarly assault any patient who came into her room uninvited. The sheriff's deputy again lectured Mrs. Brown to control her temper and then left, saying he could do nothing.

Your Turn:

1. It is 5:30 p.m. Saturday. What should the administrator and staff do?

Part C

Results: The ADON was finally able to prevail on a family member to pick up Mrs. Brown at 10:00 a.m. the following day (Sunday). The staff kept a careful watch on Mrs. Brown throughout Saturday night and Sunday morning. The administrator and the ADON personally assisted Mrs. Brown with packing and loading her and her possessions into the family member's car.

Mrs. Wood returned to the facility 2 days later. All the wounds eventually healed without infection.

The ADON resolved this situation solely through informal initiative and persuasive abilities. The California legal and healthcare systems appear to have policies that prevented this nursing facility from enlisting outside help in managing this situation.

Your Turn:

1. Should residents of nursing facilities be legally responsible for their behavior toward staff and other residents?
2. While Mrs. Brown's efforts to keep unwanted persons out of her room were extreme, do residents have a right to privacy from the intrusion of others in their rooms?
3. Should the facility staff manage Mrs. Wood's constant intrusion into other residents' rooms? If so, how?

5.3.4 DIGESTIVE SYSTEM

Section Concepts

- *The parts of the digestive system: mouth, esophagus, stomach, intestines*
- *Possible effects of aging on the digestive system*
- *Problems associated with the digestive system*

Consider as the Administrator . . .

- *The digestive system is especially sensitive in the nursing facility population. With limited funds for raw food costs, how can dietary compensate for a typically barely sufficient operating budget?*
- *How important are teeth to the resident? How crucial is good dental health to proper nutrition and digestion?*

NAB DOMAIN 1A: QUALITY OF CARE; 1B: QUALITY OF LIFE; 1B1: PSYCHOSOCIAL NEEDS (E.G., SOCIAL, SPIRITUAL, COMMUNITY, CULTURAL)

NAB DOMAIN 1A3: DISEASE MANAGEMENT (E.G., ACUTE VS. CHRONIC CONDITIONS)

Digestion is how the body breaks down food into needed nutrient particles small enough to pass through tissues into the bloodstream for delivery to the appropriate tissues and organs. After absorbing nutrients, the leftover materials or waste products are discarded from the body.

The digestive system is commonly referred to as the GI tract or alimentary canal, including the various organs that participate in the digestive process (Figure 5.5).

A diagram representing food's route through the digestive system is presented in Figure 5.6.

MOUTH

Digestion begins when food enters the mouth. Chewing is an essential step in preparing food for digestion. Salivary glands produce saliva, which contains enzymes that start breaking down food in the mouth.

ESOPHAGUS

Swallowed food enters the esophagus, a smooth muscle tube connecting the mouth to the stomach. Swallowing initiates a wavelike movement of the esophagus (called peristalsis) that propels food toward the stomach, where the gastric (stomach) sphincter relaxes to allow food into the stomach.

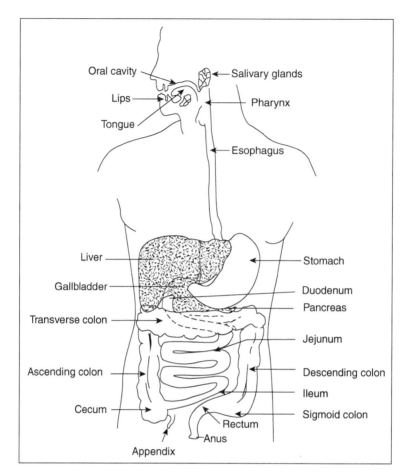

FIGURE 5.5 Organs involved in the digestive process.

STOMACH

The next phase of digestion begins in the stomach. The sphincters (muscles) at both ends of the stomach close when the stomach is full, enabling the stomach acids to have sufficient time to break down the food. The brain controls the digestive process in the stomach through the nerves, which constantly carry impulses directing the digestion process.

INTESTINES

The intestines, also referred to as the bowels or lower GI tract, are a long tube. The first section of the small intestine, the duodenum, has significant chemical digestion actions. The food is liquid at this stage (called chyme) and has been mixed with powerful enzymes that break down specific substances. The intestines are also filled with a supply of bacteria that help digestion. These bacteria are often harmful to any other part of the body if allowed to escape or invade.

Like the stomach, the intestines have nerves that carry impulses to and from the brain. These nerves are vital in stimulating the bowel to move waste materials along the intestinal tract. As in the esophagus, the intestines contract in rhythmic movements (peristalsis), propelling the food through the digestive tract.

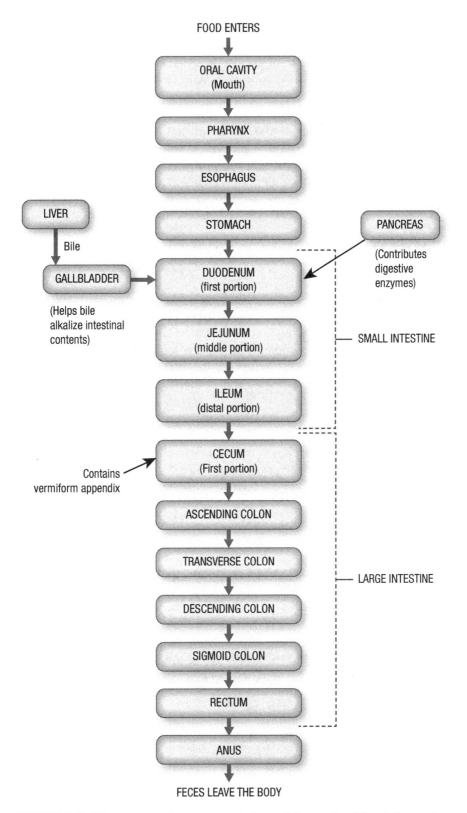

FIGURE 5.6 Diagrammatic representation of the path of food through the digestive system.

If the brain does not send the appropriate impulses to the intestines, the waste moves much more slowly through these organs. Unlike the esophagus, the intestines do not have the added force of gravity to assist in this process.

LARGE INTESTINE

The large intestine is a shorter and wider continuation of the small intestine that plays a different role in the digestive process. The primary function of the large intestine is to store waste so that the body has time to absorb excess fluids and nutrients before elimination. When waste materials are excreted from the body, they are solid, often referred to as feces or stool.

POSSIBLE EFFECTS OF AGING

Mouth

The amount of saliva secreted by the salivary glands may decrease. The saliva also may become thicker until it is almost like mucus. The loss of teeth may also cause digestive complications. Increasingly, it is suspected that gum disease (periodontal disease) and tooth disease are entry points where germs get into the body cavity, causing various systemic diseases. In light of this, oral hygiene in the nursing facility is a significant aspect of maintaining the resident's health.

Esophagus

In some older adults, food may not travel as quickly down the esophagus. The slower movement appears to be caused by a reduced swallowing mechanism effectiveness and a slower response of the gastric sphincter.

Stomach

The lining of the stomach can thin with age. This decreased thickness of the lining may allow the stomach's size to increase and the amount of acid produced to decrease.

DIGESTIVE DISEASES

The digestive tract is a body system that often troubles older adult nursing facility residents. The term *GI distress* is often referred to as a general term to describe issues with the digestive tract.

Mouth

Xerostomia

A common concern in older adults is xerostomia or dry mouth. Many medications are considered "xerogenic," or ones that cause dry mouth. Common medications with this effect include beta-blockers, antidepressants, antihistamines, antipsychotics, benzodiazepines, glucocorticoids, diuretics, and analgesics (Treister et al., 2020).

Dry mouth can cause digestion concerns, including tooth decay, candidiasis (yeast infection of the mouth), difficulty swallowing, issues with the digestion of food, speech concerns, and decreased quality of life (Fornari et al., 2021; Halter et al., 2017; Treister et al., 2020).

Esophagus

Esophagitis

The esophagus may be a common site of discomfort for the older adult resident. Esophagitis (inflammation or irritation of the esophagus) can be caused by acid reflux, a frequent problem for older individuals. This sharp, burning pain may be confused with chest pain or angina and may worsen when the person lies flat, allowing stomach contents to reenter the esophagus.

Dysphagia

Dysphagia is difficulty swallowing or transferring food from the mouth to the esophagus (Michel et al., 2017). Persons with neurological damage from trauma or a CVA may be subject to this problem. Dysphagia increases the risk of aspiration (inhaling food particles) into the lungs (Fass, 2020; Halter et al., 2017). A CVA may impair the gag reflex, which governs the epiglottis in the back of the throat. The epiglottis is the anatomy that directs food to the esophagus or air to the trachea. When a gag reflex is absent, a resident can no longer take food orally due to fear of aspiration and potential aspiration pneumonia. Speech therapy is the first-line approach to recover the gag reflex. When this is unsuccessful, residents are often equipped with a PEG tube into the stomach, through which they receive nutrition.

Gastroesophageal Reflux Disease

Gastroesophageal reflux disease (GERD) is one of the more common GI disorders affecting the nursing facility population. This problem occurs when the stomach contents move back up into the esophagus due to failure or weakening of the lower esophageal sphincter (National Institute of Diabetes and Digestive and Kidney Diseases, 2020). Left untreated, GERD can lead to complications of peptic strictures, esophageal ulcers with bleeding, erosive esophagitis, and Barrett's esophagus (Kahrilas, 2020; National Institute of Diabetes and Digestive and Kidney Diseases, 2020).

The primary focus for treatment is ensuring adequate nutrition and preventing aspiration. Patients receive prescribed diets with food of a consistency that can be safely swallowed, ranging from soft to pureed. Raising the heads of beds can also deter reflux. Lifestyle changes, antacids, proton pump inhibitors (PPIs), and other medications are used to manage the disease (Kahrilas, 2020).

Stomach

Peptic Ulcers

Peptic ulcers may occur anywhere in the GI tract (Halter et al., 2017). Two of the most common types are gastric ulcers that affect the stomach and duodenal ulcers that involve the first section of the small intestine (Michel et al., 2017; Vakil, 2020a).

An ulcer is a wearing away of the inner lining of the stomach wall due to a chronic buildup of excessive acid, excessive stress, inactivity, prolonged bed rest, severe trauma, and irritating drugs. Ulcer symptoms can include no symptoms, a sharp burning abdominal pain 2 to 5 hours after eating ("classic pain"), nausea, and weight loss. Blood in vomitus or stools is considered a major complication due to hemorrhage or perforation (Vakil, 2020a; Walter & Chang, 2020).

Common causes of peptic ulcers include a *Helicobacter pylori* infection or prolonged NSAID use (Vakil, 2020a). Standard treatment includes eradicating the *H. pylori* infection, discontinuing any NSAID drug use, and PPI therapy (Vakil, 2020b).

Dyspepsia

Dyspepsia is chronic or recurrent pain in the upper abdomen thought to arise from the upper GI tract. The term refers to what many would call a stomachache and is common in a nursing facility. Symptoms include postprandial (after meal) fullness, nausea, bloating, early satiety, epigastric pain or burning, or reflux symptoms (Vakil, 2020a; Walter & Chang, 2020).

Intestines

Constipation

Constipation is an irregularity or a lack of elimination of waste materials from the body. Symptoms may include straining at stool, lumpy or hard stools, sensations of incomplete evacuation, the use of digital evacuation, a sense of bowel blockage, or decreased stool frequency to less than three bowel movements per week (Rao, 2020). Constipation may initially present as fewer stools passed, progressing to a complete lack of stool or bowel movements. When the person cannot pass stool for an extended time, an impaction (blockage) has probably occurred. Impaction is an accumulation of hardened waste in a large intestine area due to prolonged fluid reabsorption by the body.

The treatment of constipation can include laxative medications, which vary in strength, including bulk laxatives, osmotic laxatives, stimulant laxatives, suppositories, and enemas. However, the use of laxatives can cause dependence upon them over time (Rao, 2020). Increased activity and exercise are among the best treatments.

An evaluation of constipation interventions should include over-the-counter, prescription medications, daily fluid and fiber intake, and exercise (Rao, 2020; Walter & Chang, 2020). The review result may indicate a need to change the care plan.

Hemorrhoids

Hemorrhoids are a painful condition that can affect eliminating waste materials from the body. A hemorrhoid is an enlarged vein in the rectum (internal), around the anus (external), or both (Bleday & Breen, 2020). The external type is usually more painful, but both types are often associated with bleeding, a sense of fullness, irritation, or itching (Bleday & Breen, 2020). Hemorrhoids may either be the cause or the result of chronic constipation (Walter & Chang, 2020).

Fecal Incontinence

Incontinence is the inability to control the timing of elimination (Halter et al., 2017). Some of the causes of this dysfunction may be neurological (due to disease or trauma to the brain and spinal cord), anal surgery, chronic diarrhea, or mental disturbance (Kane et al., 2018; Robson & Lembo, 2020). Fecal incontinence often leads to bacteriuria.

Bacteriuria

Bacteriuria (urinary tract infection [UTI]) is often associated with fecal incontinence due to the increased number of bacteria present in the perineal area. UTIs are commonly associated with women (due to a shorter urethra) and the use of catheters. Catheter-associated UTIs (CAUTIs) can be decreased by appropriately cleaning with antiseptics in the periurethral area when a catheter is in place (Meddings et al., 2017).

5.3.5 NUTRITION

Section Concepts

- *Food as an important aspect of the nursing facility resident's daily life*
- *How nutritional status directly affects the well-being of the facility population*
- *Minerals needed by the body*
- *Body fluids and their functions*
- *The types of prescribed diets*
- *Aspects of anemia and diabetes: Two metabolic diseases often present in the facility population*

Consider as the Administrator . . .

- *How can residents' rights and the availability of snack foods to residents with diabetic control needs be reconciled?*

> **NAB DOMAIN 1A: QUALITY OF CARE; 1A4: NUTRITION AND HYDRATION (E.G., SPECIALIZED DIETS); 1B: QUALITY OF LIFE; 1B15: FOODSERVICE (E.G., CHOICE AND MENU PLANNING, DIETARY MANAGEMENT, FOOD STORAGE AND HANDLING, DINING SERVICES)**

> **NAB DOMAIN 1A3: DISEASE MANAGEMENT (E.G., ACUTE VS. CHRONIC CONDITIONS)**

Food provides the body with the nutrients necessary for cell functions. Adequate nutrition can help maintain fitness, independence, and disease prevention.

The digestive process was previously described as the breakdown of food into absorbable nutrients. The next phase is the metabolic process, during which absorbed nutrients are converted to energy and essential elements for various body functions. Consuming food is therefore essential to body functions. Many nursing facility residents are dependent on staff for eating. This "eating dependence" is a complex problem due to differences in resident abilities and eating preferences (Palese et al., 2018).

Food contains both calories and nutrients that must be balanced in resident intake. Calories are the units of measurement for determining the amount of energy contained in foods or used by the body. Foods naturally contain essential nutrients that must be consumed to maintain normal cellular functions.

Protein is broken down into amino acids during digestion. Amino acids are necessary for cell production, tissue repair, nutrient transport, and production of hormones and enzymes.

Carbohydrates from starches and sugars are quickly broken down into readily available fuel for the body. The brain is sensitive to decreased levels of carbohydrates in the body and may be permanently damaged from reduced levels over time (Halter et al., 2017).

Fats are stored in the body for energy reserves during starvation. Fat forms a protective padding around the major organs, prevents heat loss, and facilitates the absorption of vitamins A, D, E, and K (Michel et al., 2017).

Minerals essential to the body include the following:

- *Calcium.* Used to build and strengthen bones and teeth, contract muscles, and clot blood.
- *Iron.* Red blood cell (RBC) formation and carries oxygen in the blood.
- *Sodium.* Part of buffering mechanisms, dissolves substances in the bloodstream, essential for nerve conduction, adjusts fluid in the body.
- *Potassium.* Required for nerve conduction and muscle contraction, essential to blood buffering and cardiac contraction.
- *Vitamins.* Act to convert nutrients into energy and control certain body functions.

FLUIDS

Up to 60% of the body's volume is water. The body is bathed in fluids that help eliminate waste and facilitate chemical reactions. Fluids help maintain the body's integrity by protecting the skin and distributing nutrients to promote healing.

Body fluids include the following:

- *Plasma.* Carries RBCs, hormones, and essential nutrients throughout the body.
- *Cerebrospinal fluid.* Protects the brain and spinal cord and transports nutrients and gases.
- *Lymphatic fluid.* Transports fats, houses immune cells, and carries fluids from the tissues.

In all phases of life, adequate nutrition sustains the building-up processes of the body and impedes the wearing-out processes. However, older adult residents suffering from multiple chronic diseases may need even more nutrients than healthy adults.

POSSIBLE EFFECTS OF AGING

Older adults are susceptible to involuntary weight loss, which can be driven by inadequate dietary intake, appetite loss, muscle atrophy, social and medical factors, psychiatric concerns, inflammatory effects of diseases, and physiological changes of aging (Ritchie & Yukawa, 2021). They have an increased demand for nutrients to resist the effects of diseases. Thus, the appropriate diet for the resident is complex and often changing based on their needs.

Osteoporosis, a decrease of bone mass causing skeletal fragility, is a concern among numerous older persons (Rosen, 2021). A lack of dietary calcium and vitamin D may contribute to osteoporosis, making some nursing facility residents especially susceptible to bone breakage in falls or other accidents (Rosen, 2021; Saxon et al., 2021; Walter & Chang, 2020).

Dehydration may occur more easily among older persons with reduced fluid intake due to a lessened thirst perception. Dehydration can occur quickly when an older adult has a fever without presenting symptoms or signs (Michel et al., 2017). Less fat under the skin permits body fluids to evaporate more readily. Rapid weight loss can be a clinical indicator of dehydration. Dehydration can occur due to physiological issues in the GI tract (Saxon et al., 2021).

Aging may affect other structures that aid digestion. The loss of teeth can result in changes in the types of foods eaten. Denture refitting can be needed due to weight loss or changes in the dentition.

A loss in the overall number of cells and muscle mass may decrease body weight. In this situation, the body may no longer need as many calories to provide sufficient energy.

As with any person, consuming more calories than needed while remaining relatively inactive can lead to obesity. Obesity from increased fat storage in the tissues as reserve energy is a frequent form of malnutrition in older adults.

PRESCRIBED DIETS

Although most nursing facility residents will eat typical diets, some residents will have unique nutritional needs.

Physicians may prescribe special therapeutic diets for those with chronic disease or affected by institutionalization. There are many different types of diets available. The following are among the most common therapeutic diets seen in a nursing facility:

- *Soft diet.* For residents who need a low fiber, softer texture, and mild flavor.
- *Mechanical soft diet.* Same content as a soft diet, but the texture is either chopped, pureed, or ground to make foods easier to ingest. (*Note*: Dietary staff can use molds to shape the pureed food close to its regular appearance.)
- *Strict full-liquid diet.* Foods that are liquid at body temperature but can include ice cream and hot soup.
- *High-fiber diet.* To provide bulk, similar to a regular diet, but with foods that add bulk with fiber through fruits, vegetables, whole grain bread and cereals, nuts, and bran.
- *High-calorie, high-protein diet.* May include shakes, meats, and similar foods to provide additional protein.

Physicians may prescribe enteral feeding through nasogastric (NG) tubes or gastrostomy tubes (G-tubes) for residents who cannot consume food orally (Michel et al., 2017).

NG tubes are inserted through the nose and enter the stomach. G-tubes are surgically inserted directly into the stomach.

G-tubes may be preferred to NG tubes for long-term tube feeding for comfort and less chance for aspiration (fluid inhaled into the lungs). Nutrition in the lungs often leads to aspiration pneumonia if the NG tube is placed incorrectly. Enteral feeding is provided via bottled nutritional "formula" through the feeding tube by an electronic pump or gravity and a syringe.

It can be challenging for a nursing facility setting to meet both the nutritional needs and residents' preferences. Budgetary considerations usually limit dietary choices to the most wholesome and least expensive foods available. It is possible to identify and meet resident food preferences. Recording residents' food likes and dislikes in the EHR system, and meal cards available on the tray line during food placement facilitate substituting similarly nutritious foods according to preferences. The dining experience is also essential. Careful attention to the dining room's ambiance promotes healthy intake. Many facilities meet this need through a fine-dining system or allowing the resident their choice of meals.

Every expectation applied to dining out should be applied to the facility dining experience. The administrator should periodically request to receive a standard tray in the dining room unannounced to ensure a quality dining experience.

ANEMIA AND DIABETES: DISEASES AFFECTING METABOLISM

Two of the most common diseases that disrupt the metabolism of important nutrients are anemia and diabetes.

Anemia

Anemia is a condition of low RBCs as measured by hemoglobin, hematocrit, or RBC count (Means & Brodsky, 2021).

RBC deficiency decreases the amount of oxygen circulating throughout the body (Kane et al., 2018). The RBCs contain hemoglobin, an iron-rich protein that carries oxygen to the tissues and carbon dioxide waste to the lungs (OpenStax College, 2021).

Various types of anemia are found in the nursing facility. Treatment is based on the cause of the anemia and must be specialized to each resident. Anemia is a significant decrease in the number of RBCs produced. Having multiple chronic diseases can lead to anemia. Symptoms of anemia are similar to heart disease because they also result in oxygenation problems. When anemia is combined with other diseases, such as peripheral vascular disease (PVD) or CAD, it can be severe and painful for the resident. Resident symptoms include shortness of breath, fatigue, weakness, cold hands or feet, and other various symptoms that are common among other disorders (National Heart, Lung, and Blood Institute, 2021d).

Diabetes

Diabetes occurs when there is an error in glucose (sugar) metabolism. Glucose metabolism requires proper levels and cellular response to the hormone insulin. Insulin is produced by the pancreas, a ductless gland associated with the digestive system (National Institute of Diabetes and Digestive and Kidney Diseases, 2016). Insulin encourages glucose movement from the blood into the cell for metabolism. The proper use of insulin requires the pancreas to produce sufficient amounts of insulin and for the cells to react to circulating insulin appropriately.

Type 1 diabetes (insulin-dependent diabetes mellitus) occurs when the body does not make enough insulin (National Institute of Diabetes and Digestive and Kidney Diseases, 2016). The most common cause is the body's immune system attacking the pancreas and destroying it over time, preventing insulin production. Typically, type 1 diabetes is diagnosed in children and young adults. However, since the advent of COVID-19, there has been an increase in spontaneous type 1 diabetes in adults (DiMeglio, 2021).

Type 2 diabetes (non-insulin-dependent diabetes mellitus) occurs when the body is still making insulin, but either in insufficient quantity or the body cannot use it correctly (National Institute of Diabetes and Digestive and Kidney Diseases, 2016). Type 2 diabetes is the most common type of diabetes, which can occur at any age but usually occurs in adults of middle to older age.

Both types of diabetes result in large amounts of sugar continually circulating in the bloodstream, a condition known as hyperglycemia (high blood sugar). Chronic hyperglycemia can damage many tissues, including peripheral limbs, the heart, kidneys, and eyes. The damage can eventually lead to amputations, heart disease, kidney failure requiring dialysis, and blindness (Walter & Chang, 2020).

5.3.6 EXTERNAL AND INTERNAL DEFENSE MECHANISMS

Section Concepts

- *The body has external defense mechanisms (the skin) and internal defense mechanisms (chemical defenses)*
- *How infections present a unique challenge to the nursing facility*
- *Types of infections: nosocomial, community-acquired*
- *How the facility responds to the omnipresence of infections: the infection control program*
- *Role of the infection control practitioner (ICP): The importance of handwashing*
- *Skin diseases: Herpes zoster, decubitus ulcers*
- *Pressure injury formation and treatment*

Consider as the Administrator . . .

- *Compliance with handwashing requirements remains very low, even in the times of COVID-19. What can be done about this?*

NAB DOMAIN 1A: QUALITY OF CARE; 1B: QUALITY OF LIFE; 1B1: PSYCHOSOCIAL NEEDS (E.G., SOCIAL, SPIRITUAL, COMMUNITY, CULTURAL)

NAB DOMAIN 1A3: DISEASE MANAGEMENT (E.G., ACUTE VS. CHRONIC CONDITIONS)

The body uses two defense mechanism types, barrier and chemical, to protect it from harmful environmental disruptions.

THE BARRIER SYSTEM OF DEFENSE

Barriers prevent harmful bacteria, viruses, and other pathogens from entering the body. Skin is the largest barrier protecting the body from harmful organisms, sealing in essential body fluids and regulating body temperature. The respiratory, intestinal, and urinary tracts are lined with mucous membrane barriers to protect the body from foreign materials entering the systems.

The mucous membranes of the respiratory tract also have thousands of cilia (tiny hairlike elements) to help propel inhaled foreign materials back toward the mouth. Coughing expels these particles from the body and back into the environment.

Two additional barrier-like protections are the acid of gastric juices, which protects the digestive system, and urine's acidic pH, which guards the urinary tract.

THE CHEMICAL DEFENSE SYSTEM

The immune system is often referred to as the second line of defense because it protects the body's internal structures from pathogens that have made it past the barrier system. Whenever foreign material or an antigen enters the body, the components of the immune system recognize this and mobilize for an attack response. Most often, the foreign material is a small bacterial or viral pathogen.

Antibodies and the cell-mediated response produce chemicals and proteins that fight these pathogens. Antibodies are developed through exposure to pathogens by fighting a disease or via vaccinations (active immunity) or introduced artificially through transfusion (passive immunity; Saxon et al., 2022).

INFECTIONS

NAB DOMAIN 3A7: INFECTION CONTROL AND SANITATION (E.G., LINENS, KITCHEN, HAND WASHING, HEALTHCARE-ACQUIRED INFECTIONS, HAZARDOUS MATERIALS)

When bacteria or viruses successfully defeat the body's defense mechanisms in large numbers, they create a disruption known as an infection (Michel et al., 2017; Saxon et al., 2022). The shared community environment of nursing facilities creates a higher risk for infections. Shared space allows for easy transmission among residents with additional concern for staff spreading infections. Infection control has entered the spotlight with COVID-19 and how one facility in Kirkland, Washington, was an epicenter of the infection in the United States.

Additional transmission concerns arise from the increased susceptibility of nursing facility residents to infection due to the following:

- Age-related changes in the body's immune systems
- Changes in the effectiveness of the skin as a barrier
- The presence of multiple chronic diseases (weakening the defenses)
- Use of multiple medications with side effects that may compromise the body
- Increased incidence of immobility and incontinence
- Frequent use of invasive devices such as indwelling urinary catheters
- Antibiotic use (Halter et al., 2017; Kane et al., 2018)

New infectious processes are being identified in nursing facilities. Most state regulatory bodies have some reporting expected for specific infections or outbreaks within the facility. More recently documented infections include the following:

- COVID-19
- Legionnaires' disease
- Methicillin-resistant *Staphylococcus aureus* (MRSA)
- Vancomycin resistant enterococci (VRE)
- Carbapenem-resistant *Klebsiella pneumoniae*
- Hepatitis B
- Noroviruses
- *Mycoplasma pneumoniae*
- Influenza A (H1N1)
- Rotavirus (CDC, 2020a)

HEALTHCARE-ASSOCIATED INFECTIONS

NAB DOMAIN 3A7: INFECTION CONTROL AND SANITATION (E.G., LINENS, KITCHEN, HAND WASHING, HEALTHCARE-ACQUIRED INFECTIONS, HAZARDOUS MATERIALS)

Infections acquired while in a healthcare facility are called healthcare-associated infections (HAIs), healthcare acquired infections, or nosocomial infections. Nursing facility residents are considered at risk of developing these infections because of frequent group interaction and shared care providers and environments (Singh, 2016).

Any HAI is a sentinel event because they are assumed to be preventable. The four categories of HAIs that occur in all healthcare institutions, including nursing facilities, are:

- Central-line associated bloodstream infections (CLABSI)
- CAUTIs
- Surgical site infections (SSI)
- Ventilator-associated pneumonia (VAP; CDC, 2021e; National Healthcare Safety Network, 2021)

CLABSIs are associated with any "permanent central line," including tunneled catheters, tunneled dialysis catheters, peripherally inserted central catheter (PICC) lines, and ports, all of which are seen in the nursing facility.

CAUTIs can occur in patients with long-term indwelling catheters, which should be cleansed appropriately every 12 hours or as needed and are usually changed monthly. This type of catheter may be placed for urine diversion in an incontinent resident with a sacral wound to avoid urine contamination or secondary to a bladder obstruction or surgery. Some urinary catheters (suprapubic) are surgically placed to exit the bladder above the pubic bone rather than through a urethral opening.

Special Difficulties in Identifying Infections

Infections in older adults may be more challenging to diagnose because the symptoms may present differently than expected or similar to other chronic diseases. Additionally, older adult residents may be reluctant to report symptoms.

Most infections are not considered chronic diseases because they respond to treatment, and their damage to the body can often be reversed. Some of the possible effects of aging on the immune system are discussed subsequently.

Possible Effects of Aging

The skin contains fibers that change as a person ages. These changes may make the skin and other connective tissue drier and less resilient. Skin, nail, and hair cells, which are among the fastest to grow during younger years, often do not replace themselves as quickly with age. Together, these changes help explain why many older adults have some degree of tough, dry, wrinkled skin. These changes diminish the skin's barrier function as a person ages, thus increasing the chances for an HAI to occur.

The most remarkable alteration in the internal immune system is the thymus gland's involution (decrease in size). This change is suspected to influence the function of the immune system, but it is still too early to determine the full range of implications this may have for the health of older adults. Some impairment of the immune response makes older individuals more susceptible to infection.

DISEASE PROCESSES

NAB DOMAIN 1A3: DISEASE MANAGEMENT (E.G., ACUTE VS. CHRONIC CONDITIONS); 2B5: RISK MANAGEMENT PROCESS AND PROGRAMS; 2B6: QUALITY IMPROVEMENT PROCESSES (E.G., ROOT CAUSE ANALYSIS, PDCA/PDSA); 3A7: INFECTION CONTROL AND SANITATION (E.G., LINENS, KITCHEN, HAND WASHING, HEALTHCARE-ACQUIRED INFECTIONS, HAZARDOUS MATERIALS)

Facility Responses to the Presence of Infections: Infection Prevention and Control

The federal requirements for participation in the Medicare program require nursing facilities to establish monitoring programs for infection control performance. Occupational Safety and Health Administration (OSHA) has issued the Bloodborne Pathogens Standard (29 CFR 1910.1030) in addition to the 2000

Needlestick Safety and Prevention Act to provide safeguards to keep residents and staff healthy. Federal regulations surrounding infection control are covered under 483.80 Infection Control (F880–F886). F880 speaks specifically to Infection Prevention and Control (IPC). The CDC has also issued guidance and tools for infection control assessment and response (ICAR), which the facility can use to assess their own IPC practices and guide quality improvement efforts. All tools have recently been updated to include COVID-19 protocols and prevention.

Facility workers are expected to follow standard precautions (universal precautions), which are fundamental steps to prevent the spread of germs. Standard precautions include hand hygiene, use of appropriate PPE (gloves, masks, gowns, face shields, eye protection), use of safety-engineered needles, and guidance on working after being sick with a cold, cough, or flu (Agency for Healthcare Research and Quality, 2017).

Depending on the nature of the infection, various isolation precautions must be taken to protect other residents, staff, and visitors from acquiring the infection. The administrator must ensure that residents with certain communicable diseases are reported to the state health department. In cooperation with the U.S. Public Health Service, each state specifies which diseases must be reported to the state health department.

Infections complicate the older adult residents' disease status and may increase their chance of death (mortality). Besides this risk, infections may increase the likelihood of a resident being transferred to a hospital for more intensive care than the facility provides. Finding and treating infections quickly are paramount to positive patient outcomes, including transfer to the hospital (Mileski et al., 2020).

Risk Control—Infection Control: The Infection Control Practitioner

The risk of an epidemic is always present in the nursing facility. An epidemic is a cluster of infections involving multiple individuals. Nursing facility epidemics include COVID-19, influenza, staphylococcal skin infections, antibiotic-resistant bacteria, infectious diarrhea, scabies, TB, and others. As part of their IPC, facilities often have a dedicated infection control practitioner (ICP) monitoring trends within the facility. The ICP is often a specially trained nurse hired purely for IPC or who splits time with other facility responsibilities.

HANDWASHING

Neglect of proper handwashing remains a significant factor in spreading infections in healthcare settings. Healthcare providers clean their hands less than half the times they should, and about one in 31 of all hospital patients have at least one HAI (CDC, 2019). Keeping current with best practices for expectations of handwashing and the use of alcohol-based hand sanitizers is necessary. Information specific to hand hygiene is available at many sites on the internet. The CDC maintains a site worth noting for facility standards: https://www.cdc.gov/handhygiene/providers/index.html

SKIN DISEASE

Herpes Zoster (Shingles)

One disease that primarily affects older individuals is herpes zoster, more commonly called shingles (Michel et al., 2017). This infection is caused by a reactivation of the varicella zoster virus (VZV) that became dormant in the ganglia of the spinal cord during the initial infection phase of chickenpox (Albrecht & Levin, 2021). Skin shows lesions associated with innervation by the affected nerve root. Residents who suffer from chronic diseases, such as cancer or other immunocompromising disorders, are at greater risk of developing this infection (Albrecht & Levin, 2021).

Signs and symptoms include itching, usually preceding a rash; reddened areas of the skin; vesicles (fluid-filled pimples) erupting over reddened areas; and pain described as burning and stabbing. This infection is excruciating. It is also very contagious, requiring the actively infected resident to be isolated from all other residents in the facility.

At present, there is no cure for this infection or its outbreak, so treatment consists of symptom control. Antivirals, steroids, and analgesics are often used to shorten the length of the infection and relieve some of the inflammation pain (Albrecht, 2020). Antibiotics are sometimes prescribed to prevent secondary infections (Albrecht, 2020; Halter et al., 2017).

Pressure Injuries

Pressure injuries are known by many names, including pressure ulcers, pressure-induced injuries, bedsores, decubitus ulcers, and stasis ulcers, which all refer to tissue breakdown (Kane et al., 2018). Pressure-induced skin injuries are common among hospitalized patients and long-term care residents (Berlowitz, 2020a).

Tissue breakdown often occurs over a bony prominence (buttocks, elbow, heel, hip, shoulder) secondary to unrelieved pressure over that area. With these injuries, tissues do not receive adequate oxygen, so they break down and begin to die. The process is similar to the heart muscle in a myocardial infarction or the brain during a stroke.

Risk factors for developing these wounds are chronic immobility from stroke or other incapacitating illnesses, poor nutritional status, constant pain, incontinence, or dementia (Walter & Chang, 2020). Wounds may enlarge to form cavities of dead tissue prone to the development of infection. The larger and deeper the wound, the more difficult it is to heal.

Pressure Injury Formation

The formation of a pressure injury usually occurs from the body's weight exerting pressure on internal soft tissues, compressing them between skeletal bone and another hard surface or causing shear when only part of the weight is moved, and skin drags behind the movement (Michel et al., 2017). Because immobile residents cannot independently change position frequently, there is the danger of continuous pressure on one area of the body. The main forces causing pressure injuries are direct pressure, friction, or shearing, with continued moisture worsening any of these (Grada & Phillips, 2021).

Many residents spend much of their time lying on their back, also known as the decubitus position (*decubitus* means "lying down," the source of older names for these wounds). The areas most likely to develop sores from this position are the buttocks, hips, heels, shoulders, tips and backs of ears, and elbows. Similarly, residents who spend long periods sitting up in a chair without moving have an increased risk to low back, coccyx, buttocks, posterior thigh, and elbows. Proper pressure redistribution, support surface use, and repositioning are necessary for residents at risk for pressure injury (Berlowitz, 2020b).

Signs and symptoms of decubitus ulcers include the following:

- Nonblanchable erythema (often over a bony prominence)
- Tingling, pale skin color, or other signs that there is a loss of circulation to an area
- Reddened area of skin over a bony prominence
- Temperature changes over affected areas
- A sore that will not heal
- Edema (swelling) of the lower legs and shiny skin

Note that these signs often occur after the tissue has already been injured (Grada & Phillips, 2021; Michel et al., 2017).

Pressure injuries are classified as Grades I, III, IV, unstageable, or deep tissue pressure injury:

- Stage 1 Pressure Injury—nonblanchable erythema of intact skin
- Stage 2 Pressure Injury—partial thickness skin loss with exposed dermis
- Stage 3 Pressure Injury—full-thickness skin loss
- Stage 4 Pressure Injury—full-thickness skin and tissue loss
- Unstageable Pressure Injury—obscured full-thickness skin and tissue loss
- Deep Tissue Pressure Injury—persistent nonblanchable deep red, maroon, or purple discoloration (Berlowitz, 2020a; National Pressure Injury Advisory Panel, n.d.)

The following are some of the principal preventions and treatments the facility may use:

- Providing special equipment, such as alternating pressure surfaces
- Keeping the resident clean and dry
- Eliminating the source of pressure/redistributing pressure
- Working to improve the resident's circulation
- Ensuring frequent position change (at least every 2 hours) for those who are unable or unlikely to do so themselves
- Padding feet, elbows, and other areas at high risk of tissue breakdown
- Frequently assessing the integrity of a resident's skin
- Changing the diet to include foods higher in protein, vitamin C, and calorie content to promote healing
- Further optimization of nutrition for the resident
- Preventing infection by applying dressings and dispensing antibiotic medications as prescribed

- Using elastic stockings or Ace wrap bandages, which are often prescribed for the person with peripheral vascular insufficiency (poor blood circulation in the arms and legs)
- Appropriate use of wound dressings
- Wound debridement, when necessary
- Pain control (Berlowitz, 2020a)

CASE STUDY (AN ACTUAL CASE)

Combative

Mr. Ray is an 84-year-old male admitted to The Laurels from the hospital with a diagnosis of resolved small bowel obstruction, probable Alzheimer's disease, and "failure to thrive." Mr. Ray lived at home with his wife until 2 months before admission. Mr. Ray was admitted to the hospital due to a fractured hip. His wife could not meet his care needs at home, so he remained in the hospital pending placement.

During his hospital admission, he became increasingly agitated and combative. He refused to eat and became progressively weaker until prescribed NG tube placement for nourishment.

Two months later, Mr. Ray was admitted to The Laurels for long-term care. At admission, he ambulated only with assistance, mumbled constantly, and became combative whenever approached hurriedly. Due to his combativeness, the staff placed him in a wheelchair daily and left him alone until bedtime.

The nursing assistant noticed redness in his sacral area during bathing one morning. The next day she noticed the redness was still present and notified the charge nurse, who decided to monitor the redness for changes. Two days later, Mr. Ray had a 1 cm × 1 cm × 0 depth superficial area of breakdown, inflamed, with clear drainage. At this time (4 days from initial documentation), the charge nurse placed a call to Mr. Ray's doctor, leaving a message with his secretary. The physician never returned the call. Three days later, a new charge nurse noted a 2 cm × 1 cm × 0 depth superficial area of breakdown, inflamed with yellow drainage and a foul odor about which nearby residents complained.

- *How should your staff address combative behaviors?*
- *What measures should be in place to not only identify but also prevent pressure injuries?*

Acute Skin Failure and Kennedy Terminal Ulcers

Acute skin failure (ASF) and Kennedy terminal ulcers are skin considerations often seen when a resident is fragile after a significant illness or near death. Both syndromes are indicated when intact skin develops a pressure injury within a day. Neither lesion is caused by the same forces as a traditional pressure injury.

ASF occurs as the skin and underlying tissue become necrotic due to blood hypoperfusion, often in conjunction with dysfunction or failure of other organ systems (Langemo & Brown, 2006; Mileski et al., 2021). ASF is often difficult to discern from a pressure injury; however, proper delineation is imperative. ASF is not a preventable situation, but pressure injuries are. This difference can prevent regulatory and liability concerns for the facility.

Kennedy terminal ulcers are similar to ASF; however, they correlate to within 2 weeks of death (Kennedy, 1989). This type of injury appears at the end of life, usually located in the area of the sacrum or coccyx, in the shape of a pear, butterfly, or horseshoe, with rapid progression to a total thickness injury (Stage 4) and is often an indicator of imminent death (Kennedy, 1989; Roca-Biosca et al., 2021).

Both ASF and Kennedy terminal ulcers are unavoidable skin conditions. Proper documentation and identification are of utmost importance.

5.3.7 MUSCULOSKELETAL SYSTEM

Section Concepts

- *The components of the musculoskeletal system*
- *Possible effects of aging on this system*
- *Disease processes associated with the musculoskeletal system*
  - *Osteoporosis*
  - *Arthritis*
  - *Osteoarthritis*
  - *Rheumatoid arthritis*
- *The problem of falls within nursing facilities*
- *Fractures, amputations, and contractures in the facility*
- *Rehabilitation services available*

Consider as the Administrator . . .

- *Falls are a major problem in every facility. Can falls be prevented? Do residents "have the right to fall"?*

NAB DOMAIN 1A: QUALITY OF CARE; 1B: QUALITY OF LIFE; 1B1: PSYCHOSOCIAL NEEDS (E.G., SOCIAL, SPIRITUAL, COMMUNITY, CULTURAL)

NAB DOMAIN 1A3: DISEASE MANAGEMENT (E.G., ACUTE VS. CHRONIC CONDITIONS)

The muscles and skeleton work together, providing several functions: a supporting framework for all the other body structures, mobility (closely related to the nursing facility resident's degree of independence and autonomy), and protection of the internal organs of the body (OpenStax College, 2021).

THE SKELETON AND MUSCLES

The skeleton is composed of bones that meet in joints to form the body's supporting framework and to protect soft tissues and organs. Muscles are attached to the skeleton. This combination dictates an individual's posture, directly affecting personal appearance.

SYNOVIAL JOINTS

Synovial joints are a common type of joint where the ends of two bones meet. These joints have bones covered by cartilage and surrounded by a capsule that contains synovial fluid lubrication, enhancing movement. Ligaments stabilize the joint enabling weight-bearing movement.

MOVEMENT

Movement occurs when muscles receive a nerve impulse from the brain directing them to contract. Because the muscles are attached to bones across joints, when muscles move, the attached bones move. When the muscle contracts or relaxes, this causes the joint to move. Thus, mobility requires coordination between the nervous and musculoskeletal systems. Opposing muscles surrounding each joint allow for smooth and controlled movement.

POSSIBLE EFFECTS OF AGING

Bones contain an inner compartment housing bone marrow that produces red and white blood cells. The outer shell of bone is a network of fibrous tissue containing mineral salts, primarily calcium and phosphorus, that harden and strengthen the bone.

The current consensus is that the total amount of bone in the body is decreased during the aging process, but the cause of loss is debated in the research literature (Michel et al., 2017; Yu, 2021). Bone mass peaks around age 35, then there is a slow degradation of bone mass and density over time (osteopenia; Saxon et al., 2022). This process is a standard expectation of aging but can be affected by lifestyle factors such as smoking, exercise, and alcohol use. Genetics and hormonal levels also factor into bone loss with aging (Saxon et al., 2022).

Joints are also affected by aging. Cartilage can break down or become thinner over time, decreasing the ability to cushion normal movement. Dehydration from the aging body's decreased ability to absorb water can decrease the synovial fluid production or presence in the joint (Saxon et al., 2022).

Bone Loss Later in Life

Women are at a high risk of experiencing some degree of bone loss following menopause due to hormonal changes (Michel et al., 2017; Saxon et al., 2022). Lifestyle changes such as increased intake of vitamin D and calcium, appropriate diet, and exercise can help prevent the changes associated with the already higher risk for women (Rosen & Drezner, 2021).

DISEASE PROCESSES

Age-related changes in the musculoskeletal system occur as a manifestation of the aging process or distinct disease processes. Following is a discussion of some common disruptions of musculoskeletal functioning experienced in the nursing facility population.

Osteoporosis

Osteoporosis is characterized by low bone mass with microarchitectural disruptions in the bone, causing skeletal fragility and increased fracture risk (Yu, 2021). The cause of osteoporosis remains unclear, but the mechanism of bone loss appears related to increased reabsorption of bone tissue by the body. Osteoporosis is associated with prolonged use of some medications, immobility, or underlying disease.

Bone loss can cause shortened stature and a slumped posture due to the high likelihood of compression of the vertebrae (bones in the spine) and the separating cartilage discs (Halter et al., 2017). Vertebral compression fractures create a stooped appearance and a humped back (Dowager's hump) due to the resultant wedge shape of the vertebrae's front (Rosen & Walega, 2020).

The treatment of osteoporosis can include managing pain, treating complications such as fractures, rehabilitation to correct physical inactivity, increasing protein and vitamin intake, and treating underlying conditions. Medications often used are calcium and vitamin D supplements, hormone replacement therapy, oral bisphosphonates, and other bone antiresorptive agents (Rosen & Drezner, 2021).

Arthritis

There are many types of arthritis, some specific to certain body areas. There are five types of arthritis commonly seen in the nursing facility: osteoarthritis (OA), rheumatoid arthritis (RA), psoriatic arthritis, gout, and lupus. OA and RA are the most common and are discussed in the following sections.

Osteoarthritis

Hallmarks of OA include joint pain and functional impairment, which may occur on one side of the body or a single joint (Deveza, 2021). OA is the most common form of arthritis and is a degenerative joint disease from the cartilage at the ends of the bones degrading over time. It is most commonly seen in the hips, knees, hands, neck, and lower back but can occur in any movable joint.

Symptoms of OA include the following:

- Pain in the affected joint
- Joint stiffness
- Swelling around the joint
- Tenderness around the joint
- Loss of the joint's free movement
- Joint deformity
- A loose or unstable feeling in the joint (Doherty & Abhishek, 20212; National Institute of Arthritis and Musculoskeletal and Skin Diseases, 2019)

Treatment consists of relieving symptoms. Exercise, weight loss, and assistive devices (walking aids and braces) are the first line of treatment (Deveza, 2021).

Further treatment includes pharmacological agents, including NSAIDs, duloxetine, topical capsaicin, and intraarticular hyaluronic acid (Deveza, 2021). Continual degeneration of the joints may require total joint replacement surgery, commonly seen in knees and hips.

Rheumatoid Arthritis

RA is a chronic autoimmune disorder primarily involving the body's synovial joints (Venables & England, 2021). Intriguingly, the disease has a symmetrical presentation, affecting the same joints on both sides of the body. The inflammation of the disease often leads to joint destruction due to erosion of cartilage and bone, leading to joint deformities (Venables & England, 2021).

"Typical" presentation of RA usually includes pain, stiffness, and swelling of many joints, most often fingers and thumb joints. Later presentation of the disease can include wrists, toes, and other synovial joints of the upper and lower limbs (Venables & England, 2021).

Signs and symptoms include the following:

- Symmetric inflammation of joints
- Frequent pain flare-ups and remissions
- Joint stiffness and swelling, especially in the hands
- Pain often occurs in the morning and decreases with exercise
- Weight loss
- Fever
- Fatigue
- Weakness (CDC, 2020b; Venables & England, 2021)

The treatment of RA aims to achieve decreased disease activity or remission. Management strategies include the following:

- A balance of rest and exercise
- Physical and occupational therapy
- Nutritional and dietary counseling
- Pharmacological therapies: nonbiological disease-modifying antirheumatic drugs (DMARDs) and biologic DMARDs
- Anti-inflammatory therapies: NSAIDs and glucocorticoids

FALLS

NAB DOMAIN 1B4: CARE RECIPIENT SAFETY (E.G., FALL PREVENTION, ELOPEMENT PREVENTION, ADVERSE EVENTS)

Falls are a significant occurrence in nursing facilities and a major health concern for residents. Falls can lead to an overall functional decline in the resident, unfortunate hospital stays, and increased liability concerns for the facility (Berry & Kiel, 2020). Older adults who fall and require hospitalization have a 50% greater chance of dying within 1 year (Saxon et al., 2022). Appropriate interventions and prevention strategies are a necessity in addressing falls.

Principles of Fall Prevention

Personalized Fall Prevention Program

The most effective fall intervention strategy is a personalized fall risk reduction program for each resident based on the comprehensive assessment of each resident.

Attention to Creating a Safe Physical Environment

The physical environment of the nursing facility must carefully implement the standards of the Americans with Disabilities Act, which is designed to provide a safe physical environment that minimizes falls. Personalized fall risk management plans should account for requiring ambulation assistance or the need for an assistive device when moving about the room or the facility. Considerations in the individual comprehensive assessment can be muscle strength, gait, and balance problems. An effective exercise program is a preventive effort to reduce risk.

Attention to Changes in the Resident's Vision

Regular vision examinations and vision correction are important for reducing resident fall risk.

Attention to Blood Pressure and Other Fall Risk Factors

Falling and balance issues may be due to chronic illness or decreased blood pressure upon standing (orthostatic hypotension; Michel et al., 2017; Walter & Chang, 2020). Another cause of occasional low blood pressure is postprandial hypotension, reduced blood pressure after eating (Ferrini & Ferrini, 2012; Michel et al., 2017). It appears that the blood supply is routed to the digestive system, causing lower blood pressure when the resident stands up from the meal, making those who just finished a large meal especially vulnerable (Halter et al., 2017).

Other fall risks include sensory impairments, strokes, Parkinson's disease, cardiovascular issues, cognitive changes, dementia, behavior issues, musculoskeletal weakness, and certain medications (Berry & Kiel, 2020; Saxon et al., 2022).

Environmental hazards beyond design should also be considered. Resident rooms may be cluttered or overcrowded with furniture, contributing to trip and fall risk. Due to cleaning or other concerns, wet floors can become fall hazards, as can carpeted flooring. Toilet and bed height may not be correct for residents increasing fall risk (Berry & Kiel, 2020).

Many tools are available to assist facilities in fall prevention efforts. Following are examples of national programs available; however, many states also provide fall prevention programs to facilities.

- **Agency of Healthcare Research and Quality—On-Time Falls Prevention.** This program provides tools based on electronic medical records to monitor fall risk and implement strategies in preventing falls. https://www.ahrq.gov/patient-safety/settings/long-term-care/resource/ontime/fallspx/index.html
- **Centers for Disease Control and Prevention—STEADI Initiative.** Stopping Elderly Accidents, Deaths, and Injuries (STEADI) is an approach that works

to implement clinical practice guidelines for fall prevention. https://www.cdc.gov/steadi/materials.html

AMPUTEES

Amputees are a group of nursing facility residents who need specific mobility assistance. A large proportion of all amputations are performed on patients 65 years of age and older. The most common amputations are removal of the leg above or below the knee (abbreviated as above-knee amputation [AKA] or below-knee amputation [BKA]). Amputation is the treatment of last resort for severe infection, peripheral vascular disease, or injury that is often related to diabetes. Many prosthetics and other devices are available to restore lost function, and the environment can be changed to accommodate the resident's skills.

CONTRACTURES

Contractures are deformities from muscle shortening, which pulls the adjacent joint into a flexed position. Over time, the joint becomes fixed in this position causing permanent deformity. Contractures are another disruption likely to occur in the immobilized resident or those with RA. Joints likely to develop contractures are those in the hand, wrist, foot, hip, and leg.

The best treatment for contractures is to help prevent them by exercising the joints of those unable to do so themselves. These exercises are called passive range of motion and can be performed by facility staff and taught to the resident's family. Proper positioning at rest, sometimes using prescribed devices or splints, also helps prevent the development of contractures. Contractures are major health problems that must be identified and addressed as early as possible. All facility staff, including nursing assistants, are responsible for the early identification of contracture onset.

REHABILITATION SERVICES

NAB DOMAIN 1A6: REHABILITATION AND RESTORATIVE PROGRAMS

Rehabilitation services to improve function are provided under the direction of a rehabilitation professional, usually a physical therapist, occupational therapist, or speech therapist. Typically, these services are offered to residents as part of a skilled stay related to utilizing their Medicare Part A benefits after a qualifying hospital stay. Medicare Part B also covers a limited amount of rehabilitation services. Many states offer limited rehabilitation coverage for residents who utilize Medicaid to pay for services. Once residents reach their prior level of function, plateau in recovery (do not improve any further), or no longer qualify for skilled care, they are transitioned to restorative care. Restorative staff can be used in creative ways to provide some level of rehabilitation to residents. Facilities often use restorative nursing and nursing assistants to provide limited rehabilitation to those residents who require some oversight but do not qualify for services provided by a licensed therapist. The restorative care program in facilities is often responsible for range-of-motion services and possibly even resident group exercise classes.

5.3.8 URINARY (RENAL) SYSTEM

Section Concepts

- *How the renal system works and possible effects of aging on this system*
- *The problem of chronic renal failure*
- *How end-stage renal disease and renal calculi along with urinary incontinence affect facilities*
- *The importance of identifying and managing UTIs*
- *How to deal with asymptomatic bacteriuria*
- *The problems with indwelling catheters*

Consider as the Administrator . . .

- *An odor-free environment is a daily challenge for every facility. How do you manage this in an environment which continuously creates odors?*

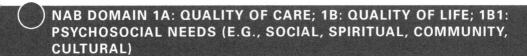

NAB DOMAIN 1A: QUALITY OF CARE; 1B: QUALITY OF LIFE; 1B1: PSYCHOSOCIAL NEEDS (E.G., SOCIAL, SPIRITUAL, COMMUNITY, CULTURAL)

NAB DOMAIN 1A3: DISEASE MANAGEMENT (E.G., ACUTE VS. CHRONIC CONDITIONS)

The renal system consists of the two kidneys, which filter wastes from the blood, two ureters, which transmit the filtered waste (urine) from the kidneys to the bladder. The urine is stored in the bladder until discharged through the urethra (OpenStax College, 2021).

The kidneys also regulate the body's fluid volume and electrolytes. The electrolytes sodium (Na), potassium (K+), calcium (Ca++), and the molecule bicarbonate (HCO$_3$) are closely adjusted within the kidney. These regulatory functions influence body processes from blood pressure to heart rhythms and respiratory rate.

Nephrons are the filtration centers of the kidney. Nephrons filter the blood and concentrate waste products. The filtered blood is returned to the general circulation by the renal vein while the nephron empties the urine to the kidney pelvis, which drains into the ureter.

The bladder is a balloon-like muscular structure that stores the continuous arrival of urine from the ureters. When the bladder senses sufficient fullness, signals are sent to the brain identifying the need to urinate. While some control can be exerted over when to urinate, bladder emptying through the urethra is a reflex called micturition.

Individuals have voluntary control over the sphincter controlling the opening of the bladder and transitional cells that contract the bladder to initiate micturition. See Figure 5.7 for an illustration of the renal system for both men and women.

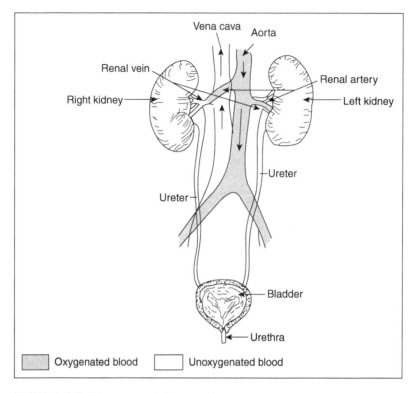

FIGURE 5.7 Diagram of the renal system.

EFFECTS OF AGING ON THE URINARY SYSTEM

As the body ages, renal (nephron) function tends to diminish. An 80-year-old adult has approximately half the renal function of an average 30-year-old (Michel et al., 2017). With age, kidneys lose mass, and nephrons lose the ability to concentrate urine (Denic et al., 2016; Saxon et al., 2022). Because kidney filtration depends on permeable capillaries, age-associated atherosclerosis (hardening) in blood vessels diminishes kidney filtration (Halter et al., 2017). Because of the bladder and urethra location, age-related changes in the reproductive organs can also influence their function.

The bladder muscle undergoes age-related changes similar to other muscles, and its urine capacity decreases. Due to these changes, the body also begins to have issues with maintaining acid–base balance and electrolyte levels (Saxon et al., 2022).

Alterations in Renal Function

It is estimated that nearly half of all nursing facility residents have a level of chronic kidney disease (Hall et al., 2013). Disruptions in renal function may be caused by changes in associated systems, such as arteriosclerotic blood vessels, sugar-crusted blood cells with diabetes, or destruction from high blood pressure, all leading to renal failure.

Internal disruption may be due to a structural malfunction or an internal blockage of the kidney or ureters, like kidney stones or tumors.

Chronic Kidney Failure

Kidney failure is the decreased filtration ability of the kidney, which can be acute (short-term) or, more likely in older adults, a chronic (long-term) process (Halter et al., 2017). Chronic kidney failure (CKD) is defined as the presence of kidney damage or decreased kidney function for 3 or more months, no matter the cause (Fatehi & Hsu, 2020).

The most common causes of CKD are poorly controlled diabetes and hypertension (Fatehi & Hsu, 2020). However, cardiovascular changes decreasing blood flow through the kidneys can permanently damage nephrons (Halter et al., 2017).

CKD symptoms develop gradually with the most apparent signs of renal failure: uremia (decreased urine output), which may progress to oliguria (no urine output). Other early symptoms include dehydration, electrolyte imbalance, osteoporosis, nocturia (producing much urine at night), and anemia (Saxon et al., 2022; Walter & Chang, 2020). Most residents experience fatigue and weakness secondary to these symptoms (Ferrini & Ferrini, 2012). But be mindful that residents may experience no clinical indications and only be diagnosed incidentally (Fatehi & Hsu, 2020). Progressive renal failure leads to a buildup of nitrogenous wastes, causing GI symptoms (nausea, anorexia, hiccups) early and later neurological symptoms (sleepiness, confusion, irritability).

Other toxic waste material buildup can damage other organs and cause painful symptoms, including itching and dry skin, weakness, muscle cramps, nausea, vomiting, diarrhea, mental confusion, and delirium (Halter et al., 2017). Due to already reduced renal function, older adults are particularly prone to end-stage kidney disease and are one of the largest groups entering kidney dialysis programs (Halter et al., 2017).

End-Stage Renal Disease (Now Chronic Kidney Failure Stage 5)

CKD that has progressed to the stage where renal function is insufficient and the body depends on dialysis is CKD stage 5, also called end-stage renal disease (ESRD). The two most common forms of treatment are kidney transplantation and dialysis (American Kidney Fund, 2021). ESRD is considered a permanent disability, and the diagnosis of ESRD causes any standard insurance or Medicare Part C plan to be discontinued with automatic coverage by traditional Medicare insurance coverage for the individual at any age.

Kidney replacement dialysis (hemodialysis; i.e., filtering the blood) requires special filtration equipment to filter unwanted waste materials and fluids from the blood. The process is usually performed in special clinics on multiple days a week over several hours. The patient's blood is circulated externally through a machine that filters the blood. While some nursing facilities have in-house dialysis services, it is very uncommon.

Peritoneal dialysis may be performed for the bedridden patient. This process involves filtering out excess fluids from the peritoneum, a membrane around the abdominal organs. A dialyzing fluid that will absorb waste products is pumped into the abdominal cavity and then drains into receiving bags over many hours. Hemodialysis is much more efficient and effective, but peritoneal dialysis is an option for patients unable to tolerate the strain of removing and returning blood.

Nephrolithiasis

Kidney stones (nephrolithiasis, urolithiasis, or renal calculi) form due to chemistry imbalances in the body. These stones are crystalline, stonelike substances that become a problem when they block the flow of urine within the renal system.

The residents at highest risk of developing kidney stones are those with limited mobility or prolonged bed rest. However, any resident who has decreased fluid intake, high sodium intake, or dietary practices which contribute to the formation of kidney stones is at risk (Curhan et al., 2021). Eighty percent of stones are formed of calcium oxalate or calcium phosphate, which is why dietary concerns are essential for treatment (Curhan et al., 2021).

Symptoms are typically flank pain (along the back and side), hematuria (blood in urine), and decreased urine outflow. Further symptoms may include nausea, vomiting, and urinary urgency (Curhan et al., 2021). Treatment focuses on pain relief and medications to relax ureters, allowing the stones to pass. The best practice is to expel stones. For cases where stones do not pass with drug intervention, ureteroscopy with laser lithotripsy is often used to remove the stones. When retrieved from filtered urine, the stone composition is analyzed to determine further treatment or prevention (Curhan et al., 2021).

Urinary Incontinence

Urinary incontinence is the inability to control the timing of urination consciously. More often than weekly urinary incontinence is a common problem in nursing facility residents. Reasons for incontinence may include stress incontinence, obesity, neurological damage, chronic constipation, impactions, and cognitive impairment (Lukacz, 2021). A defect in the nervous system (stroke patients who lose nervous control of the bladder), UTIs, or constant pressure on the bladder from other disorders, such as constipation, all may cause incontinence (Kane et al., 2018; Lucacz et al., 2021; Michel et al., 2017; Saxon et al., 2022).

Problems in mobility complicate reaching the toilet quickly, exacerbating incontinence. The nursing staff must be prompt in assisting the resident to the bathroom regularly to allow residents to empty the bladder. We often see residents with toileting schedules to assist in this concern.

Bladder retraining is used to assist the resident in using the bathroom at appropriate times. Several bladder retraining programs are suitable after assurance that the condition is not linked to a medical issue. Bladder retraining programs involve relying on a set schedule, such as assistance to the toilet 2 hours after fluid consumption, rather than physiology, to dictate when to urinate (International Cystitis Association, 2015).

Devices such as bedpans, urinals, and bedside commodes can assist the limited motion resident in controlled and dignified urination. Residents who cannot use a toilet sometimes have internal catheters threaded through the urethra into the bladder to drain it consistently. However, indwelling catheters are a choice of last resort and are usually saved for urinary occlusion due to the risk of complications and infection (CAUTIs). Men may use either an external condom-like or an indwelling catheter. Women now have an external option, but the external catheter must be attached to a suction canister. Both internal and external catheters collect urine in clear plastic drainage bags, which keep the system closed to control the introduction of bacteria or other harmful microorganisms into the urinary tract.

Urinary Tract Infections

NAB DOMAIN 3A7: INFECTION CONTROL AND SANITATION (E.G., LINENS, KITCHEN, HAND WASHING, HEALTHCARE-ACQUIRED INFECTIONS, HAZARDOUS MATERIALS)

The bladder is usually sterile. UTIs frequently result from fecal microbes introduced into the urethra and ascending to the bladder (potentially up to the ureters and kidneys; Hooton & Gupta, 2021). Increased risk for UTIs includes prostatic hypertrophy (in men), neurogenic bladder from stroke or diabetes, incontinence, and use of urinary catheters (Hooton & Gupta, 2021; National Institute of Diabetes and Digestive and Kidney Diseases, 2021).

Asymptomatic Bacteriuria

Asymptomatic bacteriuria occurs when two or more urine specimens show greater than 100,000 colonies/mL on two consecutive samples in patients with no symptoms of infection (Walter & Chang, 2020). In the nursing facility, asymptomatic bacteriuria is more likely to be antibiotic-resistant than in the general population. Distinguishing asymptomatic from symptomatic infection is complicated because older adults may not exhibit traditional UTI symptoms and may have difficulty reporting subjective symptoms. Pyuria (fever) may or may not be present. In the absence of objective evidence of infection (fever, pain, or change in cognitive or functional status), the resident should be carefully observed for the need to treat with antibiotics to avoid contributing to antibiotic-resistant strains (Fekete & Hooton, 2021; Nicolle et al., 2019; Walter & Chang, 2020).

Infection from long-term urinary catheters is nearly impossible to prevent, and many patients with asymptomatic bacteriuria utilize indwelling catheters to assist in urinary urgency. CAUTI are significant events in the nursing facility (or anywhere in healthcare, for that matter). The female rate of UTIs is higher than the male rate because pathogenic organisms traveling up the outside of the catheter have a shorter distance to travel in women (2 inches) than men (6–8 inches). UTI can increase the risk for pyelonephritis (inflammation of the kidney), a significant cause of death in patients with long-term use of indwelling catheters.

The most common causes of UTI are a lack of handwashing between resident contacts (poor infection control staff practices), urinary catheters, dehydration, improper perineal and perianal care, and bowel incontinence, causing fecal contamination. Improper Foley techniques, including nonsterile insertion and poor drainage bag positioning, have also been identified as infection causes.

Symptomatic Bacteriuria

Symptomatic bacteriuria is a UTI in which the resident experiences symptoms associated with the infection. Symptoms can include pyuria, suprapubic tenderness, altered mental status, hypotension, chills, fatigue, malaise, flank pain, or pelvic or perineal pain (Fekete & Hooton, 2021; Hooton & Gupta, 2021). The most common cause of UTI is *Escherichia coli* (*E. coli*) from fecal contamination. Risk factors for this type of infection are the recent use of broad-spectrum antibiotics and the risk factors discussed earlier in asymptomatic infection (Hooton & Gupta, 2021).

Treatment for symptomatic UTI includes immediate urine cultures to determine the infective organism followed by broad-spectrum antibiotics, which may be adjusted after obtaining culture information (often 2–4 days; Hooton & Gupta, 2021). Additional treatment includes reversing the causing or contributing factors such as rehydration or Foley exchange. Residents are at risk of dehydration because of physiological changes with aging and medical factors (acute disease, infection, medication, fluid restriction for chronic disease treatments; Hooton & Gupta, 2021; Paulis et al., 2018). UTI and dehydration are of significant concern and focus for the surveyor. Impeccable documentation by physicians and nursing staff—and a care plan for expected dehydration when appropriate—can support and protect the facility conditions and procedures.

CASE STUDY

Urinary Tract Infection and Antibiotics

As the administrator, you learn Dr. Brown has consistently prescribed antibiotics for several of his patients in your facility based on laboratory reports indicating UTI. However, none of the patients has been febrile or complaining of symptoms. Your medical director has stated that as Dr. Brown is in his practice group, he is not in a position to take any action if any action needs to be taken.

- *How would you handle this situation?*

5.3.9 REPRODUCTIVE SYSTEM

Section Concepts

- *Sexuality among the nursing facility population is no different from sexuality among the general population*

Consider as the Administrator . . .

- *Should consensual sexual relations among cognitively competent residents be routinely permitted?*

NAB DOMAIN 1A: QUALITY OF CARE; 1B: QUALITY OF LIFE; 1B1: PSYCHOSOCIAL NEEDS (E.G., SOCIAL, SPIRITUAL, COMMUNITY, CULTURAL)

NAB DOMAIN 1A3: DISEASE MANAGEMENT (E.G., ACUTE VS. CHRONIC CONDITIONS)

The reproductive system in the younger adult serves to promote species reproduction and facilitate intimacy expression through human contact. Some of the most notable changes in older adults include the woman's loss of reproductive capabilities following menopause, whereas a man retains reproductive capabilities. However, both sexes have continued needs to express their sexuality throughout life.

This section describes the reproductive organs and age-associated changes for each sex; the next section discusses sexuality and the nursing facility resident.

WOMEN

The reproductive organs in women include the ovaries, which house mature eggs that travel down the fallopian tubes to the uterus about once every month. Hormones act to control the reproductive cycle. Estrogen is the female sex hormone that directs female sexual maturation and most reproductive processes.

The organs of the lower reproductive tract are the cervix, the uterus, and the vagina. The cervix is the opening of the uterus leading into the vagina. The vagina is a barrel-shaped organ that leads to the external genitals in the female reproductive tract, such as the labia and the clitoris. Most women go through menopause (cessation of egg production and therefore of menstruation) in their 40s or 50s and are no longer fertile.

Diseases of the uterus tend to decrease with age. The changes are closely related to decreases in secretions of estrogen.

Some of the physical changes that older women may experience include a loss of tone and elasticity in the breast, uterus, cervix, and vagina; a thinning and drying of vaginal walls; a loss of pubic hair; and decreased ducts and milk glands of the breasts.

These changes may cause uncomfortable irritations, increased infections, and bleeding. The incidence of breast cancer continues to rise with age, and it is the second-most common type of cancer affecting older women after skin cancer (Mauk & Silva-Smith, 2018). The signs and symptoms of breast cancer are a hardened lump or thickening in the breast, change in size, shape, or skin of the breast or nipples, and any nipple discharge other than milk (CDC, 2021f). Treatment depends on the extent of the disease and may include surgery, radiation, or chemotherapy.

Another age-related disorder is pelvic organ prolapse. The muscle tone of the pelvic organs (bladder, rectum, uterus, urethra) becomes weakened, and the organs slip down and may seem to fall out of the vagina (Saxon et al., 2022). Women with weak muscles are at risk. Some of the signs and symptoms associated with pelvic organ prolapse include constant pressure on the bladder, incontinence of urine, and a sense of weight in the pelvis. Usually, this disorder can be reversed with bladder training, pessaries, or Kegel exercises. However, prolapsed organs may need to be repaired surgically.

MEN

The primary organs of the male reproductive tract are the testes, scrotum, prostate, and penis.

The testes are encased within the scrotum and produce the male hormone testosterone and sperm cells. Sperm cells are continually produced, mature as they travel through the epididymis, and are released through the vas deferens, ejaculatory ducts, and urethra. Associated ducts and the prostate gland secrete seminal fluid, which provides nutrients and lubrication for the sperm. During ejaculation, the sperm travel down the penis through the urethra and are emitted from the body (OpenStax College, 2021).

Some of the age-related changes in the male reproductive tract are an enlargement of the prostate gland; decreased production of testosterone, which may result in slight decreases in sexual desire; and a reduction in muscle bulk and strength. Sperm production continues into advanced old age, allowing males to maintain the ability to impregnate.

Problems with the prostate gland are a concern for many older men. Benign prostatic hyperplasia (BPH; a benign enlargement of the prostate) is a common age-related change in men. BPH may interfere with the ability to urinate for some men, causing frequency (including nocturia at night), urgency, slowness, inability, or incontinence (McVary, 2021). BPH can also be entirely asymptomatic.

Prostatic enlargement may develop into prostate cancer, the second-most common form of cancer in older men (Saxon et al., 2022). Initial symptoms for this disease are rare. Later symptoms can include urethra obstruction, urinary frequency, hematuria, genital pain, pain in the lower back, pelvis, and upper thighs, nausea, and weakness (Saxon et al., 2022; Taplin & Smith, 2020). Treatment choices vary depending on tumor type and spread and may include radiation therapy, brachytherapy (internal radioactive seeding), removal of the prostate, or active surveillance (Klein, 2021).

COPING WITH SEXUALITY

Sexual needs persist into old age, with continued activity considered healthy and health-preserving. Older adults, including those residing in facilities, have self-image and esteem needs, closely associated with the needs for intimacy and sexuality (Hajjar & Kamel, 2004). Often, society and individuals discourage sexual activity in the nursing facility because of existing stereotypes and misunderstandings about sex and old age (Lester et al., 2016).

Sexuality is not only achieved exclusively by sexual intercourse but may also incorporate various activities related to touch and displays of affection. Older people may be more likely to express their sexuality in these more diffuse and varied terms.

Nursing facilities are often perceived as disapproving and actively discouraging displays of love or affection among residents. A frequent suggestion in the literature is that nursing facility staff be educated concerning sexuality in old age and that more efforts be made to deal with problems of morality and understanding that may arise. Sexuality in the nursing facility simply remains a taboo issue, as many staff simply believe that older adults no longer have sexual needs (Jankowiak, 2009).

It is likely true that:

- Older people do remain interested in sex
- Older people find each other physically attractive
- Sexuality contributes to overall well-being

Contrary to public perceptions, the incidence of a heart attack or stroke during sexual intercourse is very low, and sexual activity is sometimes recommended for patients with diseases such as arthritis because of the therapeutic effects of exercise and intimacy.

Allowing for the privacy of some residents to develop closer relationships is important. Encouraging the development of programs to deal with quality-of-life issues such as loneliness and isolation that are important to residents is often recommended. Sexual expression fits in as a component of this effort.

SEXUAL COMPLICATIONS

The sexual partners of those who have confirmed HIV antibody tests are at risk for HIV infection that will progress to AIDS. Education to prevent disease transmission in the facility should be addressed. Many facilities provide condoms, lubricants, and other aids to residents who engage in sexual behavior to ensure that it is done safely.

Erectile dysfunction (erectile disorder or impotence) is characterized by an inability to achieve or sustain an erection that is adequate for sexual function and is the most common form of sexual dysfunction in men (Agronin, 2021). It is appropriate for adults with autonomy and sexual desires to receive treatment for this disorder.

5.3.10 EMOTIONAL AND MENTAL WELL-BEING

Section Concepts

- *Attaining and maintaining emotional and mental well-being among the nursing facility population is a significant challenge*
- *How losses may affect the nursing facility resident*
- *Information on mental illness in the facility*
- *Many facilities have a high rate of psychoactive drug prescriptions*
- *How to identify organic brain syndrome*
- *Restraints: A major daily challenge to facilities*
- *Basic understanding of mental health issues*
- *Basic understanding of cognitive impairments*

- *Depression*
  - *The importance of treating depression*
  - *How to identify a depression on top of dementia*

Consider as the Administrator . . .

- *How possible is it to achieve robust emotional and mental well-being among the resident population of the nursing facility?*
- *To what extent is cognitive impairment a "normal" part of aging?*

NAB DOMAIN 1A: QUALITY OF CARE; 1B: QUALITY OF LIFE; 1B1: PSYCHOSOCIAL NEEDS (E.G., SOCIAL, SPIRITUAL, COMMUNITY, CULTURAL); 1B11: TRAUMA-INFORMED CARE (E.G., PTSD)

NAB DOMAIN 1B10: MENTAL AND BEHAVIORAL HEALTH (E.G., COGNITIVE IMPAIRMENT, DEPRESSION, SOCIAL SUPPORT SYSTEMS)

A number of the physical system disruptions discussed earlier can have profound effects on the mental well-being of the nursing facility resident.

EFFECTS OF AGING

Differences of opinion exist as to whether intelligence declines with age. One difficulty is using tests that may not be appropriate for older adults.

Aging is associated with unique problems that may not be as disruptive for younger individuals, such as behavioral problems and mental illness. Specific behaviors residents employ to cope with these problems vary. Studies show that many nursing facility recurrent issues are related to behavioral problems stemming from cognitive impairments (Dillon et al., 2013). Behavioral concerns may be related to unmet resident needs. Unmet needs can be indicators of worse outcomes than functional or cognitive decline and may include physical dependency, the inability of self-expression, or the inability to make needs known (Ferreira et al., 2016). Long-term effects of unmet needs are decreased quality of life, feelings of resignation and hopelessness, increased distress, increased dissatisfaction with life, and potentially increased levels of depression, anxiety, somatic disorders, or behavioral symptoms (Ferreira et al., 2016). And while identifying unmet needs may be difficult, it is crucial.

Upon admission, residents may display symptoms of anxiety and apprehension regarding their new surroundings. Admission forces residents to face chronic illness and the process of dying. Even temporary admission to a nursing facility can herald a sense of mortality for a resident due to stereotyping as places to die.

Each person deals with anxiety in a particular way: fantasizing, hostile or dependent behavior, avoiding eye contact, fidgeting, insomnia, and isolation from others (Halter et al., 2017).

INSOMNIA

Insomnia, or sleep disorders, occur frequently among older adults. Human sleep pattern studies have shown that older adults spend more time in bed, have more difficulty getting to sleep, and tend to awaken frequently during sleep periods (Halter et al., 2017).

Insomnia can be associated with other medical concerns. Pain, nocturia, shortness of breath, obstructive sleep apnea, restless legs syndrome, or psychiatric disorders can all contribute to the inability to sleep adequately (Winkleman, 2021). Sleep problems may result from polypharmacy as well. Antidepressants, opioids, and glucocorticoids used to treat other disorders can cause insomnia (Winkelman, 2021).

The treatment of insomnia first utilizes sleep strategies to assist the resident with sleeping. Pharmacological interventions to promote sleep are second-string choices due to complications and medication interactions.

LONELINESS/DEPRESSION

Behaviors associated with loneliness are similar to those of a mild depressive mood and include isolation, constipation, weight loss, insomnia, fatigue, and a loss of appetite. Depression is often associated with losses, some of which are depicted in Exhibit 5.1. Identifying and addressing mild depression are significant concerns in nursing facility care (Kane et al., 2018). A substantial proportion of nursing facility residents experience mild depression, often underidentified and unaddressed by the facility staff (Singh, 2016).

Treatment is to discern the cause of depression and support effective coping measures (Halter et al., 2009, p. 756). Many facilities have vigorous activities programs that decrease loneliness and social isolation. If behaviors persist and worsen, the resident may be progressing toward mental illness requiring antidepressive medications (Halter et al., 2017). While some residents will have depression due to chemical or other imbalances, the nursing facility resident is especially susceptible to situational depression. Situational depression occurs in response to actual or perceived elements of one's environment. Real and perceived losses

EXHIBIT 5.1 Losses, Adjustments, and Gains of a Person Admitted to Long-Term Care.

Loneliness and associated depression are strongly correlated with serious health risks, so addressing these concerns is essential. Some of the health risks associated with loneliness are as follows:

- Increase risk of premature death from all causes
- 50% increased risk of dementia
- 29% increased risk of heart disease
- 32% increased risk of stroke
- Higher rates of depression, anxiety, and suicide
- For residents with heart failure as well:
  - Four times increased risk of death
  - 68% greater risk of hospitalization
  - 57% greater risk of ED visits

Source: Data from Centers for Disease Control and Prevention. (2021). *Loneliness and social isolation linked to serious health conditions.* https://www.cdc.gov/aging/publications/features/lonely-older -adults.html; National Academies of Sciences, Engineering, and Medicine. (2020). *Social isolation and loneliness in older adults: Opportunities for the health care system.* The National Academies Press. https://doi.org/10.17226/25663.

associated with admission to a nursing facility are conducive to creating situational depression.

MENTAL ILLNESS

Who is mentally ill? What is mental illness? These are difficult questions in the setting of the nursing facility. The changes brought about by chronic physical illnesses and by the "normal" social changes faced by older persons are sometimes powerful enough to overwhelm even a well-adjusted person. The line between disabling mental illnesses and the day-to-day effects of attempting to cope with aging, especially in the institutionalized setting of the nursing facility, is often blurred.

It is estimated that mental illness occurs in one fourth to one half of nursing facility residents. This high prevalence may be a result of preexisting concerns. The term *senile* was historically used to describe various behaviors in older adults caused by mental illness, ranging from slight forgetfulness to a generalized cognitive decline.

Beers Criteria are important for monitoring the quality of care surrounding medication usage in residents. The STOPP (Screening Tool of Older Person's Prescriptions) and START (Screening Tool to Alert to Right Treatment) criteria can screen for potentially inappropriate medications and prescribing omissions in older adults. STOPP and START are criteria that facilitate medication review in clinical settings (O'Mahony, 2020).

PSYCHOACTIVE DRUG USE RATES

Psychoactive (also called psychotropic) drugs affect the mind, and their use is not uncommon in the nursing facility to calm and control resident behavior. However, they are not without their side effects. Psychoactive drugs include antidepressants, antianxiety drugs, sedatives and hypnotics, and antipsychotics. Antipsychotics are among the most used and are associated with the most adverse effects, including falls (Rochon, 2021). There has been pressure from the federal government for facilities to prescribe fewer psychoactive drugs and adequately diagnose depression and other mental conditions associated with decreased quality of life. The amount of residents receiving psychoactive medications has dropped dramatically in response. A better understanding of medication side effects, fall risk, and limited effects addressing disease processes has also caused declined use (Groot Kormelinck et al., 2019).

ORGANIC BRAIN SYNDROMES

Organic brain syndromes have two subgroups: acute (due to delirium, metabolic dysfunction, or infection) and chronic (due to dementia with brain changes).

Acute confusional state refers to a state of altered consciousness characterized by disordered attention and diminished speed, clarity, and coherence of thought (Francis & Young, 2020; Ropper et al., 2019). Acute confusional state also can include reduced alertness and altered psychomotor activity (Francis & Young, 2020; Ropper et al., 2019).

Acute organic brain syndromes are often not recognized by clinicians in 70% or more cases (Francis & Young, 2020). Acutely caused organic brain syndromes are frequently entirely reversible when identified and treated quickly.

Acute Causes

Five key features characterize acute delirium:

1. Disturbances in attention and awareness
2. Developed over a short period (hours to days), representing a shift from the resident's baseline
3. Disturbance in cognition (memory deficit, disorientation, language issues, issues with visuospatial ability, perception concerns)
4. The disturbances are not explained by preexisting, evolving, or established neurocognitive disorders
5. Evidence from history, physical examination, or laboratory results that the disturbance is caused by a medical condition, substance intoxication or withdrawal, or medication side effects (American Psychiatric Association, 2013)

Chronic brain syndromes are permanent neurodegenerative diseases or dementias, with treatment to decrease symptoms and behaviors. When possible, the focus is also on slowing the progression of the disease. Nonpharmacological interventions such as massage, activities, sensory interventions, music therapy, and person-centered communication skills can be beneficial (Mileski et al., 2018; Press & Alexander, 2021). Further treatment focuses on decreasing specific symptoms through the use of pain management, antidementia drugs, antidepressants, and sleeping aids (Press & Alexander, 2021).

Chronic Causes

Neurodegenerative conditions commonly seen in the nursing facility include:

- Alzheimer's disease
- Dementia with Lewy bodies
- Frontotemporal dementia
- Parkinson's disease dementia
- Microvascular ischemic disease (Larson, 2019)

Diagnosis of any of the preceding conditions is difficult due to overlapping symptomatology. A complete differential diagnosis cannot occur between Alzheimer's disease and Lewy body dementia until brain biopsy after death. Permanent and progressive symptoms of chronic organic brain syndromes can include the following:

- Forgetfulness
- Difficulty in retaining new information
- Inability to handle complex tasks

- Unable to reason or cope with unexpected events
- Problems with spatial ability and orientation (getting lost in familiar surroundings)
- Inability to find words plus language concerns
- Behaviors (Larson, 2019)

DEPRESSION

Depression often goes undetected and significantly impacts the quality of life, medical outcomes, morbidity, and mortality (Gallo et al., 1997; Heflin, 2021). Depression can also present with cognitive, functional, or sleep dysfunction or fatigue (Heflin, 2021). It is estimated that 50% or more of nursing facility residents suffer from depression (Espinoza & Unutzer, 2019; Hoover et al., 2010).

Factors increasing the risk of depression include the following:

- Female gender
- Recent onset of physical illness
- Severe physical illness
- Functional disability or limited mobility
- Poor pain management
- Multiple illnesses (Espinoza & Unutzer, 2019)

Signs of depression include a loss of appetite resulting in weight loss, feelings of sadness, a loss of interest in people, and a sense of great effort needed to perform daily activities. Older adults may also have physical symptoms attributable to depression. The underlying problem is often loss of autonomy over daily activities and a lack of decision-making opportunities.

The treatment of depression can include antidepressant medications. However, these drugs also have strong side effects, drug interactions, and require continuous monitoring. Staff efforts to preserve or restore a sense of worth and importance to the resident may be among the most powerful tools available. Exercise and social interactions are beneficial for the treatment of depression. So, activities such as aerobics geared to the resident's level of physical capacity, dance therapy, recreation therapy, work therapy, and bibliotherapy (reading books) should be added to facility activities (Espinoza & Unutzer, 2019; Mileski et al., 2018). Brain stimulation techniques are becoming more available, including transcranial magnetic stimulation or deep brain stimulation with varying effects. For residents who have not responded to otherwise traditional treatments, electroconvulsive therapy may be a viable treatment option.

BEHAVIOR MANAGEMENT

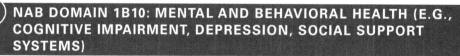

NAB DOMAIN 1B10: MENTAL AND BEHAVIORAL HEALTH (E.G., COGNITIVE IMPAIRMENT, DEPRESSION, SOCIAL SUPPORT SYSTEMS)

Behavior management is similar to behavior modification and less intensive than behavior therapy. Behavior modification focuses on changing behavior, whereas the focus is on maintaining order in behavior management. Behavior management includes all actions taken to enhance the probability that people will choose personally fulfilling, productive, and socially acceptable behaviors.

There is a great deal of research related to "behavior change" and "behavior management." B. F. Skinner and Carl Rogers have given two distinctly different approaches for addressing behavior. Skinner believes behavior can be managed by identifying what the individual finds rewarding and exchanging an acceptable version of that reward for good behavior. Skinner calls this "Positive Reinforcement Psychology." Rogers proposes that effectively addressing problem behaviors requires persuasion that makes the individual want to behave appropriately. Rogers believes that the individual must have an internal awareness of right and wrong. Creating this awareness is done by teaching the individual the difference between right and wrong, including why they should pick right.

Behavior management is part of everyday life for an administrator. Management seeks to manage the behavior of employees. Staff similarly looks to adjust the behavior of residents. Altering behavior can be a sticky area. The federal requirements require facility staff to allow each resident the maximum opportunity to be their highest-functioning self. In the course of the daily life of a nursing facility, the staff must manage some resident behaviors. A common approach to managing inappropriate behaviors is redirecting the resident's attention to more appropriate behaviors.

Person-centered care is a paradigm shift in modern care. It refocuses choices and goals of care to the resident preferences, emphasizing self-determination, choices, worth, values, history, and interests, to promote a life-affirming, satisfying experience. There are many tools providing guidance:

- The Nursing Home Toolkit for Promoting Positive Behavioral Health: https://www.nursinghometoolkit.com/index.html
- The Pioneer Network: https://www.pioneernetwork.net/
- Artifacts of Culture Change 2.0: https://www.pioneernetwork.net/artifacts -culture-change/

CASE DISCUSSIONS

Ms. Sims Leans Forward (An Actual Case, Deidentified)

Given Ms. Sims's history of right-sided weakness and history of stroke, Nurse Riley clearly should have suspected and checked for a possible TIA. Nurse Riley failed to take Ms. Sims seriously. Facility policy should include a checklist for such events— a checklist of what to do when a patient is suspected of possibly having a stroke. The facility needs to do some in-service training on stroke recognition. The facility may also need to consider replacing nurses like Nurse Riley. His response was not appropriate or acceptable.

Wandering California Hallways and Byways—On Haldol (An Actual Case)

This case illustrates several dimensions of caring for persons with dementia. Wandering and disruptive behaviors are hard to control—sometimes nearly impossible. The nursing facility setting is very complex for the caregivers because state regulations require facilities to successfully care for residents such as Ms. Wood.

(continued)

Ms. Wood brings many risks to the facility, particularly for the safety of her fellow residents.

The case illustrates the difficulty of getting mental health assistance for residents in the facility.

Combative (An Actual Case)

The skin breakdown resulted from the failure of several care processes in the facility, beginning with failure to plan appropriate care for Mr. Ray. He was clearly at high risk of pressure injury, but the staff failed to implement a plan that accounted for his lack of exercise and movement.

The nurse's aide did well to notify the charge nurse about the area of redness in the sacral area but should have done so immediately. Intervention should be as soon as possible, not to wait a day to notify the charge nurse.

The charge nurse did well to monitor the redness for changes, but this passive approach permitted the breakdown to occur. An active intervention plan would have improved Mr. Ray's outcome. Redness in the sacral area of a resident who uses a wheelchair for most of the day should be a deafening warning bell, not a signal to "observe" and see what happens. The facility staff's daily care behaviors resulted in a possible decubitus ulcer. Without immediate intervention and a new approach to Mr. Ray's care, the likelihood that the care routine would lead to actual skin breakdown was high. The care staff did not seem to know or care.

Facilities typically have a wound care nurse. The wound care nurse should have become active in Mr. Ray's care plan when the redness was first noted.

True, the charge nurse did call Mr. Ray's doctor but did not follow up. The facility is responsible for obtaining the care needed for Mr. Ray. It is not enough to place a call to the doctor's office. Active care planning to prevent skin breakdown should have occurred immediately. If the doctor fails to return a call, the facility's medical director must be informed and become active in providing Mr. Ray's care.

Ulceration can occur very fast, and the care system broke down for this resident. It was a new charge nurse who noticed the rapidly enlarging ulcer. No one seemed to be in charge at this facility. The staff was observing the warning signs and noting the results without intervention. A new plan of care, wound care nurse involvement, and escalation to the medical director were indicated but never occurred.

Sometimes pressure ulcers are not preventable due to illness or patient condition. In this case, the ulcer was likely wholly preventable if the facility functioned adequately.

Urinary Tract Infection and Antibiotics

Good medical practice is the responsibility of the facility medical director. But in the end, it is the administrator's responsibility to ensure all residents receive proper care. There is some residual debate about prescribing antibiotics for afebrile and asymptomatic residents. The best evidence-based approach is to save antibiotic prescriptions for active infections with fever and clinical symptoms. Overprescribing

(*continued*)

antibiotics has been shown to result in antibiotic resistance and reduced effectiveness when antibiotics are needed.

It appears that Dr. Brown may be overprescribing antibiotics for ease, to the possible detriment of residents in the facility. Perhaps he does not know he is overprescribing, or maybe he suspects but has not changed his practice out of convenience.

This case illustrates the complex responsibility of the administrator. As an administrator, you must know enough about the medical practice to know if your residents are receiving good medical care. It is not always safe to rely on the nursing staff monitoring medical practice in the facility. The administrator is responsible for the level of medical care occurring in the facility. If the medical director acknowledges that Dr. Brown is overprescribing antibiotics to the possible detriment of residents' well-being, perhaps it is time to look for a new medical director. The current medical director appears to be placing comfortable working relationships with his fellow practitioners above the well-being of your residents.

WHAT WOULD YOU DO?

Shimmering Grain Care Home has an issue with UTIs. Based on your quality assurance programs conclusions, your staff has found that your residents are dehydrated due to a lack of free water intake. You put several useful programs into place with the involvement of nursing staff, which made a difference, but the results were limited.

When your activities director heard about this, the director set up a hydration cart offering an afternoon snack. This cart is quite impressive and is aptly decorated for the season. The cart also often has music emanating from it that the residents appreciate and that the nursing staff can also "get into." Each afternoon the cart is pushed throughout the facility, and residents who can take hydration in the form of the day's offering receive it. Those who are restricted are offered appropriate substitutions such as thickened liquids. Cart offerings may include lemonade, pina coladas, or watermelon slices. There is always water provided as well.

When the activity director comes down the hall, all the staff come running. They were not asked to or coerced. They simply jumped in and had a good time with it. If the music playing is appropriate, they might put on a show right there in the hall with line dance, singing, or other fun happenings. Residents get hydration. The staff are happy to give it.

1. What would you do from here?
2. Is this something to recognize your activity director for or ridicule them?
3. How do you think this will be received by surveyors who observe this hydration cart and show?
4. Should *you* get involved in this activity?

REFERENCES

Agency for Healthcare Research and Quality. (2017). *A unit guide to infection prevention for long-term care staff.* https://www.ahrq.gov/hai/quality/tools/cauti-ltc/modules/resources/guides/infection-prevent.html

Agronin, M. (2021). Sexual dysfunction in older adults. *UpToDate.* https://www.uptodate.com/contents/sexual-dysfunction-in-older-adults

Albrecht, M. A. (2020). Treatment of herpes zoster in the immunocompromised patient. *UpToDate.* https://www.uptodate.com/contents/treatment-of-herpes-zoster-in-the-immunocompetent-host

Albrecht, M. A., & Levin, M. J. (2021). Epidemiology, clinical manifestations, and diagnosis of herpes zoster. *UpToDate.* https://www.uptodate.com/contents/epidemiology-clinical-manifestations-and-diagnosis-of-herpes-zoster

Aldwin, C. M., Igarashi, H., Gilmer, D. F., & Levenson, M. R. (2017). *Health, illness, and optimal aging: Biological and psychosocial perspectives* (3rd ed.). Springer Publishing Company.

Alzheimer's Association. (2021). *What is dementia?* https://www.alz.org/alzheimers-dementia/what-is-dementia

American Geriatrics Society Beers Criteria® Update Expert Panel. (2019). American Geriatrics Society 2019 updated AGS Beers Criteria® for potentially inappropriate medication use in older adults. *Journal of the American Geriatrics Society, 67*(4), 674–694. https://doi.org/10.1111/jgs.15767

American Kidney Fund. (2021). *Kidney failure (ESRD) causes, symptoms, and treatments.* https://www.kidneyfund.org/kidney-disease/kidney-failure/#what-are-the-treatment-options-for-kidney-failure

American Lung Association. (2021). *The basics of pulmonary rehabilitation.* https://www.lung.org/lung-health-diseases/lung-procedures-and-tests/pulmonary-rehab

American Psychiatric Association. (2013). *Diagnostic and statistical manual of mental disorders* (5th ed.). https://doi.org/10.1176/appi.books.9780890425596

American Speech-Language-Hearing Association. (2021a). *Conductive hearing loss.* https://www.asha.org/public/hearing/conductive-hearing-loss/

American Speech-Language-Hearing Association. (2021b). *Sensorineural hearing loss.* https://www.asha.org/public/hearing/sensorineural-hearing-loss/

American Stroke Association. (2021). *Stroke symptoms.* https://www.stroke.org/en/about-stroke/stroke-symptoms

Baer, A. N., & Sankar, V. (2020). Treatment of dry mouth and other non-ocular sicca symptoms in Sjögren's syndrome. *UpToDate.* https://www.uptodate.com/contents/treatment-of-dry-mouth-and-other-non-ocular-sicca-symptoms-in-sjogrens-syndrome

Basile, J., & Bloch, M. J. (2021). Overview of hypertension in adults. *UpToDate.* https://www.uptodate.com/contents/overview-of-hypertension-in-adults

Baumann, S. L., & Greif, N. (2017). The use of PRNs medications with hospitalized older adults. *Geriatric Nursing, 38*(6), 596–598. https://doi.org/10.1016/j.gerinurse.2017.10.010

Beckman, K. B., & Ames, B. N. (1998). The free radical theory of aging matures. *Physiological Reviews, 78*(2), 547–581. https://doi.org/10.1152/physrev.1998.78.2.547

Bengtson, V. L., & Settersten, R. A. (2016). Theories of aging: Developments within and across disciplinary boundaries. In V. L. Bengtson & R. A. Settersten (Eds.), *Handbook of theories of aging* (3rd ed.; pp. 1–8). Springer Publishing Company.

Berlowitz, D. (2020a) Clinical staging and management of pressure-induced skin and soft tissue injury. *UpToDate.* https://www.uptodate.com/contents/clinical-staging-and-management-of-pressure-induced-skin-and-soft-tissue-injury

Berlowitz, D. (2020b). Prevention of pressure-induced skin and soft tissue injury. *UpToDate.* https://www.uptodate.com/contents/prevention-of-pressure-induced-skin-and-soft-tissue-injury

Berry, S., & Kiel, D. P. (2020). Falls: Prevention in nursing care facilities and the hospital setting. *UpToDate.* https://www.uptodate.com/contents/falls-prevention-in-nursing-care-facilities-and-the-hospital-setting

Bjorksten, J. (1968). The crosslinkage theory of aging. *Journal of the American Geriatrics Society, 16*(4), 408–427. https://doi.org/10.1111/j.1532-5415.1968.tb02821.x

Bleday, R., & Breen, E. (2020). Hemorrhoids: Clinical manifestations and diagnosis. *UpToDate.* https://www.uptodate.com/contents/hemorrhoids-clinical-manifestations-and-diagnosis

Blevins, N. H. (2020). Presbycusis. *UpToDate.* https://www.uptodate.com/contents/presbycusis

Bohr, V. A., & Anson, R. M. (1995). DNA damage, mutation and fine structure DNA repair in aging. *Mutation Research/DNAging, 338*(1–6), 25–34. https://doi.org/10.1016/0921-8734(95)00008-T

Brett, L., Traynor, V., & Stapley, P. (2016). Effects of physical exercise on health and well-being of individuals living with a dementia in nursing homes: A systematic review. *Journal of the American Medical Directors Association, 17*(2), 104–116. https://doi.org/10.1016/j.jamda.2015.08.016

Brosch, J. R., & Farlow, M. R. (2021). Early-onset dementia in adults. *UpToDate.* https://www.uptodate.com/contents/early-onset-dementia-in-adults

Cadenas, R., Diez, M. J., Fernández, N., García, J. J., Sahagún, A. M., Sierra, M., López, C., Susperregui, J., & Díez, R. (2021). Prevalence and associated factors of polypharmacy in nursing home residents: A cross-sectional study. *International Journal of Environmental Research and Public Health, 18*(4), 2037. https://doi.org/10.3390/ijerph18042037

Celli, B. R. (2021). *Pulmonary rehabilitation. UpToDate.* https://www.uptodate.com/contents/pulmonary-rehabilitation

Centers for Disease Control and Prevention. (2019). *Hand hygiene in healthcare facilities.* https://www.cdc.gov/handhygiene/index.html

Centers for Disease Control and Prevention. (2020a). *Serious infections and outbreaks occurring in LTCFs.* https://www.cdc.gov/longtermcare/staff/report-publications.html

Centers for Disease Control and Prevention. (2020b). *Rheumatoid Arthritis (RA).* https://www.cdc.gov/arthritis/basics/rheumatoid-arthritis.html

Centers for Disease Control and Prevention. (2021a). *Leading causes of death.* https://www.cdc.gov/nchs/fastats/leading-causes-of-death.htm

Centers for Disease Control and Prevention. (2021b). *Coronary heart disease.* https://www.cdc.gov/heartdisease/coronary_ad.htm

Centers for Disease Control and Prevention. (2021c). *Chronic Obstructive Pulmonary Disease (COPD).* https://www.cdc.gov/copd/index.html

Centers for Disease Control and Prevention. (2021d). *Pneumonia.* https://www.cdc.gov/pneumonia/causes.html

Centers for Disease Control and Prevention. (2021e). *Types of healthcare-associated infections.* https://www.cdc.gov/hai/infectiontypes.html

Centers for Disease Control and Prevention. (2021f). *What are the symptoms of breast cancer?* https://www.cdc.gov/cancer/breast/basic_info/symptoms.htm

Chamberlain, A. M., Dunlay, S. M., Gerber, Y., Manemann, S. M., Jiang, R., Weston, S. A., & Roger, V. L. (2017). Burden and timing of hospitalizations in heart failure: A community study. *Mayo Clinic Proceedings, 92*(2), 184–192. https://doi.org/10.1016/j.mayocp.2016.11.009

Chau, K. L. (2021). Clinical manifestations of Parkinson disease. *UpToDate.* https://www.uptodate.com/contents/clinical-manifestations-of-parkinson-disease

Chies, S. (2021). *Pratt's long-term care: Managing across the continuum* (5th ed.). Jones and Bartlett.

Clark, D. G. (2021). Aphasia: Prognosis and treatment. *UpToDate.* https://www.uptodate.com/contents/aphasia-prognosis-and-treatment

Coll, P. (2019). *Healthy aging : A complete guide to clinical management.* Springer Cham. https://doi.org/10.1007/978-3-030-06200-2

Colucci, W. S. (2021). Overview of the management of heart failure with reduced ejection fraction in adults. *UpToDate.* https://www.uptodate.com/contents/overview-of-the-management-of-heart-failure-with-reduced-ejection-fraction-in-adults

Colucci, W. S., & Dunlay, S. M. (2021). Clinical manifestations and diagnosis of advanced heart failure. *UpToDate.* https://www.uptodate.com/contents/clinical-manifestations-and-diagnosis-of-advanced-heart-failure

Cornelius, E. A. (1972). Increased incidence of lymphomas in thymectomized mice-Evidence for an immunological theory of aging. *Experientia, 28*(4), 459–459. https://doi.org/10.1007/BF02008340

Curhan, G. C. (2021). Kidney stones in adults: Prevention of recurrent kidney stones. *UpToDate.* https://www.uptodate.com/contents/kidney-stones-in-adults-prevention-of-recurrent-kidney-stones

Curhan, G. C., Aronson, M. D., & Preminger, G. M. (2021). Kidney stones in adults: Diagnosis and acute management of suspected nephrolithiasis. *UpToDate.* https://www.uptodate.com/contents/kidney-stones-in-adults-diagnosis-and-acute-management-of-suspected-nephrolithiasis

Daga, L. C., Kaul, U., & Mansoor, A. (2011). Approach to STEMI and NSTEMI. *Journal of Association of Physicians of India, 59*(12), 19–25. PMID: 22624277.

Davidovic, M., Sevo, G., Svorcan, P., Milosevic, D. P., Despotovic, N., & Erceg, P. (2010). Old age as a privilege of the "selfish ones." *Aging and Disease, 1*(2), 139–146. PMID: 22396861.

Denic, A., Glassock, R. J., & Rule, A. D. (2016). Structural and functional changes with the aging kidney. *Advances in Chronic Kidney Disease, 23*(1), 19–28. https://doi.org/10.1053/j.ackd.2015.08.004

Deveza, L. A. (2021). Overview of the management of osteoarthritis. *UpToDate.* https://www-uptodate-com/contents/overview-of-the-management-of-osteoarthritis

Dillon, C., Serrano, C. M., Castro, D., Pérez Leguizamón, P., Heisecke, S. L., & Taragano, F. E. (2013). Behavioral symptoms related to cognitive impairment. *Neuropsychiatric Disease and Treatment, 2013*(9), 1443–1455. https://doi.org/10.2147/NDT.S47133

DiMeglio, L. A. (2021). COVID-19 and Type 1 diabetes: Addressing concerns and maintaining control. *Diabetes Care, 44*(9), 1924–1928. https://doi.org/10.2337/dci21-0002

Doherty, M., & Abhishek, A. (2021). Clinical manifestations and diagnosis of osteoarthritis. *UpToDate.* https://www.uptodate.com/contents/clinical-manifestations-and-diagnosis-of-osteoarthritis

Douglas-Hall, P., & Whicher, E. V. (2015). "As required" medication regimens for seriously mentally ill people in hospital. *Cochrane Database of Systematic Reviews, 12*, CD003441. https://doi.org/10.1002/14651858.CD003441.pub3

Eliopoulos, C. (2018). *Gerontological nursing* (9th ed.). Wolters Kluwer.

Elliott, A. F., Dreer, L. E., McGwin, G., Jr., Scilley, K., & Owsley, C. (2010). The personal burden of decreased vision-targeted health-related quality of life in nursing home residents. *Journal of Aging and Health, 22*(4), 504–521. https://doi.org/10.1177/0898264310361368

Ernstmeyer, K., & Christman, E. (2020). *Open RN nursing pharmacology textbook.* WI Technical Colleges Open Press.

Espinoza, R. T., & Unutzer, J. (2019). Diagnosis and management of late-life unipolar depression. *UpToDate.* https://www.uptodate.com/contents/diagnosis-and-management-of-late-life-unipolar-depression

Fabiani-Longo, D., Bishop, K., Mullen, J., Murphy, C., Allen, J., Cornelius, V., Dismore, J., McGeoch, K., & Grabbe, J. W. (2017). Physical changes in age. In J. W. Grabbe (Ed.), *Recent advances in geriatric medicine volume 2: An interdisciplinary approach to geriatric medicine* (pp. 25–38). Bentham Science Publishers Ltd.

Fass, R. (2020). Approach to the evaluation of dysphagia in adults. *UpToDate.* https://www.uptodate.com/contents/approach-to-the-evaluation-of-dysphagia-in-adults

Fatehi, P., & Hsu, C. (2020). Chronic kidney disease (newly identified): Clinical presentation and diagnostic approach in adults. *UpToDate.* https://www.uptodate.com/contents/chronic-kidney-disease-newly-identified-clinical-presentation-and-diagnostic-approach-in-adults

Fekete, T., & Hooton, T. M. (2021). Asymptomatic bacteriuria in adults. *UpToDate.* https://www.uptodate.com/contents/asymptomatic-bacteriuria-in-adults

Ferrah, N., Lovell, J. J., & Ibrahim, J. E. (2017). Systematic review of the prevalence of medication errors resulting in hospitalization and death of nursing home residents. *Journal of the American Geriatrics Society, 65*(2), 433–442. https://doi.org/10.1111/jgs.14683

Ferreira, A. R., Dias, C. C., & Fernandes, L. (2016). Needs in nursing homes and their relation with cognitive and functional decline, behavioral and psychological symptoms. *Frontiers in Aging Neuroscience, 8,* 72. https://doi.org/10.3389/fnagi.2016.00072

Ferrini, A. F., & Ferrini, R. L. (2012). *Health in the later years* (5th ed.). McGraw Hill.

Fornari, C. B., Bergonci, D., Stein, C. B., Agostini, B. A., & Rigo, L. (2021). Prevalence of xerostomia and its association with systemic diseases and medications in the elderly: A cross-sectional study. *Sao Paulo Medical Journal, 139*(4), 380–387. https://doi.org/10.1590/1516-3180.2020.0616.r3.1902021

Francis, J., & Young, G. B. (2020). Diagnosis of delirium and confusional states. *UpToDate.* https://www.uptodate.com/contents/diagnosis-of-delirium-and-confusional-states

Furie, K. L., & Rost, N. S. (2021). Initial evaluation and management of transient ischemic attack and minor ischemic stroke. *UpToDate.* https://www.uptodate.com/contents/initial-evaluation-and-management-of-transient-ischemic-attack-and-minor-ischemic-stroke

Gallo, J. J., Rabins, P. V., Lyketsos, C. G., Tien, A. Y., & Anthony, J. C. (1997). Depression without sadness: Functional outcomes of nondysphoric depression in later life. *Journal of the American Geriatrics Society, 45*(5), 570–578. https://doi.org/10.1111/j.1532-5415.1997.tb03089.x

Gecaite-Stonciene, J., Hughes, B. M., Burkauskas, J., Bunevicius, A., Kazukauskiene, N., van Houtum, L., Brozaitiene, J., Neverauskas, J., & Mickuviene, N. (2021). Fatigue is associated with diminished cardiovascular response to anticipatory stress in patients with coronary artery disease. *Frontiers in Physiology, 12,* 692098. https://doi.org/10.3389/fphys.2021.692098

Glaucoma Research Foundation. (2020). *Types of glaucoma.* https://www.glaucoma.org/glaucoma/types-of-glaucoma.php

Global Initiative for Asthma. (2021). *Global strategy for asthma management and prevention.* https://ginasthma.org/wp-content/uploads/2021/05/GINA-Main-Report-2021-V2-WMS.pdf

Global Initiative for Chronic Obstructive Lung Disease. (2021). *Global strategy for the diagnosis, management, and prevention of chronic obstructive pulmonary disease: 2021 report.* https://goldcopd.org/2021-gold-reports/

Goorang, S., Ausman, L., Houser, R., & Whiting, S. J. (2015). Profile of use of vitamin and mineral supplements among elderly institutionalized adults: A systematic review. *Journal of Nursing Home Research, 1,* 1–5. https://www.jnursinghomeresearch.com/385-profile-of-use-of-vitamin-and-mineral-supplements-among-elderly-institutionalized-adults-a-systematic-review.html

Grada, A., & Phillips, T. J. (2021). Pressure injuries. *Merck manual—Professional version.* https://www.merckmanuals.com/professional/dermatologic-disorders/pressure-injury/pressure-injuries

Grant, R. A., Morales-Nebreda, L., Markov, N. S., Swaminathan, S., Querrey, M., Guzman, E. R., Abbott, D. A., Donnelly, H. K., Donayre, A., Goldberg, A. I., Klug, Z. M., Borkowski, N., Lu, Z., Kihshen, H., Politanska, Y., Sichizya, L., Kang, M., Shilatifard, A., Qi, C., . . . The NU SCRIPT Study Investigators. (2021). Circuits between infected macrophages and T cells in SARS-CoV-2 pneumonia. *Nature, 590,* 635–641. https://doi.org/10.1038/s41586-020-03148-w

Griffin, S. (2020). COVID-19: Continued outbreaks in care homes risk extending pandemic, say experts. *BMJ, 369,* m2530. https://doi.org/10.1136/bmj.m2530

Groot Kormelinck, C. M., van Teunenbroek, C. F., Kollen, B. J., Reitsma, M., Gerritsen, D. L., Smalbrugge, M., & Zuidema, S. U. (2019). Reducing inappropriate psychotropic drug use in nursing home residents with dementia: Protocol for participatory action research in a stepped-wedge cluster randomized trial. *BMC Psychiatry, 19*(1), 298. https://doi.org/10.1186/s12888-019-2291-4

Hajjar, R. R., & Kamel, H. K. (2004). Sexuality in the nursing home, Part 1: Attitudes and barriers to sexual expression. *Journal of the American Medical Directors Association, 5*(2), S43–S47. https://doi.org/10.1016/S1525-8610(04)70092-4

Hall, R. K., O'Hare, A. M., Anderson, R. A., & Colón-Emeric, C. S. (2013). End-stage renal disease in nursing homes: A systematic review. *Journal of the American Medical Directors Association, 14*(4), 242–247. https://doi.org/10.1016/j.jamda.2013.01.004

Hallal, P. C., Andersen, L. B., Bull, F. C., Guthold, R., Haskell, W., & Ekelund, U. (2012). & Lancet Physical Activity Series Working Group. Global physical activity levels: Surveillance progress, pitfalls, and prospects. *The Lancet, 380*(9838), 247–257. https://doi.org/10.1016/S0140-6736(12)60646-1

Halter, J. B., Ouslander, J. G., Studenski, S., High, K. P., Asthana, S., Supiano, M. A., & Ritchie, C. (2017). *Hazzard's geriatric medicine and gerontology* (7th ed.). McGraw Hill.

Han, M. K., Dransfield, M. T., & Martinez, F. J. (2020). Chronic obstructive pulmonary disease: Definition, clinical manifestations, diagnosis, and staging. *UpToDate.* https://www.uptodate.com/contents/chronic-obstructive-pulmonary-disease-definition-clinical-manifestations-diagnosis-and-staging

Harman, D. (1956). Aging: A theory based on free radical and radiation chemistry. *Journal of Gerontology, 11,* 298–300. https://doi.org/10.1093/geronj/11.3.298

Hayflick, L., & Moorehead, M. (1961). The serial cultivation of human diploid cell strains. *Experimental Cell Research, 25,* 585–621. https://doi.org/10.1016/0014-4827(61)90192-6

Heflin, M. T. (2021). Geriatric health maintenance. *UpToDate.* https://www.uptodate.com/contents/geriatric-health-maintenance

Hochberg, N. S., Rekhtman, S., Burns, J., Ganley-Leal, L., Helbig, S., Watts, N. S., Brandeis, G. H., Ellner, J. J., & Horsburgh, J. C. R. (2016). The complexity of diagnosing latent tuberculosis infection in older adults in long-term care facilities. *International Journal of Infectious Diseases, 44,* 37–43. https://doi.org/10.1016/j.ijid.2016.01.007

Hooton, T. M., & Gupta, K. (2021). Acute complicated urinary tract infection (including pyelonephritis) in adults. *UpToDate.* https://www.uptodate.com/contents/acute-complicated-urinary-tract-infection-including-pyelonephritis-in-adults

Hoover, D. R., Siegel, M., Lucas, J., Kalay, E., Gaboda, D., Devanand, D. P., & Crystal, S. (2010). Depression in the first year of stay for elderly long-term nursing home residents in the USA. *International Psychogeriatrics, 22*(7), 1161–1171. https://doi.org/10.1017/S1041610210000578

Huang, J., Zou, Y., Huang, W., Zhou, Y., Lin, S., Chen, J., & Lan, Y. (2020). Factors associated with physical activity in elderly nursing home residents: A path analysis. *BMC Geriatrics*, *20*(1), 274. https://doi.org/10.1186/s12877-020-01676-8

International Cystitis Association. (2015). *Bladder retraining*. https://www.ichelp.org/diagnosis-treatment/management-of-ic-pain/bladder-retraining/

Jacobs, D. S. (2021a). Open-angle glaucoma: Treatment. *UpToDate*. https://www.uptodate.com/contents/open-angle-glaucoma-treatment

Jacobs, D. S. (2021b). Cataract in adults. *UpToDate*. https://www.uptodate.com/contents/cataract-in-adults

Jankowiak, M. (2009). Sexuality in nursing facilities. *Provider*, *35*(1), 33–35. PMID: 19226873.

Jin, K. (2010). Modern biological theories of aging. *Aging and Disease*, *1*(2), 72. https://www.ncbi.nlm.nih.gov/pmc/articles/PMC2995895/

Kahrilas, P. J. (2020). Medical management of gastroesophageal reflux disease in adults. *UpToDate*. https://www.uptodate.com/contents/medical-management-of-gastroesophageal-reflux-disease-in-adults

Kane, R. L., Ouslander, J. G., Resnick, B., & Malone, M. (2018). *Essentials of clinical geriatrics* (8th ed.). McGraw Hill.

Kannam, J. P., Aroesty, J. M., & Gersh, B. J. (2021). Chronic coronary syndrome: Overview of care. *UpToDate*. https://www.uptodate.com/contents/chronic-coronary-syndrome-overview-of-care

Kennedy, K. L. (1989). The prevalence of pressure ulcers in an intermediate care facility. *Decubitis*, *2*(2), 44–45. PMID: 2787655.

Khan, A., Rebhan, A., Seminara, D., & Szerszen, A. (2019). Enduring challenge of latent tuberculosis in older nursing home residents: A brief review. *Journal of Clinical Medicine Research*, *11*(6), 385–390. https://doi.org/10.14740/jocmr3763

Kim, A. Y., & Gandhi, R. T. (2021). COVID-19: Management in hospitalized adults. *UpToDate*. https://www.uptodate.com/contents/covid-19-management-in-hospitalized-adults

Klein, E. A. (2021). Prostate cancer: Risk stratification and choice of initial treatment. *UpToDate*. https://www.uptodate.com/contents/prostate-cancer-risk-stratification-and-choice-of-initial-treatment

Lalic, S., Sluggett, J. K., Ilomäki, J., Wimmer, B. C., Tan, E. C. K., Robson, L., Emery, T., & Bell, J. S. (2016). Polypharmacy and medication regimen complexity as risk factors for hospitalization among residents of long-term care facilities: A prospective cohort study. *Journal of the American Medical Directors Association*, *17*(11), 1067. https://doi.org/10.1016/j.jamda.2016.08.019

Langemo, D. K., & Brown, G. (2006). Skin fails too: acute, chronic, and end-stage skin failure. *Advances in Skin & Wound Care*, *19*(4), 206–211. https://doi.org/10.1097/00129334-200605000-00014

Langston, J. (2006). The Parkinson's complex: Parkinsonism is just the tip of the iceberg. *Annals of Neurology*, *59*(4), 591–596. https://doi.org/10.1002/ana.20834

Larson, E. B. (2019). Evaluation of cognitive impairment and dementia. *UpToDate*. https://www.uptodate.com/contents/evaluation-of-cognitive-impairment-and-dementia

Lee, C. M., & Afshari, N. A. (2017). The global state of cataract blindness. *Current Opinion in Ophthalmology*, *28*(1), 98–103. https://doi.org/10.1097/ICU.0000000000000340

Lester, P. E., Kohen, I., Stefanacci, R. G., & Feuerman, M. (2016). Sex in nursing homes: a survey of nursing home policies governing resident sexual activity. *Journal of the American Medical Directors Association*, *17*(1), 71–74. https://doi.org/10.1016/j.jamda.2015.08.013

Lok, N., Lok, S., & Canbaz, M. (2017). The effect of physical activity on depressive symptoms and quality of life among elderly nursing home residents: Randomized controlled trial. *Archives of Gerontology and Geriatrics*, *70*, 92–98. https://doi.org/10.1016/j.archger.2017.01.008

Lucacz, E. S. (2021). Evaluation of females with urinary incontinence. *UpToDate*. https://www.uptodate.com/contents/evaluation-of-females-with-urinary-incontinence

Mauk, K., & Silva-Smith, A. (2018). Management of common illnesses, diseases, and health conditions. In K. Mauk (Ed.), *Gerontological nursing* (4th ed.; pp. 305–386). Jones & Bartlett.

McGarrigle, L., Irving, K., van Boxtel, M. P. J., & Boran, L. (2019). Cognitive reserve capacity: Exploring and validating a theoretical model in healthy ageing. *Journal of the International Neuropsychological Society*, 25(6), 603–617. https://doi.org/10.1017/S1355617719000250

Mcnamara, J. J., Molot, M. A., Stremple, J. F., & Cutting, R. T. (1971). Coronary artery disease in combat casualties in Vietnam. *JAMA*, 216(7), 1185–1187. https://doi.org/10.1001/jama.1971.03180330061012

McVary, K. T. (2021). Clinical manifestations and diagnostic evaluation of benign prostatic hyperplasia. *UpToDate*. https://www.uptodate.com/contents/clinical-manifestations-and-diagnostic-evaluation-of-benign-prostatic-hyperplasia

Means, R. T., & Brodsky, R. A. (2021). Diagnostic approach to anemia in adults. *UpToDate*. https://www.uptodate.com/contents/diagnostic-approach-to-anemia-in-adults

Meddings, J., Saint, S., Krein, S. L., Gaies, E., Reichert, H., Hickner, A., McNamara, S., Mann, J. D., & Mody, L. (2017). Systematic review of interventions to reduce urinary tract infection in nursing home residents. *Journal of Hospital Medicine*, 12(5), 356–368. https://doi.org/10.12788/jhm.2724

Meehan, R., & Shura, R. (2016). Residents' perspectives on living with vision impairment in long-term care: An unseen factor in quality of life and appropriateness of care. *Journal of Nursing Home Research*. https://www.jnursinghomeresearch.com/646-residents-perspectives-on-living-with-vision-impairment-in-long-term-care-an-unseen-factor-in-quality-of-life-and-appropriateness-of-care.html

Michel, J. P., Beattie, B. L., Martin, F. C., & Walston, J. (2017). *Oxford textbook of geriatric medicine* (3rd ed.). Oxford University Press.

Mikkelsen, M. E., & Abramoff, B. (2021). COVID-19: Evaluation and management of adults following acute viral illness. *UpToDate*. https://www.uptodate.com/contents/covid-19-evaluation-and-management-of-adults-following-acute-viral-illness

Mileski, M., McClay, R., & Natividad, J. (2021). Facilitating factors in the proper identification of acute skin failure: A systematic review. *Critical Care Nurse*, 41(2), 36–42. https://doi.org/10.4037/ccn2021145

Mileski, M., Pannu, U., Payne, B., Sterling, E., & McClay, R. (2020, June). The impact of nurse practitioners on hospitalizations and discharges from long-term nursing facilities: A systematic review. *Healthcare*, 8(2), 114. https://doi.org/10.3390/healthcare8020114

Mileski, M., Topinka, J. B., Brooks, M., Lonidier, C., Linker, K., & Vander Veen, K. (2018). Sensory and memory stimulation as a means to care for individuals with dementia in long-term care facilities. *Clinical Interventions in Aging*, 13(967), 967–974. https://doi.org/10.2147/CIA.S153113

Mitteldorf, J. (2010). Aging is not a process of wear and tear. *Rejuvenation Research*, 13(2–3), 322–326. http://doi.org/10.1089/rej.2009.0967

Moermans, V. R. A., Bleijlevens, M. H. C., Verbeek, H., Tan, F. E. S., Milisen, K., & Hamers, J. P. H. (2018). The use of involuntary treatment among older adults with cognitive impairment receiving nursing care at home: A cross-sectional study. *International Journal of Nursing Studies*, 88, 135–142. https://doi.org/10.1016/j.ijnurstu.2018.09.004

Mora, J. C., & Valencia, W. M. (2018). Exercise and older adults. *Clinics in Geriatric Medicine*, 34(1), 145–162. https://doi.org/10.1016/j.cger.2017.08.007

Morbidity and Mortality Weekly Report. (1990). *Prevention and control of tuberculosis in facilities providing long-term care to the elderly recommendations of the Advisory Committee for the Elimination of Tuberculosis*. Centers for Disease Control and Prevention. https://www.cdc.gov/mmwr/preview/mmwrhtml/00001711.htm

National Academies of Sciences, Engineering, and Medicine. (2020). *Social isolation and loneliness in older adults: Opportunities for the health care system.* The National Academies Press. https://doi.org/10.17226/25663

National Health Service. (2019). *Diagnosis—Heart attack.* https://www.nhs.uk/conditions/heart-attack/diagnosis/

National Healthcare Safety Network. (2021). *Bloodstream infection event (central-line associated bloodstream infection and non-central line associated bloodstream infection.* https://www.cdc.gov/nhsn/pdfs/pscmanual/4psc_clabscurrent.pdf

National Heart, Lung, and Blood Institute. (2021a). *Coronary heart disease.* https://www.nhlbi.nih.gov/health-topics/coronary-heart-disease

National Heart, Lung, and Blood Institute. (2021b). *Heart failure.* https://www.nhlbi.nih.gov/health-topics/heart-failure

National Heart, Lung, and Blood Institute. (2021c). *COPD.* https://www.nhlbi.nih.gov/health-topics/copd

National Heart, Lung, and Blood Institute. (2021d). *Anemia.* https://www.nhlbi.nih.gov/health-topics/anemia

National Institute of Arthritis and Musculoskeletal and Skin Diseases. (2019). *Osteoarthritis.* https://www.niams.nih.gov/health-topics/osteoarthritis/advanced

National Institute of Diabetes and Digestive and Kidney Diseases. (2016). *What is diabetes?* https://www.niddk.nih.gov/health-information/diabetes/overview/what-is-diabetes

National Institute of Diabetes and Digestive and Kidney Diseases. (2020). *Symptoms & causes of GER & GERD.* https://www.niddk.nih.gov/health-information/digestive-diseases/acid-reflux-ger-gerd-adults/symptoms-causes

National Institute of Diabetes and Digestive and Kidney Diseases. (2021). *Bladder infection (urinary tract infection—UTI) in adults.* https://www.niddk.nih.gov/health-information/urologic-diseases/bladder-infection-uti-in-adults

National Pressure Injury Advisory Panel. (n.d.). *NPIAP pressure injury stages.* https://cdn.ymaws.com/npiap.com/resource/resmgr/online_store/npiap_pressure_injury_stages.pdf

Neschis, D. G., & Golden, M. A. (2021). Clinical features and diagnosis of lower extremity peripheral artery disease. *UpToDate.* https://www.uptodate.com/contents/clinical-features-and-diagnosis-of-lower-extremity-peripheral-artery-disease

Nicolle, L. E., Gupta, K., Bradley, S. F., Colgan, R., DeMuri, G. P., Drekonja, D., Eckert, L. O., Geerlings, S. E., Köves, B., Hooton, T. M., Juthani-Mehta, M., Knight, S. L., Saint, S., Schaeffer, A. J., Trautner, B., Wullt, B., & Siemieniuk, R. (2019). Clinical practice guideline for the management of asymptomatic bacteriuria: 2019 update by the Infectious Diseases Society of America. *Clinical Infectious Diseases: An Official Publication of the Infectious Diseases Society of America, 68*(10), e83–e110. https://doi.org/10.1093/cid/ciy1121

Nolen, M. S., & Patton, R. M. (2009). ASHP statement on bar-code-enabled medication administration technology. *American Society of Health-Systems Pharmacists, 66,* 588–590. https://www.ashp.org/-/media/assets/policy-guidelines/docs/statements/bar-code-enabled-medication-administration-technology.pdf

Northey, J. M., Cherbuin, N., Pumpa, K. L., Smee, D. J., & Rattray, B. (2018). Exercise interventions for cognitive function in adults older than 50: A systematic review with meta-analysis. *British Journal of Sports Medicine, 52*(3), 154–160. https://doi.org/10.1136/bjsports-2016-096587

Nyborg, G., Brekke, M., Straand, J., Gjelstad, S., & Romøren, M. (2017). Potentially inappropriate medication use in nursing homes: An observational study using the NORGEP-NH criteria. *BMC Geriatrics, 17*(1), 1–11. https://doi.org/10.1186/s12877-017-0608-z

O'Mahony, D. (2020). STOPP/START criteria for potentially inappropriate medications/ potential prescribing omissions in older people: Origin and progress. *Expert Review of Clinical Pharmacology, 13*(1), 15–22. https://doi.org/10.1080/17512433.2020.1697676

Onder, G., Vetrano, D. L., Villani, E. R., Carfi, A., Lo Monaco, M. R., Cipriani, M. C., Manes Gravina, E., Denkinger, M., Pagano, F., van der Roest, H. G., & Bernabei, R. (2019). Deprescribing in nursing home residents on polypharmacy: Incidence and associated factors. *Journal of the American Medical Directors Association, 20*(9), 1116–1120. https://doi.org/10.1016/j.jamda.2019.01.130

OpenStax College. (2021). *Anatomy and physiology.* https://openstax.org/books/anatomy-and-physiology/pages/1-introduction

Paffenbarger, R. S., Jr, Wing., L, A., & Hyde, R. T. (1978). Physical activity as an index of heart attack risk in college alumni. *American Journal of Epidemiology, 108*(3), 161–175. https://doi.org/10.1093/oxfordjournals.aje.a112608

Palese, A., Bressan, V., Kasa, T., Meri, M., Hayter, M., & Watson, R. (2018). Interventions maintaining eating Independence in nursing home residents: A multicentre qualitative study. *BMC Geriatrics, 18*(1), 292. https://doi.org/10.1186/s12877-018-0985-y

Park, D. C., & Yeo, S. G. (2013). Aging. *Korean Journal of Audiology, 17*(2), 39–44. https://doi.org/10.7874/kja.2013.17.2.39

Paulis, S. J. C., Everink, I. H. J., Halfens, R. J. G., Lohrmann, C., & Schols, J. M. G. A. (2018). Prevalence and risk factors of dehydration among nursing home residents: A systematic review. *Journal of the American Medical Directors Association, 19*(8), 646–657. https://doi.org/10.1016/j.jamda.2018.05.009

Pitkälä, K., Savikko, N., Poysti, M., Strandberg, T., & Laakkonen, M. L. (2013). Efficacy of physical exercise intervention on mobility and physical functioning in older people with dementia: A systematic review. *Experimental Gerontology, 48*(1), 85–93. https://doi.org/10.1016/j.exger.2012.08.008

Press, D., & Alexander, M. (2021). Management of neuropsychiatric symptoms of dementia. *UpToDate.* https://www.uptodate.com/contents/management-of-neuropsychiatric-symptoms-of-dementia

Protenus. (2021). *2021 drug diversion digest.* https://www.protenus.com/resources/2021-drug-diversion-digest

Rao, S. S. C. (2020). Constipation in the older adult. *UpToDate.* https://www.uptodate.com/contents/constipation-in-the-older-adult

Reeder, G. S., & Kennedy, H. L. (2021). Diagnosis of acute myocardial infarction. *UpToDate.* https://www.uptodate.com/contents/diagnosis-of-acute-myocardial-infarction

Ritchie, C., & Yukawa, M. (2021). Geriatric nutrition: Nutritional issues in older adults. *UpToDate.* https://www.uptodate.com/contents/geriatric-nutrition-nutritional-issues-in-older-adults

Robson, K. M., & Lembo, A. J. (2020). Fecal incontinence in adults: Etiology and evaluation. *UpToDate.* https://www.uptodate.com/contents/fecal-incontinence-in-adults-etiology-and-evaluation

Roca-Biosca, A., Rubio-Rico, L., molina-Fernández, De., I, M., Martinez-Castillo, J. F., Pancorbo-Hidalgo, P. L., & García-Fernández, F. P. (2021). Kennedy terminal ulcer and other skin wounds at the end of life: An integrative review. *Journal of Tissue Viability, 30*(2), 178–182. https://doi.org/10.1016/j.jtv.2021.02.006

Rochon, P. A. (2021). Drug prescribing for older adults. *UpToDate.* https://www.uptodate.com/contents/drug-prescribing-for-older-adults

Rodnitzky, R. L. (2020). Cognitive impairment and dementia in Parkinson disease. *UpToDate.* https://www.uptodate.com/contents/cognitive-impairment-and-dementia-in-parkinson-disease

Ropper, A. H., Samuels, M. A., Klein, J. P., & Prasad, S (Eds.). (2019). *Adams and Victor's principles of neurology* (11th ed.). McGraw Hill.

Rosen, H. N., & Drezner, M. K. (2021). Overview of the management of osteoporosis in postmenopausal women. *UpToDate.* https://www.uptodate.com/contents/overview-of-the-management-of-osteoporosis-in-postmenopausal-women

Rosen, H. N., & Walega, D. R. (2020). Osteoporotic thoracolumbar vertebral compression fractures: Clinical manifestations and treatment. *UpToDate.* https://www.uptodate.com/contents/osteoporotic-thoracolumbar-vertebral-compression-fractures-clinical-manifestations-and-treatment

Rozemuller, A. J., van Gool, W. A., & Eikelenboom, P. (2005). The neuroinflammatory response in plaques and amyloid angiopathy in Alzheimer's disease: Therapeutic implications. *Current Drug Targets-CNS & Neurological Disorders, 4*(3), 223–233. https://doi.org/10.2174/1568007054038229

Saxon, S. V., Etten, M. J., & Perkins, E. A. (2022). *Physical change and aging* (7th ed.). Springer Publishing Company.

Schöllgen, I., Huxhold, O., & Schmiedek, F. (2012). Emotions and physical health in the second half of life: Interindividual differences in age-related trajectories and dynamic associations according to socioeconomic status. *Psychology and Aging, 27*(2), 338–352. https://doi.org/10.1037/a0026115

Sesso, H. D., Paffenbarger, R. S., Jr., & Lee, I. M. (2000). Physical activity and coronary heart disease in men: The Harvard Alumni Health Study. *Circulation, 102*(9), 975–980. https://doi.org/10.1161/01.CIR.102.9.975

Shah, K., Lo, C., Babich, M., Tsao, N. W., & Bansback, N. J. (2016). Bar code medication administration technology: A systematic review of impact on patient safety when used with computerized prescriber order entry and automated dispensing devices. *The Canadian Journal of Hospital Pharmacy, 69*(5), 394. https://doi.org/10.4212/cjhp.v69i5.1594

Singh, D. A. (2016). *Effective management of long-term care facilities* (3rd ed.). Jones & Bartlett.

Statista. (2022). *Population projections for the United States from 2015 to 2060.* https://www.statista.com/statistics/183481/united-states-population-projection/

Tache-Codreanu, D. L., & Cucu, C. D. (2020). The neuromuscular electrical stimulation associated with speech therapy exercises in dysphagia and dysarthria after stroke (clinical case). *Journal of Sport & Kinetic Movement, 1*(35), 42–48. https://jskm.ro/images/pdfs/35volI/THE-NEUROMUSCULAR-ELECTRICAL-STIMULATION-ASSOCIATED-WITH-SPEECH-THERAPY-EXERCICES-IN-DYSPHAGIA-AND-DYSARTHRIA-AFTER-STROKE.pdf

Taplin, M. E., & Smith, J. A. (2020). Clinical presentation and diagnosis of prostate cancer. *UpToDate.* https://www.uptodate.com/contents/clinical-presentation-and-diagnosis-of-prostate-cancer

Tatar, M., Bartke, A., & Antebi, A. (2003). The endocrine regulation of aging by insulin-like signals. *Science, 299*(5611), 1346–1351. https://doi.org/10.1126/science.1081447

Treister, N. S., Villa, A., & Thompson, L. (2020). Palliative care: Overview of mouth care at the end of life. *UpToDate.* https://www.uptodate.com/contents/palliative-care-overview-of-mouth-care-at-the-end-of-life

Troen, B. R. (2003). The biology of aging. *Mount Sinai Journal of Medicine, 70*(1), 3–22. PMID: 12516005.

Vaismoradi, M., Vizcaya Moreno, F., Sletvold, H., & Jordan, S. (2019). PRN medicines management for psychotropic medicines in long-term care settings: A systematic review. *Pharmacy, 7*(4), 157. https://doi.org/10.3390/pharmacy7040157

Vakil, N. B. (2020a). Peptic ulcer disease: Clinical manifestations and diagnosis. *UpToDate.* https://www.uptodate.com/contents/peptic-ulcer-disease-clinical-manifestations-and-diagnosis

Vakil, N. B. (2020b). Peptic ulcer disease: Treatment and secondary prevention. *UpToDate.* https://www.uptodate.com/contents/peptic-ulcer-disease-treatment-and-secondary-prevention

Van Gulick, L., Saby, C., Morjani, H., & Beljebbar, A. (2019). Age-related changes in molecular organization of type I collagen in tendon as probed by polarized SHG and Raman microspectroscopy. *Scientific Reports, 9*(1), 1–12. https://doi.org/10.1038/s41598-019-43636-2

Van Heemst, D. (2010). Insulin, IGF-1 and longevity. *Aging and Disease, 1*(2), 147–157. https://www.ncbi.nlm.nih.gov/pmc/articles/PMC3295030

Venables, P. J. W., & England, B. R. (2021). Clinical manifestations of rheumatoid arthritis. *UpToDate.* https://www.uptodate.com/contents/clinical-manifestations-of-rheumatoid-arthritis

Vetrano, D. L., Grande, G., Villani, E. R., Giovannini, S., Cipriani, M. C., Manes-Gravina, E., Bernabei, R., & Onder, G. (2018). Association of polypharmacy with 1-year trajectories of cognitive and physical function in nursing home residents: Results from a multicenter European study. *Journal of the American Medical Directors Association, 19*(8), 710–713. https://doi.org/10.1016/j.jamda.2018.04.008

Walter, L., & Chang, A. (2020). *Current diagnosis & treatment: Geriatrics* (3rd ed.). Lange Medical Books/McGraw Hill.

Williams, J., & Williams, C. (2020). Responsibility for vitamin D supplementation of elderly care home residents in England: falling through the gap between medicine and food. *BMJ Nutrition, Prevention & Health, 3*(2), 256–262. https://doi.org/10.1136/bmjnph-2020-000129

Winkelman, J. W. (2021). Overview of the treatment of insomnia in adults. *UpToDate.* https://www.uptodate.com/contents/overview-of-the-treatment-of-insomnia-in-adults

World Health Organization. (2021a). *Noncommunicable diseases.* https://www.who.int/health-topics/noncommunicable-diseases#tab=tab_1

World Health Organization. (2021b). *Hypertension.* https://www.who.int/news-room/fact-sheets/detail/hypertension

Yu, E. Q. (2021). Screening for osteoporosis in postmenopausal women and men. *UpToDate.* https://www.uptodate.com/contents/screening-for-osteoporosis-in-postmenopausal-women-and-men

Yu, L., Liang, Q., Zhou, W., Huang, X., Hu, L., You, C., Li, J., Wu, Y., Li, P., Wu, Q., Wang, Z., Gao, R., Bao, H., & Cheng, X. (2018). Association between physical activity and stroke in a middle-aged and elderly Chinese population. *Medicine, 97*(51), e13568. http://doi.org/10.1097/MD.0000000000013568

Putting the Systems Together

6.1 SETTING POLICIES FOR THE FACILITY

Section Concepts

- *Administrative policies*
- *Compliance with laws*
- *Health Information Management (HIM) policies and incentives*
- *Governing bodies*

Consider as the Administrator . . .

- *You are left with two choices; both involve violating regulations which conflict with each other. Which regulation do you violate?*

NAB DOMAIN 3B: REGULATORY COMPLIANCE; 3B1: FEDERAL HEALTHCARE LAWS, RULES, AND REGULATIONS; 3B2: GOVERNMENT PROGRAMS AND ENTITIES (E.G., MEDICARE, MEDICAID, WAIVERS); 3B3: CERTIFICATION AND LICENSURE REQUIREMENTS FOR THE ORGANIZATION

The following is a set of policies that, if followed, will enable a nursing facility to comply with the multitude of national rules and regulations that shape the nursing facility environment of today. The policies are based on the federal requirements for nursing facilities and are divided among the various functional areas of the nursing facility.

6.1.1 ADMINISTRATION POLICIES

RESOURCE UTILIZATION

The facility will be administered in a manner that enables it to use its resources effectively and efficiently to attain or maintain the highest practicable physical, mental, and psychosocial well-being of each resident (F835/§483.70).

COMPLIANCE WITH LAWS

The facility will be licensed under and adhere to applicable state and local laws (F836/§483.70(a)).

The facility will operate and provide services in compliance with all applicable federal, state, and local laws, regulations, and codes, and with accepted professional standards and principles that apply to professionals providing services in such a facility (F836/§483.70(b)).

HEALTH INFORMATION MANAGEMENT

NAB DOMAIN 1A8: CLINICAL AND MEDICAL RECORDS AND DOCUMENTATION REQUIREMENTS (E.G., STORAGE, RETENTION, DESTRUCTION); 2B11: HEALTHCARE RECORD REQUIREMENTS (E.G., CONFIDENTIALITY, DISCLOSURE, SAFEGUARDING, HIPAA, HITECH); 3B1: FEDERAL HEALTHCARE LAWS, RULES, AND REGULATIONS; 3B2: GOVERNMENT PROGRAMS AND ENTITIES (E.G., MEDICARE, MEDICAID, WAIVERS); 3B3: CERTIFICATION AND LICENSURE REQUIREMENTS FOR THE ORGANIZATION

In 2004, Executive Order 13335 provided incentives for developing and using health information technology (HIT) and established a National Health Information Technology Coordinator Office to implement the president's order. The Health Information Technology for Economic and Clinical Health (HITECH) Act of the American Recovery and Reinvestment Act (ARRA) of 2009 created reimbursement incentives for healthcare organizations that use electronic health records (EHRs) in meaningful ways (HITECH Act, 2009). Unfortunately, long-term care facilities were excluded from these incentives and were deemed "ineligible providers" under the ARRA (Kruse et al., 2015, 2017). This slight caused irreparable damage to the nursing facility in fully adopting EHR. Many facilities today use some level of EHRs, but all too many only use small components of otherwise larger suites of software that they can afford. The promise of interoperable HIT enables all healthcare providers to track patients across the entire healthcare spectrum, such as physicians' offices, outpatient services, pharmacies, home healthcare providers, assisted living facilities, and nursing facilities. Nursing facility residents make frequent transitions among all these providers. Having a single interoperable care record available to all providers can improve the quality of care at all levels (Kruse et al., 2017; Office of the National Coordinator for Health Information Technology, 2019).

Information technology is primarily federally driven. Nursing facilities must already provide information electronically to state Medicaid offices and Medicare intermediaries. Reimbursement is already tied to the Minimum Data Set (MDS) healthcare information recorded by facilities. Because Medicaid can vary from state to state, the details of the HIT required will vary. HIT can result in improvements across the spectrum of caregiving: improved quality measurements, better clinical and pharmaceutical accuracy, reduced errors of many types, and enhanced communication among the caregivers.

GOVERNING BODY

NAB DOMAIN 4A5: GOVERNANCE (E.G., BOARD OF DIRECTORS, GOVERNING BODIES, CORPORATE ENTITIES, ADVISORY BOARDS)

NAB DOMAIN 4B5: PUBLIC RELATIONS AND EXTERNAL STAKEHOLDERS (E.G., HOSPITALS, REFERRALS SOURCES, LOCAL COMMUNITY, DONORS)

The facility will have a governing body, or designated persons functioning as a governing body, that establishes and implements policies regarding the management and operation of the facility. The governing body is the group of persons who are legally responsible for the proper management and operation of the facility. The board bears ultimate responsibility for the acts of the organization. Sometimes the governing body is called the board of trustees, or sometimes the governing board. The governing body establishes the policies that the facility staff must implement. Occasionally, the governing body will also develop specific procedures that implement the broader policies set by the governing body (F837/§483.70(d)).

The governing body's role is to manage the organizational resources to carry out the wishes of the stakeholders as fully as possible. The governing body sets the mission for the organization and then provides policies and resources for the organization to implement.

Generally, the governing body is a group appointed by the owners to represent the owners' interests. The governing body has the general obligation to operate within the applicable national, state, and local laws and standards of practice. There is no formal governing body of persons appointed to manage the facility in some cases. This lack of governing body occurs when one person has been appointed to manage the facility, such as in many not-for-profit situations. There is no immediate governing body setting policies for the facility in this case. In a landmark case known as the Pacific Homes in California, the Methodist Church's Annual Conference that governs all the churches and church-owned healthcare facilities in Southern California and Arizona served as the "governing body." A court decision held the Annual Conference of the Methodist Church to be financially responsible for poor care given in its Pacific Homes facility.

TRANSFER AGREEMENT

NAB DOMAIN 1A11: TRANSITION OF CARE (E.G., ADMISSION, MOVE-IN, TRANSFER, DISCHARGE, AND MOVE-OUT)

The facility has a written transfer agreement with one or more hospitals approved for participation under the Medicare and Medicaid programs, which reasonably ensures that (a) residents receive timely admission to the hospital when medically appropriate as determined by the attending physician, and (b) medical and other information needed for care and treatment of residents is available for determining whether residents can receive appropriate care and services in the hospital, or if transfer to a less restrictive setting is in order (F843/§483.70(j)).

CHANGES IN OWNERSHIP

NAB DOMAIN 3B1: FEDERAL HEALTHCARE LAWS, RULES, AND REGULATIONS; 3B2: GOVERNMENT PROGRAMS AND ENTITIES (E.G., MEDICARE, MEDICAID, WAIVERS); 3B3: CERTIFICATION AND LICENSURE REQUIREMENTS FOR THE ORGANIZATION

The facility will provide written notice to the state agency responsible for licensing the facility at the time of change if a change occurs in (a) persons with an ownership or controlling interest; (b) the officers, directors, agents, or managing employees; (c) the corporation, association, or other company responsible for the management of the facility; or (d) the facility's administrator or director of nursing (DON; F844/§483.70(k)(2))).

COMMON PITFALLS IN PRACTICE

- There are always conflicting laws and regulations with which to contend. Best practice is to comply with *all* these different laws and regulations (federal, state, local, city, county, etc.). There is no correct answer on which one to follow if they conflict. You must answer to all of them or explain why you cannot comply with certain local, city, or county regulations.
- Ultimately, *you* as the administrator are responsible for notifying the state of a change in administrator. Follow your corporate policies but ensure that this crucial paperwork is done and that you have proof to show surveyors when they enter your facility.

6.1.2 PERSONNEL POLICIES

Section Concepts

- *Facility human resource policies*
- *The personnel staff person needs to be aware of qualification requirements for:*
  - *Activities staff*
  - *Social services staff members*
  - *All nurses*
  - *Pharmacists, dietitians, and other consultants*
  - *Medical director and medical providers (i.e., MD/DO/NP)*
- *Why the staff person handling personnel functions needs to be aware of special requirements regulating the following:*
  - *Training of nurse's aides*
  - *Regular in-service education requirements for various staff*
  - *Uses of outside resources*
  - *Disaster and emergency preparedness*
  - *Employee screening and training, and nonemployment of specific individuals*

Consider as the Administrator . . .

- *You are but only one person. Is it possible for you to understand and enforce all these differing policies for each of your staff members?*

NAB DOMAIN 1B17: THERAPEUTIC RECREATION AND ACTIVITY PROGRAMS; 2C: HUMAN RESOURCES

ACTIVITIES

Properly Qualified Activities Program Professional

The activities program will be directed by a professional who is a qualified therapeutic recreation specialist or an activities professional who—(i) is licensed or registered, if applicable, by the state in which they are practicing and (ii) is eligible for certification as a therapeutic recreation specialist or as an activity professional by a recognized accrediting body on or after October 1, 1990; or (b) has 2 years of experience in a social or recreational program within the last 5 years, one of which was full-time in a therapeutic activities program; or (c) is a qualified occupational therapist or occupational therapy assistant; or (d) has completed a training course approved by the state (F680/§483.24(c)(2))).

Activities will achieve multiple goals, such as promoting a sense of well-being, building self-esteem, giving pleasure, creating a sense of fulfillment, providing a sense of accomplishment, promoting physical and mental fitness, and accomplishing social fulfillment (Singh, 2016). Activities will be individualized to meet each resident's unique needs.

SOCIAL SERVICES

NAB DOMAIN 1B16: SOCIAL SERVICES PROGRAMS

The facility will provide medically related social services to attain or maintain the highest practicable physical, mental, and psychosocial well-being of each resident to ensure that sufficient and appropriate social services are provided to meet the resident's needs (F745/§483.40(d)). Whenever the facility has more than 120 beds, it will employ a qualified social worker full time (F850/§483.70(p)).

Qualifications of the Social Worker

It is facility policy that a qualified social worker is an individual with (a) a bachelor's degree in social work or a bachelor's degree in a human services field, including, but not limited to, sociology, gerontology, special education, rehabilitation counseling, or psychology, and (b) 1 year of supervised social work experience in a healthcare setting working directly with individuals (F850/§483.70(p)).

REGISTERED NURSE

NAB DOMAIN 2C5: STAFF CERTIFICATION AND LICENSURE REQUIREMENTS

The facility will use the services of a registered nurse for at least 8 consecutive hours a day, 7 days a week (F727/§483.35(b)(1)). A registered nurse will be designated to serve as the DON on a full-time basis (F727/§483.35(b)(2)). The DON may serve as a charge nurse only when the facility has an average daily occupancy of 60 or fewer residents (F727/§483.35(b)(3)).

SPECIALIZED REHABILITATIVE SERVICES PERSONNEL

NAB DOMAIN 2B13: CONTRACTED SERVICES (E.G., ROLES, RESPONSIBILITIES, OVERSIGHT, BACKGROUND CHECKS); 2C5: STAFF CERTIFICATION AND LICENSURE REQUIREMENTS; 2C14: LABOR RELATIONS (E.G., UNION, COLLECTIVE BARGAINING [CBA], CONTRACT/POOL STAFF)

Specialized rehabilitative services will be provided under the written order of a physician by qualified personnel (F826/§483.65(b)). Qualified personnel refers to physical therapists, occupational therapists, respiratory therapists, speech/language pathologists, physicians, nurse practitioners, clinical nurse specialists, or physician assistants. Qualified personnel also refers to physical therapy assistants and occupational therapy assistants furnishing services under a qualified therapist.

CONSULTANT PHARMACIST

The facility will employ or obtain the services of a licensed pharmacist who (a) provides consultation on all aspects of the provision of pharmacy services in the facility (F755/§483.45(b)(1)), (b) establishes a system of records of receipt and disposition of all controlled drugs in sufficient detail to enable an accurate reconciliation (F755/§483.45(b)(2)), and (c) determines that drug records are in order and that an account of all controlled drugs is maintained and periodically reconciled (F755/§483.45(b)(3)).

TRAINING OF NURSE'S AIDES

The facility will not use any individual working in the facility as a nurse's aide for more than 4 months, on a full-time basis, unless (a) that individual is competent to provide nursing and nursing-related services and (b) that individual has completed a training and competency evaluation program, or a competency evaluation program approved by the state as meeting the requirements (F728/§483.35(d)(1)). The facility will not use nonpermanent employees as nurse's aides unless they have completed either a training and competency evaluation program or a state-approved competency evaluation program (F728/§483.35(d)(2)).

Regular In-Service Education

NAB DOMAIN 2C6: PROFESSIONAL DEVELOPMENT (E.G., MAINTENANCE OF CREDENTIALS, CONTINUING EDUCATION); 2C7: EMPLOYEE TRAINING AND ORIENTATION

The facility will complete a performance review of every nurse's aide at least once every 12 months and will provide regular in-service education based on the outcome of these reviews (F730/§483.35(d)(7)).

STAFF QUALIFICATIONS

NAB DOMAIN 2C5: STAFF CERTIFICATION AND LICENSURE REQUIREMENTS

The facility will employ, on a full-time, part-time, or consultant basis, those professionals necessary to carry out the provisions of these requirements (F839/§483.70(f)(1)). Professional staff will be licensed, certified, or registered per applicable state laws (F839/§483.70(f)(2)).

USE OF OUTSIDE RESOURCES

If the facility does not employ a qualified professional person to furnish a specific service to be provided by the facility, the facility will have that service furnished to residents by a person or agency outside the facility under an appropriate agreement (F840/§483.70(g)(1)).

MEDICAL DIRECTOR

NAB DOMAIN 1A9: MEDICAL DIRECTOR

The facility will designate a physician to serve as a medical director (F841/§483.70(h) (1)) who is responsible for the implementation of resident care policies and the coordination of medical care in the facility (F841/§483.70(h)(2)).

SAFETY, DISASTER, AND EMERGENCY PREPAREDNESS: TRAINING FOR ALL EMPLOYEES IN EMERGENCY PROCEDURES

NAB DOMAIN 1B18: COMMUNITY RESOURCES, PROGRAMS, AND AGENCIES (E.G., MEALS ON WHEELS, HOUSING VOUCHERS, AREA AGENCIES ON AGING, VETERANS AFFAIRS)

NAB DOMAIN 3A7: INFECTION CONTROL AND SANITATION (E.G., LINENS, KITCHEN, HAND WASHING, HEALTHCARE-ACQUIRED INFECTIONS, HAZARDOUS MATERIALS)

NAB DOMAIN 2C7: EMPLOYEE TRAINING AND ORIENTATION; 3A8: DISASTER AND EMERGENCY PLANNING, PREPAREDNESS, RESPONSE, AND RECOVERY (E.G., APPENDIX Z)

The facility will train all employees in emergency preparedness policies and procedures when they begin to work in the facility, provide emergency preparedness training at least annually, and demonstrate staff knowledge of emergency procedures (§483.73(d)(1)). The facility must conduct exercises to test the emergency plan at least annually and carry out unannounced staff drills using those procedures (§483.73(d)(2)). The facility will have detailed written plans and procedures to address all potential emergencies and disasters, such as fire, severe weather, and missing residents, which must be updated annually (§483.73(b)).

Few nursing facilities can afford to employ a full-time disaster coordinator or security staff. Thus, the responsibility for safety and disaster preparedness typically falls on the administrator. Safety applies to everyone having contact with the facility: the public, the employees, and the residents. It is necessary to pay attention to providing a safe environment for all who interact with the facility; this includes fire safety and environmental safety, including accident prevention. Accident prevention becomes an all-hands operation, from planning a safe building to planning how each resident can safely move about the facility. Life safety from a fire can be achieved by following the Life Safety Code requirements and recommendations. A safe physical environment begins with implementing the Americans with Disabilities Act requirements. Physical safety extends from controlling for outside intruders to controlling residents' behavior toward each other.

Disaster preparedness requires the administrator and staff to imagine all possible disaster scenarios that might occur to the specific facility. Common to all facilities are disaster concerns such as fire; loss of potable water; storm damage (such as losing a roof or other parts of the building); loss of electrical power; water damage from flooding toilets, bathing areas, the kitchen, or other areas; and the sudden outbreak of a highly infectious disease. A *disaster* is any event that threatens the functioning and safety of any aspect of delivering safe and effective quality care to residents—not just tornados, earthquakes, and hurricanes.

The facility should have disaster plans with appropriate outside agencies such as the local fire department, the local water department, the local emergency medical services agency, the local hospital(s), and any other group or agency that can respond to facility disasters.

Actual readiness for a disaster requires that the staff be trained with actual drills, which are randomly announced, participated in, and evaluated in postdrill debriefing. Fire drills are the most common in the nursing facility. Still, other drills may be appropriate, such as calling 911 and conducting emergency care for a resident or visitor on the premises.

There are numerous resources in the community to assist a facility in times of disaster. Planning with these agencies is key to a smooth response to disasters.

Emergency Materials

The facility is required to keep an emergency kit containing medications to meet the needs of each resident (F755/§483.45). The pharmaceutical committee determines the contents, such as drugs for life-threatening situations like heart attacks, severe allergic reactions to medications, and seizures. Although the drugs in the emergency kit are the pharmacist's responsibility, the staff using the kit must keep records of when each item is used and trigger a reorder as needed to keep the kit fully stocked. Generally, a 72-hour supply of drugs is permitted in these kits. The kit must remain unlocked for quick access but be stored in a secure area known to all involved staff. Automated external defibrillators (AEDs) are a common feature in healthcare facilities and must be maintained in good working order.

Increasingly, facilities also must store oxygen canisters, which must be secured upright and in a safe place. If the facility maintains canisters of other gaseous substances, they must be well marked and kept in identifiably separate spaces to minimize staff errors when in rushed circumstances.

EMPLOYEE SCREENING AND TRAINING POLICIES

NAB DOMAIN 2C7: EMPLOYEE TRAINING AND ORIENTATION

The facility will develop and operationalize policies and procedures for screening and training employees on the rights of residents and the responsibilities of the facility to properly care for its residents (F942/§483.95(b)). The facility must also provide training to their staff that educates on activities that constitute abuse, neglect, exploitation, and misappropriation of resident property (F942/§483.95(c)(1)). Training must also include procedures for reporting incidents of abuse, neglect, exploitation, or the misappropriation of resident property (F942/§483.95(c)(2)). Further training must provide knowledge of dementia management and resident abuse prevention (F942/§483.95(c)(3)). Effective communication techniques are also mandatory training for direct care staff (F941/§483.95(a)).

Of note, these trainings, especially those surrounding abuse, neglect, exploitation, and misappropriation, should be ongoing as a best practice. Training is expected in these areas to have occurred recently should surveyors arrive for a complaint visit.

NONEMPLOYMENT OF CERTAIN INDIVIDUALS

NAB DOMAIN 1B9: RECOGNITION OF MALTREATMENT (E.G., ABUSE, NEGLECT, EXPLOITATION); 2C1: FEDERAL HUMAN RESOURCES LAWS, RULES, AND REGULATIONS (E.G., ADA, FMLA, WAGE AND HOUR, FLSA); 2C2: SELECTION AND HIRING PRACTICES (E.G., EEOC, INTERVIEWING, ADVERSE IMPACT, PROTECTED CLASSES, OCCUPATIONAL QUALIFICATIONS)

The facility will not employ individuals who (a) have been found guilty of abusing, neglecting, or mistreating residents by a court of law or (b) have had a finding entered into the state nurse's aide registry concerning abuse, neglect, mistreatment of residents, or misappropriation of their property; or have a disciplinary action in effect against their professional license by a state licensure board as a result of a finding of abuse, neglect, exploitation, mistreatment of residents, or misappropriation of resident property (F606/§483.12(a)(3)). The facility must also report any knowledge it has of actions by a court of law against an employee, which would indicate unfitness for service as a nurse's aide or other facility staff to the state nurse's aide registry or licensing authorities (F606/§483.12(a)(4)).

FACILITY REPORTING POLICIES

NAB DOMAIN 1B9: RECOGNITION OF MALTREATMENT (E.G., ABUSE, NEGLECT, EXPLOITATION); 2B8: INTERNAL INVESTIGATION PROTOCOLS AND TECHNIQUES (E.G., INCIDENTS, ADVERSE EVENTS); 2B9: MANDATORY REPORTING REQUIREMENTS (E.G., INCIDENTS, ADVERSE EVENTS, ABUSE, NEGLECT, FINANCIAL EXPLOITATION, FRAUD)

The facility will ensure that all alleged violations involving mistreatment, neglect, or abuse, including injuries of unknown source and misappropriation of resident property, are reported immediately to the facility's administrator and other officials per state law (F607/§483.12(b)). The facility will maintain evidence that all alleged violations are thoroughly investigated and will prevent further potential abuse while the investigation is in progress. The results of all investigations will be reported to the administrator or the administrator's designated representative and other officials per state law (including to the state survey and certification agency) within the specified timeframe. If the alleged violation is verified, appropriate corrective action will be taken.

COMMON PITFALLS IN PRACTICE

- It seems that "overtraining" may be a best practice, as when an incident occurs, surveyors ask for all the training that your facility has done over the particular concern.
- Many administrators keep their own binder with employee training ready for when surveyors request it.
- As abuse, neglect, exploitation, and misappropriation are often reportable items, many administrators in-service on these topics each time they are in front of their staff—to the point of overtraining. However, when surveyors ask the staff if they have been trained on these topics, the exasperated eye roll and "in-serviced constantly" coming from the staff goes a long way toward your compliance.

6.1.3 DIETARY

Section Concepts

- *Dietary staffing and personnel functions*

Consider as the Administrator . . .

- *Who says what "sufficient staff" is when it comes to your kitchen?*

NAB DOMAIN 1B15: FOODSERVICE (E.G., CHOICE AND MENU PLANNING, DIETARY MANAGEMENT, FOOD STORAGE AND HANDLING, DINING SERVICES)

STAFFING

The facility will employ a qualified dietitian or another clinically qualified nutrition professional on a full-time, part-time, or consultant basis (F801/§483.60(a)). If a qualified dietitian is not employed full time, the facility will designate a person to serve as the director of food service who receives frequently scheduled consultation from a qualified dietitian (F801/§483.12(a)(2)). A *qualified dietitian* holds a bachelor's or higher degree in a program in nutrition or dietetics accredited by an appropriate national accreditation organization, has completed at least 900 hours of supervised dietetics practice under the supervision of a registered dietitian or nutrition professional, is licensed or certified as a dietitian or nutrition professional by the state where services are performed (F801/§483.60(a)(1)).

DIETARY: SUFFICIENT STAFF

The facility will employ sufficient support personnel to safely and effectively carry out the functions of the dietary service (F802/§483.60(a)(3)).

6.1.4 ADMISSIONS POLICIES

Section Concepts

- *Admission orders*
- *Policies for admissions and preadmissions*

Consider as the Administrator . . .

- *Can a misstep in the admissions process haunt you for years to come?*

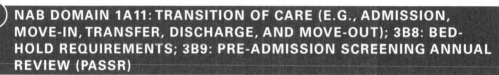

NAB DOMAIN 1A11: TRANSITION OF CARE (E.G., ADMISSION, MOVE-IN, TRANSFER, DISCHARGE, AND MOVE-OUT); 3B8: BED-HOLD REQUIREMENTS; 3B9: PRE-ADMISSION SCREENING ANNUAL REVIEW (PASSR)

ADMISSION ORDERS

When each resident is admitted, the facility will have physician orders for the resident's immediate care (F635/§483.20(a)). "Physician orders for immediate care" means written orders mentioning that facility staff needs to provide essential care to the resident, consistent with the resident's mental and physical status on admission. These orders will include dietary, drugs (if necessary), and routine care to maintain or improve the resident's functional abilities until staff can conduct a comprehensive assessment and develop an interdisciplinary care plan.

PREADMISSION SCREENING AND RESIDENT REVIEW (PASRR)

The facility will not admit any new residents with a mental disorder unless the state mental health authority has determined, based on an independent physical and mental evaluation performed by a person or entity other than the state mental health authority, before admission that (a) because of the physical and mental condition of the individual, the individual requires the level of services provided by a nursing facility and (b) if the individual requires such level of services, whether the individual requires specialized services or specialized services for intellectual disability (ID; F645/§483.20(k)(1)).

Preadmission for Each Resident

NAB DOMAIN 1B1: PSYCHOSOCIAL NEEDS (E.G., SOCIAL, SPIRITUAL, COMMUNITY, CULTURAL); 1B2: PERSON-CENTERED CARE AND COMPREHENSIVE CARE PLANNING; 1B3: CARE RECIPIENT BILL OF RIGHTS AND RESPONSIBILITIES; 2C13: CULTURAL COMPETENCE AND DIVERSITY AWARENESS

The facility owes it both to the resident and to itself to be conscientious about the preadmission process. Each new admission affects the ambiance of the facility and, potentially, the facility's profitability. It is vital to ensure that the facility can meet the identified needs of each newly admitted resident (F656/§483.21(b)). Because the facility assumes specific financial obligations for each new resident's medical needs, it is essential to calculate whether the facility will be reimbursed for the care required. For example, the facility may be required to assume transportation and treatment costs for a long series of outside-the-facility cancer treatments, which would cost more than the facility is permitted to charge for such a potential resident's care needs.

Diversity awareness is critical to include in the planning of admissions. To the extent possible, the facility should reflect the culture, ethnicity, race, sexual orientation, gender, religion, and language of the surrounding community. It may not be possible to admit as many men as women because men die sooner than women. It is possible to seek admissions that reflect the community consciously. In every case, it is important not to discriminate in admissions based on race, culture, national origin, sex, age, or disability (F836/§483.70(c)).

COMMON PITFALLS IN PRACTICE

- Preadmission requirements are general but differ in each state. Ensure you are knowledgeable surrounding your state requirements in this area. Noncompliance with preadmission requirements can quickly spin out of control and cause significant citations.

6.1.5 SOCIAL SERVICES POLICIES

Section Concepts

- *Social services requirements*

Consider as the Administrator . . .

- *Can the facility exist without a great social worker? Does the social worker provide more services than those that are simply necessary due to regulations?*

NAB DOMAIN 1B16: SOCIAL SERVICES PROGRAMS

SOCIAL SERVICES REQUIREMENTS

The facility will provide medically related social services to attain or maintain the highest practicable physical, mental, and psychosocial well-being of each resident (F745/§483.40(d)).

6.1.6 REHABILITATION POLICIES

Section Concepts

- *Rehabilitative services policies*
- *Qualifications of rehabilitation personnel*

Consider as the Administrator . . .

- *How important is a great rehab program? Can you maintain a good Part A census with a bad rehab provider?*

NAB DOMAIN 1A6: REHABILITATION AND RESTORATIVE PROGRAMS

REHABILITATION POLICIES FOR THE FACILITY

Provision of Services

If specialized rehabilitative services such as but not limited to physical therapy, speech/language pathology, occupational therapy, respiratory therapy, and mental health rehabilitative services for mental illness and ID are required in the resident's comprehensive plan of care, the facility will (a) provide the required services (F825/§483.65(a)(1)) or (b) obtain the required services from an outside resource from a provider of specialized rehabilitative services (F825/§483.65(a)(2)).

QUALIFICATIONS OF SPECIALIZED REHABILITATIVE SERVICES PERSONNEL

Specialized rehabilitative services will be provided under the written order of a physician by qualified personnel (F826/§483.65(b)). Once the assessment for specialized rehabilitative services is completed, a care plan will be developed, followed, and monitored by a licensed professional. Once a resident has met their care plan goals, a licensed professional will either discontinue treatment or initiate a maintenance program, which either nursing or restorative aides will follow to maintain functional and physical status.

"QUALIFIED PERSONNEL"

Qualified personnel means that professional staff is licensed, certified, or registered to provide specialized therapy/rehabilitative services under applicable state laws. Health rehabilitative services for mental disorders and ID will be implemented consistently by all staff unless the nature of the services is such that they are designated or required to be implemented only by licensed or credentialed personnel.

6.1.7 RESIDENTS' RIGHTS

Section Concepts

- *Residents have numerous rights that the facility will have policies to implement and protect*

Consider as the Administrator . . .

- *How are residents' rights within a facility different from noninstitutionalized citizens' rights? Or do our residents have the same rights as those living in the community?*

NAB DOMAIN 1B3: CARE RECIPIENT BILL OF RIGHTS AND RESPONSIBILITIES; 1B7: CARE RECIPIENT DECISION-MAKING (E.G., CAPACITY, POWER OF ATTORNEY, GUARDIANSHIP, CONSERVATORSHIP, CODE STATUS, ADVANCE DIRECTIVES, ETHICAL DECISION-MAKING); 1B8: CARE RECIPIENT (AND REPRESENTATIVE) SATISFACTION

NAB DOMAIN 1B5: CARE RECIPIENT (AND REPRESENTATIVE) GRIEVANCE, CONFLICT, AND DISPUTE RESOLUTION

NURSING FACILITY RESIDENTS' RIGHTS AND PROTECTIONS

The resident has a right to a dignified existence, self-determination, and communication with and access to persons and services inside and outside the facility (F550/§483.10(a)). As such, it is understandable that residents' rights are an essential part of the facility's operation.

The Centers for Medicare & Medicaid Services (CMS) provides clear information to residents regarding their rights and protections in the nursing facility. Residents have the right to the following:

- Be treated with respect
- Participate in activities
- Be free from discrimination
- Be free from abuse and neglect
- Be free from restraints
- Make complaints
- Get proper medical care with the following rights:
  - To be fully informed about your total health status in a language you understand
  - To be fully informed about your medical condition, prescription, and over-the-counter drugs, vitamins, and supplements
  - To be involved in the choice of your doctor
  - To participate in decisions that affect your care
  - To take part in developing your care plan
  - To access all your records and reports, including clinical records, promptly
  - To express any complaints about care or treatment

- To create advance directives
- To refuse to participate in experimental treatment
- Have your representative notified regarding the following:
  - You are involved in an accident and are injured or need to see a doctor
  - Your physical, mental, or psychosocial status starts to get worse
  - You have a life-threatening condition
  - You have medical complications
  - Your treatment needs to change significantly
  - The facility decides to transfer or discharge you
- Get information on services and fees
- Manage your money, in addition:
  - If you deposit money with the facility or ask them to hold or account for your money, you must do so in writing
  - The facility must allow you access to your bank accounts, cash, and other financial records
  - The facility must have a system that ensures full accounting for your funds and cannot combine your funds with facility funds
  - The facility must protect your funds from any loss by providing acceptable protection (surety bond)
  - The facility must return funds with a final accounting to the person or court handling the estate within 30 days of a death
- Get proper privacy, property, and living arrangements, including the following rights:
  - To keep and use your personal belongings and property if they do not interfere with the rights, health, or safety of others
  - To have private visits
  - To make and get private phone calls
  - To have privacy in sending and getting mail and email
  - To have your belongings protected from theft
  - To share a room with your spouse, if you both live in the same nursing facility and agree to share a room
  - To have proper notification before your room or roommate is changed, and your preferences should be considered
  - To review the facilities health and fire safety inspection results
- Spend time with visitors, including the following rights:
  - To spend private time with visitors
  - To have visitors at any time, for as long as you wish to see them, if the visit does not interfere with the provision of care and privacy rights of other residents
  - To see any person who gives you help with your health, social, legal, or other services at any time—including your doctors, health department representatives, and long-term care ombudsmen
- Get social services
- Leave the nursing facility by either outside visitation or moving out
- Have protection against unfair transfer or discharge, including the following rights:
  - To appeal a transfer or discharge to the state
  - To not be discharged if you are waiting to get Medicaid
  - To have a 30-day written notice of the facility plan and reason for discharge or transfer

■ To be safely and orderly transferred or discharged and provided notice of bed hold or readmission requirements
- Form or participate in resident groups
- Have your friends and family involved (CMS, 2021, pp. 1–4)

From the Facility Perspective

The following are the facility residents' rights policies:

- The facility must treat each resident with respect and dignity and care for each resident in a manner and in an environment that promotes maintenance or enhancement of their quality of life, recognizing each resident's individuality (F550/§483.10(a)(1))
- The facility must protect and promote the rights of the resident (F550/§483.10(a)(1))
- The facility must provide equal access to quality care regardless of diagnosis, severity of condition, or payment source (F550/§483.10(a)(2))
- The facility must maintain identical policies and practices regarding transfer, discharge, and provision of services regardless of payment source (F550/§483.10(a)(2))

Exercise of Rights Despite Barriers

The facility will promote the exercise of rights for each resident, including any who face barriers (such as communication problems, hearing problems, and cognition limits) in the exercise of these rights (Halter et al., 2017). A resident, even though determined to be incompetent, will be able to assert these rights based on their degree of capability (F551/§483.10(b)(7)).

Resident Exercise of Rights Without Reprisal

The resident has the right to exercise their rights as a resident of the facility and as a citizen or resident of the United States (F550/§483.10(b)).

The resident has the right to be free of interference, coercion, discrimination, and reprisal from the facility in exercising their rights and to be supported by the facility in the exercise of their rights (F550/§483.10(b)(2)).

The facility must ensure that the resident can exercise their rights without interference, coercion, discrimination, or reprisal from the facility (F550/§483.10(b)(1)). The facility must not hamper, compel, treat differentially, or retaliate against a resident for exercising their rights.

NAB DOMAIN 1B4: CARE RECIPIENT SAFETY (E.G., FALL PREVENTION, ELOPEMENT PREVENTION, ADVERSE EVENTS); 1B5: CARE RECIPIENT (AND REPRESENTATIVE) GRIEVANCE, CONFLICT, AND DISPUTE RESOLUTION; 1B9: RECOGNITION OF MALTREATMENT (E.G., ABUSE, NEGLECT, EXPLOITATION)

The resident has the right to be free from abuse, neglect, misappropriation of resident property, and exploitation; this includes freedom from corporal punishment, involuntary seclusion, and any physical or chemical restraint not required to treat the resident's medical symptoms (F600/§483.12). The facility must not use verbal, mental, sexual, or physical abuse, corporal punishment, or involuntary seclusion (F600/§483.12(a)(1)).

Residents must not be subjected to abuse by anyone, including, but not limited to, facility staff, other residents, consultants or volunteers, staff of other agencies serving the resident, family members or legal guardians, friends, or other individuals.

Signs and Symptoms

Abuse is the willful infliction of injury, unreasonable confinement, intimidation, or punishment with resulting physical harm, pain, or mental anguish (§483.50). This also includes the deprivation by an individual, including a caretaker, of necessary goods or services to attain or maintain physical, mental, and psychosocial well-being. This presumes that instances of abuse of all residents, even those in a coma, cause physical harm, pain, or mental anguish. This includes verbal abuse, sexual abuse, physical abuse, and mental abuse—including abuse facilitated or enabled using technology.

Neglect is the failure of the facility, employers, or providers to provide goods and services to a resident that are necessary to avoid physical harm, pain, mental anguish, or emotional distress (§483.50).

Mental abuse includes, but is not limited to, the use of verbal or nonverbal conduct, which has the potential to cause the resident humiliation, intimidation, fear, shame, agitation, or degradation.

Verbal abuse is a type of mental abuse and is defined as the use of oral, written, or gestured communication or sounds to residents within hearing distance, regardless of age, ability to comprehend, or disability.

Sexual abuse includes, but is not limited to, sexual harassment, sexual coercion, or sexual assault (§483.50).

Physical abuse includes, but is not limited to, hitting, slapping, punching, biting, and kicking. It also includes controlling behavior through corporal punishment. Corporal punishment can consist of pinching, spanking, slapping, flicking, or hitting with objects.

Involuntary seclusion is defined as the separation of a resident from other residents or from their room or confinement to their room (with or without roommates) against the resident's will or the will of the resident's legal representative (§483.12). Emergency or short-term monitored separation from other residents will not be considered involuntary seclusion. It may be permitted if used for a limited period as a therapeutic intervention to reduce agitation until professional staff can develop a plan of care to meet the resident's needs.

Misappropriation of resident property means the deliberate misplacement, exploitation, or wrongful, temporary, or permanent use of a resident's belongings or money without the resident's consent (§483.50).

Exploitation means taking advantage of a resident for personal gain using manipulation, intimidation, threats, or coercion (§483.50).

NAB DOMAIN 2B8: INTERNAL INVESTIGATION PROTOCOLS AND TECHNIQUES (E.G., INCIDENTS, ADVERSE EVENTS); 2B9: MANDATORY REPORTING REQUIREMENTS (E.G., INCIDENTS, ADVERSE EVENTS, ABUSE, NEGLECT, FINANCIAL EXPLOITATION, FRAUD)

The facility will ensure that all alleged violations involving mistreatment, neglect, or abuse, including injuries of unknown source and misappropriation of resident property, are reported immediately to the administrator of the facility and other officials per state law through established procedures (including to the state survey and certification agency; F609/§483.12(c)(1)).

The facility will have evidence that all alleged violations are thoroughly investigated (F610/§483.12(c)(2)) and will prevent further potential abuse, neglect, exploitation, or mistreatment while the investigation is in progress (F610/§483.12(c)(3)). The results of all investigations will be reported to the administrator or the administrator's designated representative and other officials per state law (including to the state survey and certification agency) within 5 working days of the incident. If the alleged violation is verified, appropriate corrective action must be taken by the facility (F610/§483.12(c)(4)).

Facility Policy on Incompetence

NAB DOMAIN 1B7: CARE RECIPIENT DECISION-MAKING (E.G., CAPACITY, POWER OF ATTORNEY, GUARDIANSHIP, CONSERVATORSHIP, CODE STATUS, ADVANCE DIRECTIVES, ETHICAL DECISION-MAKING)

In the case of a resident adjudged incompetent under the laws of the state by a court of competent jurisdiction, the rights of the resident will be exercised by the person appointed under state law to act on the resident's behalf (F551/§483.10(b)(7)).

In the case of a resident who has not been adjudged incompetent by the state court, the resident has the right to designate a representative per state law, and any legal surrogate designated may exercise the resident's rights to the extent provided by state law (F551/§483.10(b)(3)).

When reference is made to "resident," it also refers to any person who may, under state law, act on the resident's behalf when the resident is unable to act for themselves (551/§483.10(b)(3)-(7)). That person is referred to as the *resident's surrogate* or *representative*. If the resident has been formally declared incompetent by a court, the surrogate or representative is appointed by the court—a guardian, conservator, or committee. The facility will verify that any surrogate or representative has the necessary authority. For example, a court-appointed conservator might have the power to make financial decisions but not healthcare decisions.

A resident may wish to delegate decision-making to specific persons, or the resident and family may have agreed on a decision-making process. To the degree permitted by state law and to the maximum extent practicable, the facility will respect the resident's wishes and follow that process.

The rights of the resident that the surrogate or representative may exercise include the right to make healthcare decisions. However, the facility will seek a healthcare decision (or any other decision or authorization) from a surrogate or representative only when the resident cannot make the decision. Suppose there is a question about whether the resident can make a healthcare decision. In that case, staff will discuss the matter with the resident at a suitable time and judge how well the resident understands the information. In the case of a resident who has been formally declared incompetent by a court, lack of capacity is presumed. Notwithstanding those as mentioned earlier, if such a resident can understand the situation and express a preference, the resident will be informed, and their wishes respected to the degree practicable.

The involvement of a surrogate or representative does not automatically relieve the facility of its duty to protect and promote the resident's interests. For example, a surrogate or representative does not have the right to insist that treatment be performed that is not medically appropriate. The right of a surrogate or representative to reject treatment may be subject to state law limits.

CASE STUDY (AN ACTUAL CASE)

Squabbles With Roommates: "Man Accused of Using Cane to Kill Two in Home"

Dade City, FL—A resident of a cramped retirement home beat to death two sleeping residents with his walking cane and injured four others in a room-to-room rampage sparked by disputes with roommates, police said Monday.

Henry T., 88, a retired fruit picker and sometimes junk collector, was charged with two counts of first-degree murder in the deaths of his 90-year-old roommate, Max N., and resident Myrtle S., 73, Dade City Police Chief Phil Thompson said. He said that charges were being prepared for the injuries to the other four residents and will be filed this week.

- *The vice president of your chain has arrived in your office the day after these killings occurred in your facility. He wants to know why this happened and how you plan to prevent future recurrences.*

Resident Rights to All Records

The resident or their legal representative has the right (a) upon an oral or written request, to access all records pertaining to themselves, including current clinical records, within 24 hours (excluding weekends and holidays) and (b) after receipt of their records for inspection, to purchase at a cost not to exceed the community standard photocopies of the records or any portions of them on request and 2 working days advance notice to the facility (F573/§483.10(g)(2)).

NAB DOMAIN 1A8: CLINICAL AND MEDICAL RECORDS AND DOCUMENTATION REQUIREMENTS (E.G., STORAGE, RETENTION, DESTRUCTION); 2B11: HEALTHCARE RECORD REQUIREMENTS (E.G., CONFIDENTIALITY, DISCLOSURE, SAFEGUARDING, HIPAA, HITECH)

An oral request is sufficient to produce the current record for review. In addition to clinical records, the term "records" includes all records about the resident, such as trust fund ledgers pertinent to the resident and contracts between the resident and the facility (F573/§483.10(g)(2)-(3)).

Residents' Rights to Full Total Health Status Information

The resident has the right to be fully informed, in language that they can understand, of their total health status, including, but not limited to, their medical condition (F552/§483.10(c)(1)). "Total health status" includes functional status, nutritional status, rehabilitation, and restorative potential, ability to participate in activities, cognitive status, oral health status, psychosocial status, and sensory and physical impairments (F552/§483.10(c)(1), (4)-(5)). Information on health status will be presented in language that the resident can understand (F552/§483.10(c)(1)). This includes minimizing the use of technical jargon in communicating with the resident, having the ability to communicate in a foreign language, and the use of sign language or other aids, as necessary.

Information in Advance About Care Treatment

The resident has the right to be fully informed in advance about care and treatment (F552/§483.10(c)(4)) and of any changes in that care or treatment that may affect the resident's well-being (F553/§483.10(c)(2)-(3)).

"Informed in advance" means that the resident receives information necessary to make a healthcare decision, including information about their medical condition and changes in medical condition, about the benefits and reasonable risks of the treatment, and about reasonably available alternatives.

Residents' Rights to Advance Directives and to Refuse Treatment or Research

NAB DOMAIN 1B7: CARE RECIPIENT DECISION-MAKING (E.G., CAPACITY, POWER OF ATTORNEY, GUARDIANSHIP, CONSERVATORSHIP, CODE STATUS, ADVANCE DIRECTIVES, ETHICAL DECISION-MAKING)

The resident has the right to request, refuse, or discontinue treatment, to participate in or refuse to participate in experimental research, and to formulate an advance directive (F578/§483.10(c)(6)).

Treatment is defined as medical care, nursing care, and interventions provided to maintain or restore health and well-being, improve the functional level, or relieve symptoms.

Experimental research is defined as the development, testing, and use of clinical treatment, such as an investigational drug or therapy that has not yet been approved by the U.S. Food and Drug Administration or medical community as effective and conforming to accepted medical practice.

Advance directive means a written instruction, such as a living will or durable power of attorney for healthcare, recognized under state law relating to the provision of healthcare when the individual is incapacitated.

Right to Withhold Consent

As provided under state law, a resident who has the capacity to make a healthcare decision and who withholds consent to treatment or makes an explicit refusal of treatment, either directly or through an advance directive, may not be treated against their wishes (F578/§483.10(c)(6), (c)(8), (g)(12)).

Discharge Rights

The facility will not transfer or discharge a resident for refusing treatment unless the criteria for transfer or discharge are met (F578/§483.10(c)(6), (c)(8), (g)(12)).

Decision-Making Rights

If the resident is unable to make a healthcare decision, a decision by the resident's surrogate or representative to forego treatment may, subject to state law, be equally binding on the facility. The facility will determine what the resident is refusing and why. To the extent the facility is able, it will address the resident's concern (F578/§483.10(c)(6), (c)(8), (g)(12)). For example, a resident requires physical therapy to walk again after sustaining a fractured hip. The resident refuses treatment. Staff in the facility will assess the reasons for this resident's refusal, clarify, and educate the resident about the consequences of refusal, offer alternative treatments, and continue to provide all other services. If a resident's refusal of treatment brings about a significant change, the facility will reassess the resident and institute care planning changes (F578/§483.10(c)(6), (c)(8), (g)(12)).

Resident Conduct and Resident Responsibilities

The facility will inform the resident both orally and in writing, in a language that the resident understands, of their rights and all rules and policies governing resident conduct and responsibilities during the stay in the facility (F572/§483.10(g)(1)).

Rights at Admission

The facility will ensure that each resident knows their rights and responsibilities and that the facility communicates this information before or on admission, as appropriate during the resident's stay, and when the facility rules change (F572/§483.10(g)(16)).

Medicaid Benefits

NAB DOMAIN 2A5: REVENUE AND REIMBURSEMENT (E.G., PDPM, PDGM, ACOs, HMOs, MEDICAID, PRIVATE PAYORS)

The facility will (a) inform each resident who is entitled to Medicaid benefits, in writing, at the time of admission to the nursing facility or when the resident becomes eligible for Medicaid, of (i) the items and services that are included in nursing facility services under the state plan and for which the resident may not be charged; (ii) those other items and services that the facility offers and for which the resident may be charged, and the amount of charges for those services; and (b) inform each resident when changes are made to the items and services (F582/§483.10(g)(17)). The facility will inform each resident before or at the time of admission, and periodically during the resident's stay, of services available in the facility and of charges for those services, including any charges for services not covered under Medicare or by the facility's per diem rate (F582/§483.10(g)(18)).

Written Legal Rights Descriptions

NAB DOMAIN 1B6: CARE RECIPIENT ADVOCACY (E.G., OMBUDSMAN, RESIDENT AND FAMILY COUNCIL); 2A10: RESIDENT TRUST ACCOUNTS FOR PERSONAL FUNDS

The facility will furnish a written description of legal rights, which includes (a) a description of the manner of protecting personal funds; (b) a description of the requirements and procedures for establishing eligibility for Medicaid, including the right to request an assessment that determines the extent of a couple's resources under section 1924(c) of the Social Security Act; (c) a list of names, addresses, and telephone numbers of all pertinent state regulatory and informational agencies, resident advocacy groups, such as the state survey agency, the state licensure office, the state long-term care ombudsman program, the protection and advocacy agency, adult protective services where state law provides them jurisdiction in a facility, the local contact agency for information about returning to the community, and the Medicaid fraud control unit; and (d) a statement that the resident may file a complaint with the state survey agency concerning any suspected violation of state or federal nursing facility regulations, including but not limited to resident abuse, neglect, exploitation, misappropriation of resident property, noncompliance with the advance directives requirements, and requests for returning to the community (F574/§483.10(g)(4)).

States have enacted a long-term care ombudsman program to advocate for residents. An *ombudsman* is a person appointed to look out for the interests of specific groups such as nursing facility residents. Ombudspersons do not have any direct enforcement authority but are typically part of the local government structure in which their recommendations can carry weight. Surveyors actively seek out ombudsman opinions and perceptions during the survey process. The facility's goal is to provide quality care. The ombudsperson's job is to ensure that the facility offers good-quality care. The ombudsperson can and should be a valued positive resource for the facility. Having an additional set of eyes can offer different valuable inputs.

Similarly, advocacy groups for nursing facility residents have the same goals and values as the facility staff. Advocacy groups typically begin in an adversarial model. It is essential to respond positively to advocacy group concerns with the hope of using their inputs to improve the quality of care.

Display of Information

The facility will prominently display in the facility written information and provide to residents and applicants for admission oral and written information about how to apply for and use Medicare and Medicaid benefits and how to receive refunds for previous payments covered by such benefits (F579/§483.10(g)(13)).

Change of Condition Notifications

Notifications required by the facility on a change in the resident's condition or the resident's rights are as follows: (a) The facility will immediately inform the resident; consult with the resident's physician, and notify the resident's representatives when there is (i) an accident involving the resident which results in injury and has the potential for requiring physician intervention; (ii) a significant change in the resident's physical, mental, or psychosocial status (i.e., a deterioration in health, mental, or psychosocial status in either life-threatening conditions or clinical complications); (iii) a need to alter treatment significantly (i.e., a need to discontinue an existing form of treatment due to adverse consequences, or to commence a new form of treatment); or (iv) a decision to transfer or discharge the resident from the facility, a change in room or roommate assignment; or (v) a change in resident rights under federal or state law or policies. (b) The facility will record and periodically update the address and telephone number of the resident's legal representative or interested family member (F580/§483.10(g)(14)).

Protection of Resident Funds

The resident has the right to manage their financial affairs, and the facility will not require residents to deposit their personal funds with the facility. On written authorization of a resident, the facility will hold, safeguard, manage, and account for the personal funds of the resident deposited with the facility (F567/§483.10(f)(10)).

Deposit of Funds

(a) The facility must deposit any residents' personal funds in excess of $100 in an interest-bearing account that is separate from any of the facility's operating accounts that credit interest earned on the funds to the resident's account. For funds that do not exceed $100, these funds can be maintained in an interest-bearing account, a non-interest-bearing account, or a petty cash fund.

(b) For residents funded by Medicaid, all the same is true; however, the funds must be more than $50 (F567/§483.10(f)(10)).

Notice of Certain Balances

The facility will notify each resident who receives Medicaid benefits (a) when the amount in the resident's account reaches $200 less than the Supplemental Security Income (SSI) resource limit for one person and (b) that if the amount in the account, in addition to the value of the resident's other nonexempt resources, reaches the SSI resource limit for one person, the resident may lose eligibility for Medicaid or SSI (F569/§483.10(f)(10)).

Conveyance of Resident's Funds Within 30 Days of Discharge or Death

Upon the discharge, eviction, or death of a resident with a personal fund deposited with the facility, the facility must convey within 30 days the resident's funds and a final accounting of those funds to the resident or, in the case of death, the individual or probate jurisdiction administering the resident's estate (F569/§483.10(f)(10)).

Surety Bond or Equivalent to Protect Resident Funds

Assurance of Financial Security

The facility must purchase a surety bond or otherwise provide assurance satisfactory to the secretary to assure the security of all personal funds of residents deposited with the facility (F570/§483.10(f)(10)).

The Facility Will Not Be Named as a Beneficiary

Self-insurance is not an acceptable alternative to a surety bond. Likewise, funds deposited in bank accounts protected by the Federal Deposit Insurance Corporation, or similar entity, also are not good alternatives (F570/§483.10(f)(10)).

Limitations on Charges to Personal Funds: Chargeable and Nonchargeable Items

The facility must not impose a charge against the personal funds of a resident for any item or service for which payment is made under Medicaid or Medicare (except for applicable deductible and coinsurance amounts) (F571/§483.10(f)(11)).

1. *Services included in Medicare or Medicaid payment.* During a covered Medicare or Medicaid stay, facilities will not charge a resident for the following categories of items and services: (a) nursing services as required; (b) food and nutrition services as required; (c) an activities program as required; (d) room/bed maintenance services; (e) routine personal hygiene items and services as required to meet the needs of residents, including, but not limited to, hair hygiene supplies, comb, brush, bath soap, disinfecting soaps, or specialized cleansing agents when indicated to treat special skin problems or to fight infection, razor, shaving cream, toothbrush, toothpaste, denture adhesive, denture cleaner, dental floss, moisturizing lotion, tissues, cotton balls, cotton swabs, deodorant, incontinence care and supplies, sanitary napkins and related supplies, towels, washcloths, hospital gowns, over-the-counter drugs, hair and nail hygiene services, bathing assistance, and basic personal laundry; (f) medically related social services; and (g) hospice services elected by the resident and paid for under the Medicare hospice benefit or paid for by Medicaid under a state plan (F571/§483.10(f)(11)).

2. *Items and services that may be charged to a resident's funds.* The following list shows the general categories and examples of items and services that the facility may charge to a resident's funds if they are requested by a resident if they are not required to achieve the goals stated in the resident's care plan if the facility informs the resident that there will be a charge, and if payment is not made by Medicare or Medicaid: (a) telephone (including cellular); (b) television/radio for personal use, personal computer, or other electronic devices for personal use; (c) personal comfort items, including smoking materials, notions and novelties, and confections; (d) cosmetic and grooming items and services above those for which payment is made under Medicaid or Medicare; (e) personal clothing; (f) personal reading matter; (g) gifts purchased on behalf of a resident; (h) flowers and plants; (i) costs to participate in social events and entertainment offered outside the scope of the activities program; (j) noncovered special care services

such as privately hired nurses or aides; (k) private room, except when therapeutically required (e.g., isolation for infection control); and (l) specially prepared or alternative food requested instead of the food generally prepared by the facility (F571/§483.10(f)(11)).

Consider as the Administrator . . .

- *This is a long and complicated list. Is it worth the administrator's attention?*
- *How important is complying implicitly with the regulations provided by federal and state entities?*

Requests for Items and Services

1. The facility can only charge a resident for any noncovered item or service if the resident explicitly requests such item or service.
2. The facility must not require a resident to request any item or service as a condition of admission or continued stay.
3. The facility must inform, orally and in writing, the resident requesting an item or service for which a charge will be made that there will be a charge for the item or service and what the cost will be (F571/§483.10(f)(11)).

Privacy and Confidentiality in Records, Treatments, Visits, Accommodations, Communications, and Meetings

NAB DOMAIN 1A1: MEDICAL AND NURSING CARE PRACTICES; 1B3: CARE RECIPIENT BILL OF RIGHTS AND RESPONSIBILITIES; 2B11: HEALTHCARE RECORD REQUIREMENTS (E.G., CONFIDENTIALITY, DISCLOSURE, SAFEGUARDING, HIPAA, HITECH)

The resident has the right to personal privacy and confidentiality of their personal and clinical records (F583/§483.10(h)). Personal privacy includes accommodations, medical treatment, written and telephone communications, personal care, visits, and meetings of family and resident groups, but this does not require the facility to provide a private room for each resident (F583/§483.10(h)(1)). The resident has the right to refuse the release of personal and medical records except as provided by law (F583/§483.10(h)(3)).

Voice Grievances Without Reprisal

NAB DOMAIN 1B5: CARE RECIPIENT (AND REPRESENTATIVE) GRIEVANCE, CONFLICT, AND DISPUTE RESOLUTION; 1B8: CARE RECIPIENT (AND REPRESENTATIVE) SATISFACTION

A resident has the right to voice grievances without discrimination or reprisal and without fear of discrimination or reprisal (F585/§483.10(j)(1)). Such grievances include those concerning treatment that has been furnished and that has not been furnished, the behavior of staff and other residents, and other concerns regarding their stay.

Prompt Facility Effort to Resolve Grievances

A resident has the right to, and the facility must make prompt efforts to resolve grievances the resident may have (F585/§483.10(j)(2)).

Examination of Survey Results by Residents

A resident has the right to examine the results of the most recent survey of the facility conducted by federal or state surveyors and any plan of correction in effect concerning the facility (F577/§483.10(g)(10)). The facility will make the results available for examination in a place readily accessible to residents, family members, and legal representatives of residents. It will post a notice of their availability (F577/§483.10(g)(11)).

Information Reception by Resident From Client Advocate Agencies

A resident has the right to receive information from agencies acting as client advocates and be allowed to contact those agencies (F577/§483.10(g)(10)).

Work

The resident has the right to refuse to perform services for the facility, and the facility must not require a resident to perform services for the facility. The resident may perform services for the facility, if they choose to do so, when (a) the facility has documented the resident's need or desire for work in the plan of care; (b) the plan specifies the nature of the services performed and whether the services are voluntary or paid; (c) compensation for paid services is at or above prevailing rates; and (d) the resident agrees to the work arrangement described in the plan of care (F566/§483.10(f)(9)).

Mail Rights in Sending and Receiving

The resident has the right to send and promptly receive mail that is unopened and other letters, packages, and other materials delivered to the facility for the resident, including those delivered through a means other than a postal service (F583/§483.10(h)(2)).

Access and Visitation Rights

The resident has the right to receive visitors of their choosing at the time of their choosing, subject to the resident's right to deny visitation when applicable, and in a manner that does not impose on the rights of other residents. The facility must provide the following: (a) immediate access to a resident by immediate family and other relatives of the resident and (b) immediate access to a resident by others who are visiting with the consent of the resident (F563/§483.10(f)(4)).

The facility must have written policies and procedures regarding visitation rights of residents, including those setting forth any clinically necessary or reasonable restriction or the limitation or safety restriction or limitation, when the facility may need to place limitations on such rights and reasons for the clinical or safety restriction or limitation (F563/§483.10(f)(4)).

Reasonable Access

The facility will provide reasonable access to any resident by any entity or individual that provides health, social, legal, or other services to the resident, subject to the resident's right to deny or withdraw consent at any time (F563/§483.10(f)(4)).

State Ombudsman Access to Patient's Clinical Records

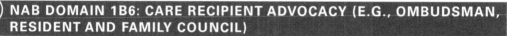

NAB DOMAIN 1B6: CARE RECIPIENT ADVOCACY (E.G., OMBUDSMAN, RESIDENT AND FAMILY COUNCIL)

The facility will allow representatives of the state ombudsman to examine a resident's medical, social, and administrative records per state law (F583/§483.10(h)(3)).

Resident Access to Telephone

The resident has the right to have reasonable access to the use of a telephone, including teletypewriter (TTY) and telecommunications device for the deaf (TDD) services, and a place in the facility where calls can be made without being overheard. This includes the right to retain and use a cellular phone at the resident's own expense (F576/§483.10(g)(6)).

Personal Property

The resident has the right to retain and use personal possessions, including some furnishings and appropriate clothing, as space permits, unless to do so would infringe on the rights or health and safety of other residents (F557/§483.10(e)(2)).

Respect for Possessions

All residents' possessions, regardless of their apparent value to others, will be treated with respect, for what they are and what they may represent to the resident. The right to retain and use personal possessions ensures that the residents' environment will be as homelike as possible and that residents will retain as much control over their lives as possible. The facility has the right to limit the resident's exercise of this right on the grounds of space and health or safety (F557/§483.10(e)(2)).

Married Couples Sharing a Room

The resident has the right to share a room with their spouse when married residents live in the same facility and both spouses consent to the arrangement (F559/§483.10(e)(4)).

Self-Administration of Drugs (Requirements)

An individual resident may self-administer drugs if the interdisciplinary team has determined that this practice is clinically appropriate (F554/§483.10(c)(7)). If a resident requests to self-administer medications, it is the responsibility of the interdisciplinary team to determine that it is safe for the resident to self-administer drugs before the resident may exercise that right. The interdisciplinary team will also decide who will be responsible (the resident or the nursing staff) for storage and documentation of the administration of drugs and the location of the drug administration (e.g., resident's room, nurses' station, or activities room). Appropriate notation of these determinations will be placed in the resident's care plan.

Refusal of Certain Transfers

 NAB DOMAIN 1A11: TRANSITION OF CARE (E.G., ADMISSION, MOVE-IN, TRANSFER, DISCHARGE, AND MOVE-OUT)

An individual has the right to refuse a transfer to another room within the institution if the purpose of the transfer is to relocate (a) a resident of a skilled nursing facility (SNF) from the distinct part of the institution that is an SNF to a part of the institution that is not an SNF; (b) a resident of a nursing facility from the distinct part of the institution that is a nursing facility to a distinct part of the institution that is an SNF; or (c) solely for the convenience of the staff (F560/§483.10(e)(7)).

A resident's exercise of the right to refuse transfer does not affect the individual's eligibility or entitlement to Medicare or Medicaid benefits (F560/§483.10(e)(8)).

Admission, Transfer, and Discharge Rights

Transfer and discharge include movement of a resident to a bed outside of the certified facility whether that bed is in the same physical plant or not. Transfer and discharge do not refer to the movement of a resident to a bed within the same certified facility (F622/§483.15(c)).

Transfer and Discharge Provisions

Transfer and discharge provisions significantly restrict a facility's ability to transfer or discharge a resident once that resident has been admitted to the facility. The facility will not transfer or discharge the resident unless:

- The transfer or discharge is necessary to meet the resident's welfare and the resident's welfare cannot be met in the facility
- The transfer or discharge is appropriate because the resident's health has improved sufficiently so that the resident no longer needs the services provided by the facility
- The safety of individuals in the facility is endangered due to the clinical or behavioral status of the resident
- The health of individuals in the facility would otherwise be endangered

- The resident has failed, after reasonable and appropriate notice, to pay for a stay at the facility
- The facility ceases to operate (F622/§483.15(c)(1))

Notice to Resident Before Transfer

Before the facility transfers or discharges a resident, it will (a) notify the resident and the resident's representatives of the transfer or discharge and the reasons for the move in writing and in a language and manner they understand (a copy of the notice must be sent to the ombudsman) and (b) record the reasons in the resident's medical record (F623/§483.15(c)(3)).

Timing of the Notice

The notice of transfer or discharge will be made by the facility at least 30 days before the resident is transferred or discharged. Notice may be made as soon as practicable before transfer or discharge when (a) the safety of the individuals in the facility would be endangered, (b) the health of individuals in the facility would be endangered, (c) the resident's health improves sufficiently to allow a more immediate transfer or discharge, (d) an immediate transfer or discharge is required by the resident's urgent medical needs, or (e) a resident has not resided in the facility for 30 days (F623/§483.15(c)(4)).

Contents of Transfer Notice

The written notice of this section will include the following: (a) the reason for transfer or discharge; (b) the effective date of transfer or discharge; (c) the location to which the resident is transferred or discharged; (d) a statement of the resident's appeal rights and information on how to obtain an appeal form and assistance in completing the form and submitting the appeal hearing request; (e) the name, address, and telephone number of the state long-term care ombudsman; (f) for nursing facility residents with intellectual and developmental disabilities, the mailing address and telephone number of the agency responsible for the protection and advocacy of individuals with developmental disabilities established under Part C of the Developmental Disabilities Assistance and Bill of Rights Act of 2000; and (g) for nursing facility residents who have a mental disorder or related disabilities, the mailing and email address and telephone number of the agency responsible for the protection and advocacy of individuals with a mental disorder established under the Protection and Advocacy for Mentally Ill Individuals Act (F623/§483.15(c)(5)).

Resident Orientation for Transfer or Discharge

The facility will provide and document sufficient preparation and orientation to residents to ensure safe and orderly transfer or discharge from the facility. This orientation must be provided in a form and manner that the resident can understand (F623/§483.15(c)(7)).

Notice of Bed-Hold Policy and Readmission

NAB DOMAIN 1A11: TRANSITION OF CARE (E.G., ADMISSION, MOVE-IN, TRANSFER, DISCHARGE, AND MOVE-OUT); 3B8: BED-HOLD REQUIREMENTS

Notice Before Transfer

Before the facility transfers a resident to a hospital or allows a resident to go on therapeutic leave, the nursing facility will provide written information to the resident or resident representative that specifies the duration of the state bed-hold policy, if any, during which the resident is permitted to return and resume residence in the nursing facility and the reserve bed payment policy (F625/§483.15(d)(1)).

Notice of Bed Hold on Transfer

At the time of transfer of a resident for hospitalization or therapeutic leave, the nursing facility will provide to the resident and resident representative written notice which specifies the duration of the bed-hold policy (F625/§483.15(d)(2)).

Permitting Resident to Return to the Facility

The facility will establish and follow a written policy on permitting residents to return after they are hospitalized or placed on therapeutic leave. The policy must provide that a resident whose hospitalization or therapeutic leave exceeds the bed-hold period under the state plan returns to the facility to their previous room if available or immediately upon the first availability of a bed in a semi-private room if the resident (a) requires the services provided by the facility and (b) is eligible for Medicare SNF services or Medicaid nursing facility services (F626/§483.15(e)(1)).

Equal Access to Quality Care

NAB DOMAIN 2C13: CULTURAL COMPETENCE AND DIVERSITY AWARENESS

The facility must establish, maintain, and implement identical policies and practices regarding transfer and discharge and the provision of services for all individuals regardless of the source of payment (F621/§483.15(b)(1)).

Admission and Placement Policies: Permissible Charges

The facility will (a) not request or require residents or potential residents to waive their rights to Medicare or Medicaid and (b) not request or require oral or written assurance that residents or potential residents are not eligible for, or will not apply for, Medicare or Medicaid benefits or (c) not request or require residents or potential residents to waive potential facility liability for losses of personal property (F620/§483.15(a)(2)).

Third-Party Guarantee Limitations

The facility will not require a third-party guarantee of payment as a condition of admission or expedited admission or continued stay in the facility. However, the facility may request and require an individual who has legal access to a resident's income or resources available to pay for facility care to sign a contract, without incurring personal financial liability, to provide facility payment from the resident's income or resources (F620/§483.15(a)(3)).

Residents' Rights in Paying the Facility Bills

The facility may not require a third person to accept personal responsibility for paying the facility bill out of their funds. However, they may use the resident's money to pay for care. A third-party guarantee is not the same as a third-party payer, for example, an insurance company, and this provision does not preclude the facility from obtaining information about Medicare or Medicaid eligibility or the availability of private insurance.

Medicaid-Eligible Residents' Rights

NAB DOMAIN 2A5: REVENUE AND REIMBURSEMENT (E.G., PDPM, PDGM, ACOs, HMOs, MEDICAID, PRIVATE PAYORS)

In the case of a person eligible for Medicaid, the facility will not charge, solicit, accept, or receive, in addition to any amount otherwise required to be paid under the state plan, any gift, money, donation, or other consideration as a precondition of admission, expedited admission, or continued stay in the facility. However, the facility may charge a resident who is eligible for Medicaid for items and services the resident has requested and received and that are not specified in the state plan as included in the term "nursing facility services," so long as the facility gives proper notice of the availability and cost of these services to residents and does not condition the resident's admission or continued stay on the request for and receipt of such additional services (F620/§483.15(a)(4)).

COMMON PITFALLS IN PRACTICE
- As you have seen here, resident rights are a *huge* area of concern for the administrator (and surveyors). Doing everything you can to ensure that *you* are an advocate for your residents can only help you be successful.
- One of the most important things you can do in this area is to become a good listener. Have an open door, a hot pot of coffee, and open ears. Many times, we see problems in this area to be perceptions of others. When we help them understand our perspective—and the law—we see an understanding of our perspective on their behalf and fewer concerns from them.

CASE STUDIES (ACTUAL CASES)

Much has been said about patient rights. Nowhere is the right to die directly addressed. Consider the following.

MS. ABBOTT'S DECISION: A CONTINUING CARE RETIREMENT COMMUNITY CASE

Ms. Abbott's next-door neighbor noticed with alarm that Ms. Abbott's newspaper was still outside the door of her two-room apartment at 7:30 a.m. Ms. Abbott "always" took in her paper well before 7:30 a.m.

The neighbor knocked loudly on Ms. Abbott's door and then called her on the phone. No response. She quickly summoned the nurse on duty at the life care center's nursing facility one block away. On entering the living room, they discovered Ms. Abbott's nearly lifeless body, her head tightly covered by a plastic bag, an empty bottle of Darvon nearby. Carefully written suicide notes were visible on the coffee table.

The physician at the hospital emergency department worked quickly to revive Ms. Abbott. During the resuscitation efforts, Ms. Abbott's neighbor told the physician that Ms. Abbott had a living will stipulating no heroic efforts to keep her alive. The physician replied that living wills do not apply in these circumstances.

Two weeks later, Ms. Abbott's daughter and Ms. Abbott, a member of the former Hemlock Society, were both still angry at the community administrator. Both felt Ms. Abbott's rights had been compromised. Ms. Abbott was thinking about getting into her car and visiting her lawyer.

Instead, Ms. Abbott had the life care center's Ethics Committee (she herself a member) convene. She has asked the Ethics Committee to write a policy to cover situations such as hers.

- *As a member of the Ethics Committee, write out the policy you would adopt.*

MISS WHITING'S ICE PITCHER

It was late afternoon. Ms. Janus, the administrator of The Laurels, had just started down the hall to leave for the day when she overheard one of the nurses laughing and announcing to several aides and nurses standing around at the nurses' station, "She'll never do that again on my shift."

The rest of the nurses were giggling. Striding up to the nurses' station, Ms. Janus asked, "What won't she ever do again? Who won't do what again?"

Nurse McCarthy replied, "I caught Miss Whiting playing with herself again. That's the third time I've taken her supper in this week, and there she's been, sitting on the bed doing it to herself. Fortunately, the aide had just filled her ice water pitcher, so I poured it on her." Nurse McCarthy seemed very pleased with himself.

The other staff members seemed amused and a little bit pleased. "Maybe you ought to start remembering to knock," one of the nurses chimed in.

Ms. Janus smiled weakly and walked on out the corridor to her car.

(continued)

"I've told them a hundred times that our patients have full rights to their personal lives," she said to herself. "How many times have I told them that if a patient's behavior is not infringing on other patients' rights or harmful to themselves, each patient's privacy and behavioral preferences will be respected?"

"If Nurse McCarthy keeps on disrespecting patients' rights, I'm going to have to call him into my office and tell him to conform or find another job. He knows that is cause for suspension and disciplinary action, but he continues to ignore our policies. Well, I'll just keep my fingers crossed I don't catch him doing it again."

- *What is your evaluation of Ms. Janus's response?*

6.1.8 QUALITY ASSESSMENT AND ASSURANCE: MEETING THE HOLISTIC NEEDS OF THE RESIDENT

Section Concepts

- *Resident quality of life includes dignity, self-determination, participation inside and outside the facility, accommodation to the resident's needs, receiving notices before facility actions, appropriate dining and nutrition, and sanitary conditions, among others. These are described here and included as facility policy*

Consider as the Administrator . . .

- *How can the dining experience be deinstitutionalized?*

NAB DOMAIN 1B: QUALITY OF LIFE; 1B1: PSYCHOSOCIAL NEEDS (E.G., SOCIAL, SPIRITUAL, COMMUNITY, CULTURAL); 1B2: PERSON-CENTERED CARE AND COMPREHENSIVE CARE PLANNING; 1B3: CARE RECIPIENT BILL OF RIGHTS AND RESPONSIBILITIES; 1B4: CARE RECIPIENT SAFETY (E.G., FALL PREVENTION, ELOPEMENT PREVENTION, ADVERSE EVENTS); 1B5: CARE RECIPIENT (AND REPRESENTATIVE) GRIEVANCE, CONFLICT, AND DISPUTE RESOLUTION; 1B6: CARE RECIPIENT ADVOCACY (E.G., OMBUDSMAN, RESIDENT AND FAMILY COUNCIL); 1B7: CARE RECIPIENT DECISION-MAKING (E.G., CAPACITY, POWER OF ATTORNEY, GUARDIANSHIP, CONSERVATORSHIP, CODE STATUS, ADVANCE DIRECTIVES, ETHICAL DECISION-MAKING); 1B8: CARE RECIPIENT (AND REPRESENTATIVE) SATISFACTION

QUALITY OF LIFE

The facility will care for each resident with respect and dignity and care for each resident in a manner and in an environment that promotes maintenance or enhancement of each resident's quality of life, recognizing each resident's individuality (F550/§483.10(a)(1)).

Dignity

Each resident has a right to be treated with respect and dignity, including the right to retain and use personal possessions, including furnishings, and clothing as space permits, unless to do so would infringe on the rights or health and safety of other residents (F557/§483.10(e), (e)(2)).

Self-Determination and Participation

The resident has the right to (a) choose activities, schedules, and healthcare and providers of healthcare consistent with their interests, assessments, and plans of care (F561/§483.10(f)(1)); (b) make choices about aspects of their life in the facility that are significant to the resident (F561/§483.10(f)(2)); (c) interact with members of the community and participate in community activities both inside and outside the facility (F561/§483.10(f)(3)); and (d) participate in other activities, including social, religious, and community activities that do not interfere with the rights of other residents in the facility (F561/§483.10(f)(8)).

Participation in Resident and Family Groups

A resident has the right to organize and participate in resident groups in the facility (F565/§483.10(f)(5)). The facility must provide a resident or family group with private space and take steps to make residents and family members aware of upcoming meetings. Staff, visitors, or other guests may attend these meetings only at the group's invitation. The facility must provide a staff person whom the group approves to provide assistance and respond to written requests that result from group meetings.

Required Facility Responses to Resident or Family Groups

The facility must consider the views of the resident or family group and act promptly on the grievances and recommendations of such groups concerning issues of resident care and life in the facility (F565/§483.10(f)(5)). The facility must demonstrate its response and rationale for such a response. The facility does not have to implement every recommendation or request of the group.

Transportation Options

NAB DOMAIN 1C3: TRANSPORTATION FOR CARE RECIPIENTS

For residents to participate in community activities or even meet personal shopping needs, some form(s) of transportation must be provided beyond meeting the requirement to transport the resident to and from healthcare appointments. Providing a facility car or van for transportation is ideal. If, however, the facility is unable to provide its transportation, most communities offer some type(s) of transportation for persons without a means. Beyond this, the facility may consider encouraging resident families to assist in transportation, although not without careful thought regarding safety and insurance coverage.

Accommodation of Individual Needs and Preferences

A resident has a right to reside and receive services in the facility with reasonable accommodation of resident needs and preferences except when the health or safety of the individual or other residents would be endangered (F558/§483.10(e)(3)).

Receive Notice Before Resident's Room or Roommate Is Changed

NAB DOMAIN 1A11: TRANSITION OF CARE (E.G., ADMISSION, MOVE-IN, TRANSFER, DISCHARGE, AND MOVE-OUT)

A resident has a right to receive written notice, including the reason for the change, before the resident's room or roommate in the facility is changed (F559/§483.10(e)(6)).

Quality Assessment and Assurance

The facility must maintain a quality assessment and assurance (QAA) committee consisting of (a) the DON services, (b) the medical director or their designee, and (c) at least three other members of the facility's staff, one of which must be the administrator, owner, board member, or another individual in a leadership role and the infection preventionist (F868/§483.75(g)(1)).

Quarterly Meeting of Quality Assessment and Assurance Committee

NAB DOMAIN 2B6: QUALITY IMPROVEMENT PROCESSES (E.G., ROOT CAUSE ANALYSIS, PDCA/PDSA); 3B7: QUALITY ASSURANCE AND PERFORMANCE IMPROVEMENT (QAPI)

The QAA committee (a) meets at least quarterly and as needed to coordinate and evaluate activities under the Quality Assurance Performance Improvement (QAPI) program, such as identifying issues concerning which QAA activities, including performance improvement projects required under the QAPI program, are necessary (F868/§483.75(g)(2)).

6.1.9 DIETARY

Section Concepts

- *The importance of proper resident dining areas*
- *Weight loss as a concern for the facility*
- *Meals not only meeting nutritional adequacy, but also needs of the individual resident*

Consider as the Administrator . . .

- *Should you know what your own food tastes like?*
- *Should you consider spending time with your residents to learn more about them and their concerns? Is a meal a good place to do this?*

NAB DOMAIN 1A4: NUTRITION AND HYDRATION (E.G., SPECIALIZED DIETS); 1B15: FOODSERVICE (E.G., CHOICE AND MENU PLANNING, DIETARY MANAGEMENT, FOOD STORAGE AND HANDLING, DINING SERVICES)

RESIDENT DINING AND ACTIVITY AREAS

The facility will maintain acceptable parameters of nutritional status for each resident, such as body weight or desirable body weight range and electrolyte balance unless the resident's clinical condition demonstrates that this is not possible or resident preferences indicate otherwise (F692/§483.25(g)(1)).

PROVIDE THERAPEUTIC DIETS FOR EACH NUTRITIONAL PROBLEM

The facility will provide a therapeutic diet when there is a nutritional problem, and the healthcare provider orders a therapeutic diet (F692/§483.75(g)(3)).

WEIGHT

Weight loss or gain will be examined within the context of the individual's personal history and overall condition. Weight goals should be based on a resident's usual body weight or desired body weight (F692/§483.75(g)).

Parameters for evaluating the significance of unplanned and undesired weight loss are as follows:

Interval (months)	Significant Loss (%)	Severe Loss (%)
1	5	Greater than 5
3	7.5	Greater than 7.5
6	10	Greater than 10

The following formula determines the percentage of loss:

$$\% \text{ of body weight loss} = \frac{\text{Usual weight} - \text{Actual weight} \times 100}{\text{Usual weight}}$$

OTHER DIETARY CONCERNS

Assistive devices. The facility will provide special eating equipment and utensils for residents who need them and appropriate assistance to ensure that the resident can use the assistive devices when consuming meals and snacks (F810/§483.60(g)).

Food and nutrition services. The facility will provide each resident with a nourishing, palatable, well-balanced diet that meets the daily nutritional and special dietary needs of each resident, taking into consideration the preferences of each resident (F800/§483.60).

Food and drink. Each resident receives, and the facility provides, the following:

- Food prepared by methods that conserve nutritive value, flavor, and appearance (F804/§483.60(d)(1))
- Food and drink that is palatable, attractive, and at a safe and appetizing temperature (F804/§483.60(d)(2))

- Food prepared in a form designed to meet individual needs (F804/§483.60(d)(3))
- Food that accommodates resident allergies, intolerances, and preferences (F804/§483.60(d)(4))
- Appealing options of similar nutritive value to residents who choose not to eat food that is initially served or who request a different meal choice (F804/§483.60(d)(5))
- Drinks, including water and other liquids consistent with resident needs and preferences and sufficient to maintain resident hydration (F804/§483.60(d)(6))

Food safety requirements. Food must be procured from sources approved or considered satisfactory (F812/§483.60(i)(1)). Food must be stored, prepared, distributed, and served following professional standards for food service safety (F812/§483.60(i)(2)).

Frequency of meals. Each resident must receive, and the facility must provide at least three meals daily, at regular times comparable to normal mealtimes in the community or per resident needs, preferences, requests, and plans of care (F809/§483.60(f)(1)). There will be no more than 14 hours between a substantial evening meal and breakfast the following day, except when a nourishing snack is provided at bedtime, then 16 hours may elapse between meals (F809/§483.60(f)(2)). The facility will offer suitable, nourishing alternative meals and snacks to residents who want to eat at nontraditional times or outside normal meal service times, consistent with the plan of care (F809/§483.60(f)(3)).

Menus and nutritional adequacy. Menus will meet the nutritional needs of residents following established national guidelines (F803/§483.60(c)(1)); be prepared in advance (F803/§483.60(c)(2)); be followed (F803/§483.60(c)(4)); reflect reasonable efforts in meeting religious, cultural, and ethnic needs of the resident population as well as input from residents and resident groups (F803/§483.60(c)(4)); be updated periodically (F803/§483.60(c)(5)); be reviewed by the facility dietitian or other clinically qualified nutritional professional for nutritional adequacy (F803/§483.60(c)(6)); and not limit the resident's right to make personal dietary choices (F803/§483.60(c)(7)).

Sufficient staff. The facility will employ sufficient staff with the appropriate competencies and skills sets to carry out the food and nutrition service functions, considering resident assessments, individual plans of care, and the number, acuity, and diagnoses of the resident population (F801/§483.60(a)).

Therapeutic diets. Therapeutic diets will be prescribed by the attending physician (F808/§483.60(e)(1)) or delegated by the attending physician to a registered or licensed dietitian with the task of prescribing the resident's diet, including therapeutic diets (F808/§483.60(e)(2)).

COMMON PITFALLS IN PRACTICE

- You will need to find a happy medium between what you *can* do to meet all these holistic needs discussed here and what you are asked to do by residents and responsible parties. You can usually accomplish this. When you cannot, ensure proper documentation as to why. Follow the regulations. You simply will not be able to meet everyone's wants. You will, however, be able to meet their needs.

Milk

Dr. Brown admitted Ms. Farrington to The Laurels 5 days ago. Ms. Farrington was 96 and had a history of problems with swallowing that sometimes caused particles to be forced into her lungs, resulting in choking symptoms and later pneumonia. Dr. Brown ordered that no liquid thinner than honey be permitted.

The evening of the fifth day after Ms. Farrington was admitted, she was served milk with dinner, whereupon she began choking. The nurse in charge wheeled Ms. Farrington into the hallway to get her out of sight. A few minutes later, a staff member who went into the hallway to check on Ms. Farrington found her gagging and vomiting undigested food.

The nurse called the attending physician and told him Ms. Farrington was suffering from "congestion" but never mentioned the choking. Two hours later, Ms. Farrington died.

- *What went wrong with the facility's systems to ensure quality care?*

6.1.10 ENVIRONMENTAL MANAGEMENT

Section Concepts

- *That the facility, through its policies, will ensure:*
  - *A clean, safe, and homelike environment*
  - *Necessary housekeeping and maintenance services*
  - *Adequate and comfortable lighting*
  - *Comfortable and safe temperature levels*
  - *Comfortable sound levels*
  - *An accident-free environment*
  - *Emergency power*
  - *Preventive maintenance*
  - *A resident call system*
  - *Water available at all times*
  - *Adequate outside ventilation*
  - *Firmly secured handrails*
  - *Effective pest control*

Consider as the Administrator . . .

- *What is the balance between meeting requirements and meeting resident wishes? For example, if a resident says, "Do not serve me breakfast of any kind, I have never eaten breakfast," and the facility does not serve the resident any kind of breakfast, might the facility be cited for deficient practice?*

NAB DOMAIN 3A4: FACILITY MANAGEMENT AND ENVIRONMENTAL SERVICES

RESIDENTS' ENVIRONMENT

 NAB DOMAIN 3A2: PERSON-CENTERED ENVIRONMENT (E.G., HOME-LIKE ENVIRONMENT)

 NAB DOMAIN 2B11: HEALTHCARE RECORD REQUIREMENTS (E.G., CONFIDENTIALITY, DISCLOSURE, SAFEGUARDING, HIPAA, HITECH)

 NAB DOMAIN 2B12: SECURITY (E.G., CAMERAS, MONITORING SYSTEMS, LOCKS, STAFF LOCATION REPORTING)

A Safe, Clean, Comfortable, and Homelike Environment: Allowing the Residents to Use Their Personal Belongings to the Extent Possible

Powerful legal and economic forces ensure that providing a homelike environment remains a continuing challenge. Fire safety rules govern what materials may be in a resident's room. The fire codes and environmental safety codes require handrails, grab bars, signage, and many other features that create an institutional feel. However, in recent years, both federal and state officials have become aware of the need to make the facility as homelike as possible within the scope of permitted practices. Personal possessions and furniture within the resident's room bring memories of the past. Options such as increased ability to choose food, wake-up time, bath time, and many similar personal choices can foster a more homelike environment. It is important to decide when one eats breakfast or whether one eats breakfast. Choice, the ability to determine one's daily life, is essential to residents. With increased options comes increased control over one's life.

Changing marketing expectations are leading many nursing facility chains to build single-room facilities. Few, if any, residents prefer having a "roommate." Many owners realize that providing long-term care is like providing resort care. The more owners view the residents as their customers whose preferences matter, the more satisfied everyone may be. Today's market is dominated by Medicare and Medicaid policies. Only a few facilities have the luxury of serving only private-pay residents who have sufficient funds to afford resort-like amenities.

Choice, comfort, and dignity for care recipients are increasingly the focus of not just owners but also federal and state surveyors. Furthermore, we see culture change making waves within the field to improve the quality of care being given. This culture change is often very dependent on the regulatory environment.

Necessary Housekeeping and Maintenance Services

The facility will provide housekeeping and maintenance services necessary to maintain a sanitary, orderly, and comfortable interior (F584/§483.10(i)(2)). The facility will provide clean bed and bath linens that are in good condition (F584/§483.10(i)(3)).

Adequate and Comfortable Lighting Levels

The facility will provide adequate and comfortable lighting levels in all areas (F584/§483.10(i)(5)).

Comfortable and Safe Temperature Levels

The facility will maintain comfortable and safe temperature levels at a range of 71°F to 81°F (F584/§483.10(i)(6)).

Comfortable Sound Levels

The facility will provide for the maintenance of comfortable sound levels (F584/§483.10(i)(7)). "Comfortable" sound levels will not interfere with residents' hearing and will enhance privacy when privacy is desired and encourage interaction when social participation is desired. Of particular concern to comfortable sound levels is the resident's control over unwanted noise.

Accident-Free Environment

The facility will ensure that the resident environment remains as free of accident hazards as is possible (F689/§483.10(d)(1)).

Physical Environment

The facility will be designed, constructed, equipped, and maintained to protect the health and safety of residents, personnel, and the public (F895/§483.90).

Emergency Power

NAB DOMAIN 3A8: DISASTER AND EMERGENCY PLANNING, PREPAREDNESS, RESPONSE, AND RECOVERY (E.G., APPENDIX Z)

An emergency electrical power system will supply adequate power, at least for lighting all entrances and exits; equipment to maintain the fire detection, alarm, and extinguishing systems; and life support systems in the event the normal electrical supply is interrupted (F906/§483.90(c)(1)).

Environmental and Maintenance Services for Property, Plant, and All Equipment, Including Preventive Maintenance

NAB DOMAIN 3A1: FEDERAL CODES AND REGULATIONS FOR BUILDING EQUIPMENT, MAINTENANCE, AND GROUNDS; 3A4: FACILITY MANAGEMENT AND ENVIRONMENTAL SERVICES; 3A6: PREVENTATIVE AND ROUTINE MAINTENANCE PROGRAMS (E.G., PEST CONTROL, EQUIPMENT, MECHANICAL SYSTEMS)

Policy. The facility will maintain all essential mechanical, electrical, and patient care equipment in safe operating condition (F908/§483.90(d)(2)).

Maintenance work can be classified into categories such as immediate calls for repair or service, routine service requests, and preventive work. An overflowing toilet demands prompt resolution. The request for a light bulb replacement can be put on the daily schedule. The maintenance head must be able to prioritize service requests appropriately.

Maintenance logs. A documented and reported inspection program is a necessity. Operating system checks must be made and documented in a log available for the administrator's inspection. The fire alarm system must be tested quarterly (or, more often, according to state regulations). The emergency electricity generator must be tested; smoke detectors, fire door operation, and fire alarms must be tested and kept in complete working condition. Hot-water temperatures throughout the facility must be checked and documented. Resident wandering systems should be checked each shift and documented. A schedule to inspect each facility area must be established, logged, and reported periodically to the administrator. These inspections include patient rooms, dietary, laundry, loading docks, and the front lobby. In short, all areas of the building must be inspected and maintained. During these inspections, such issues as slowly leaking toilets, leaking faucets, doors that no longer close properly, burned-out light bulbs, areas accumulating visible dirt, missing ceiling tiles, broken floor tiles, and the like are discovered. On the outside, pests may be observed near the garbage area; parking lot lighting may be burned out or broken; pavement may require repair; signs may be missing; debris may be littering the lawn; shrubbery may be overgrown and in need of trimming. A well-maintained facility will have a daily touch-up painting program that maintains the facility's appearance. Typically, outside contracts are used for routine maintenance areas such as pest control, grounds maintenance, equipment inspection, and repairs.

The environment includes protecting the structure(s) themselves and providing a safe, comfortable, user-friendly, and clean environment. The facility may be thought of as a resort, but with stricter requirements for air temperature and humidity and water temperatures, air quality, waste management, and safety. Typically, the environment includes the functions of housekeeping, laundry, maintenance, and safety. One full-time maintenance person is required for a typical nursing facility of around 100 beds.

Various maintenance and repair services are typically contracted out, such as grounds maintenance or HVAC (heating, ventilation, and air conditioning) services and repair. Contracted services should be for 1 year to allow for periodic review of the terms and effectiveness of contractors. All contractors' work is deemed to be *respondeat superior* work; that is, the facility is responsible for all behaviors of contractors. It is essential to assign a regular employee to supervise contractors' work.

Painting must be done on a schedule that results in painting resident rooms at least every 2 to 3 years. Qualifications for the maintenance head need not call for expertise in any area. However, the maintenance head should be capable of performing simple repair and maintenance functions such as simple plumbing and electrical repairs. The maintenance head can learn to do more sophisticated repairs and maintenance as they observe outside repair persons at work when systems break down. *Preventive maintenance* means servicing systems on a routine basis to keep them running in good condition, like the preventive maintenance each of us performs for our automobiles by having the vehicles lubricated, the oil changed, and the brakes maintained on a preplanned schedule.

Physical Building Policies

- Bedroom limited to four residents (before November 28, 2016), two residents after that (F911/§483.90(e)(1)(i))
- Direct access to an exit corridor for resident rooms (F913/§483.90(e)(1)(iii))
- Be designed or equipped to ensure total visual privacy for each resident (F911/§483.90(e)(1)(iv))
- Resident room window to the outside (F915/§483.90(e)(1)(vi))
- Resident rooms that are at or above grade level (F916/§483.90(e)(1)(vii))
- The facility will provide each resident with (a) a separate bed of proper size and height for the safety and convenience of the resident; (b) a clean, comfortable mattress; (c) bedding appropriate to the weather and climate; and (d) functional furniture appropriate to resident needs and individual closet space in the bedroom with clothes racks and shelves accessible to the resident (F917/§483.90(e)(2)). Each resident must have private closet space in each resident room (F917/§483.10(i)(4)). Each resident room will be equipped with or located near toilet and bathing facilities. After November 28, 2016, construction must include resident rooms with their own bathroom equipped with at least a toilet and sink (F918/§483.90(f))

Resident Call System

The facility must be adequately equipped to allow residents to call for staff assistance through a communication system that relays the call directly to a staff member or a centralized staff work area from (a) resident bedside and (b) toilet and bathing facilities (F919/§483.90(g)(1), (2)) The call system will be both audio and visual—both at the nurses' station and the patient's room. Wireless communication devices are also available that permit instant communication among the resident, the nurses' station, and staff in the halls.

Resident Dining and Activity Area

The facility will provide one or more rooms designated for resident dining and activities. These rooms will be well lighted, well ventilated, adequately furnished, and have sufficient space to accommodate all activities (F920/§483.90(h)(1-4)).

Water Available at All Times

The facility will establish procedures to ensure that water is available to essential areas when there is a loss of normal water supply (F922/§483.90(i)(1)).

Adequate Outside Ventilation

The facility will have adequate outside ventilation through windows, mechanical ventilation, or a combination of the two (F923/§483.90(i)(2)).

Firmly Secured Handrails in Corridors

The facility will equip corridors with firmly secured handrails on each side (F924/§483.90(i)(3)).

Pest Control

Maintain an effective pest control program so that the facility is free of pests and rodents (F925/§483.90(i)(4)).

COMMON PITFALLS IN PRACTICE
- Do not be afraid to get your hands dirty. You are not too good to clean up a spill or to plunge a clogged toilet—and both are within your purview.
- Understand and be a part of facility maintenance. Administrators who are not a part of maintenance are part of the problem with it. You must see and understand what is happening in this area.

6.1.11 INFECTION CONTROL

Section Concepts

- *An effective infection control program is one of the most important aspects of facility function*

Consider as the Administrator ...

- *How can the facility ensure that nurses and aides follow handwashing requirements?*

NAB DOMAIN 3A7: INFECTION CONTROL AND SANITATION (E.G., LINENS, KITCHEN, HAND WASHING, HEALTHCARE-ACQUIRED INFECTIONS, HAZARDOUS MATERIALS)

NAB DOMAIN 3A6: PREVENTATIVE AND ROUTINE MAINTENANCE PROGRAMS (E.G., PEST CONTROL, EQUIPMENT, MECHANICAL SYSTEMS)

The facility will establish and maintain an infection prevention and control program designed to provide a safe, sanitary, and comfortable environment and to help prevent the development and transmission of communicable diseases and infections (F880/§483.80).

INFECTION CONTROL PROGRAM

The facility will establish an infection control and prevention program (ICPP) that must include (a) a system for preventing, identifying, reporting, investigating, and controlling infections and communicable disease for all residents, staff, volunteers, visitors, and other individuals; (b) written standards, policies, and procedures for the program; and (c) a system for recording incidents identified and their corrective actions (F880/§483.80(a)(1-4)). The intent is to ensure that the facility has an infection control program that effectively investigates, controls, and prevents infections.

Preventing the Spread of Infection

The facility must have standard and transmission-based precautions to be followed to prevent the spread of infections (F880/§483.80(a)(2)).

Employees With Communicable Disease or Infected Skin Lesions

NAB DOMAIN 2C9: HUMAN RESOURCE POLICIES (E.G., DRUG-FREE WORKPLACE, DISCIPLINE, JOB CLASSIFICATION, PHOTOGRAPHY AND VIDEO, SOCIAL MEDIA USAGE, MOBILE PHONE USAGE)

The facility must have policies under which the facility must prohibit employees with a communicable disease or infected skin lesions from direct contact with residents or their food if direct contact will transmit the disease (F880/§483.80(a)(2)).

Staff Handwashing After Direct Resident Contact

The facility will require staff to follow proper hand hygiene procedures after each direct resident contact as by accepted professional practice (F880/§483.80(a)(2)).

Linens

Personnel will handle, store, process, and transport linens to prevent the spread of infection (F880/§483.80(e)).

COMMON PITFALLS IN PRACTICE

- You will see amazing things when it comes to infections. They come from everywhere. Residents, families, staff, visitors—anybody can be your source. Keep your eyes open and act when you need to. Do not be afraid to ask someone to mask up or leave the facility. Remember, *you* are entrusted with the health of those who live under your roof.

6.1.12 PHYSICIAN SERVICES

Section Concepts

- *Policies for the following:*
  - *Physician services*
  - *Physician supervision*
  - *Physician visits*
  - *Frequency of physician visits*
  - *Availability of physicians for emergency care*
  - *Physician delegation of tasks in SNFs*
  - *Performance of physician tasks in NFs*

Consider as the Administrator . . .

- *Many physicians don't know the federal regulations governing facility practice and often state that they do not intend to learn federal regulations. How can the facility staff manage in this circumstance?*

NAB DOMAIN 1A1: MEDICAL AND NURSING CARE PRACTICES; 1C7: HEALTHCARE PARTNERS AND CLINICAL PROVIDERS (E.G., MD/DO, NURSE PRACTITIONER, PSYCHIATRIST, PODIATRIST, DENTIST)

PHYSICIAN SUPERVISION OF CARE

A physician must personally approve in writing a recommendation that an individual is admitted to the facility. Each resident must remain under the care of a physician. A physician, physician assistant, nurse practitioner, or clinical nurse specialist must provide orders for the resident's immediate care and needs (F710/§483.30).

PHYSICIAN REVIEW OF TOTAL PLAN OF CARE, OTHER REQUIREMENTS

Physician Visits

The physician will (a) review the resident's total program of care, including medications and treatments, at each visit; (b) write, sign, and date progress notes at each visit; and (c) sign and date all orders except for influenza and pneumococcal polysaccharide vaccines, which may be administered per physician-approved facility policy after an assessment for contraindications (F711/§483.30(b)(1-3)).

Frequency of Physician Visits

The resident will be seen by a physician at least once every 30 days for the first 90 days after admission, and at least once every 60 days after that. A physician visit is considered timely if it occurs not later than ten days after the date the visit was required (F712/§483.30(c)(1-2)).

Physician Visits: Personal, Permitted Alternates

At the option of the physician, required visits in SNFs, after the initial visit, may alternate between personal visits by the physician and visits by a physician assistant, nurse practitioner, or clinical nurse specialist (F712/§483.30(c)(4)).

Availability of Physicians for Emergency Care

The facility will provide or arrange for the provision of physician services 24 hours a day, in case of an emergency (F713/§483.30(d)).

Physician Delegation of Tasks

A physician may delegate tasks to a physician assistant, nurse practitioner, or clinical nurse specialist who acts within the scope of practice as defined by state law and is under the supervision of the physician (F714/§483.30(e)(1)). A physician may not delegate a task when the policies specify that the physician will perform it personally or when the delegation is prohibited under state law or by the facility's policies.

MEDICAL DIRECTOR

NAB DOMAIN 1A9: MEDICAL DIRECTOR; 2B8: INTERNAL INVESTIGATION PROTOCOLS AND TECHNIQUES (E.G., INCIDENTS, ADVERSE EVENTS)

NAB DOMAIN 1C7: HEALTHCARE PARTNERS AND CLINICAL PROVIDERS (E.G., MD/DO, NURSE PRACTITIONER, PSYCHIATRIST, PODIATRIST, DENTIST)

NAB DOMAIN 2B6: QUALITY IMPROVEMENT PROCESSES (E.G., ROOT CAUSE ANALYSIS, PDCA/PDSA); 3A7: INFECTION CONTROL AND SANITATION (E.G., LINENS, KITCHEN, HAND WASHING, HEALTHCARE-ACQUIRED INFECTIONS, HAZARDOUS MATERIALS); 3B7: QUALITY ASSURANCE AND PERFORMANCE IMPROVEMENT (QAPI)

The facility will designate a physician to serve as the medical director for (a) implementation of resident care policies and (b) the coordination of medical care in the facility (F841/§483.70(h)(1-2)). The medical director is responsible for "resident care policies," including the following:

- Recommending, developing, and approving facility policies related to residents' care (physical, mental, and psychosocial well-being)
- Issues related to the coordination of medical care identified through the facility QAA committee and other activities related to the coordination of care
- Organizing physician services and services provided by other professionals relating to resident care
- Participation in the QAA committee
- Ensuring the appropriateness and quality of medical and medically related care
- Assisting in the development of educational programs for facility staff
- Working with the facility clinical team to provide surveillance and develop policies to prevent the potential infection of residents
- Cooperating with facility staff to establish policies ensuring the rights of individuals (residents, staff members, community members) are respected
- Supporting and promoting person-centered care such as the formation of advance directives, end-of-life care, and provisions that enhance resident decision-making, including choice in medical care options
- Identifying performance expectations and facilitating feedback to physicians and other practitioners regarding performance and practice
- Discussing and intervening with practitioners regarding medical care that is inconsistent with current standards of care

NAB DOMAIN 2B9: MANDATORY REPORTING REQUIREMENTS (E.G., INCIDENTS, ADVERSE EVENTS, ABUSE, NEGLECT, FINANCIAL EXPLOITATION, FRAUD)

Each state has requirements for reporting care recipient incidents, accidents, and emergencies. Each facility must have written policies and procedures that conform to state health authority reporting requirements.

An *incident* is any unexpected negative occurrence involving a patient, employee, visitor, or any person on the premises.

An *accident* is any unexpected or unintentional incident, which results or may result in injury or illness to the person(s) involved.

An *emergency* is any event requiring immediate action for the safety or well-being of person(s) involved.

Accident and incident reports are a vital part of caregiving. Each facility needs written policies and procedures that enable staff to recognize, act on, and carefully document each incident, accident, and emergency. These reports are typically reviewed by state and federal health officials, as well as attorneys who may become involved.

When the medical director identifies or receives a report of possible inadequate medical care, including drug irregularities, they are responsible for evaluating the situation and taking appropriate steps to correct the problem. This may include any necessary consultation with the resident and their physician concerning care and treatment. The medical director's coordination role also includes ensuring the support of essential medical consultants as needed (F841/§483.70(h)).

Increasingly, the typical facility is acquiring an increasing number of healthcare partners. These partners range from laboratory services to x-ray and diagnostic services brought into the facility to the ambulatory care offices of numerous health caregivers such as local physician offices, dental offices, physical therapy providers, laboratory services—the entire range of ambulatory care providers at one time or another. All these services must be obtained under the authority of the resident's personal physician or the facility's medical director. Nurses, for example, may recognize the need for a follow-up medical procedure or a medication change. Nurses and the other allied health personnel in the facility have no authority to authorize such care. The resident's healthcare remains under the direction of the resident's personal physician.

LABORATORY SERVICES

NAB DOMAIN 1C5: DIAGNOSTIC SERVICES (E.G., RADIOLOGY, LAB SERVICES)

The facility will provide or obtain laboratory services to meet the needs of its residents. The facility is responsible for the quality and timeliness of the services (F770/§483.50(a)(1)).

> *Lab work only when ordered by the attending physician.* Provide or obtain laboratory services only when ordered by the physician, physician assistant, nurse practitioner, or clinical nurse specialist (F773/§483.50(a)(2)). The intent of this policy is to ensure that only medically necessary laboratory services are ordered.

Prompt notification to physicians of laboratory results received. Promptly notify the ordering physician, physician assistant, nurse practitioner, or clinical nurse specialist of laboratory results that fall outside of clinical reference ranges following facility policies and procedures (F773/§483.50(a)(2)). The intent of this policy is to ensure that the physician is notified of all lab results so that prompt, appropriate action may be taken if indicated for the resident's care.

Assist resident to laboratory work if needed. Assist the resident in making transportation arrangements to and from the source of service if the resident needs assistance (F774/§483.50(a)(2)).

Facility responsibility for radiology and other diagnostic services. The facility will provide or obtain radiology and other diagnostic services to meet the needs of its residents. The facility is responsible for the quality and timeliness of the services (F776/§483.50(b)(1)).

Radiology and other diagnostic services only on order of a physician. The facility will provide or obtain radiology and other diagnostic services only when ordered by a physician, physician assistant, nurse practitioner, or clinical nurse specialist. The facility will notify the physician or practitioner of results that fall outside clinical reference ranges (F777/§483.50(b)(2)).

Assist resident with radiological services transportation. Assist the resident in making transportation arrangements to and from the source of service if the resident needs assistance (F778/§483.50(b)(2)) and file in the resident's clinical record signed and dated reports of radiologic and other diagnostic services (F779/§483.50(b)(2)).

NAB DOMAIN 1C2: SPECIALIZED MEDICAL EQUIPMENT (E.G., OXYGEN, DURABLE MEDICAL EQUIPMENT)

The facility administrator and staff frequently interact with salespersons representing various medical specialties, especially at industry trade shows. Oxygen is a routine aspect of daily facility life, as is durable medical equipment such as wheelchairs and other mobility devices. Similarly, podiatric services must be ensured by the facility. Each aspect of care remains under the physician's order and must be a documented part of the resident's care plan. Often these matters are best handled by obtaining standing physician orders, such as a standing order by the resident's physician for annual (or more often, as needed) podiatric services to be provided in the facility.

COMMON PITFALLS IN PRACTICE

- Doctors are people. These individuals are people you can talk to, discuss things with, and rely on. Become acquainted and friendly with your providers. They can help you as much as you can help them.

6.1.13 DENTAL CARE

Section Concepts

- *Maintaining proper dental services is key for resident health*

Consider as the Administrator . . .

- *Just because you are in a rural area, does this negate the need for a dentist, even if you are unable to find one?*

NAB DOMAIN 1C6: DENTAL AND ORAL CARE SERVICES; 1C7: HEALTHCARE PARTNERS AND CLINICAL PROVIDERS (E.G., MD/DO, NURSE PRACTITIONER, PSYCHIATRIST, PODIATRIST, DENTIST)

DENTAL SERVICES

The facility will assist residents in obtaining routine and 24-hour emergency dental care (F791/§483.55(b)).

The facility will provide or obtain from an outside resource routine and emergency dental services to meet the needs of each resident and will, as necessary, assist the resident in making appointments; arrange for transportation to and from the dentist's office; and promptly (within 3 days) refer residents with lost or damaged dentures to a dentist.

6.1.14 NURSING REQUIREMENTS

Section Concepts

- *The federal government enforces a 1300-plus page set of requirements known as the Long-Term Care Resident Assessment Instrument (RAI). The RAI is part of the MDS. Here you will be introduced to the significant aspects of the RAI, including the following:*
  - *Comprehensive assessments*
  - *Frequency of assessments*
  - *Review of assessments*
  - *Coordination of assessments with other programs*
  - *Comprehensive care plans*

Consider as the Administrator . . .

- *Which staff in the facility will be familiar with the RAI? What staff in the facility should be knowledgeable with the RAI? What is the difference between these staff?*

NAB DOMAIN 1A: QUALITY OF CARE; 1A1: MEDICAL AND NURSING CARE PRACTICES; 1A7: CARE RECIPIENT ASSESSMENT AND INTERDISCIPLINARY CARE PLANNING

NURSING POLICIES

Comprehensive Assessments

The facility will conduct, initially and periodically, a comprehensive, accurate, standardized, and reproducible assessment of each resident's functional capacity (F636/§483.20).

Resident Assessment Instrument

The facility will make a comprehensive assessment of a resident's needs, strengths, goals, life history, and preferences using the Resident Assessment Instrument (RAI) specified by the CMS (F636/§483.20(b)(1)). The assessment will include at least the following:

1. Identification and demographic information
2. Customary routine
3. Cognitive patterns
4. Communication
5. Vision
6. Mood and behavior patterns
7. Psychological well-being
8. Physical functioning and structural problems
9. Continence
10. Disease diagnosis and health conditions
11. Dental and nutritional status
12. Skin conditions
13. Activity pursuit
14. Medications
15. Special treatments and procedures
16. Discharge planning
17. Documentation of summary information regarding the additional assessment performed on the care areas triggered
18. Documentation of participation in assessment

Frequency of Assessments

When required, the facility will conduct a comprehensive assessment of a resident as follows: within 14 calendar days after admission, excluding readmissions in which there is no significant change in the resident's physical or mental condition or not less than once every 12 months (F636/§483.20(b)(2)).

Frequency of Assessments: Promptly After a Significant Change in Physical or Mental Condition

Within 14 days after the facility determines, or should have determined, that there has been a significant change in the resident's physical or mental condition. A "significant change" means a major decline or improvement in the resident's status that will not normally resolve itself without further intervention by staff or by the implementation of standard disease-related clinical interventions that have an impact on more than one area of the resident's health status and requires interdisciplinary review or revision of the care plan, or both (F637/§483.20(b)(2)).

Quarterly Review Assessment

The facility must assess a resident using the quarterly review instrument specified by the state and approved by the CMS not less frequently than once every 3 months between comprehensive assessments (F638/§483.20(c)).

A facility must maintain all resident assessments completed within the previous 15 months in the resident's active record and use the results of the assessments to develop, review, and revise the resident's comprehensive plan (F639/§483.20(d)).

Encoding data. Within 7 days after a facility completes a resident's assessment, the facility will encode the following information for each resident in the facility: (a) admission assessment; (b) annual assessment updates; (c) significant change in status assessments; (d) quarterly review assessments; (e) a subset of items upon a resident's transfer, reentry, discharge, or death; and (f) background (face-sheet) information, if there is no admission assessment (F640/§483.20(f)(1)).

Transmitting data. Within 7 days after the facility completes a resident's assessment, the facility will be capable of transmitting to the CMS system information for each resident contained in the MDS in a format that conforms to standard record layouts and data dictionaries and that passes standardized edits defined by the CMS and the state (F640/§483.20(f)(2)).

Transmittal requirements. Within 14 days after a facility completes a resident's assessment, a facility must electronically transmit encoded, accurate, and complete MDS data to the CMS system, including the following (F640/§483.20(f)(3)):

1. Admission assessment
2. Annual assessment
3. Significant change in status assessment
4. Significant correction of prior full assessment
5. Significant correction of prior quarterly assessment
6. Quarterly review
7. A subset of items upon a resident's transfer, reentry, discharge, or death
8. Background (face-sheet) information for an initial transmission of MDS data on a resident who does not have an admission assessment

Data format. The facility will transmit data in the format specified by the CMS or state alternative RAI requirements (F640/§483.20(f)(4)).

Comprehensive care plans goal. The facility will use the results of all resident assessments completed within the previous 15 months in the resident's active record and use the results of the assessments to develop, review, and revise the resident's comprehensive care plan (F639/§483.20(d)).

Comprehensive care plans. The facility will develop a comprehensive person-centered care plan for each resident, consistent with resident rights, including measurable objectives and timeframes to meet a resident's medical, nursing, and mental and psychosocial needs identified in the comprehensive assessment. The care plan will describe the services to be furnished to attain or maintain the resident's highest practicable physical, mental, and psychosocial well-being (F656/§483.21(b)).

Emergency Medical Services and Techniques

NAB DOMAIN 1A10: EMERGENCY MEDICAL SERVICES (E.G., CPR, FIRST AID, HEIMLICH MANEUVER, AED)

Facility personnel are to provide basic life support, including CPR, to a resident requiring such emergency care before the arrival of emergency medical personnel and subject to related physician orders and the resident's advance directives (F678/§483.24(a)(3)).

Nursing staff is typically trained to administer emergency medical services such as first aid, Heimlich maneuvers, cardiopulmonary resuscitation (CPR), and automated external defibrillator (AED).

An AED is a portable electronic device that automatically diagnoses the life-threatening cardiac arrhythmias of ventricular fibrillation and ventricular tachycardia in a resident and can treat them through defibrillation, the application of electrical therapy which stops the arrhythmia, allowing the heart to reestablish an effective rhythm. With simple audio and visual commands, AEDs are designed to be simple to use for the layperson. AEDs use is taught in first aid, certified first responder, and basic life support (BLS)–level CPR classes.

Facility policy must specify which additional staff must be trained in such life-saving techniques. The dietary staff, for example, may be required to know the Heimlich maneuver in case a resident in the dining room chokes.

COMMON PITFALLS IN PRACTICE

It is just as important for you to understand nursing policy as anyone else in your facility. An explanation to surveyors that "this is my DON's job" does not make you any less responsible for their action or lack of it. *You* are the administrator; everything begins and ends in your office. Remember *respondeat superior.*

6.1.15 QUALITY OF CARE USING THE RESIDENT ASSESSMENT INSTRUMENT TO ENSURE CARE RECIPIENT SATISFACTION

Section Concepts

- *That quality of care involves:*
  - *Activities of daily living (ADLs)*
  - *No diminishment of ADL skills*
  - *Appropriate treatment and services to the resident*
  - *Providing necessary services*
  - *Treating hearing and vision problems*
  - *Managing pressure sores and urinary incontinence*
  - *Maintaining range of motion*
  - *Ensuring mental and psychosocial well-being*
  - *Using nasogastric tubes properly*
  - *Providing an accident-free environment*
  - *Meeting special needs vis-à-vis injections and related procedures*
  - *Ensuring that no unnecessary drugs are given*
  - *Minimizing use of antipsychotic drugs*
  - *Making drug discontinuance efforts*
  - *Ensuring a medication error rate of less than 5%*

Consider as the Administrator . . .

- *Much of quality of care appears to be directly related to nursing. How much of this should you be monitoring? How much of this agenda should you be moving forward toward excellent resident care? How much of this is your responsibility?*

NAB DOMAIN 1A: QUALITY OF CARE; 1A1: MEDICAL AND NURSING CARE PRACTICES; 1A5: ACTIVITIES OF DAILY LIVING (ADLs) AND INSTRUMENTAL ACTIVITIES OF DAILY LIVING (IADLs); 1A6: REHABILITATION AND RESTORATIVE PROGRAMS; 1A7: CARE RECIPIENT ASSESSMENT AND INTERDISCIPLINARY CARE PLANNING; 1B: QUALITY OF LIFE; 1B1: PSYCHOSOCIAL NEEDS (E.G., SOCIAL, SPIRITUAL, COMMUNITY, CULTURAL); 1B2: PERSON-CENTERED CARE AND COMPREHENSIVE CARE PLANNING; 1B10: MENTAL AND BEHAVIORAL HEALTH (E.G., COGNITIVE IMPAIRMENT, DEPRESSION, SOCIAL SUPPORT SYSTEMS)

QUALITY OF LIFE

Each resident will receive, and the facility will provide, the necessary care and services to attain or maintain the highest practicable physical, mental, and psychosocial well-being, per the comprehensive assessment and plan of care (F675/§483.24(b)). The facility will ensure that the resident obtains the highest possible level of functioning and well-being, limited by the individual's recognized pathology and the normal aging process

A resident's abilities in activities of daily living (ADLs) do not diminish unless circumstances of the individual's clinical condition demonstrate that diminution was unavoidable. This includes the resident's ability to perform tasks related to (a) hygiene (bathing, dressing, grooming, oral care), (b) mobility (transfer and ambulation), (c) elimination (toileting), (d) dining (eating), and (e) communication (speech, language, or other functional communication systems; F676/§483.24(b)).

Appropriate Treatment and Services to Residents

A resident is given the appropriate treatment and services to maintain or improve their ability to carry out the ADLs (F676/§483.24(a)(1)).

Providing Necessary Services

A resident who is unable to carry out ADLs receives the necessary services to maintain good nutrition, grooming, and personal and oral hygiene (F677/§483.24(a) (2)).

Vision and Hearing

To ensure that residents receive proper treatment and assistive devices to maintain vision and hearing abilities, the facility will, if necessary, assist the resident (a) in making appointments and (b) in arranging transportation to and from the office of a practitioner specializing in the treatment of vision or hearing impairment or the office of a professional specializing in the provision of vision or hearing assistive devices (F685/§483.25(a)(1-2)).

Pressure Ulcers (Pressure Injuries)

Based on the comprehensive assessment of a resident, the facility will ensure that (a) a resident receives care consistent with professional standards of practice to prevent pressure ulcers and does not develop pressure ulcers unless the individual's clinical condition demonstrates that they were unavoidable and (b) a resident with pressure ulcers receives necessary treatment and services, consistent with professional standards of practice, to promote healing, prevent infection, and prevent new ulcers from developing (F686/§483.25(b)(1)). Pressure ulcers are now termed *pressure injuries*; however, the reference to pressure ulcers has been left here to reflect current regulatory verbiage.

Urinary Incontinence

Based on the resident's comprehensive assessment, the facility will ensure that (a) a resident who enters the facility without an indwelling catheter is not catheterized unless the resident's clinical condition demonstrates that catheterization was necessary, (b) a resident who enters the facility with an indwelling catheter or subsequently receives one is assessed for removal of the catheter as soon as possible unless the resident's clinical condition demonstrates that catheterization is necessary, and (c) a resident who is incontinent of bladder receives appropriate treatment and services to prevent urinary tract infections and to restore continence to the extent possible (F690/§483.25(e)(1-2)).

Range of Motion

The facility must ensure that residents who enter the facility without a limited range of motion do not experience reductions in range of motion unless the resident's clinical condition demonstrates that a decrease in range of motion was unavoidable (F688/§483.25(c)(1)).

Treatment of Residents With Limited Range of Motion

Based on the comprehensive assessment of a resident, the facility will ensure that a resident with a limited range of motion receives appropriate treatment and services to increase range of motion or to prevent further decrease in range of motion (F688/§483.25(c)(2)).

Mental and Psychosocial Functioning

Residents whose assessments did not reveal or who do not have a diagnosis of a mental or psychosocial adjustment difficulty or a documented history of trauma and/or posttraumatic stress disorder do not display a pattern of decreased social interaction and/or increased withdrawn, angry, or depressive behaviors, unless the resident's clinical condition demonstrates that such a pattern is unavoidable (F743/§483.40(b)(2)).

Conditions for Using Nasogastric Tubes

A resident who has been able to eat enough alone or with assistance is not fed by enteral methods unless the resident's clinical condition demonstrates that enteral feeding was clinically indicated and consented to by the resident (F693/§483.25(g)(4)).

Nasogastric Tube Requirement for Preventing Aspiration and Restoration of Normal Eating

A resident who is fed by enteral means receives the appropriate treatment and services to restore, if possible, oral eating skills and to prevent complications of enteral feeding, including but not limited to aspiration pneumonia, diarrhea, vomiting, dehydration, metabolic abnormalities, and nasal–pharyngeal ulcers (F693/§483.25(g)(5)).

Resident Environment Free of Accident Hazards

NAB DOMAIN 3A2: PERSON-CENTERED ENVIRONMENT (E.G., HOME-LIKE ENVIRONMENT); 3A3: SAFETY AND ACCESSIBILITY (E.G., ADA, SAFETY DATA SHEETS)

Accidents. The facility will ensure that the environment remains as free of accident hazards as is possible and that each resident receives adequate resident supervision and assistive devices to prevent accidents (F689/§483.25(d)(1-2)).

Resident Hydration

The facility will provide each resident with sufficient fluid intake to maintain proper hydration and health (F692/§483.25(g)(2)).

Internal Investigation Protocols and Techniques

NAB DOMAIN 2B8: INTERNAL INVESTIGATION PROTOCOLS AND TECHNIQUES (E.G., INCIDENTS, ADVERSE EVENTS); 2B9: MANDATORY REPORTING REQUIREMENTS (E.G., INCIDENTS, ADVERSE EVENTS, ABUSE, NEGLECT, FINANCIAL EXPLOITATION, FRAUD)

The facility must respond to abuse, neglect, exploitation, or mistreatment allegations. The facility must have evidence that all alleged violations are thoroughly investigated; that preventing further potential abuse, neglect, exploitation, or mistreatment occurs during the investigation; and that results are reported according to state law. If the alleged violation is verified, appropriate corrective action must be taken (F610/§483.12(c)(2-4)).

CASE STUDY

Ms. Brown's Six Episodes

On Thursday morning, the administrator of The Laurels received a copy of an incident report written the day before by the charge nurse on the day shift. The report indicated that the day-shift nurse's aide responsible for Ms. Brown's care had made six consecutive observations of Ms. Brown experiencing unusual and significant postprandial orthostatic hypotension on her shift. The report indicated that after a brief consultation with the aide (the only follow-up to the report), the extent of action to be taken is for Ms. Brown to be watched by the reporting day-shift aide for the rest of the week for any continuation of these occurrences.

The DON chanced to pass by the administrator's office (Ms. Howard), shortly afterward. Ms. Howard asked the DON if the proposed action of further observations by the nurse's aide was all that was planned. The DON nodded affirmatively, indicating that she had read the report also and felt that nothing further was necessary. The charge nurse and aide, she thought,

(continued)

were overreacting. Simple observation was all that seemed indicated, the DON felt.

- *What is happening with Ms. Brown?*
- *How appropriate is the incident report? And how appropriate are the actions taken?*
- *How should the administrator respond to this situation?*
- *From the point of view of risk management, is the charge nurse reporting a potentially compensable event (opening the facility to a lawsuit)?*

Special Needs

Regarding special needs situations, the facility must ensure that residents who are utilizing any of the following are cared for consistent with professional standards of practice, the comprehensive person-centered care plan, the resident's goals and preferences, and so forth:

- Foot care (F687/§483.25(b)(2))
- Colostomy, urostomy, or ileostomy care (F691/§483.25(f))
- Nasogastric tubes, gastrostomy tubes, other tubes, and enteral fluids (F692/§483.25(g))
- Respiratory care, including tracheostomy care and tracheal suctioning (F695/§483.25(i))
- Prosthetics (F696/§483.25(j))
- Injections (F880/§483.80)

Minimization of Psychotropic Drugs

NAB DOMAIN 1A2: MEDICATION MANAGEMENT AND ADMINISTRATION

Psychotropic drugs are not given to those residents who have not used these drugs unless the medication is necessary to treat a specific condition as diagnosed and documented in the clinical record (F758/§483.45(e)(1)).

Psychotropic Drugs: Discontinuance Efforts

Residents who use psychotropic drugs receive gradual dose reductions and behavioral interventions, unless clinically contraindicated, to discontinue these drugs (F758/§483.45(e)(2)).

Medication Error Rate Less Than 5%

Residents Free of Significant Medication Errors

The facility will ensure that it is free of medication error rates of 5% or greater (F759/§483.45(f)(1)) and that residents are free of any significant medication errors (F760/§483.45(f)(2)).

6.1.16 PHARMACY

Section Concepts

- *Federal requirements related to pharmacy functions:*
  - *Need for a consultant pharmacist*
  - *Reviews of the drug regimens*
  - *Policies on unnecessary drugs*
  - *Minimization of antipsychotic drugs*
  - *Actions required on pharmacist reports*
  - *How to label drugs and biologicals*
  - *How to store drugs and biologicals*
  - *Medication management*

Consider as the Administrator . . .

- *What is the best way to safeguard narcotics in the facility considering the information that the use of facility-obtained narcotics is the most frequent reason state nursing boards discipline or suspend nurses?*
- *How can medications be effectively managed?*

NAB DOMAIN 1A2: MEDICATION MANAGEMENT AND ADMINISTRATION; 1C7: HEALTHCARE PARTNERS AND CLINICAL PROVIDERS (E.G., MD/DO, NURSE PRACTITIONER, PSYCHIATRIST, PODIATRIST, DENTIST)

CONSULTANT PHARMACIST REQUIRED

The facility will employ or obtain the services of a licensed pharmacist who (a) provides consultation on all aspects of the provision of pharmacy services in the facility, (b) establishes a system of records of receipt and disposition of all controlled drugs in sufficient detail to enable an accurate reconciliation, and (c) determines that drug records are in order and that an account of all controlled drugs is maintained and periodically reconciled (F755/§483.45(b)(1-3)).

DRUG REGIMEN USE

The drug regimen of each resident will be reviewed at least once a month by a licensed pharmacist (F756/§483.45(c)(1)). It may be necessary to review more frequently (e.g., every week) depending on the resident's conditions and the drugs they are taking.

UNNECESSARY DRUGS

Each resident's drug regimen will be free from unnecessary drugs. An *unnecessary drug* is any drug when used (a) in excessive dose (including duplicate therapy); (b) for excessive duration; (c) without adequate monitoring; (d) without adequate indications for its use; (e) in the presence of adverse consequences, which indicate the dose should be reduced or discontinued; or (f) any combinations of the reasons as mentioned earlier (F757/§483.45(d)(1-6)).

Beers' List

Proper medication selection and prescribing (including dose, duration, and type of medications) may help stabilize or improve a resident's outcome, quality of life, and functional capacity. The *Beers' Criteria for Potentially Inappropriate Medication Use in Older Adults* provides information on safely prescribing medications for older adults (F758/§483.45).

ANTIPSYCHOTIC DRUG DOSAGE LEVELS

Minimization of Psychotropic Drugs

Psychotropic drugs are not given to those residents who have not used these drugs unless the medication is necessary to treat a specific condition as diagnosed and documented in the clinical record (F758/§483.45(e)(1)).

Psychotropic Drugs: Discontinuance Efforts

Residents who use psychotropic drugs receive gradual dose reductions and behavioral interventions, unless clinically contraindicated, to discontinue these drugs (F758/§483.45(e)(2)).

ACTION REQUIRED ON PHARMACIST REPORTS

NAB DOMAIN 1A9: MEDICAL DIRECTOR

The attending physician must document in the resident's medical record that the identified irregularities on the consultant pharmacists' reports have been reviewed and what, if any, action has been taken to address it. If there is to be no change in the medication, the attending physician should document their rationale in the resident's medical record (F756/§483.45(c)(4)).

Labeling of Drugs and Biologicals

Drugs and biologicals used in the facility will be labeled per currently accepted professional principles and include the appropriate accessory and cautionary instructions and the applicable expiration date (F761/§483.45(g)).

Storage of Drugs and Biologicals

Per state and federal laws, the facility will store all drugs and biologicals in locked compartments under proper temperature controls and permit only authorized personnel to access the keys. The facility will provide separately locked, permanently affixed compartments for storage of controlled drugs listed in Schedule II of the Comprehensive Drug Abuse Prevention and Control Act of 1979 and other drugs subject to abuse, except when the facility uses single-unit package drug distribution systems in which the quantity stored is minimal, and a missing dose can be readily detected (F761/§483.45(h)(1-2)).

6.1.17 MEDICAL RECORDS

Section Concepts

- *The importance of proper medical records*
- *Timing of medical record entries*
- *Medical record retention*

Consider as the Administrator . . .

- *Is it possible for you to know where all your medical records are at any given time? Is it your responsibility?*

NAB DOMAIN 1A8: CLINICAL AND MEDICAL RECORDS AND DOCUMENTATION REQUIREMENTS (E.G., STORAGE, RETENTION, DESTRUCTION)

MEDICAL RECORDS POLICIES FOR THE FACILITY

Medical Records

The facility will maintain medical records on each resident following accepted professional standards and practices that are (a) complete, (b) accurately documented, (c) readily accessible, and (d) systematically organized (F842/§483.70(i)(1)).

Within 7 days after the facility completes the resident's assessment, it will encode information for each resident in the facility and, within 14 days, will electronically transmit encoded, accurate, and complete MDS data to the CMS system, including (F640/§483.20(f)(2-3)):

1. Admission assessments
2. Annual assessments
3. Significant change in status assessment
4. Significant correction of prior full assessments
5. Significant correction of prior quarterly assessments
6. Quarterly reviews
7. A subset of items upon a resident's transfer, reentry, discharge, and death
8. Background (face-sheet) information, if there is no admission assessment

Retention of Medical Records

Medical records will be retained for (a) the period required by state law, (b) 5 years from the date of discharge when there is no requirement in state law, or (c) for a minor, 3 years after a resident reaches legal age under state law (F842/§483.70(i)(4)).

NAB DOMAIN 2B11: HEALTHCARE RECORD REQUIREMENTS (E.G., CONFIDENTIALITY, DISCLOSURE, SAFEGUARDING, HIPAA, HITECH)

Safeguards of Patient's Clinical Record

Resident-identifiable information. (a) The facility will not release information that is resident-identifiable to the public. (b) The facility may release information that is resident-identifiable to an agent only per a contract under which the agent agrees not to use or disclose the information except to the extent the facility itself is permitted to do so (F842/§483.70(i)(1)). The facility will safeguard medical record information against loss, destruction, or unauthorized use (F842/§483.70(i)(3)).

COMMON PITFALLS IN PRACTICE
- Of the many policies discussed here, those surrounding quality of care should always be abided by. It is at the root of what we do to provide the highest quality service possible. Be certain to follow the regulations and do what is right by those entrusted to you.

6.1.18 DISCHARGE POLICIES

Section Concepts
- *Proper discharge includes many individual parts*
- *Postdischarge plans of care are imperative for good follow up into the community*

Consider as the Administrator . . .
- *Should a good discharge plan begin at admission?*

NAB DOMAIN 1A11: TRANSITION OF CARE (E.G., ADMISSION, MOVE-IN, TRANSFER, DISCHARGE, AND MOVE-OUT)

Upon discharge, a resident will have a discharge summary that includes (a) a recapitulation of the resident's stay and (b) a final summary of the resident's status at the time of the discharge that is available for release to authorized persons and agencies, with the consent of the resident or resident's representative (F661/§483.21(c)(2)).

A POSTDISCHARGE PLAN OF CARE DEVELOPED WITH PARTICIPATION

A postdischarge plan of care will be developed with the resident's participation and with the resident's consent, the resident's representatives, which will assist the resident in adjusting to their new living environment. This postdischarge plan of care must indicate where the individual plans to reside, any arrangements that have been made for resident's follow-up care, and any postdischarge medical and non-medical services (F661/§483.21(c)(2)).

This ends our formal presentation of useful policies for the nursing facility. We now turn to the process of developing a care plan.

6.2 DEVELOPING A PERSON-CENTERED CARE PLAN

Section Concepts

- *Developing the care plan is at the heart of what successful facilities do*
- *You will learn:*
  - *Use of the RAI to gather information*
  - *The components of the RAI*
  - *What the care area assessment (CAA) will include*
  - *How to identify outcomes in care planning*
  - *That the care planning process focuses specifically on the individual person*
  - *The facility's care plan*

Consider as the Administrator . . .

- *What is your part in the care plan? Is this a meeting you should be attending for each resident?*

NAB DOMAIN 1B2: PERSON-CENTERED CARE AND COMPREHENSIVE CARE PLANNING

NAB DOMAIN 1A7: CARE RECIPIENT ASSESSMENT AND INTERDISCIPLINARY CARE PLANNING

THE RESIDENT ASSESSMENT INSTRUMENT AND THE MINIMUM DATA SET 3.0

The MDS and RAI are a set of screening, clinical, and functional status elements that form the foundation of a comprehensive assessment for each resident in the nursing facility. The items within the MDS standardize communication about resident problems and conditions within the nursing facility, with other nursing facilities, and with other community agencies.

Facility staff will use the RAI to gather information, address each resident's needs and goals, and monitor the planned interventions' results. This instrument enables staff to evaluate goal achievement and revise care plans by tracking resident status changes. In combining problem identification with clinical interventions, the care plan becomes each resident's unique path toward achieving or maintaining their highest practical level of well-being. This interdisciplinary team approach involves dietary, social work, physical therapy, occupational therapy, speech/language pathology, pharmacy, activities, and others.

The RAI, utilizing the care area assessment (CAA) process, enables the staff to audit care recipient services and outcomes. Typically, a resident care planning conference is held for each resident at least monthly. At this time, all staff caregivers are invited to participate in assessing the past month's care plan implementation and establishing the coming month's care plan goals, including which staff will be responsible for implementing and measuring each goal. Additionally, the DON typically makes daily rounds to assess the care being given in the facility. Beyond that, each staff member is responsible for continuously observing each resident 24 hours a day, observing for changes in behavior or other signs that attention must be paid to that resident.

THE RESIDENT ASSESSMENT INSTRUMENT COMPONENTS USED BY THE FACILITY

The RAI consists of three basic components: the MDS 3.0, the CAA process, and the RAI utilization guidelines. The MDS is a core set of screening, clinical, and functional status elements that forms the basis for a comprehensive assessment for each resident. In addition to the main MDS, there are subsets of data items for each MDS assessment and tracking documents for comprehensive quarterly, annual, significant change, discharge, entry, and similar changes. The CAA process is designed to help systemically interpret the information recorded on the MDS. Once a care area need has been triggered or identified, the facility will determine whether to care plan for it. This process applies current, evidence-based clinical resources to conduct the assessments.

The CAA process in the facility will include care area triggers (CATs), which are specific resident responses for one or a combination of MDS elements. The triggers identify residents who have or are at risk for developing functional problems and require further assessment. There are extensive utilization guidelines providing instruction to staff for when and how to use the RAI.

The MDS care planning process can be visualized as follows:

Assessment Minimum Data Set -->	Care Area Assessment -->	Decision-Making Development -->	Care Plan Implementation -->	Care Plan Evaluation

Assessment. Taking stock of all observations, information, and knowledge about a resident from all available sources (e.g., medical records, the resident, resident's representative, or guardian).

Decision-making. Determining with the resident, the resident's physician, and the interprofessional team the severity, functional impact, and scope of a resident's problems.

Care planning. Establishing a course of action with input from the resident, the physician, and the interdisciplinary team moves a resident toward resident-specific goals utilizing individual resident strengths and interprofessional expertise. This is the "how" of resident care.

Discharge Planning: Working With the Community

Discharge planning is a process that begins at admission and involves identifying each resident's discharge goals and needs, developing and implementing interventions to address them, and continuously evaluating them throughout the resident's stay to ensure a successful discharge (F660/§483.21(c)(1)). Resident records must show that the potential for discharge is being constantly assessed and charted.

All residents have the right to choose the services they receive and the settings in which they receive those services. Individuals have a right to receive care in the least restrictive (most integrated) setting, and governments are responsible for enforcing and supporting these choices. An individual in a nursing facility can choose to leave the facility at any time. (Be sure to document this event fully!) An individual can request to talk to someone about returning to the community at any time. The return to community referral (required as part of the discharge plan) focuses on residents who want to speak to someone about returning to the community and enables nursing facility staff to directly open the discussion about the individual's preferences for service settings.

Expectations about returning to community living are unique for each individual. An individual may expect to return to their former home or return to a different community home, or the individual may identify a desire to stay in the nursing facility. Each person's level of understanding about their health status and needs for physical assistance and the availability of family and other supports also varies. The discharge assessment process requires nursing facility staff to apply a systematic and objective protocol so that every individual can assess meaningful information about community living options and community service alternatives, with the goal being to assist the individual in maintaining or achieving the highest level of functioning. This includes ensuring that the individual or representative is fully informed and involved, identifying individual strengths, assessing risk factors, implementing comprehensive plan of care interventions, coordinating interdisciplinary care providers, fostering independent functioning, using rehabilitative programs, and using community referrals.

When this care need is triggered, nursing facility staff should follow their facility's chosen protocol or policy for performing the CAA. This CAA is triggered when a resident expresses interest in returning to the community. The information gleaned from the assessment should be used to assess the resident's situation and begin appropriate care planning, discharge planning, and other follow-up measures. The next step is to develop a resident-specific care plan based directly on these findings. Care planning aims to initiate and maintain collaboration between the nursing facility and the local contact agency to support the individual's expressed interest in being transitioned to community living. This includes facility support for the individual in achieving their highest level of functioning and the involvement of the designated contact agency providing informed choices for community living. This collaboration will enable the state-designated local contact agency to initiate communication by telephone or visit with the individual (and their family or representatives, if the individual so chooses) to talk about returning to community living opportunities.

Identification of Outcomes in Care Planning

Determining the expected outcomes forms the basis for evaluating resident-specific goals and interventions to help residents achieve those goals.

Implementation is putting that course of action (specific interventions derived through interdisciplinary individualized care planning) into motion by staff knowledgeable about the resident's care goals and approaches. This carries out the "how" and "when" of resident care.

Evaluation is critically reviewing individualized care plan goals, interventions, and implementation in terms of achieved resident outcomes as identified and assessing the need to modify the care plan (i.e., change interventions) to adjust to changes in the resident's status, goals, or improvement or decline.

NAB DOMAIN 2A7: INTEGRATION OF CLINICAL AND FINANCIAL SYSTEMS (E.G., EMR/EHR, MDS)

The MDS consists of several sections:

A. Identification Information
B. Hearing, Speech, and Vision
C. Cognitive Patterns
D. Mood
E. Behavior
F. Preferences for Customary Routine and Activities
G. Functional Status
GG. Functional Abilities and Goals
H. Bladder and Bowel
I. Active Diagnoses
J. Health Conditions
K. Swallowing/Nutritional Status
L. Oral/Dental Status
M. Skin Conditions
N. Medications
O. Special Treatments, Procedures, and Programs
P. Restraints
Q. Participation in Assessment and Goal Setting
V. CAA Summary
X. Correction Request
Z. Assessment Administration

Initially, the MDS was used to determine the quality of care being given. Today, the MDS is also used to determine Medicare's reimbursement each month. The staff person who serves as the MDS coordinator has become a critically important position within the facility staff.

The goal of all care planning is to focus on and accommodate each resident's unique characteristics and needs. The MDS provides the basis for each facility's personal care plan for each individual resident. There are a variety of formats used by facilities to embody the care plan in a way that enables staff to use the information to provide hour-by-hour care of each resident.

COMMON PITFALLS IN PRACTICE

- Understanding care planning is important. Being a part of care planning and resident care is a crucial part of your success. Many administrators simply choose to distance themselves from this part of the facility. We urge you to be a part of this, as it can truly improve resident care and your relationship with those you serve.

CASE STUDY

Ms. Jacobs's Decision

Ms. Jacobs, 84, has lived at The Laurels for 3 years. She is diagnosed with post-cerebrovascular accident (CVA) with right-sided weakness and bilateral hearing loss. She is alert and oriented, enjoys watching TV and listening to classical music, but rarely participates in group activities. She has three daughters who all visit regularly. When she entered the facility, she indicated under the Patient Self-Determination Act papers signed that she wanted all reasonable measures to be taken to treat any reversible condition.

Each day, Ms. Jacobs gets up with the assistance of one person and performs her morning ADLs with minimum aid. She ambulates daily for short distances with her walker and standby assistance.

One Friday, Ms. Jacobs refused her breakfast and lunch, saying she did not feel well and wanted someone to perform her ADLs. Nurse Casey noticed that her speech was slightly slurred, blood pressure was 130/74, pulse was 84 and regular, respirations were 24 and unbalanced. Ms. Jacobs was alert; was oriented to person, place, and time; and showed no other changes in following commands or ambulating.

Dr. Greg was called. He asked the staff to encourage oral intake and to call him if Ms. Jacobs showed any other changes.

On Saturday, Ms. Jacobs had difficulty transferring herself from her bed to her chair and complained of leg weakness. She continued to refuse to eat and drank only small amounts of liquids. Dr. Greg visited and decided to admit her to the hospital to perform some tests to assess if she had had another CVA.

Dr. Greg explained his concerns to Ms. Jacobs, and she understood. However, Ms. Jacobs told Dr. Greg and her daughters, "I don't want to go to the hospital. I am old and tired. Please leave me alone and let me die. I am ready to die. " Dr. Greg and Ms. Jacobs's daughters decided to honor her wishes. Dr. Greg then wrote the following orders on her chart:

"Encourage patient to take fluids orally. Do not resuscitate in the event of cardiac or respiratory arrest. Do not transport to the hospital. Do not place a nasogastric tube or start intravenous fluids."

Many of the staff were confused and angry. A debate among staff ensued as to whether Dr. Greg and Ms. Jacobs's family were correct in following her wishes expressed after her status changes and not transferring her to the hospital.

- *Is the physician correct?*
- *Are the confused and angry staff correct?*
- *Are the daughters correct?*
- *Is Ms. Jacobs correct?*
- *Do we need more than some notes in a resident chart to make all this happen for the resident?*

6.3 THE QUALITY INDICATORS SURVEY: THE REGULATORY SURVEY AND INSPECTION PROCESS AND PLAN OF CORRECTION

Section Concepts

- *What the survey is*
- *The purposes of the survey*
- *How surveyors prepare*
- *About the entrance conference*
- *What is required by surveyors after entry within 1 hour, 4 hours, and 24 hours*
- *Procedures used by surveyors*
- *How the MDS sample is constructed*
- *The stages in the survey process*
- *How survey results are presented: The exit conference*
- *How deficiencies are determined*
- *How plans of correction are written*
- *How facilities may appeal deficiencies*
- *How to read the Scope and Severity chart*

Consider as the Administrator . . .

- *How can the facility defend itself against what it feels is an unfair survey result?*

NAB DOMAIN 3B4: REGULATORY SURVEY AND INSPECTION PROCESS; 3B6: CENTERS FOR MEDICARE AND MEDICAID SERVICES (CMS) QUALITY MEASURES; 3B7: QUALITY ASSURANCE AND PERFORMANCE IMPROVEMENT (QAPI)

The Quality Indicators Survey (QIS) is used as the survey-of-record only for states that have received CMS approval and only by surveyors who have completed QIS training. The QIS survey is a "substitute" for the traditional standard survey, where allowed.

PURPOSE OF THE SURVEY

The government surveys to determine the extent to which the facility has implemented facility policies and the rules and regulations that apply to operating a nursing facility. The actual QIS survey consists of nine tasks, ranging from offsite preparation by surveyors to the exit conference.

PREPARATION BY THE SURVEYORS

This unannounced annual survey begins with the surveyor team reviewing (a) current government data records on the facility (quality measure/indicator reports, Online Survey Certification & Reporting System [OSCAR]), (b) current complaints and ombudsman information, and (c) the current MDS data. Based on this information, the surveyors choose a random sample of residents.

ENTRANCE CONFERENCE

At Entrance

The surveyor team leader meets with the administrator and requests an alphabetical resident census, a copy of the facility floor plan, a staffing schedule for licensed and registered nurses, the formula used to calculate the emergency water source, and the new admission form used by the facility.

The survey team leader provides to the administrator an OSCAR (data) report, Medicare/Medicaid application (671), Resident Census and Conditions (672), the Quality Indicator Survey Demonstration Brochure, and signs to post in the facility so that residents know a survey is being conducted.

Within 1 Hour

The administrator will provide the following to the survey team leader within 1 hour:

- Name of the resident council president
- Medication pass times
- All admission sample closed records
- Mealtimes and dining locations
- List of key facility personnel

Within 4 Hours

The facility will provide the following to the surveyors within 4 hours:

- Influenza/pneumococcal policy
- List of any rooms with four or more residents, less than required square footage, or no window access
- QAA committee information
- Location of Preadmission Screening and Resident Review (PASRR) information
- Contact person for complaints, abuse, or grievances
- List of ventilator-dependent residents
- List of residents in hospice care
- List of dialysis patients
- List of residents with end-stage renal disease (ESRD) diagnosis
- Description of any experimental research occurring in the facility

Within 24 Hours

The facility will provide the following to the surveyors within 24 hours:

- A list of any Medicare residents who have requested demands bills since the last survey
- Five most recent denial notices issued
- Completed Medicare/Medicaid (CMS 671) application
- Completed Resident Census and Conditions (CMS 672)

Survey Procedures Expected by the Facility

Based on the MDS reports and other information, the survey team uses the Quality Indicator Survey Data Collection Tool (QIS DCT) to generate at least three lists of residents to be interviewed: an MDS sample, an admission sample, and a census sample. The surveyors can generate additional lists of residents to be interviewed; for example, they may decide to interview all residents with bed sores or all residents with restraints of any kind.

The Three Samples

The *MDS sample* focuses on residents who had an MDS assessment completed at any time within the past 180 days. The *admission sample* focuses on postadmission care, maximizing function before decline occurs, long-stay admissions, and review of 30 current or discharged resident records. The *census sample* includes observations, interviews, and record reviews for up to 40 residents residing in the facility.

Stages

The survey can take 2 to 5 days and occurs in two stages. Stage 1 is a preliminary investigation of the regulatory areas identified in the admission and census samples. Stage 2 is an in-depth investigation of residents who related Quality Care Indicators (QCIs) exceeded thresholds in care areas through completion of Stage 1. Finally, the team interviews the resident council president.

The administrator must carefully manage the survey process. Staff must be educated on what the surveyors will do and appropriate staff responses. Each staff member must know what surveyors are permitted and not permitted to do. A surveyor may not, for example, require a staff caregiver to reveal a care recipient's genitals. Every staff member, from housekeeping to the front office staff, needs to be educated on their appropriate roles when surveyors are in the building.

The Exit Conference

During the exit conference, the surveyors share their observations and preliminary findings with designated facility personnel, the ombudsman, the resident council president, and, if invited, one or two residents. Facility personnel may provide any additional information they want the surveyors to have in response to their preliminary findings.

Survey Results

After returning to their agency, the surveyors decide what their findings will be, perhaps in consultation with their supervisors as needed. Within 10 working days, the facility will receive a report (CMS-2567 form). If any deficiencies are found, the surveyors provide the prefix and tag number (e.g., Tag F686), citing what practice was deficient or the requirement that was not met, together with the evidence supporting the deficiency or deficiencies.

Deficiencies

If any deficiencies are cited, the facility will submit a plan of correction to the survey agency by the 10th day after receiving the CMS-2567 report. Within 10 days, the surveyors will notify the facility whether the plan of correction is acceptable. If the facility plan is not acceptable, the process repeats until a plan is accepted.

The preparation of an acceptable plan of correction must address the following:

- How corrective action will be accomplished for those residents found to have been affected by the deficient practice
- How the facility will identify other residents having the potential to be affected by the same deficient practice
- What measures will be put into place or systemic changes will be made to ensure that the deficient practice does not recur
- How the facility plans to monitor its performance to ensure that solutions are sustained
- Dates when corrective action will be completed (SOM, 7317)

Plans for Follow-Up

The CMS offers no guarantee of a revisit. However, should one be conducted, one revisit will normally be conducted after a survey that found noncompliance and another before the expiration of the 6-month period. A facility must be in substantial compliance to avoid termination of its provider agreement.

NAB DOMAIN 3B5: PROCEDURES FOR INFORMAL DISPUTE RESOLUTION (IDR)

Informal Dispute Resolution

The facility may ask for a meeting to dispute the cited deficiencies. However, requesting an informal dispute resolution (IDR) does not delay any enforcement action. The facility may not dispute the team's decision as to scope and severity of a practice (except when a finding of immediate jeopardy or substandard quality of care is made), the remedies imposed, alleged failure of the survey team to comply with a requirement of the survey process, or alleged inconsistency of the survey team in citing deficiencies among other facilities. The IDR is often a valuable step because it allows the facility an additional opportunity to demonstrate that its practices did meet standards.

All the information available to the survey team is available to the facility.

This allows an alert facility to be fully prepared when a survey team arrives at the facility door.

We have looked at a set of policies a facility may wish to adopt. We have further examined the care planning process and the survey process. The final result of these complicated processes is the formal findings of the inspectors.

6.4 THE REPORT CARD

Section Concepts

* *Understanding compliance is the key to eliminating deficiencies*
* *Scope and severity can quickly become a nightmare situation when immediate jeopardy level deficiencies occur*

Consider as the Administrator . . .

* *Is it fair that your license is referred for immediate jeopardy level citations, especially in areas you have less control over (such as nursing)?*

NAB DOMAIN 2B4: COMPLIANCE PROGRAMS; 3B4: REGULATORY SURVEY AND INSPECTION PROCESS

The surveyors determine the level of compliance with each of the federal requirements through the survey process. Deficiencies are issued for standards of care not met. Deficiencies are divided into resident-centered and facility-centered. A dietary food handling violation would be a facility-related deficiency. Resident-centered requirements must be met for every resident regardless of whether that resident is receiving Medicare or Medicaid reimbursement for care or any payer source.

The deficiencies are reportable outcome measures applied by the surveyors to care given in the facility.

SCOPE AND SEVERITY LEVELS FOR DEFICIENCIES ISSUED BY SURVEYORS

The surveyors use the Scope and Severity grid in judging the seriousness of each deficiency issued to a facility. If there are only one or two deficiencies at Level A, the facility might not be required to write a plan of correction. A level A deficiency might involve one resident who did not receive proper access to nutritious snacks as required. A level C deficiency might be issued for the hot water for the entire facility being 2 degrees warmer than permitted. This would be level C because the scope was widespread (the entire facility), but no actual harm occurred, and there was potential for only minimal harm. Deficiencies at the higher levels of scope and severity can result in large fines imposed on the facility. Deficiencies at the highest levels of scope and severity risk the facility being placed on a "fast track," which could lead to decertification of the facility for Medicare and Medicaid funding within a matter of 60 days if satisfactory corrections are not accomplished.

Scope and Severity Grid			
	Scope of the Deficiency		
Severity of the Deficiency	**ISOLATED**	**PATTERN**	**WIDESPREAD**
Immediate jeopardy to resident health or safety	J	K	L
Actual harm that is not immediate	G	H	I

(continued)

Scope and Severity Grid (*continued*)

Severity of the Deficiency	Scope of the Deficiency		
	ISOLATED	PATTERN	WIDESPREAD
No actual harm with potential for more than minimal harm that is not immediate jeopardy	D	E	F
No actual harm with potential for minimum harm	A	B	C

Shaded areas within the grid denote deficiencies that may constitute substandard quality of care. Any deficiency in the top row of the grid (J, K, L) constitutes immediate jeopardy.

Scope and Severity is a system of rating the seriousness of deficiencies. A *deficiency* is a nursing facility's failure to meet a participation requirement. Scope and Severity is a national system used by all state survey agencies and the CMS when conducting nursing facility Medicare and Medicaid certification surveys. For each deficiency, the surveyor determines the level of harm to the resident or resident(s) involved and the scope of the problem within the nursing facility. The surveyor then assigns an alphabetical scope and severity value, A through L, to the deficiency. "A" is the least serious and "L" is the most serious rating. The Scope and Severity matrix is an integral part of how nursing facility scores are calculated in the scoring system.

COMMON PITFALLS IN PRACTICE
It is imperative that you understand the survey process and know it as well as the surveyor. Appendix PP (what this chapter is based on) needs to be a document with which you are intimately acquainted. The best advice that you can be given is to always know more than your surveyors. Be able to assist in their understanding of the regulations.

6.5 GETTING REIMBURSED FOR CARE GIVEN

Section Concepts

- *How facilities are reimbursed by Medicare*
- *Use of the Prospective Payment System (PPS) in determining reimbursement for care given by the facility*
- *The role of the MDS in reimbursement*
- *The Resource Utilization Group classification system*
- *How the ADL score is used in figuring reimbursement*
- *How to compete in today's marketplace*
- *How to bill for care rendered to Medicare*
- *Residents' providers' role in the healthcare continuum*

Consider as the Administrator . . .

- *Is the profitability or.unprofitability of the typical nursing facility primarily in the hands of the Medicare and Medicaid system administrators?*

NAB DOMAIN 1A7: CARE RECIPIENT ASSESSMENT AND INTERDISCIPLINARY CARE PLANNING; 2A5: REVENUE AND REIMBURSEMENT (E.G., PDPM, PDGM, ACOs, HMOs, MEDICAID, PRIVATE PAYORS); 2A7: INTEGRATION OF CLINICAL AND FINANCIAL SYSTEMS (E.G., EMR/EHR, MDS)

PATIENT DRIVEN PAYMENT MODEL

For many years now, the CMS has used a Prospective Payment System (PPS) to determine reimbursement to nursing facilities for care given. In 2019, we saw a significant shift in how payments were made to the Patient Driven Payment Model (PDPM). The PDPM was expected to improve payment accuracy and appropriateness by focusing on resident-centered services rather than on the volume of services (as was previously the focus). It was also expected to reduce the administrative burden on providers and improve SNF care payments to underserved beneficiaries.

The PDPM focuses on five case mix-adjusted components, all based on data derived from the MDS and provider. These five components are physical therapy, occupational therapy, speech/language pathology, nursing, and nonancillaries. The PDPM allows for a specific focus surrounding payment accuracy based on resident needs in these five specific areas. The PDPM is a rather complicated system in scoring for payment. It has been revised since its inception as well and undergoes frequent change. It is in the best interests of the administrator to keep up with these changes.

THE MINIMUM DATA SET

The MDS contains items that reflect the acuity level of the resident, including diagnoses, treatments, and an evaluation of the resident's functional status. The MDS is used as a data collection tool to identify specific resident information for billing purposes. The MDS is used by Medicare, Medicaid, private insurers, and others to determine billing levels. As such, the MDS document must be completed accurately, correctly, and completely—and skillfully.

Understanding the specifics for each payer is crucial for billing success. It is most certainly the job of the MDS coordinator to ensure that MDS documentation is correct, but it is the job of the administrator to ensure that this is occurring. It is also the administrator's job to understand the MDS and all other processes and players that figure into billing. These players include the physical therapist, the occupational therapist, the speech therapist, the business office manager, billers, the social worker, and many individuals who are part of the interdisciplinary care team.

REIMBURSEMENT

NAB DOMAIN 2A5: REVENUE AND REIMBURSEMENT (E.G., PDPM, PDGM, ACOs, HMOs, MEDICAID, PRIVATE PAYORS)

How much a facility is reimbursed for the care given typically determines whether the facility will be reimbursed for its actual costs. As Medicare requires the facility to pay various expenses associated with each resident, some residents may cost the facility too much to admit. For instance, a cancer patient receiving intensive therapies requiring frequent out-of-facility transportation may cost more than the facility can hope to be reimbursed under Part A.

The Reimbursement Process

The government seeks to control its care costs, and the facility aims to maximize its income. This has not always been true. Initially, the government did not care how many dollars healthcare providers charged. The government paid whatever the healthcare providers charged, believing healthcare providers to be professionals who would not take advantage of government generosity and trust. This turned out not to be the case. Having been given the ability to write checks on the U.S. Treasury, healthcare providers began a spending spree in 1965 that ended only in the 1980s when Congress realized that healthcare costs had mushroomed out of control. The government decided to control healthcare costs by telling the providers ahead of time what the government would pay for each service or item. Enter the era of cost controls. The system is now known as the PPS.

Competing in Today's Healthcare Marketplace

Today it is accepted practice that the government actively seeks to pay the least amount possible for services rendered. In contrast, providers seek to be paid the maximum amount possible for services provided. These attitudes have introduced the era of cost shifting, where each player aims to minimize its own cost at the likely cost of the other players. Hospitals have sought to shift care costs to nursing facilities for services provided to the resident discharged from the hospital. Who will pay for the cancer treatments once the patient has moved from the hospital to the nursing facility? As both the hospital and the nursing facility receive a predetermined number of dollars to provide care for each patient, these questions of who pays for what services have moved to the forefront of healthcare reimbursement disputes. Today, healthcare is provided in an era of scarcity.

The provider's role is to offer and receive payment for the healthcare services society specifies. The nursing facility industry's role is to respond to the stated societal need for 24-hour-a-day nursing care for persons who do not need acute care in a hospital but who require sufficient nursing care on a 24-hour basis that care in a facility setting is necessary.

Deciding How to Bill

In reality, the government expects the healthcare providers to maximize their income by placing care given in the most expensive permitted care reimbursement category. The government constantly monitors the care charges submitted by healthcare providers and makes adjustments if the government feels it is being overcharged. How much a facility can charge is a moving target. As a result, the federal government has produced several statutes to discover and prevent fraudulent billing over time. Some of these are the Health Care Fraud and Abuse Control Program as part of the Health Insurance Portability and Accountability Act (HIPAA). Violations can carry fines of up to $25,000 and up to 5 years in prison. Upcoding and kickbacks are the primary foci.

Upcoding

NAB DOMAIN 2B3: ETHICAL CONDUCT AND STANDARDS OF PRACTICE; 2B4: COMPLIANCE PROGRAMS

Upcoding is billing for a higher reimbursement than services provided or should have been provided, given the resident's need profile. In reality, all healthcare providers seek to be reimbursed at the highest level of care justifiable. Still, what is justifiable remains a moving target. It is essential to bill at the highest reasonable level for needed and provided care. It is equally important to know current rules and billing practices. The U.S. Department of Health and Human Services Office of Inspector General estimated that nursing facilities overbilled Medicare for more than $1 billion in a past year.

Kickbacks

Kickbacks occur when an effort is made to induce referrals of Medicaid or Medicare, whether in cash or in kind. Gifts to physicians or others in a position to refer patients, such as the hospital discharge social worker, may be interpreted as an inducement. A policy of paying for all services in arm's-length transactions is always advisable if fraud is to be avoided.

Today, the nursing facility administrator's job requires skill in leading the facility by providing excellence in care while simultaneously ensuring that the facility receives sufficient reimbursement to allow the facility to survive economically. As the years have passed, the skill level required of the administrator has risen.

The Stark Laws and the Anti-Kickback Statutes are crucial considerations in this area. The administrator must stay knowledgeable of these laws and any changes that occur with them.

We are near the end of this text. A lot has been said about what nursing facility administrators should and should not do as they go about the daily task of managing a nursing facility.

COMMON PITFALLS IN PRACTICE

- Money. In the end, no matter the type of facility you work for, you *must* make money. Money is what allows you to care for your residents, to pay your staff, and to pay your bills. Sadly, you must make it, and to do this, you need census.
- You must know, just as well as your business office manager, how to bill.

CASE STUDY

A Final Case: Ms. Jensen's Management Style

The administrator in training (AIT) had been assigned to Ms. Jensen for a 2-day period. Ms. Jensen, the administrator at The Laurels, had been told only the day before. Not having had much advance notice, when the AIT arrived, Ms. Jensen suggested that he shadow her for 2 days as an excellent way to see her administrative style in action. The first meeting of the day was with Ms. Wellborn, the head of housekeeping. Ms. Wellborn had been trying for 2 weeks to decide on the employees' request, which she had discussed with Ms. Jensen, to change their schedule to 10 hours a day, 4 days a week. Ms. Jensen told Ms. Wellborn to reject the request and keep the staff on their 8-hour-a-day, 5-days-a-week work schedule.

Later that morning Ms. Jensen met with the DON, seeking to revise the patient admission policy. The DON wanted to reduce the proportion of heavy-care patients. Ms. Jensen told the DON to rewrite the admissions policy before the next staff meeting and distribute it for review at the staff meeting.

While walking down the hall on her way to lunch, the head of maintenance stopped her and said he couldn't decide between the four different mowing machines she and he had looked at for purchase. Ms. Jensen said, "I don't care which machine you buy. You and your staff ride them, you decide," and continued down the hall to the lunchroom.

Shortly after lunch, she had a meeting with the comptroller. The comptroller had been bugging her about going to a new type of depreciation schedule for the past month. Ms. Jensen saw no advantages. After a half-hour discussion, she told the comptroller to stay with the current depreciation method and consider the matter closed.

Ms. Jensen arrived early the next morning, AIT in tow, before the night shift had left. She decided to go on rounds with the DON. The round was conducted by the night supervisor. Three of the night-shift workers left rounds for home partway through. The day-shift supervisor arrived at the facility and joined them near the end of rounds.

After rounds were over, the DON returned to her office to open mail. Ms. Jensen suggested that she and the DON have a cup of coffee from the DON's ever-ready coffeepot. Ms. Jensen shut the office door. She told the DON to speak to the night-shift workers who left early and to the day supervisor who arrived late, commenting, "The staff have to understand that rounds are as important as any other aspect of the job."

The weekly staff meeting was scheduled for that afternoon. The DON distributed copies of her proposed policy for balancing the case mix more evenly. Aside from the usual reports, one action item came up. The night nurses' aides had been complaining for some time that they should not have to fold and sort resident clothes. They felt this was more appropriately a job of the laundry staff. Ms. Jensen tells the two department heads to get together after the staff meeting and settle the matter between them.

(continued)

After the staff meeting, Ms. Jensen invited the AIT, who had shadowed her for these 2 days, into her office and asked him first to describe what he saw as her management style and then give her his frank opinions about her managerial effectiveness.

She wanted his advice about whether he thought she needed to change her style to be more effective.

- *How would you respond to Ms. Jensen's two questions to the AIT?*

6.6 A GLANCE AT THE HORIZON

Section Concepts

- *Work at the facility is 24/7*
- *Patient acuity has increased exponentially and will continue to do so over time*
- *Nursing facilities provide customer service; it is the administrator's job to ensure that the quality of the service endures*

Consider as the Administrator . . .

- *Can you possibly meet all the needs of each resident and of the facility that are coming your way? Is time management a key? Is stress management a necessity?*

THE CHANGING FACILITY ROLE

Sicker and Quicker

NFs are no longer warehouses for older adults until the end of their life. Facilities now provide care and rehabilitation for residents admitted as a step in their healing process after hospitalization or provide involved care for residents seeking a meaningful life but requiring ongoing healthcare support. The current trend is admitting sicker residents than ever before, as hospitals are discharging earlier than ever before. This transition results in new considerations for the nursing facility of today:

1. Relationship building for the nursing facility administrator is a crucial skill. You need to be the first administrator that discharge planners, social workers, transition care coordinators, and hospital CEOs think of when movement needs to happen in their facilities.
2. Admissions is a 24/7/365 job. In the past, weekend admissions were frowned upon and sometimes even strategically avoided by intake personnel. Today, they are necessary and expected. Making hospitals wait kills relationships with your source of census.
3. Therapy is a 7-days-a-week expectation. With residents being admitted for more extensive care and rehabilitation, the team must be ready to care for them. A full complement of therapists needs to work every day of the week to provide the services required for positive resident outcomes and reimbursement.

4. Understanding tiered resident needs is vital to their success and yours. Many residents need further extensive rehab. Often residents admitted to SNFs arrive there because they cannot meet the requirements to qualify for subacute, step-down, rehab hospital, or long-term acute care facilities. Nursing facilities are expected to provide high-quality services for short-term rehab or long-term support care, optimizing resident function. These are all facility goals for balanced census and quality resident outcomes.

6.7 SUMMARY OBSERVATIONS FROM A CAREER OF NURSING FACILITY ADMINISTRATION

FIX IT ALL THE TIME

You will need to make some assumptions on your trek to becoming an administrator. Rarely does a new job come from a "perfect" administrator leaving an exquisite building. If it were perfect, understand that administrator would probably still be working at the facility. Each facility will have clean-up projects, even if it is running well. Consider using your new eyes, opinions, and perspective to make a successful facility a magical one.

On the other hand, if your inherited facility is terribly broken, you will need a lot of effort to turn around property and attitudes. At some point in your career, you will have this experience. Understand that *every* facility has something that is "broken." Your job as the administrator is to find it and *fix it* all the time. Consistently look for what needs to be fixed. If you become blind to the daily issues, listen to the people around you, their comments are your opportunities for improvement. You set the corrections in motion. You look throughout the day for your chance to make things better, newer, fresher. Before you leave for the day, you follow up on projects to ensure that what needed to be fixed *is* fixed. This is a part of all your daily duties in the facility. You are the individual tasked to make the facility run correctly, and you absolutely cannot fail to create a functioning and attractive environment for your residents and staff. You are the person with the power to do it. Be the mover and shaker that gets things done.

A few considerations:

1. Be an administrator that everyone knows. Nobody should ever be able to tell your replacement that they never met you. This goes for all shifts, all departments, all employees, all contractors, all residents, all responsible parties, and all loved ones. Understand and know your stakeholders. Build relationships. This effort will pay off without question.
2. Surround yourself with people smarter than you. Build an unbeatable team of experts. Lean on your experts and allow them to lean on you.
3. Treat your employees well. Make your team a commodity.
4. Treat all your employees as if they were the last ones available on the planet. Consistently and positively reinforce those who work with you. Employees *need* to hear what a good job they are doing. Make meaningful and specific comments that make them feel like you are noticing their efforts and tell them about it all day. Demonstrate appreciation in meaningful ways whenever you can.

5. *Follow up.* Follow up on your request when you say something, ask something, or request something. Your loss of focus with empty requests and empty employee corrections frustrates your employees and creates distrust. If you are known for not following up on your directives, your employees will assign the same importance and not bother to complete the actions.
6. Your position is not higher than anyone who works with you. Being the administrator makes you a supervisor of people. *Never expect your team to do anything you would not do yourself.*
7. Be seen. Be heard. Be present. Mop a floor. Buff a hall. Paint a wall. Serve a meal. Paint resident nails. Braid hair. Hold a hand. Being a successful administrator requires you to be a "real person" to those around you.

BE A TURNAROUND SPECIALIST

Both authors of this textbook have spent many years working in facilities with specific challenges that others might consider "broken" throughout all areas of healthcare. The key is to see the opportunities in the areas where people see concerns; this attitude is what has provided a generous career and lifestyle. We urge you to be part of creating a more perfect world. Go to work each day with a passion in your heart and your mind focused on impeccable resident care. Do the job of a turnaround specialist daily. Do everything in your power to ensure you never need a cleaner to follow you after you leave a facility. Focus on quality improvement and on making everything that you touch better than the way you found it.

Enjoy the life of an administrator. It is among the most fulfilling of jobs you can ever have.

CASE DISCUSSIONS

Squabbles With Roommates: "Man Accused of Using Cane to Kill Two in Home"

This case presents an intriguing situation with two separate considerations. The first concern here, which we will consider for our purposes completed, is the reporting of the incident to local law enforcement and state entities which are required dependent upon current regulations. The second concern is the future of the facility and how you handle the situation. The vice president of your chain has presented a question requiring answers surrounding how you plan to prevent this from happening ever again. The state surveyors will also make the same inquiry.

There is no "one answer" here. The case of Henry T. will need to be assessed to find out what went wrong and where. The case cites a "room-to-room rampage sparked by disputes with roommates," however, there was more than one room involved here, thus not necessarily all Henry's roommates. We need to find out what happened to cause Henry to behave in such a manner. Was this simply a dispute, or were there clinical conditions with Henry that caused him to misbehave (such as a bad urinary tract infection)? Was there truly a roommate issue? Was the retirement home actually "cramped" as it is accused to be? What are Henry's diagnoses?

(continued)

What is in Henry's care plan? What were the results of the PASRR before Henry was admitted? Could the facility have done things differently for Henry to prevent this from becoming an issue?

All these questions need to be answered and taken into consideration before an action plan can take place. After this occurs, whatever action plan you provided for Henry's case will need to be applied to each resident in the facility. This is necessary as a murder just occurred in the facility, and undoubtedly this action will be a requirement to release the immediate jeopardy citation against the facility which will be ongoing until this situation can be rectified.

Sadly, this is not an isolated incident.

Ms. Abbot's Decision (An Actual Case)

There is no clear answer for this case. The American public is highly conflicted about suicide and assisted and unassisted euthanasia. The U.S. Congress and most state legislatures have avoided making hard-and-fast rules, leaving it instead to the discretion of the physicians, individuals involved, and "family" members.

The Hemlock Society was dedicated to the idea that the individual should have full control over the timing and circumstances of their death: They believed that one had an absolute right to control one's own death. This Society, always controversial, disbanded in 2003.

Was the emergency department physician right to ignore Ms. Abbot's living will? Depends. Society has not agreed that individuals have a right to die. Likely, the legislature did not intend the living will legislation to include individual euthanasia rights.

The Ethics Committee has a challenging task. Given the right-to-live ethic that pervades American culture, what policy could they write? Whatever policy they come up with will be a potential problem for the administrator. The concept of a right to die is as controversial in our society as the concept of a right to life.

Miss Whiting's Ice Pitcher (An Actual Case)

Issues abound here. The most obvious is that Nurse McCarthy has violated Miss Whiting's right to privacy and her behavioral preferences. The nursing facility is not "in loco parentis" for its residents. The nursing facility is not functioning as a surrogate parent for residents. Sexual activity in the nursing facility is an ongoing issue. What rights do residents have to behave as consenting adults in the facility? Resident's children are often shocked when their parent engages in sexual activities in the nursing facility and expect the facility to control (limit or prohibit) such behavior.

Our society is as ambivalent toward sexual activity among nursing facility residents as it is toward euthanasia. Generally, it appears, society feels that nursing facility residents ought not be sexually active. Surveyors, in contrast, usually demand that, as Ms. Janus observed, if residents' behavior is not infringing on other patients' rights or harmful to themselves, each patient's privacy and behavioral preferences will be respected. One does not give up one's citizenship or status as an adult upon entering a nursing facility.

(*continued*)

In pouring water on Miss Whiting, Nurse McCarthy is guilty at least of assault and probably of assault and battery. This is a real risk management problem for the facility.

The staff members' response at the nurse's station and the administrator's response suggests deep problems for the facility. By condoning staff snickers and suggestions of "Maybe you ought to start remembering to knock," the staff are participating in the attitude that patient rights are ignored with no consequences in that facility. And that is the problem. The administrator knows the problem exists and ignores the situation through avoidance behaviors. Crossing fingers will not resolve these problems. The problem begins with the administrator who "knows" what ought to be happening but chooses not to intervene on behalf of the residents.

Milk

The systems were simply not functioning. Dietary failed to serve the prescribed diet. The nurse failed to address Ms. Farrington's coughing and need for assistance. The nurse compounded the problem by wheeling Ms. Farrington to the hallway to get her out of sight. The nurse, in effect, lied to the physician, attempting to cover up her mistakes. The nurse should have been calling 911 and other staff members to assist her.

This may be an isolated incident, but the dietary system has failed, and the nursing care system has failed. This incident is likely symptomatic of more significant systemic failures at the facility.

Ms. Brown's Six Episodes

The good news is that an incident report was written, that the administrator received a copy, and that the administrator was reading and following up on the incident report in a timely manner. The further good news is that the administrator was sufficiently aware of an appropriate healthcare response to the six episodes and knew that the facility staff was not providing quality care for Ms. Brown.

Then it becomes complicated, depending on Ms. Howard's response after being told by the DON that the charge nurse and aide were overreacting. The administrator, Ms. Howard, is not a trained nurse but knows that appropriate healthcare is not being provided to Ms. Brown. Should the administrator overrule the DON and demand an immediate assessment for Ms. Brown? Is that the administrator's job? Ultimately, yes. The administrator's job is to ensure that the facility delivers quality care at every level. Long term, the administrator may need to hire a new DON. Short term, the care planning team must address Ms. Brown's six dizzy spells. Ms. Brown's physician needs to become involved immediately. It may be a simple medication adjustment or symptomatic of a significant health change. The nursing staff is failing to assess residents properly.

(continued)

Failure to react appropriately to the six unusual and significant postprandial orthostatic hypotension episodes is a potentially compensable event.

Ms. Jacobs's Decision

Possibly all four are correct. Possibly all four are wrong.

Is the physician correct? Yes, if you feel that residents have a right to decide when they wish to be allowed to die. No, if you feel that Dr. Greg should have given Ms. Jacobs a much more extensive examination to determine whether her request to be allowed to die was an effect of a stroke and that Ms. Jacobs might feel quite different about dying once the effects of the stroke passed in the next few days or weeks. Should he have insisted she be taken to the hospital?

Are the confused and angry staff correct? Staff may feel that the doctor should have done more to assess Ms. Jacobs and only after that write orders that her wish to be allowed to die be honored. Staff often become emotionally involved with residents. Staff may be angry as advocates for Ms. Jacobs. Staff may be uncomfortable with the prospect of themselves providing the end-of-life care ordered by Dr. Greg.

Are the daughters correct? Hard to say what is correct. One might feel the daughters were more nearly "correct" if there was a supportive and loving relationship between Ms. Jacobs and the daughters and that the daughters were willing to be part of the prospective end-of-life care process for Ms. Jacobs.

Is Ms. Jacobs correct? Depends. She may or may not have been depressed or suffering from a temporary effect of a stroke or stroke-like episode. In the end, it should be her decision. The fact is, of course, she can always change her mind at any time and tell the staff, her daughters, and her physician that she has decided to live a while longer and to bring her a good meal and something good to drink.

What about the administrator? The administrator should ensure that Ms. Jacobs is making an appropriate decision and ensure that Ms. Jacobs's end-of-life care is carefully documented. If I were the administrator, I would prepare the document or documents for Ms. Jacobs, the daughters, and Dr. Greg to sign spelling out the end-of-life care being requested.

A Final Case: Ms. Jensen's Management Style

Most readers are by this point so understandably disgusted with Ms. Jensen that they remain highly critical of the management style the AIT saw during his 2-day visit to The Laurels.

This case was written to illustrate a variety of management styles employed effectively by a single administrator! Go back and reread the case event by event.

Regarding housekeeping's request for a 4-day week. If a 4-day week is granted to housekeeping, Ms. Jensen should be prepared to expect similar requests from nursing, dietary, and maintenance. Ms. Jensen gave the department head 2 weeks to decide; then Ms. Jensen decided to head this one off at the pass by saying "no" to housekeeping.

(continued)

Regarding the DON's request to revise the admissions policy. *Ms. Jensen showed unusual (too much?) confidence in the DON by asking her to write a policy and then present it to the staff. We can guess that Ms. Jensen knew enough about the DON's goals that Ms. Jensen would likely agree with what the DON proposed. If not, Ms. Jensen could gracefully refer the policy back to the DON or a committee for further refinement. In addition, it might be politically wise to have such a policy emanate from the DON rather than the administrator.*

Riding mowers. *Two weeks earlier, Ms. Jensen had gone out with the head of maintenance and picked out three equally good riding mowers. Very possibly, the director of maintenance was attempting to put the onus on Ms. Jensen's back by having her make the final decision. If Ms. Jensen made the final decision, it could be her fault if the machine she selected later failed to meet expectations!*

The comptroller's request. *Ms. Jensen had given the comptroller a month and, today, one-half hour, yet still unconvinced, telling him to end the matter. She, as the administrator, is finally responsible to the board/owner, not to the comptroller. This is her decision as the chief financial officer. She gave his ideas a thorough hearing.*

Regarding rounds. *Ms. Jensen shut the DON's door and told the DON to enforce policies whether the DON wanted to or not. It was handled so that the DON did not lose face but was firmly told to enforce essential policies.*

The staff meeting. *At the staff meeting, Ms. Jensen tells the two department heads involved in the linen issue to settle the matter between them and (by implication) to report back to her if they cannot. In this case, Ms. Jensen is not failing to exercise her responsibility to integrate the work of the departments in the facility. These two heads will settle the matter or face Ms. Jensen with their inability to settle a matter. Alternatively, some observers of this case argue that typically nursing, being more powerful in most facilities, will win and that Ms. Jensen had a legitimate role as arbiter between these two departments.*

Note that the only situation in which Ms. Jensen was "democratic" was the menu cycle. Facilities are required to develop and post menu cycles a specified number of days in advance. The staff was more voting on the *sequencing* of the menus than the substance of the menus.

WHAT WOULD YOU DO?

You are the administrator of Happy Hills Nursing Facility. You have been the administrator here for 12 years now. You have a female resident who has been on hospice for about 2 years. She has been deemed nearing the end of her life within the next 30 days.

The family for this resident consists of 11 children, 10 of whom you have never seen or interacted with. There has been one child, a daughter, who has taken an active interest in the care of her mother. The rest of the children have been estranged for many

(continued)

years. Due to the impending death, the daughter has contacted the other children, imploring them to mend their relationship with their mother before she soon dies.

This contact to the family begins a slow onslaught of family members coming into the facility. There were so many coming in and out that you had to move the resident's roommate out of the room due to the roommate's complaints. The resident now has a private room which you have outfitted with extra tables and chairs to accommodate the family during this time.

Again, you have never seen or met these family members. However, many of them and their partners have decided that the care you provide has been substandard quality. This has never been a concern previously, and you have never received any citations regarding the quality of care for this resident. You have spoken to the family members and addressed any concerns they have had. However, neither the resident nor the nonestranged daughter (responsible party) has given you any ability to discuss particulars of the case, disease progression, or any other details.

As the next couple of weeks wear on, you find yourself, having been threatened and yelled at, now subject to a complaint survey surrounding this resident. Multiple family members have called in complaints to the state regarding their perceptions of their mother's care. Smartly, you got in front of this and let your local program manager at the state know that such a situation was occurring. You notified the program manager of what you have done. The estranged (never-met) family is complaining and expecting you and your nursing staff to violate HIPAA regulations. You also let the program manager know that the estranged family has been disrupting the resident's care and other residents of the facility.

1. What would you do from here?
2. Was your contact with your program manager at the state a good idea?
3. Can you talk to the family about the resident simply because they are asking for information?
4. Is your staff right in denying the family information?
5. Can you make the estranged family happy, or at least appease them, at some level?
6. What are other resources available to you through your own facility and through hospice in dealing with this situation?

REFERENCES

Centers for Medicare & Medicaid Services. (2005). *State operations manual. Appendix P—Survey protocol for long term care facilities—Part I.* https://www.cms.gov/medicare/provider-enrollment-and-certification/guidanceforlawsandregulations/downloads/som107ap_p_ltcfpdf

Centers for Medicare & Medicaid Services. (2006). Quality indicator survey procedures for long-term care facilities.

Centers for Medicare & Medicaid Services. (2017). *State operations manual. Appendix PP—Guidance to surveyors for long term care facilities.* https://www.cms.gov/medicare/provider-enrollment-and-certification/guidanceforlawsandregulations/downloads/appendix-pp-state-operations-manual.pdf

Centers for Medicare & Medicaid Services. (2018). *State operations manual. Chapter 7—Survey and enforcement process for skilled nursing facilities and nursing facilities.* https://www.cms.gov/Regulations-and-Guidance/Guidance/Manuals/Downloads/som107c07pdf.pdf

Centers for Medicare & Medicaid Services. (2019). *Long-term care facility resident assessment instrument 3.0 user's manual.* https://downloads.cms.gov/files/mds-3.0-rai-manual-v1.17.1_october_2019.pdf

Centers for Medicare & Medicaid Services. (2021). *Rights and protections in a nursing home.* https://downloads.cms.gov/medicare/your_resident_rights_and_protections_section.pdf

Halter, J. B., Ouslander, J. G., Studenski, S., High, K. P., Asthana, S., Supiano, M. A., & Ritchie, C. (2017). *Hazzard's geriatric medicine and gerontology* (7th ed.). McGraw Hill.

Health Information Technology for Economic and Clinical Health Act, 42 U.S.C. § 201. (2009). http://www.healthit.gov/sites/default/files/hitech_act_excerpt_from_arra_with_index.pdf

Kruse, C. S., Mileski, M., Alaytsev, V., Carol, E., & Williams, A. (2015). Adoption factors associated with electronic health record among long-term care facilities: A systematic review. *BMJ Open, 5*(1), e006615. https://doi.org/10.1136/bmjopen-2014-006615

Kruse, C. S., Mileski, M., Vijaykumar, A. G., Viswanathan, S. V., Suskandla, U., & Chidambaram, Y. (2017). Impact of electronic health records on long-term care facilities: Systematic review. *JMIR Medical Informatics, 5*(3), e35. https://doi.org/10.2196/medinform.7958

Office of the National Coordinator for Health Information Technology. (2019). *Improved diagnostics and patient outcomes.* https://www.healthit.gov/topic/health-it-and-health-information-exchange-basics/improved-diagnostics-patient-outcomes

Singh, D. A. (2016). *Effective management of long-term care facilities* (3rd ed.). Jones & Bartlett.

Web Resources

AARP: https://www.aarp.org

Administration for Community Living: https://acl.gov/about-acl/administration-aging

Agency for Healthcare Research and Quality—On-Time Falls Prevention: https://www.ahrq.gov/patient-safety/settings/long-term-care/resource/ontime/fallspx/index.html

Alliance for Retired Americans: https://retiredamericans.org

American College of Health Care Administrators (ACHCA): https://www.achca.org

American College of Healthcare Executives: https://www.ache.org

American Federation for Aging Research: https://www.afar.org

American Geriatrics Society: https://www.americangeriatrics.org

American Health Care Association: https://www.ahcancal.org/Pages/default.aspx

American National Standards Institute: https://webstore.ansi.org

American Nurses Association—*Code of Ethics for Nurses With Interpretive Statements*: https://www.nursingworld.org/coe-view-only

American Society on Aging: https://www.asaging.org

Americans With Disabilities Act (ADA)—Standards for Accessible Design: https://www.ada.gov/2010ADAstandards_index.htm

Argentum: https://www.argentum.org

Centers for Disease Control and Prevention—Hand Hygiene in Healthcare Settings: https://www.cdc.gov/handhygiene/providers/index.html

Centers for Disease Control and Prevention—STEADI Initiative. Stopping Elderly Accidents, Deaths, and Injuries (STEADI) is an approach that works to implement clinical practice guidelines for fall prevention: https://www.cdc.gov/steadi/materials.html

Centers for Medicare & Medicaid Services: https://www.cms.gov

Centers for Medicare & Medicaid Services—Minimum Data Set 3.0: https://www.cms.gov/Research-Statistics-Data-and-Systems/Computer-Data-and-Systems/Minimum-Data-Set-3-0-Public-Reports

The Gerontological Society of America: https://www.geron.org

GLAAD—Media Reference Guide: https://www.glaad.org/reference

INTERACT® (Interventions to Reduce Acute Care Transfers) Tools: https://pathway-interact.com

Leading Age: https://leadingage.org

Medicare.gov—Find & compare nursing homes, hospitals & other providers near you: https://www.medicare.gov/care-compare

National Association of Long Term Care Administrator Boards: https://www.nabweb.org

National Council on Aging: https://www.ncoa.org

National Fire Protection Association: https://www.nfpa.org

National Institute on Aging: https://www.nia.nih.gov

National Labor Relations Board—About NLRB: Our History: https://www.nlrb.gov/about-nlrb/who-we-are/our-history

The Nursing Home Toolkit for Promoting Positive Behavioral Health: https://www.nursinghometoolkit.com/index.html

Occupational Safety and Health Administration—COVID-19 Healthcare ETS: https://www.osha.gov/coronavirus/ets

Occupational Safety and Health Administration—Nursing Homes and Personal Care Facilities: https://www.osha.gov/nursing-home

Occupational Safety and Health Administration—OSH Act of 1970: https://www.osha.gov/laws-regs/oshact/completeoshact

Occupational Safety and Health Administration—OSHA Injury and Illness Recordkeeping and Reporting Requirements: https://www.osha.gov/recordkeeping

Occupational Safety and Health Administration—OSHA's free workplace poster: https://www.osha.gov/publications/poster

Pioneer Network: https://www.pioneernetwork.net

Pioneer Network—Artifacts of Culture Change 2.0: https://www.pioneernetwork.net/artifacts-culture-change

U.S. Department of Labor: https://www.dol.gov

Index of NAB Domains

Index